D1616130

The Geological Society of America, Inc.
Memoir 161

Proterozoic Geology: Selected Papers from an International Proterozoic Symposium

Edited by

L. G. Medaris, Jr.
C. W. Byers
D. M. Mickelson
W. C. Shanks

1983

Published by The Geological Society of America, Inc.
3300 Penrose Place, P.O. Box 9140, Boulder, Colorado 80301

Printed in U.S.A.

Library of Congress Cataloging in Publication Data

International Proterozoic Symposium (1981: University
of Wisconsin—Madison)
Proterozoic geology.

(Memoir/Geological Society of America; 161)
Includes bibliographies.
1. Geology, Stratigraphic—Pre-Cambrian—Congresses.
I. Medaris, L. G. (L. Gordon), 1936- . II. Geological
Society of America. III. Title. IV. Series: Memoir
(Geological Society of America); 161.
QE653.I58 1981 551.7'15 83-16587
ISBN 0-8137-1161-4

Contents

Preface

An International Proterozoic Symposium was held at the University of Wisconsin, Madison, on May 18-21, 1981, to dedicate the recently completed Lewis G. Weeks Hall for Geological Sciences and to celebrate the centennial of the Department of Geology and Geophysics, which was originally established as the Department of Mineralogy and Geology in 1878.

The symposium topic was selected in view of the pioneering investigations of Precambrian geology in the Great Lakes region by department faculty, beginning with R. D. Irving in 1870, and followed by T. C. Chamberlin, C. R. Van Hise, and C. K. Leith. Precambrian studies have continued to play an important role in departmental teaching and research over the years. The symposium focused on the Proterozoic Eon because at the time few modern, comprehensive publications were available on this critical segment of earth history and because Proterozoic events played an important role in the geological development of the Great Lakes region.

The symposium was attended by approximately 150 scientists from the United States, Canada, England, Denmark, West Germany, Australia, and the People's Republic of China. Sessions were held on Proterozoic tectonics, magmatism and metamorphism, evolution of life, atmosphere and the oceans, glaciation, mineral resources, and Proterozoic geology of the Great Lakes region. Papers from the last category have been published by the Geological Society of America as Memoir 160. Papers from the other sessions are included in this volume.

Introduction

The Proterozoic Eon represents an important segment of earth history, encompassing the transition from Archean conditions to those of the Phanerozoic. The two most important aspects of the Proterozoic were 1) a declining thermal regime, resulting in the growth of stabilized continental crust and a related change from permobile Archean tectonics to the initiation of modern-style plate tectonics; and 2) emergence of an atmosphere and hydrosphere similar in characteristics to those of the present day, with attendant effects on the evolution of life, nature of sedimentation, and formation of mineral deposits.

The International Proterozoic Symposium brought together experts in various fields to discuss current research and thereby provide an overview of the latest ideas on Proterozoic evolution of the earth. This volume is divided into five broad topics, as was the Symposium, including tectonics, magmatism and metamorphism, mineral deposits, life and the oceans, and glaciation.

Tectonics

Although most workers agree that modern-style plate tectonics began by about 1000-800 Ma, the nature and style of early Proterozoic tectonics continues to be a controversial topic. Windley, in his review of Proterozoic tectonics, summarizes the evidence for Wilson cycle signatures in early Proterozoic terranes, and Anderson and Burke apply a plate tectonics interpretation to some Proterozoic problems in eastern North America. In contrast, both Baer and Kröner argue for the development of ensialic orogenic belts during the early Proterozoic, unrelated to the growth and subduction of large ocean basins.

Piper proposes the existence of a Proterozoic supercontinent, based on paleomagnetic evidence, and emphasizes the constraints placed on the relative motions of cratons bordering Proterozoic mobile belts. Dunlop and Schutts present one set of paleomagnetic data which implies little relative motion of the Superior and Churchill cratons associated with the Hudsonian Orogeny, but another set of data which is compatible with precollisional divergence between Grenvillia and the rest of the Canadian shield.

The section on tectonics concludes with an evaluation by Glikson of the possibility of a slowly expanding earth during early and middle Precambrian time.

Magmatism and Metamorphism

Proterozoic magmatic activity was marked by the emergence of relatively potassic rock types, in contrast to the relatively sodic Archean varieties. This fundamental change in magmatic character from the Archean to the Proterozoic is recorded in the geochemistries of sedimentary rocks of corresponding ages as described by Taylor and McLennan. Another distinctive feature of Proterozoic magmatism was the widespread generation of anorogenic anorthosites, rapakivi granites, and ignimbrites in the interval, 1800-1000 Ma. Anderson summarizes the occurrence of these rock types in North America and discusses their origin and evolution.

With respect to metamorphism, R. St. J. Lambert gives estimates for the pressure-temperature conditions of selected Proterozoic metamorphic complexes, discusses the difficulties in relating equilibrium geothermal gradients to thermal gradients derived from metamorphic complexes, and evaluates the heat flux from Proterozoic crust and mantle. Newton and Hansen discuss the origin of charnockites, most of which formed between 2700 and 1000 Ma and constitute a significant proportion of Proterozoic high-grade terranes, and emphasize the importance of a profound source of heat and CO_2 in the generation of such metamorphic rocks.

Mineral Deposits

The Proterozoic encompass a period of earth history

which saw the development of an incredible variety of mineral deposits. Banded iron formation, conglomerate-hosted uranium and gold deposits, stratiform base-metal deposits, and magmatic oxide and sulfide deposits have important, in some cases unique, and commonly very large representatives.

Sawkins, in his review of tectonic controls on Proterozoic metal deposits, emphasizes the time-space relation of important deposits and rifting events. Significant differences between Proterozoic and Phanerozoic deposits are noted, but are ascribed largely to differing erosional levels rather than fundamental changes in tectonic style.

Gale summarizes geologic setting and metallogenesis of Proterozoic exhalative massive sulfide deposits, including both sedimentary- and volcanic-hosted types. He reemphasizes the possible role of magmatic waters in ore genesis and offers the interpretation that some stratiform Cu-Ni sulfide deposits may be exhalative. Lambert focuses specifically on sediment-hosted Pb-Zn deposits and addresses recent controversies over diagenetic versus synsedimentary origins.

The Proterozoic is, perhaps, characterized in a metallogenic sense by the occurrence of enormous uranium and iron reserves. Kimberley examines genetic models which may account for the preponderance of banded iron formations in the Proterozoic. Langford emphasizes the occurrence of U-Th deposits in the Archean and early Proterozoic, principally as paleoplacers, and ascribes the late Proterozoic transition to U-rich vein, sandstone, and unconformity types to atmospheric evolution.

Life and the Oceans

The Proterozoic was a time of profound importance in the coevolution between life and the chemistry of the oceans and atmosphere. As a result of photosynthetically-released oxygen, the surface of the earth was irreversibly oxidized, paving the way for the development of metazoan life. Cloud summarizes the evidence for a Proterozoic earth in which the continental crust and oceans had reached approximately their present dimensions. Oxidation of the atmosphere is recorded in the changing suites of sedimentary deposits and in the fossil sequence. Perry and Ahmad present data on the oxygen isotopic composition of Proterozoic chemical sediments, which are depleted in oxygen-18 relative to the Phanerozoic. The authors discuss hypotheses to account for the difference: either hotter Proterozoic oceans or oceans depleted in oxygen-18. Vidal and Knoll review the state of the art in Proterozoic plankton studies. Late Precambrian plankton are shown to display both paleoecologic and biostratigraphic zonation. The history of eukaryotic plankton is traced from its origins through the extinctions near the end of the eon.

Glaciation

The evidence of glaciation during the Proterozoic is fairly well accepted and is outlined in a paper by Harland. Disagreement, however, exists about the interpretation of mixtites of late Proterozoic age. In the paper analyzing evidence of late Proterozoic glaciations, Schermerhorn concludes that, in many cases, evidence for widespread glaciation is poor. He suggests that in many cases tongues of ice flowing from uplifted areas reached an otherwise fairly warm environment.

Because the sedimentary record is more complete in younger rocks, two papers were chosen to provide comparison with Proterozoic glaciations. Crowell outlines the evidence necessary to recognize ancient glacial deposits of any age, including those in the Proterozoic. Observations on Quaternary glacial deposits are provided in the paper by Dreimanis. Because these are our most recent glacial sediments, they hold clues to the interpretation of sedimentary environments of the Proterozoic.

We hope that this collection of papers will provide a stimulus to scientists interested in the Proterozoic and suggest new avenues of investigation into problems associated with this important stage in the evolution of the earth.

Geological Society of America
Memoir 161
1983

A tectonic review of the Proterozoic

Brian F. Windley
Department of Geology
The University
Leicester LE1 7RH
United Kingdom

ABSTRACT

The fact that lithospheric plates were beginning to respond (2.5 b.y. B.P.) to deformation, intrusion, and deposition in a mode comparable to that of today is indicated by the development of linear/arcuate orogenic belts bordering continental plates, leaving stable interiors with little-deformed cratonic sequences and linear dike swarms, the development of aulacogens and continental-rise sequences, island arcs, Andean arcs and back-arc basins, back-arc thrust belts adjacent to high-potash minimum-melting granites and slip-line indentation fracture systems bordering linear/arcuate orogenic belts, and geochemical patterns of igneous rocks comparable to modern tectonic equivalents; all these features indicate that modern-style plate tectonics began in the early Proterozoic.

Archean-type greenstone belts and granulite-gneiss belts continued to form throughout the Proterozoic, probably in marginal basins and the deeper levels of Andean belts, respectively. In the early Proterozoic a large number of orogenic belts formed, which are increasingly being interpreted in terms of Wilson Cycle processes. In the mid-Proterozoic (1.7 to 1.2 b.y. B.P.), major abortive rifting gave rise to anorogenic sodic anorthosites and rapakivi granites. In the period 1.0 ± 0.2 b.y. B.P., the Grenville and Dalslandian belts in the North Atlantic region formed with prominent Andean-type and Himalayan-type stages of development; today we see deeply eroded levels of these belts. The 0.8 to 0.57 b.y. B.P. Pan-African/Braziliano/Cadomian belts are widely acclaimed as having formed by Wilson Cycle tectonics.

The Proterozoic was a period of substantial lateral plate motion, accretion, and subduction and of corresponding crustal growth, although less intense than in the Archean. It was also a period of differentiation of the continental crust and the formation of potash granites in upper levels.

INTRODUCTION

The Proterozoic Era occupies 50% of the geological record between the Archean (3.8 to 2.5 b.y. B.P.) and the Phanerozoic. What happened to the continents during this period is a subject of increasing debate, within which there are two dominant questions. Did the Proterozoic represent the intermediate stage of development between the permobile Archean and the start of modern-style plate tectonics soon after 1.0 b.y. ago (e.g., Hargraves, 1976; Baer, 1977), or did Wilson Cycles start in the early Proterozoic, after the period of substantial crustal growth in the late Archean (e.g., Windley, 1979; Barker and others, 1981)? As more is learnt about the make-up and variability of modern orogenic belts and as more Proterozoic belts are reassessed in the light of the Wilson Cycle theory, the balance of opinion is increasingly in favour of the operation of some form of plate tectonic scheme of events throughout the Proterozoic, suitably modified to take account of variables such as the higher rate of breakdown of radiogenic isotopes in the past.

Proterozoic tectonic history is divisible into the following stages:

1. 2.5 to 1.6 b.y. B.P. (Proterozoic X of the U.S. Geological Survey [USGS]). In southern Africa, Proterozoic-type conditions began about 3.0 b.y. ago (the Pongola Group). Many sedimentary-volcanic basins and plutonic mobile belts formed in this period.

2. 1.7 to 1.2 b.y. B.P. Major abortive rifting gave rise to sodic anorthosites and rapakivi granites.

3. 1.2 to 0.8 b.y. B.P. The Grenville-Dalslandian mobile belt formed in the North Atlantic region. Isotopic ages elsewhere in the world peak in this period.

4. 0.8 to 0.57 b.y. B.P. (Proterozoic Z of the USGS). A series of mobile belts (collectively termed the Pan-African/Braziliano) formed, and some continued their development into the early Paleozoic.

Before reviewing these stages in turn, we must establish, first, the crustal conditions operative at the start of the Proterozoic and, second, the continuity of certain Archean-type structures into and through the Proterozoic. The aim of this overview is to give an assessment of current thinking on the tectonic evolution of Proterozoic orogenic belts.

CRUSTAL CONDITIONS IN THE EARLY PROTEROZOIC

The massive thickening of lithosphere in the late Archean gave rise by the early Proterozoic to extensive, thick, rigid, and stable continental parts of plates underlain by tectospheric roots; this time-boundary, therefore, represents the most important threshold in geological history (Windley, 1977; Dewey and Windley, 1981). The fact that early Proterozoic lithospheric plates were beginning to respond to deformation, deposition, and intrusion in a mode comparable to that of today is indicated by the following features:

1. Large stable continental areas showing a high degree of rigidity, as evidenced by the deposition and preservation of little-deformed cratonic sequences (Witwatersrand, Huronian) and by the intrusion of extensive linear dyke swarms (Molson dykes, Canada; Waterberg, Botswana-Transvaal; Umkondo, Zimbabwe).

2. Continental shelf-rise sequences on and aulacogen (Milanovsky, 1981) re-entrants in continental margins (Aldan Shield), often with early alkali complexes associated with the rifted margin (Wopmay orogen, Hoffman, 1980a).

3. Linear/arcuate orogenic belts bordering continental plates leaving stable interiors (Circum-Ungava Geosyncline) with fore-arc thrust sheets over basement (Wopmay orogen).

4. Widespread basement reactivation adjacent to linear/arcuate thrust belts involving the generation of high-potash minimum-melting granites (East Labrador Trough; Hepburn batholith in Wopmay orogen) and slip-line indentation fracture systems in cratonic forelands (Wopmay orogen; Churchill Province–Slave Craton, Gibb, 1975; deep-level shear zones in west Greenland, Watterson, 1978).

5. The construction of island arcs, Andean arcs, and back-arc basins, the igneous rocks of which are chemically similar to modern equivalents (Churchill Province, Great Batholith in Wopmay orogen, Arizona, Svecokarelides, Queensland, Ketilidian; Moore, 1977; Barker and others, 1981; Hamilton, 1981; Brown, 1981).

These features indicate that modern-style plate tectonics began in the early Proterozoic.

Important litho-chemical developments at the Archean/Proterozoic boundary were as follows:

1. The chemical composition of sedimentary rocks changed markedly: the K_2O/Na_2O ratio in undifferentiated sediments increased (Engel and others, 1975), the $^{87}Sr/^{86}Sr$ ratio of carbonates increased (Veizer and Jansen, 1979), the La/Yb, ΣLREE/ΣHREE, and the total abundance of REE increased, and the Eu/Eu* decreased (Taylor and McLennan, 1981). There was also an increase in the cumulative thickness and area of sedimentary rocks (Veizer and Jansen, 1979) and a 20-fold increase in the ratio of carbonate and orthoquartzite to other sediments (Engel and others, 1975).

2. There was a substantial increase in the potash-soda ratio of igneous rocks (Engel and others, 1974) with the result that high-potash minimum-melting granites predominate over calc-alkaline silicic-intermediate igneous rocks in the Proterozoic, which implies a dominance of crustal differentiation over crustal growth (Dewey and Windley, 1981).

GREENSTONE BELTS (GB) AND GRANULITE-GNEISS BELTS (GGB)

Archean terrains are made up of two fundamentally

TABLE 1. SOME PROTEROZOIC GREENSTONE BELTS

Greenstone belt	Age (b.y.)	References
Trans-Amazonian Belts, Guiana Shield	2.25	Choudhuri, 1980 Gibb, 1980
Birrimian, West Africa	2.3-1.95	Sillitoe, 1979
Lynn Lake, Manitoba	1.85-1.65	Zwanzig and others, 1979
Amisk Group (Flin Flon-Snow Lake), Manitoba	1.85-1.65	Stauffer and others, 1975 Moore, 1977
Pecos, New Mexico	1.8-1.7	Wyman, 1980
Dalma, India	1.7-1.6	Gupta and others, 1980
Hastings area, Grenville Province	1.3	Moore, 1977
Nubian-Arabian Shield Pan-African	0.9-0.6	Engel and others, 1980
Sinai. Pan-African	0.8-0.6	Shimron, 1980

different types of tectonic units: greenstone belts and granulite-gneiss belts. It has been widely believed that they, and in particular the GB, were a characteristic feature of only the Archean and that they ceased to form in subsequent time. However, it is now apparent from recent isotopic age determinations that comparable GB and GGB continued to form throughout the Proterozoic, albeit fewer in number than in the Archean.

Tarney and Windley (1981) listed several possible Proterozoic GB, (some key examples are listed in Table 1). The early and mid-Proterozoic belts provide the link between Archean GB and the GB of the Pan-African that can reasonably be interpreted as ancient analogues of Phanerozoic arcs and marginal basins (see later). This linkage provides an explanation for the remarkable similarity between the Kuroko massive sulphide deposits in Japan that formed in a Miocene volcanic arc rift or marginal basin and the massive sulphide deposits in Archean GB (Cathles and others, 1980), and in the early Proterozoic GB at Flin Flon and Snow Lake in Manitoba and at Jerome in Arizona.

Granulite-gneiss belts (GGB) are uplifted or upturned segments of orogenic belts (Proterozoic examples are listed in Table 2). Many are comparable on the one hand with Archean GGB, and on the other with deeply eroded modern orogenic belts. Examples of uniformitarian interpretations of tectonic evolution are the Telemarkian orogen of South Norway as a remnant of a Cordilleran-type continental margin, like the Columbian orogen of the Canadian Cordillera (Torsk, 1977), the Svecokarelides of the Baltic Shield (Bowes, 1980), and the Musgrave Range of Australia (Davidson, 1973) as Himalayan-type collisional belts.

My point of emphasis here is that the two main types of Archean orogenic belt continued to evolve, although with certain differences, throughout the Proterozoic, and Mesozoic-Cenozoic equivalents should help us understand their mode of development in a plate tectonic reference frame

TABLE 2. SOME PROTEROZOIC GRANULITE-GNEISS BELTS

Granulite-Gneiss Belts	Age (b.y.)	Reference
Namaqua-Natal, South Africa	2.0-1.0	Tankard and others, 1982
Svecokarelian, Baltic Shield	1.83-1.70	Bowes, 1980
Musgrave Range, Australia	1.38	Davidson, 1973
Telemarkian, Southern Norway	1.2-0.85	Torsk, 1977
Enderby Land, Antarctica	1.1±0.8	Sheraton and others, 1980
Grenville-Dalslandian	1.0±0.2	Baer and others, 1974 Berthelsen, 1980
Mozambiquian, Pan-African	0.6±0.2	Kröner, 1980

EARLY PROTEROZOIC OROGENIC BELTS

There have been over 40 papers and abstracts in the past few years interpreting geophysical, geochemical, and geological data from early Proterozoic belts in terms of plate tectonic models; these greatly overshadow the half dozen attempts to erect nonuniformitarian *ad hoc* hypotheses. The following evidence is critical:

Sutures: Geophysical and Structural Evidence

Gibb and others (1980) summarized the findings of many authors regarding the location of many possible Proterozoic sutures in Canada. Early Proterozoic examples lie on the west (Wopmay orogen) and east (Thelon Suture) borders of the Slave Craton, along the Superior–Churchill Province boundary and in several positions within the Churchill Province. The Thelon and Circum-Ungava boundaries are marked by Bouguer gravity anomalies interpreted as edge effects between juxtaposed isostatically compensated crustal blocks of different mean density and thickness. The density discontinuity dips towards the younger crustal block, which is consistently thicker (39.5 km) and denser (2.91 g/cm^{-3}) than the older (34 km, 2.84 g/cm^{-3}). Gravity anomaly profiles by Thomas and Kearey (1980) across the Labrador Trough show that linear regional anomalies are related to major, fault-bounded crustal blocks of differing density and that the gravity model of the Churchill Province east of the trough is comparable in morphology and scale to the crustal model of the Andes across Peru. In particular, a marked negative gravity anomaly coincides with a 500-km-long granitic belt, equivalent to the Andean Coastal Batholith. The front (east side) of the Slave-Churchill boundary is marked by a negative magnetic anomaly coincident with a mylonite belt (mid-Aphebian) and by orthogonal sets of strike-slip faults (late-Aphebian) comparable in geometry to the indentation faults of Asia caused by the northward collision of the Indian plate. These geophysical-structural data provide a sound and fundamental base on which to interpret the geological features along these province boundaries.

Paleomagnetic Data

There is considerable dispute amongst palaeomagneticians about the tectonic significance of Proterozoic apparent polar wander paths (APW). According to Piper (1976, and many earlier papers) and Embleton and Schmidt (1979), the palaeomagnetic evidence is consistent with a model in which most of the Precambrian shields were aggregated together as a single supercontinent during much of Proterozoic time; accordingly, Proterozoic mobile belts developed ensialically. However, McGlynn and others (1975) pointed out that the palaeomagnetic evidence did not lead to this conclusion and, in particular, that there was not a supercontinent made up of Laurentia and West Gondwanaland between 2.2 b.y. and 1.8 b.y. ago. Burke and others (1976) plotted APW paths for suture-bounded blocks rather than present continents and found that they were compatible with the operation of the Wilson Cycle throughout the Proterozoic. Cavanaugh and Nairn (1980) found that the paucity of palaeomagnetic data of pre-1.4-b.y.-old rocks from North America and Baltic Europe precluded the drawing of any conclusions concerning the intracratonic integrity of these shields; they did, however, tentatively suggest that a Wilson Cycle may have operated between 2.2 b.y. and 1.8 b.y. B.P. (between the Superior (+ Southern and Wyoming) and Churchill (+ Slave and Labrador) provinces. In contrast, Irving and McGlynn (1981) concluded that it is impossible from current data to determine whether the Slave and Superior provinces had common or separate APW paths in the period 2.3 to 1.85 b.y. B.P. Palaeomagnetic data from Huronian red beds and Nipissing diabase indicate that the Laurentian Shield was in high latitudes from 2.2 to 2.0 b.y. B.P. and in intermediate to low latitudes from 1.9 to 1.5 b.y. B.P. (Roy and Lapointe, 1976). Finally, Ullrich and van der Voo (1981) used APW paths to estimate minimum plate velocities since the Archean. They found a positive correlation between high velocities and peaks of isotopically dated orogenic events. Although each continent has its own velocity signature, velocities were significantly higher in the past, at times reaching 10 cm/yr, as during Hudsonian times in North America, compared with recent total velocities which are usually less than 3 cm/yr. The same type of velocity pattern evolved throughout the Proterozoic and the Phanerozoic, and therefore we might expect similar mechanisms of plate motions at these times.

In summary, it must be emphasized that there is such a paucity of data, especially of isotopic and stratigraphic age control (over 60% of the palaeopoles are from one continent—North America—and for the Proterozoic there is an average of only 1 pole/9 m.y. compared with 6 from the Carboniferous to the present, and actual gaps may be as large as 100 m.y., Roy, 1980) and so many disagreements in interpretation of Proterozoic palaeomagnetic data, particularly for the early Proterozoic, that they can seldom be used as a tight constraint on interpretation based on other evidence.

Time-Space Templates in Sedimentary and Igneous Rocks

Analysis of modern orogenic belts has taught us that sedimentary and igneous rocks are arranged in specific order with predictable temporal and spatial relationships along rifts, accreting and subduction plate margins, and collisional sutures. Recognition of such rock signatures in early Proterozoic mobile belts enables us to define specific stages in the Wilson Cycle. But there is a great variety of modern plate boundaries with complex changes in geometry, and the challenge for the Proterozoic field geologist is to know enough about the multitude of modern plate histories to be able to recognize their ancient analogues, or indeed modifications caused by variations in certain parameters in the past such as plate thickness and rigidity, radiogenic heat production, and so forth.

The Wopmay orogen (2.2 to 1.8 b.y. B.P.) in northwest Canada (Hoffman, 1980a) is outstanding because it retains evidence of a complete Wilson Cycle, although Hoffman pointed out that magmatism was more intense than today in certain environments and the rise of mafic tholeiites through subducting plates in trenches seems to have been more common in the Proterozoic. The tectonic history was not simple: west-dipping was followed by oblique east-dipping subduction and rather than paired metamorphic belts there were paired plutonic (batholith) belts (Hoffman, 1980b). The Wopmay orogen is important, not only because it shows us that modern-style plate tectonics were in operation in the early Proterozoic but also because it tells us about some of the processes that were different then compared with now.

Now let us consider evidence for the successive stages in the Wilson Cycle.

Rifts and Trailing Continental Margins. The Wopmay orogen has continent-derived alluvial and deltaic clastics with bimodal lavas formed during early rifting (Hoffman, 1980a). A complete Atlantic-type continental terrace (shelf-slope) and rise was developed. Collapse of the carbonate bank was followed by continent-directed flysch and finally molasse. Several major aulacogens project into the continental margin.

The Labrador Trough has a shelf-basin slope-basin transition, inferred by Wardle (1981) to have formed as a passive continental margin sequence on the eastern margin of which flysch accumulated with submarine mafic volcanics sheeted by comagmatic basaltic sill swarms. Farther to the north, the Cape Smith belt has a stratigraphy more akin to that of a greenstone belt (Hynes and Frances, 1981), and farther along strike there is an aulacogen (the Richmond Gulf graben) projecting at a high angle from the Superior Craton into the Belcher Fold Belt (Chandler and Schwarz, 1980). Farther west, in Manitoba, the Circum-Ungava suture has cherts, pillow lavas, serpentinites, and the ultramafic cumulates of the Fox River complex (Gibb and Walcott, 1971). Current research results from the Circum-Ungava fold belt suggest that it is made up of different segments, each of which preserves its own signature of ocean opening and closure.

Island Arcs and Andean-type Belts. If there were subduction in the early Proterozoic we should see the results as calc-alkaline volcanics and plutonics in batholithic belts; these rocks tend to fare well during subsequent continental collisions and thus should be easy to document.

In Arizona there are four 1.8 to 1.71-b.y.-old volcanic belts which (1) are flanked by aprons of volcanogenic greywackes and siltstones, (2) show mafic to felsic evolution with time, (3) show vertical stratification from low-K tholeiites at the base to calc-alkaline volcanic, fragmental, and clastic tops, and (4) are of different but overlapping ages. In particular, each volcanic belt shows lateral alkali-silica polarity (Anderson, 1978). Coeval with the arcs are plutonic rocks (diorite-gabbro-tonalite-granodiorite-quartz monzonite) which also show their polarity.

Recent work by Lewry (1981) in the western Churchill Province suggested that there is a major volcanoplutonic arc (Rottenstone-La Ronge belt), a microcontinent (Glennie Lake domaine), an intervening telescoped fore-arc basin (eastern La Ronge domaine) and suture zone (Stanley Zone), and a transform fault along the Tabbernor shear zone between the microcontinent and a remnant interarc basin (Kisseynew domaine). The Rottenstone 'arc' continues along strike into the 900-km-long 1.86-b.y.-old Wathaman-Chipewyan batholith of monzogranite-granodiorite, which is of Andean type and which developed after deposition of shallow-shelf sediments in the Wollaston domaine against remobilized basement in the Mudjatik domaine (Lewry and Sibbald, 1980; Ray and Wanless, 1980). The adjacent Flin Flon domaine contains the Amisk Group of andesites and pyroclastics of island arc chemical affinity (Stauffer and others, 1975), whilst the Llynn Lake domaine (greenstone belt) contains subaqueous basaltic shield volcanoes and a younger calc-alkaline mafic to felsic succession (Zwanzig and others, 1979), probably formed in an island arc or back-arc basin. In summary, a traverse across the Churchill Province in northern Saskatchewan provides a section across a Himalayan-type mountain chain.

In Wisconsin, rhyolites, ignimbrites, and granites formed on an active continental margin about 1.79 b.y. ago (van Schmus, 1976). Calc-alkaline meta-andesites and granitic batholiths formed in a long-lived Cordilleran-type orogenic belt in southern Norway (Torsk, 1977). In southern Sweden, calc-alkaline andesites associated with granitic batholiths are regarded by Loberg (1980) as island arc volcanics, whilst the leptites have a chemistry that suggests they form an island arc suite of calc-alkaline rocks ranging from basalt to rhyolite (Löfgren, 1979). Tonalites and quartz-monzonites in Sweden have low initial $^{87}Sr/^{86}Sr$ ratios of 0.703 and are considered to have formed by subduction processes by Wilson (1980), whilst Hietanen (1975) compared the tonalite-trondhjemite suite in southern Finland with the Sierra Nevada batholith; these volcanic-plutonic suites lie within the Svecokarelide Cordilleran-type fold belt of Bowes (1980).

In Queensland, Australia, the Tweinga Group (>1.45 b.y. B.P.) consists of meta-calc-alkaline volcanics intruded by tonalitic-granitic batholiths and overlain by basalts, ignimbritic rhyolites, and dacites. Detailed analysis of the chemistry of these rocks led Wilson (1978) to conclude that they were very similar to Phanerozoic equivalents in the Central Andes and, therefore, that they formed at a convergent plate margin. The lack of andesites is postulated to result from a more hydrous early Proterozoic mantle.

In the Wopmay orogen the Great Bear Magmatic Zone contains high alumina–low TiO_2 andesites, basaltic andesites, and basaltic and dacitic to rhyolitic ash-flow tuffs, nearly identical in major and minor element geochemistry to modern continental magmatic arcs (Hildebrand, 1981; Hoffman, pers. commun.), and in southern Greenland the Julianehaab, Andean-type batholith belongs to the Ketilidian fold belt that formed as a result of northward collision against an Archean continental plate (Watterson, 1978).

According to Barker and others (1981), modern-style continental margin batholiths began to form in the early Proterozoic. In contrast to the bimodal tonalite-trondhjemite and basalt suites typical of most Archean belts, the post-Archean continental margin batholiths are compositionally continuous, having formed by interaction of mantle-derived magmas and crustal rocks.

MID-PROTEROZOIC ABORTIVE RIFTS

In the period 1.7 to 1.2 b.y. ago, and in particular from 1.5 to 1.4 b.y., extensive anorogenic magmatism gave rise to many andesine-labradorite massif anorthosite-adamellite complexes with rapakivi potassic granites and ferrodiorites which were intruded at depths of 15 to 20 km and which form major alignments across the Proterozoic continents (Emslie, 1978). Important examples are Morin, Michikamau, Harp Lake, Saguenay, and Nain in Canada; Wolf River, Adirondack, and Laramie in the eastern United States; Rogaland in southern Norway; Wiborg, Loos-Hamra, and Ahvenisto in Finland; Ukrainian Shield, southern Greenland; East Ghats belt of India; and Angola in Africa. The intrusive suite is a product of bimodal magmatism and is characterized by high contents of alkalis (Na in anorthosites and K in granites) and Fe (fayalite, hedenbergite, and annite in granites and ferrodiorites) and low content of MgO, and Sn mineralization in the granites (especially in Fennoscandia). The granitic rocks are chemically distinctive from arc-type granites and collision-zone granites (Brown, 1981).

A common comparison is with the Younger (Jurassic) suite of fayalite-riebeckite granites with Sn mineralization and sodic anorthosites of Nigeria and Niger, and the alkali-calcic to alkalic granitic rocks of the Hebridean Tertiary Province of northwest Scotland. These are both extensional magmatic suites also characterized by low Mg and high Fe and alkali geochemistry. The Nigerian suite lies on a possible northward extension of the rift that gave rise to the South Atlantic, and the British Tertiary suite is contemporaneous with the North Atlantic rifting (Brown, 1981). Thus it seems most likely that the anorogenic mid-Proterozoic complexes are a reflection of major abortive attempts to rift the continents; they coincide in time with a period of slow plate velocity (Ullrich and van der Voo, 1981).

GRENVILLE-DALSLANDIAN MOBILE BELT

In the period 1.0 ± 0.2 b.y. B.P. a series of mobile belts formed, some of which are so deeply eroded that their high-grade lower crustal segments are exposed. Prominent in the North Atlantic region is the Grenville-Dalslandian belt. Many controversial interpretations have been produced to account for the tectonic evolution of the Grenville belt. This is not surprising, not because of anything unique or unusual about the Grenville belt, but simply because very little is known about how the lower parts of modern orogenic belts formed.

Ideas on the origin of the Grenville belt include *in situ* ensialic (no lateral shortening) deformation of cover-basement (H. R. Wynne-Edwards), a dextral shear zone (A. J. Baer), very slow sideways shunting of continental crust over a hot spot (H. R. Wynne-Edwards), and a Wilson Cycle with prominent Tibetan-style late continental collision (J. F. Dewey and K. Burke, A. J. Baer, G. M. Young). As a result of a conference on the Grenville, Baer and others (1974) stated that "most experts would agree that the Grenvillian orogeny may be explained in terms of plate tectonics." A major constraint on such models is provided by palaeomagnetic data. The sequence of loops with amplitudes of 60° and period of 200 to 300 m.y. is consistent with the operation of the Wilson Cycle, four hypotheses being invoked by Irving and others (1974). In contrast, Dunlop and others (1980) concluded that the data suggest tentatively that a small ocean between 'Grenvillia' and Laurentia may have closed after 1.2 b.y. by 90° rotation about a pole northeast of Newfoundland and that the well-dated poles for the Grenville Loop in the North American APW path between 1.05 and 0.8 b.y. B.P. rule out the possibility of a collision between 'Grenvillia' and the rest of the Canadian Shield in this time interval. Evidence in the foreland that strongly supports the idea of the operation of a Grenville Wilson Cycle includes the presence of the contemporaneous Keweenawan rift system and its attendant gravity high, the rift triple junction in the Lake Superior region, the belt of alkaline complexes marginal to the northwest side of the Grenville belt, and the Abitibi dike swarm. The only suggestion for the existence of oceanic lithosphere is in southeast Ontario where there is a belt of mafic pillow basalts overlying a mafic-ultramafic meta-igneous complex and overlain by more salic volcanics, sediments, and marbles, and intruded by granodioritic to granitic plutons (Chappell and others, 1975). Also here there are 4 km of low-K tholeiites whose trace element distributions are similar to those of modern immature emerging arcs overlain by 3 km of andesite geochemically comparable to volcanic rocks from mature arc systems (Condie and Moore, 1977).

Farther to the east, according to Young (1980), there are Grenville-age rocks and deformation in southern Norway and eastern Greenland, northwest Africa, the Channel Islands, the Moines of Scotland, Brittany, and in the Nubian and Arabian Shields. However, Young (1980) suggested that the Bou Azzer ophiolite in Morocco may be of Grenville age (1.0 b.y. B.P.); this would seem to be incorrect in the light of the new isotopic data of Leblanc and Lancelot (1980), which indicate a history from 0.788 to 0.534 b.y. B.P. As yet the geochronological data do not enable us to separate clearly the events of Grenville and Pan-African age, but nevertheless, it seems that some ophiolites may be related to the Grenville orogeny. In particular, in Egypt there are serpentinites, gabbros, sheeted dikes, and mafic volcanics 1.2 to 0.85 b.y. old associated with chert and tectonic mélange (Shackleton and others, 1980); these record the presence of a former ocean or marginal basin of Grenville age, but whether it was closed in late Grenville or early Pan-African times is uncertain.

An interesting picture is emerging from the 1.0 ± 0.2-b.y.-old Dalslandian belt in southern Sweden and southern Norway where Berthelsen (1980) has recognized several low-angle thrusts on which slabs of crustal thicknesses 200 to 300 km long and 50 km wide have been piled upon each other, and he interpreted this thrust-stacking as a result of a Himalayan-style continental collision. According to Falkum and Petersen (1980), aulacogens about 1.19 b.y. old are preserved in the Telemark area of southern Norway which formed during the early stages of this Sveconorwegian orogeny. Evidence elsewhere of 1.2 to 0.8-b.y.-old crustal tectonics includes many aulacogens of the Russian plate, the granulite-gneiss belts of Antarctica, the Namaqua-Natal mobile belt of southeast Africa, and the granulite belt on the south coast of western Australia. The literature on these belts is as yet sparse, but in future they may provide further constraints on the tectonic mechanisms in this period.

PAN-AFRICAN BELTS

In the period 0.8 to 0.5 b.y. B.P. a series of mobile belts formed in many continents; the Pan-African, Braziliano, and Cadomian belts are particularly well known. As late as 1973 it was widely thought that many of these belts formed ensialically, but there has been considerable success in recent years in establishing geological relationships that point towards a plate-tectonic mode of development. A major problem still remains, however, in the lack of age constraints with regard to the subdivision of the many belts that formed in this period, as well as the fact that the older belts overlap with those of Grenville age and the younger ones with those of Caledonian-Appalachian age.

The key results indicative of modern-style plate tectonic activity are listed in Table 3. To support such conclusions based on geological and geochemical relationships is the accumulating palaeomagnetic evidence for large and rapid apparent polar wander from all major continents, and because their APW paths cannot all be matched, it follows that large relative continental movements occurred (Briden, 1977).

TABLE 3. DATA INDICATIVE OF WILSON CYCLE OPERATION IN PAN-AFRICAN BELTS

Belt	Reference
Arabian-Nubian Shields	
Ophiolite-island arc sequences	Engel and others, 1980
Calc-alkaline batholiths with chemical polarity of K, Na, and Rb/Sr, K/Rb	Rogers and others, 1980 Brown *in* Al-Shanti, v. 3, 1980
Ophiolite belts in Saudi Arabia (SA)	Frisch and Al-Shanti, 1977
Ophiolite with sheeted dikes, Jabal Ess, SA	Shanti and Roobol, 1979
Andesites, diorite-to-trondhjemite batholiths and volcaniclastic sediments of intra-oceanic island arc type and post-collisional wrench faults of indentation type	Fleck and others *in* Al-Shanti, v. 3, 1980
Andean-style zonation of Cu, Au, to Ag-Pb-Zn mineralization	Al-Shanti and Roobol *in* Al-Shanti, v. 1, 1979
W, Sn, U, Nb mineralization in peralkaline granites related to post-suturing indentation rifts	Sillitoe *in* Al-Shanti, v. 1, 1979
Complete Wilson Cycle rock suites	Brown and Jackson, Gass *in* Al-Shanti, v. 1, 1979 Shackleton, Schmidt and others *in* Al-Shanti, v. 2, 1979
Island arc volcanism and sedimentation	Shimron, 1980
Central North Africa	
Complete Wilson Cycle geology. The Hoggar	Caby and others, 1981
Calc-alkaline batholith of Andean-type with geochemical polarity	Rogers and others, 1980
Himalayan-style identation fault tectonics	Ball, 1980
North-West Africa	
Complete Wilson Cycle sequence: Anti-Atlas	Leblanc and Lancelot, 1980
Calc-alkaline volcanics of island-arc type, Morocco and Algeria	Chikhaoui and others, 1980
West Africa	
Geochemistry of calc-alkaline volcanics of arc type. Nigeria	McCurry and Wright, 1977
Ophiolites and continental margin sediments, Ghana	Grant, 1973
South-West Africa	
Glaucophane in the Gariep belt, Namibia	Kröner, 1975
Calc-alkaline lavas intruded by granite batholiths in a volcanic-plutonic arc	Watters, 1976
Complete Wilson Cycle in Damaran belt	Barnes and Sawyer, 1980
Complete Wilson Cycle in the Damaran (Namibia) and Ribeira (Brazil) belts	Porada, 1979
South America	
Complete Wilson Cycle. E. Brazil	Pedreira, 1979
Northwest Europe	
Complete Wilson Cycle in the Cadomian orogenic belt	Cogné and Wright, 1980

One group of rocks deserves special comment. Engel and others (1980) described the Pan-African 'oceanic-arc complexes' of Egypt, Sudan, and Saudi Arabia as "the largest and one of the few well-preserved greenstone belts in the Proterozoic of the world." Serpentinized ultramafic rocks, overlain by gabbros (with gabbro dikes) and pillowed tholeiitic basalts, form an oceanic substrate overlain in turn by a calc-alkaline sequence of andesitic and more felsic metavolcanics of arc type interfingered with coeval immature sediments (tuffaceous wackes and volcaniclastics intruded by sills of basaltic komatiite) and banded iron formations of Algoma type. These rocks are engulfed by synkinematic and younger granites. As Engel and others (1980) pointed out, these rocks have geological and geochemical features comparable on the one hand with modern ocean-floor ophiolites and overlying island arc suites, and on the other with many Archean greenstone belts (and by implication with early Proterozoic greenstone belts, as indicated in this paper). These Pan-African rocks thus provide an important link between modern and early Precambrian sequences. However, Engel and others (1980) also stated that "there is increasing evidence that large segments of post-Archean pre-Permian orogens may be essentially ensialic." The evidence compiled in this paper indicates that their statement is incorrect. Moreover, this evidence strongly contradicts the view of Kröner (1980) that "the Pan-African may represent a tectonic regime transitional between predominantly intraplate deformation of the older Precambrian and predominantly plate margin deformation of the Phanerozoic."

CONSTRAINTS ON THE INTERPRETATION OF PROTEROZOIC TECTONIC EVOLUTION PROVIDED BY MODERN PLATE TECTONIC REGIMES

In order to construct a plate tectonic or nonuniformitarian tectonic model for a Proterozoic orogenic belt, the geologist has to know something about Mesozoic-Cenozoic plate tectonics. A great deal is known about modern plate geometry and about the upper levels of plates, such as the accretionary prism, fore-arc basin, arc, back-arc basin, the Andean belt of Peru, and the thrust belts of Switzerland. This is very useful for interpreting weakly metamorphosed Proterozoic belts, such as the Aphebian of Saskatchewan, the Wopmay orogen, and the Pan-African of Saudi Arabia. But it does not help us at all to interpret the deeply eroded (15 to 30 km/5 to 10 kbar) Proterozoic granulite-gneiss belts like the Mozambiquian (Pan-African), the Grenville, the Laxfordian, or the Svecokarelides. The problem arises because the lower levels of very few Mesozoic-Cenozoic belts are exposed. What do we know about the way in which the lower levels of modern belts formed?—very little. Therefore, we have a situation in which there is commonly much agreement about the plate tectonic interpretation of many high-level Proterozoic belts, but much disagreement, expressed by the construction of nonuniformitarian *ad hoc* hypotheses, about the tectonic origin of Proterozoic granulite-gneiss belts. If the high levels of Proterozoic belts were created by modern-style plate tectonic processes, it seems highly unlikely that the deeper levels were not, and therefore one suspects the validity of the nonuniformitarian ideas created as a result of the lack of a modern constraint.

Table 1 shows that greenstone belts continued to form throughout the Proterozoic, although they were probably fewer in number than in the Archean. As Engel and others (1980) pointed out, the Pan-African belts of oceanic-arc complexes have similarities to many Phanerozoic ophiolites, most of which are thought these days to have formed in marginal basins. Crawford and Keays (1978) described a marginal basin in the Lachlan fold belt of southeast Australia as a greenstone belt and its age as Cambrian. Thus it seems that there may not have been such a major difference between the Precambrian and Phanerozoic belts as is commonly supposed. Whether or not they all formed in marginal basins, as proposed by Tarney and Windley (1981), the Proterozoic greenstone belts should be seen as a continuing tectonic form through the middle part of Earth history.

It would probably be premature to make such a long-range extrapolation about Proterozoic granulite-gneiss belts because so little is known about the make-up of the mid-to-lower levels of modern orogenic belts; however, it remains an interesting possibility that they represent the deeply eroded or upturned level of Andean-type belts and thus are comparable to Archean granulite-gneiss belts (Windley and Smith, 1976). It can be no coincidence that the two main additions to the crust during Mesozoic-Cenozoic orogenesis (arc-Andean belts and marginal basins) are broadly similar to those accreted during the formation of Proterozoic belts.

This review has been largely concerned with the tectonic evolution of Proterozoic orogenic belts. An important effect of the cratonization that took place across the Archean-Proterozoic boundary was the development of rigid plates with stable interiors on which were deposited intracratonic basins, such as the Dominion, Witwatersrand, Ventersdorp, Transvaal, Griqualand West, Waterberg, and Soutpansberg Groups, and the miogeoclinal Umkondo and Matsap Groups of South Africa—these are all well reviewed by Tankard and others (1982).

ACKNOWLEDGMENTS

I am grateful for useful comments by P. F. Hoffman and F.H.A. Campbell.

REFERENCES CITED

Al-Shanti, A.M.S., editor, 1979 (v. 1), 1979 (v. 2), 1980 (v. 3), Evolution and mineralization of the Arabian-Nubian Shield: Oxford, Pergamon Press.

Anderson, P., 1978, The island arc nature of Precambrian volcanic belts in Arizona: Geological Society of America Abstracts with Programs, v. 10, p. 156.

Baer, A. J., 1977, Speculations on the evolution of the lithosphere: Precambrian Research, v. 5, p. 249–260.

Baer, A. J., Emslie, R. F., Irving, E., and Tanner, J. G., 1974, Grenville geology and plate tectonics: Geoscience Canada, v. 1, p. 54–61.

Ball, E., 1980, An example of very consistent brittle deformation over a wide intracontinental area: The late Pan-African fracture system of the Tuareq and Nigerian Shield: Tectonophysics, v. 61, p. 363–379.

Barker, F., Arth, J. G., and Hudson, T., 1981, Tonalites in crustal evolution: *in* Moorbath, S., and Windley, B. F., eds., The origin and evolution of the Earth's continental crust: Philosophical Transactions Royal Society of London Series A, v. A301, p. 293–303.

Barnes, S. J., and Sawyer, E. W., 1980, An alternative model for the Damara mobile belt: Ocean crust subduction and continental convergence: Precambrian Research, v. 13, p. 297–336.

Berthelsen, A., 1980, Towards a palinspastic tectonic analysis of the Baltic Shield, *in* Cogné, J., and Slansky, M., eds., Geology of Europe: Bureau de Recherches Géologiques et Minières, Orléans, France, p. 5–21.

Bowes, D. R., 1980, Correlation in the Svecokarelides and a crustal model, *in* Mitrofanov, F. P., ed., Principles and criteria of subdivision of Precambrian in mobile zones: Leningrad, Nauka, p. 294–303.

Briden, J. L., 1977, Palaeomagnetism and Proterozoic tectonics: Tectonophysics, v. 38, p. 167–168.

Brown, G. C., 1981, Space and time in granite plutonism: Philosophical Transactions Royal Society of London Series A, v. A301, p. 321–336.

Burke, K., Dewey, J. F., and Kidd, W.S.F., 1976, Precambrian palaeomagnetic results compatible with contemporary operation of the Wilson Cycle: Tectonophysics, v. 33, p. 287–299.

Caby, R., Bertrand, J. M., and Black, R., 1981, Pan-African ocean closure and continental collision in the Hoggar-Iforas segment, central Sahara, *in* Kröner, A., ed., Precambrian plate tectonics: Elsevier, Amsterdam, p. 407–434.

Cathles, L. M., Cuber, A. L., Lenagh, T. C., Dudas, F., and Horikoshi, E., 1980, Kuroko massive sulfide deposits in Japan: Products of an attempt to form a new marginal basin?: Geological Society of America Abstracts with Programs, v. 12, p. 400.

Cavanaugh, M. D., and Nairn, A.E.M., 1980, The role of the geologic province in Precambrian paleomagnetism: Earth Science Reviews, v. 16, p. 257–276.

Chandler, F. W., and Schwarz, E. J., 1980, Tectonics of the Richmond Gulf area, northern Quebec—a hypothesis: Geological Survey of Canada, Paper 80-1A, p. 59–68.

Chappell, J. F., Brown, R. L., and Moore, J. M., Jr., 1975, Subduction and continental collision in the Grenville province of Southeastern Ontario: Geological Society of America Abstracts with Programs, v. 7, p. 733–734.

Chikhaoui, M., Dupuy, C., and Dostal, J., 1980, Geochemistry and petrogenesis of late Proterozoic volcanic rocks from North-western Africa:

Contributions to Mineralogy and Petrology, v. 73, p. 375–388.
Choudhuri, A., 1980, The early Proterozoic greenstone belts of the northern Guiana Shield, South America: Precambrian Research, v. 13, p. 363–374.
Cogné, J., and Wright, J. B., 1980, L'orogène cadomien, *in* Cogné, J., and Slansky, M., eds., Geology of Europe: Bureau de Recherches Géologiques et Minières, Orléans, France, p. 29–55.
Condie, K. C., and Moore, J. M., 1977, Geochemistry of Proterozoic volcanic rocks from the Grenville province, eastern Ontario, *in* Baragar, W.R.A., and others, eds., Volcanic regimes in Canada: Geological Association of Canada Special Paper 16, p. 149–168.
Crawford, A. J., and Keays, R. R., 1978, Cambrian greenstone belts in Victoria: marginal sea-crust slices in the Lachlan fold belt of SE Australia: Earth and Planetary Science Letters, v. 41, p. 197–208.
Davidson, D., 1973, Plate tectonics model for the Musgrave Block–Amadeus Basin complex of Central Australia: Nature, Physical Science, v. 245, p. 21–23.
Dewey, J. F., and Windley, B. F., 1981, Growth and differentiation of the continental crust, *in* Moorbath, S., and Windley, B. F., eds., The origin and evolution of the Earth's continental crust: Philosophical Transactions Royal Society of London Series A, v. A301, p. 189–206.
Dunlop, D. J., York, D., Berger, G. W., Buchank, L., and Stirling, J. M., 1980, The Grenville province: A paleomagnetic case-study of Precambrian continental drift, *in* Strangway, D. W., ed., The continental crust and its mineral deposits: Geological Association of Canada Special Paper 20, p. 487–502.
Engel, A.E.J., Itson, S. P., Engel, C. G., Stickney, D. M., and Cray, E. J., 1974, Crustal evolution and global tectonics: A petrogenetic view: Geological Society of America Bulletin, v. 85, p. 843–858.
Engel, A.E.J., Dixon, T. H., and Stern, R. J., 1980, Late Precambrian evolution of Afro-Arabian crust from ocean arc to craton: Geological Society of America Bulletin, Part 1, v. 91, p. 699–706.
Embleton, B.J.J., and Schmidt, P. W., 1979, Recognition of common Precambrian polar wandering reveals a conflict with plate tectonics: Nature, v. 282, p. 705–707.
Emslie, R. F., 1978, Anorthosite massifs, rapakivi granites and late Proterozoic rifting of North America: Precambrian Research, v. 7, p. 61–98.
Falkum, T., and Petersen, J. S., 1980, The Sveconorwegian orogenic belt, a case of late-Proterozoic plate collision: Geologisch Rundschau, v. 69, p. 622–647.
Frisch, W., and Al-Shanti, A., 1977, Ophiolite belts and the collision of island arcs in the Arabian Shield: Tectonophysics, v. 43, p. 293–306.
Gibb, A. K., 1980, The Archean-Proterozoic transition: Perspective from the Guiana Shield: Geological Society of America Abstracts with Programs, v. 12, p. 433.
Gibb, R. A., 1975, Slave-Churchill collision tectonics: Nature, v. 271, p. 50–52.
Gibb, R. A., and Walcott, R. I., 1971, A Precambrian suture in the Canadian Shield: Earth and Planetary Science Letters, v. 10, p. 417–422.
Gibb, R. A., Thomas, M. D., and Mukhopadhyay, M., 1980, Proterozoic sutures in Canada: Geoscience Canada, v. 7, p. 149–154.
Grant, N. K., 1973, Orogeny and reactivation to the west and southeast of the West African craton, *in* Nairn, A.E.M., and Stehli, F. G., eds., The ocean basins and margins: New York, Plenum Press, v. 1, p. 447–492.
Gupta, A., Basu, A., and Ghosh, P. K., 1980, The Proterozoic ultramafic and mafic lavas and tuffs of the Dalma greenstone belt, Singhbhum, eastern India: Canadian Journal of Earth Sciences, v. 17, p. 210–231.
Hamilton, W., 1981, Crustal evolution by arc magmatism, *in* Moorbath, S., and Windley, B. F., eds., The origin and evolution of the Earth's continental crust: Philosophical Transactions Royal Society of London Series A, v. A301, p. 279–291.
Hargraves, R. B., 1976, Precambrian geologic history: Science, v. 193, p. 363–371.
Hietanen, A., 1975, Generation of potassium-poor magmas in the northern Sierra Nevada and the Svecofennian of Finland: Journal of Research, U.S. Geological Survey, v. 3, p. 631–645.
Hildebrand, R. S., 1981, Early Proterozoic La Bine Group of Wopmay Orogen: Remnant of a continental volcanic arc developed during oblique convergence, *in* Campbell, F.H.A., ed., Proterozoic basins in Canada: Geological Survey of Canada Paper, v. 81–10, p. 133–156.
Hoffman, P. F., 1980a, Wopmay orogen: A Wilson cycle of early Proterozoic age in the northwest of the Canadian Shield, *in* Strangway, D. W., ed., The continental crust and its mineral deposits: Geological Association of Canada Special Paper 20, p. 523–552.
—— 1980b, Paired plutonic belts of Wopmay Orogen, NWT and signature of Proterozoic continental collisions?: Geological Society of America Abstracts with Programs, v. 12, p. 448.
Hynes, A., and Francis, D., 1981, Tectonic evolution of the Cape Smith fold belt, northern Ungava: Geological Association of Canada Abstracts, v. 6, p. A28.
Irving, E., and McGlynn, J. C., 1981, On the coherence, rotation and paleolatitude of Laurentia in the Proterozoic, *in* Kröner, A., ed., Precambrian plate tectonics: Amsterdam, Elsevier, p. 561–598.
Irving, E., Emslie, R. F., and Ueno, H., 1974, Upper Proterozoic paleomagnetic poles from Laurentia and the history of the Grenville structural province: Journal of Geophysical Research, v. 79, p. 5491–5502.
Kröner, A., 1975, Late Precambrian formation in the western Richtersveld, northern Cape Province: Royal Society South Africa Transactions, v. 41, p. 375–433.
—— 1980, Pan-African crustal evolution: Episodes, v. 1980, p. 3–8.
Leblanc, M., and Lancelot, J. R., 1980, Interprétation géodynamique du domaine pan-Africain (Précambrien terminal) de l'Anti-Atlas (Maroc) à partir de données géologiques et géochronologiques: Canadian Journal of Earth Sciences, v. 17, p. 142–155.
Lewry, J. F., 1981, Lower Proterozoic arc-microcontinent collisional tectonics in the western Churchill Province: A provisional evolutionary model: Geological Association of Canada Abstracts, v. 6, p. A35.
Lewry, J. F., and Sibbald, T.I.I., 1980, Thermotectonic evolution of the Churchill Province in northern Saskatchewan: Tectonophysics, v. 68, p. 45–82.
Loberg, B.E.H., 1980, A Proterozoic subduction zone in southern Sweden: Earth and Planetary Science Letters, v. 46, p. 287–294.
Löfgren, C., 1979, Do leptites represent Precambrian island arc rocks?: Lithos, v. 12, p. 159–165.
McCurry, P., and Wright, J. B., 1977, Geochemistry of calc-alkaline volcanics in northwestern Nigeria and a possible Pan-African suture zone: Earth and Planetary Science Letters, v. 37, p. 90–96.
McGlynn, J. C., Irving, E., Bell, K., and Pullaiah, G., 1975, Palaeomagnetic poles and a Proterozoic supercontinent: Nature, v. 255, p. 318–319.
Milanovsky, E. E., 1981, Aulacogens of ancient platforms: Problems of their origin and tectonic development: Tectonophysics, v. 73, p. 213–248.
Moore, J. M., 1977, Orogenic volcanism in the Proterozoic of Canada, *in* Baragar, W.R.A., and others, eds., Volcanic regimes in Canada: Geological Association of Canada, Special Paper 16, p. 127–148.
Pedreira, A. J., 1979, Possible evidence of a Precambrian continental collision in the Rio Pardo basin of eastern Brazil: Geology, v. 7, p. 445–448.
Piper, J.D.A., 1976, Palaeomagnetic evidence for a Proterozoic supercontinent: Philosophical Transactions Royal Society of London, v. A280, p. 469–490.
Porada, H., 1979, The Damara-Ribeira orogen of the Pan-African-Braziliano cycle in Namibia (Southwest Africa) and Brazil as interpreted in terms of continental collision: Precambrian Research, v. 57, p. 237–265.

Ray, G. E., and Wanless, R. K., 1980, The age and geological history of the Wollaston, Peter Lake, and Rottenstone domains in northern Saskatchewan: Canadian Journal of Earth Sciences, v. 17, p. 333–347.

Rogers, J.J.W., Hodges, K. V., and Ghuma, M. A., 1980, Trace elements in continental-margin magmatism: Part 2. Trace elements in Ben Ghnema batholith and nature of the Precambrian crust in central north Africa: Summary: Geological Society of America, Part 1, v. 91, p. 445–447.

Roy, J. L., 1980, Paleomagnetism of the North American Precambrian: International Geological Congress, 26th, Paris, Abstracts, p. 613.

Roy, J. L., and Lapointe, P. L., 1976, The paleomagnetism of Huronian red beds and Nipissing diabase: Post-Huronian igneous events and apparent polar path for the interval -2300 to -1500 Ma for Laurentia: Canadian Journal of Earth Sciences, v. 13, p. 749–773.

Shackleton, R. M., Ries, A. C., Graham, R. H., and Fitches, W. R., 1980. Late Precambrian ophiolitic mélange in the eastern desert of Egypt: Nature, v. 285, p. 472–474.

Shanti, M., and Roobol, M. J., 1979, A late Proterozoic ophiolite complex at Jabal Ess in northern Saudi Arabia: Nature, v. 279, p. 488–491.

Sheraton, J. W., Offe, L. A., Tingey, R. J., and Ellis, D. J., 1980, Enderby Land, Antarctica—an unusual Precambrian high-grade metamorphic terrain: Journal of the Geological Society of Australia, v. 27, p. 1–18.

Shimron, A. E., 1980, Proterozoic island arc volcanism and sedimentation in Sinai: Precambrian Research, v. 12, p. 437–458.

Sillitoe, R. H., 1979, Porphyry copper-type mineralisation in early Proterozoic greenstone belts, Upper Volta, West Africa: Geological Association of Canada Abstracts, v. 4, p. 78.

Stauffer, M. R., Mukherjee, A. C., and Koo, J., 1975, The Amisk Group: An Aphebian (?) island arc deposit: Canadian Journal of Earth Sciences, v. 12, p. 2021–2035.

Tankard, A. J., Jackson, M.P.A., Eriksson, K. A., Hobday, D. R., and Minter, W.E.L., 1982, Crustal evolution of Southern Africa: New York, Springer Verlag, 523 p.

Tarney, J., and Windley, B. F., 1981, Marginal basins through geological time, *in* Moorbath, S., and Windley, B. F., eds., Origin and evolution of the Earth's continental crust: Philosophical Transactions Royal Society of London Series a, v. A301, p. 217–232.

Taylor, S. R., and McLennan, S. M., 1981, The composition and evolution of the continental crust: Rare earth element evidence from sedimentary rocks, *in* Moorbath, S., and Windley, B. F., eds., The origin and evolution of the Earth's crust: Philosophical Transactions Royal Society of London Series A, v. A301, p. 381–399.

Thomas, M. D., and Kearey, P., 1980, Gravity anomalies, block faulting, and Andean-type tectonism in the eastern Churchill Province: Nature, v. 283, p. 61–63.

Torsk, T., 1977, The South Norway Precambrian region—a Proterozoic Cordilleran-type orogenic segment: Norsk Geologisk Tidsskrift, v. 57, p. 97–120.

Ullrich, L., and van der Voo, R., 1981, Minimum continental velocities with respect to the pole since the Archean: Tectonophysics, v. 74, p. 17–27.

van Schmus, W. R., 1976, Early and middle Proterozoic history of the Great Lakes area, North America: Philosophical Transactions Royal Society of London, v. A28, p. 605–628.

Veizer, J., and Jansen, S. L., 1979, Basement and sedimentary recycling and continental evolution: Journal of Geology, v. 87, p. 341–370.

Wardle, R. J., 1981, Eastern margin of the Labrador Trough: An Aphebian proto-oceanic rift zone: Geological Association of Canada Abstracts, v. 6, p. A59.

Watters, B. R., 1976, Possible late Precambrian subduction zone in southwest Africa: Nature, v. 259, p. 471–473.

Watterson, J., 1978, Proterozoic intra-plate deformation in the light of SE Asian neotectonics: Nature, v. 273, p. 636–640.

Wilson, I. H., 1978, Volcanism as a Proterozoic continental margin in northwestern Australia: Precambrian Research, v. 7, p. 205–235.

Wilson, M. R., 1980, Granite types in Sweden: Geologiska Föreningens i Stockholm Förhandlinger, v. 102, p. 167–176.

Windley, B. F., 1977, The evolving continents: London, John Wiley & Sons, 385 p.

—— 1979, Tectonic evolution of continents in the Precambrian: Episodes, v. 1979, p. 12–16.

Windley, B. F., and Smith, J. V., 1976, Archaean high-grade complexes and modern continental margins: Nature, v. 260, p. 671–675.

Wyman, W. F., 1980, Proterozoic komatiites from the Sangre de Cristo Mountains, south-central New Mexico: Geological Society of America Abstracts with Programs, v. 12, p. 553.

Young, G. M., 1980, The Grenville orogenic belt in the North Atlantic continents: Earth Science Reviews, v. 16, p. 277–288.

Zwanzig, H. V., Syme, E. C., and Gilbert, H. P., 1979, Volcanic and sedimentary facies relationships at Lynn Lake, Manitoba: A reconstruction of parts of an Aphebian greenstone belt: Geological Association of Canada, Program with Abstracts, v. 4, p. 86.

Manuscript Accepted by the Society April 14, 1983

Printed in U.S.A.

Geological Society of America
Memoir 161
1983

Dynamics of the continental crust in Proterozoic times

J.D.A. Piper
Sub-Department of Geophysics
University of Liverpool
P.O. Box 147
Liverpool L69 3BX
England

ABSTRACT

Studies of recent years, notably from metamorphic terrains, have resolved the magnitude and direction of apparent polar wandering (APW) motions over much of Proterozoic times. This paper re-examines the case for a Proterozoic supercontinent, and shows that both the polarities and the positions of the Proterozoic paleopoles from the major shields conform to a single APW path using a unique reconstruction. These data imply that the continental crust was amassed together as a single lens-shaped body as heat loss by extensive small-scale mantle convection correlating with low rates of APW was replaced by a large-scale mantle convection system responsible for the Proterozoic mobile belt regime and correlating with high rates of APW. The later greenstone belts (ca. 2900–2200 Ma old) formed in permobile environments and early Proterozoic straight belts (> 2200 Ma old) formed between larger stabilized divisions of continental crust are oriented parallel to the long axis of the continent. This alignment is preserved by younger mobile belts and most tectonic trends. There was a progressive contraction of rapakivi-massive anorthosite magmatism towards one margin of the supercontinent as temperature gradients declined; most features linked to ocean lithosphere subduction are associated with this margin. Large-scale fracturing with the formation of aulacogens took place along the opposite colder margin. Peripheral parts of the supercontinent broke up apparently without major separation 1100 Ma ago, and the central parts broke up at the beginning of Cambrian times with the formation of a large ocean basin between the Gondwanaland and the Laurentian, Fennoscandian, and Siberian Shields; this event marking the end of Proterozoic times is defined by a number of chemical changes linked to the faunal diversification. Both of these episodes are defined by widespread alkaline magmatism and rifting, and the latter is linked to subdivision of a simple roll mantle convection system which appears to have pertained in some form during most of Proterozoic times.

The characteristic signature of the Proterozoic APW path is a closed loop with a hairpin near the apex. These features can no longer be correlated with tectonic/magmatic episodes and appear to reflect overturn in the driving mantle system. The ensialic mobile episodes follow periods when APW movements were relatively small and may be linked to a thermal blanketing effect of the continental crust. Since 2700-to 2200-Ma-old paleopoles from Africa, Laurentia, Australia, and India are not significantly different from one another on the supercontinent reconstruction, the continental crust has evidently been a highly coherent unit since late Archean times. Movements across later mobile belts do not appear to have been on a scale large enough to be detected by paleomagnetism.

INTRODUCTION

Assessments of the distinctive characteristics of Proterozoic times identify this as an interval when large units of continental crust had stabilized with the development of extensive lineaments and dike swarms (Sutton and Watson, 1974; Davies and Windley, 1976). The way in which the continental crust moved with respect to the rotation axis is defined quantitatively by the paleomagnetic evidence and qualitatively by (very limited) paleoclimatic evidence. The former data have been evaluated in the context of several tectonic models (Piper and others, 1973; Irving and McGlynn, 1976), but in this paper I concentrate on a re-evaluation of the supercontinent model (Piper, 1976a) for the Proterozoic continental crust because, as will be seen, this both satisfies the existing paleomagnetic data and integrates closely with the geologic evidence.

TECTONIC MODELS FOR THE DATA

Paleomagnetic results from Precambrian shields have been variously examined in the context of two limiting tectonic models, namely, the opening and closing of ocean basins between cratonic nucleii moving with respect to one another, and the in situ development of ensialic mobile belts with movements between the cratons that are not (as yet) paleomagnetically detectable. It has been widely concluded that data from Africa (e.g., Piper, 1976a, 1976b), Laurentia (e.g., Irving and McGlynn, 1976), Australia (e.g., McElhinny and Embleton, 1976) conform most closely to the latter model because paleopoles (whilst seldom exhibiting precise agreement) form systematic sequences which lie along single APW tracks 10° to 20° wide (McElhinny and McWilliams, 1977). In retrospect, the early conclusions may seem optimistic because APW motions have proved to be more complex than realized at the time, but there is now little doubt that they are correct and conform with the largely, or wholly, ensialic nature of the mobile zones separating the critical data sets (Shackleton, 1973; Piper and others, 1973; Kröner, 1976). Alternative interpretations based on the former model (Burke and others, 1976; Cavanaugh and Seyfert, 1977) have not survived critical test (see McElhinny and McWilliams, 1977; Roy and others, 1978). An alternative intermediate model regards the Proterozoic mobile belts as zones of large-scale strike-slip motion on a sufficiently large scale to be paleomagnetically detectable (Onstott and Hargraves, 1981) but preserving the integrity of the shields.

With strong paleomagnetic support for the integrity of individual shields, the discussion has also been widened to intershield comparisons. Early discussion (Spall, 1972, 1973) suggested that the shields had individual APW signatures but was hampered by the paucity of data. Subsequent analyses identified similar APW signatures between Africa and North America (Piper, 1976a, 1976b) over the interval ca 2500 to 800 Ma B.P. Correlations of pre-1000-Ma paleomagnetic data between the Laurentian and Fennoscandian Shields also define a contiguous reconstruction (Piper, 1976a; Poorter, 1976) refined by subsequent studies (Piper, 1980a, 1980b), while comparisons between the pre- and post-1000-Ma record from these two shields specifically define a breakup and relative rotation at about 1100 Ma B.P. (Patchett and Bylund, 1977; Patchett and others, 1978). The Precambrian paleomagnetic record from Australia does not conform with the African record on the conventional reconstruction of Gondwanaland (Smith and Hallam, 1970; McElhinny and Embleton, 1976) but appears to conform with the African/Laurentian record in a different unique configuration (Fig. 1, Table 1), implying that the supercontinent of Gondwanaland resulted from the fusion

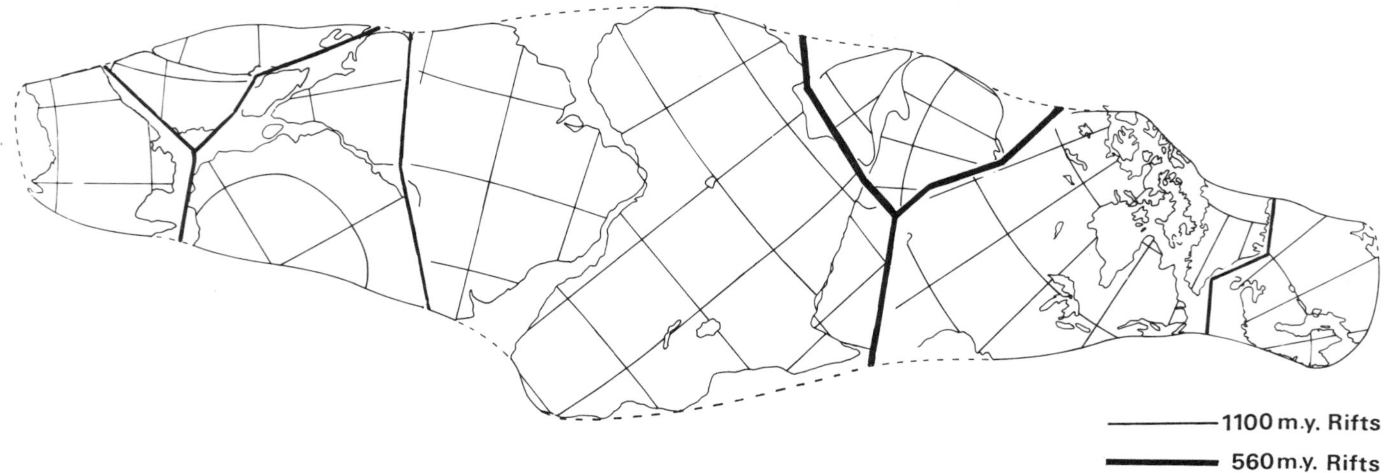

Figure 1. The Proterozoic supercontinent defined predominantly from paleomagnetic evidence (see text). The positions of the North and South China Shields and the Kazakhskaya Shield are inserted to complete the continuity of the sialic crust; these positions are supported by limited geologic evidence but no paleomagnetic data.

TABLE 1. THE PROTEROZOIC SUPERCONTINENT - EULER ROTATION POLES AND ANGLES OF THE SHIELD AREAS WITH RESPECT TO THE LAURENTIAN SHIELD

Operation	Euler Pole °E	°N	Rotation angle (°)	Reference
Fennoscandia to Laurentia (pre-1100 Ma)	8	21	-41	1*
Fennoscandia to Laurentia (post-1100 Ma)	274	80½	-66½	2
Siberia to Laurentia	309	66	+86	3*
Africa to Laurentia	138	73	+146	4
South America to Laurentia	329½	44	+57	5
and	138	73	-146	4
India to Laurentia	238	50½	+137	6
Antarctica to Laurentia	235	-75	-110	6
Australia to Laurentia	281	45	+116	6

Note: References: 1, Piper (1980a); 2, Patchett and others (1978); 3, Piper (1980b); 4, Piper (1976a); 5 Smith and Hallam (1970); 6. This paper.
*Modified to improve continuity of sialic crust (Fig. 1).

of at least two different plates in late Precambrian times (McElhinny and McWilliams, 1977). The apparent gap between Africa and Australia in the Proterozoic configuration (Fig. 1) is equivalent to the combined areas of the Indian and Antarctic Shields, and the present paleomagnetic data from India constrain the configuration to the approximate one shown in this figure; unfortunately these data have poor age control, and the model will no doubt require further adjustment here. The position of the Chinese Shield to the west of Australia follows Hurley and others (1971) and Crawford (1974); it conveniently fills the gap in the sialic crust, but there are as yet no significant paleomagnetic data to test it. The remaining gap between the African and Laurentian Shields is fitted by the Siberian Shield on the configuration proposed by Sears and Price (1978) on purely geologic grounds. The reconstruction of Figure 1 is achieved by one or more clockwise (negative) or anticlockwise (positive) rotations of the shields and paleopoles about a Euler pole or poles. The comparisons here are made with respect to the Laurentian Shield for which the relevant rotations and Euler poles are listed in Table 1.

Tarling (1979) illustrated examples from the North Atlantic area for late Paleozoic–Mesozoic times to show the limitations of using paleomagnetic data to derive paleomagnetic reconstructions: the *closest* match of the APW paths yields a reconstruction that does not accord well with the geologic and geometric constraints; these latter produce a reconstruction illustrating differences in the European and North American APW paths explicable in the context of geomagnetic field complexities and/or inadequacies in the data coverage. In Proterozoic times it would clearly be unwise to rely entirely on the paleomagnetic data. Since the well-constrained African, Laurentian, and Fennoscandian data yield reconstructions with the Precambrian Shields in direct contact, it is reasonable to infer that the remaining shields were similarly disposed; this is assumed in the reconstruction of Figure 1 but cannot be proved by the paleomagnetic data alone. Also a model such as this is only acceptable if it can be shown to satisfy the geologic constraints. Accordingly, the analysis of this paper falls into two parts: firstly, it is shown that all of the paleomagnetic data conform with this single reconstruction, and secondly, it is shown to satisfy the geologic evidence which is mainly in the form of the distributions of tectonic and magmatic events and certain paleoclimatic indicators.

THE DATA ANALYSIS

The data upon which the analysis is based are listed in Tables I to XVI of the pole listings in the *Geophysical Journal of the Royal Astronomical Society* and in papers published in the field of Precambrian paleomagnetism since the latest listing (1980). Some of these data are also listed by Irving and Hastie (1975) with annotated notes on specific studies. Paleomagnetic data from the Russian sector of the Fennoscandian Shield and the Siberian Shield are listed by McElhinny and others (1977) and McElhinny and others (1979) (after compilations by A. N. Khramov). The Ukrainian results appear to conform with the Fennoscandian data (Spall, 1973; Piper, 1980b), and the two areas are considered as part of the same shield. The data are summarized shield by shield in the figure captions.

The age assignments noted in the source listings are accepted unless they have been updated by more recent studies. All ages are adjusted to new decay constants listed by Steiger and Jäger (1977) involving a reduction of 2.1% in the Rb-Sr dates where $\lambda = 1.39 \times 10^{-11}$ yr^{-1} had previously been used and involving an adjustment of the K-Ar dates according to the table of Dalrymple (1980). In general, Rb-Sr isochron or U-Pb ages are preferred for the primary igneous magnetizations, and K-Ar and Rb-Sr mineral ages are preferred for the metamorphic uplift magnetizations and (sometimes) the secondary overprints. Rb-Sr isochron ages on sediments cannot necessarily be directly linked to the magnetizations unless the latter clearly have a dewatering origin (Perry and Turekian, 1973; Smith and others, 1983).

For the paleomagnetic data, the minimum acceptability criteria of McElhinny (1973) are also utilized. Whilst more rigid selection criteria have been argued for elsewhere, the greatest limitation on the analysis of Precambrian data is normally imposed by the age data, and no useful purpose is served by selection unless it also incorporates this. No poles with an age assignment are excluded from the analysis because they fail to fit the model; the only data not included are a number of poles from the Indian, Ukrainian, and Siberian Shields for which not even a general notion of the age is available. This very large measure of consistency is not only impressive confirmation of the model, but it also emphasizes the basic value of the paleomagnetic information: even where constituent magnetizations of a resultant vector have not been adequately resolved (common in studies prior to about 1973), one component usually predominates to the extent that the mean is interpretable in the context of either a primary or a secondary remanence. Whilst a rigid selection would not appreciably affect the overall geologic model presented here, a refinement in the data base will be necessary to answer a number of problems about which the present data are ambiguous; namely, whether (1) the APW swathes, which range from 10° to 25° in width, are really representative of actual polar movements or are just a gross average, (2) whether the Proterozoic geomagnetic field was simply an axial geocentric dipole, and (3) whether movements across mobile zones are paleomagnetically detectable.

Any continental reconstruction derived from paleomagnetic data requires that poles of the same polarity are being correlated. Owing to high rates of APW, notably in late Proterozoic times (Morris and Roy, 1977), polarities cannot be unambiguously inferred from the APW path. However, paleomagnetic studies yield the ratio of poles to antipoles in any study, and if we are correlating predominantly poles with poles and antipoles with antipoles the overall analysis is clearly reinforced. These are indicated in the figures as solid or open symbols, respectively.

THE SINGLE PROTEROZOIC APW PATH

The reconstruction of Figure 1 is confirmed by the pre-2200-Ma data from the central (Africa) and peripheral (Australia, Laurentia) parts of the reconstruction. "Track 6" defined by Irving and Naldrett (1977) from the Laurentian Shield is precisely applicable to the data from elsewhere (Fig. 2), incorporating the shift between poles older than ca 2450 Ma and younger than 2400 Ma, and the anticlockwise loop defined by Morris (1977a). In Figure 2 and subsequent figures the paleopoles applicable to each part of the Proterozoic interval are summarized together with relevant notes on key data points. The rapid APW movement

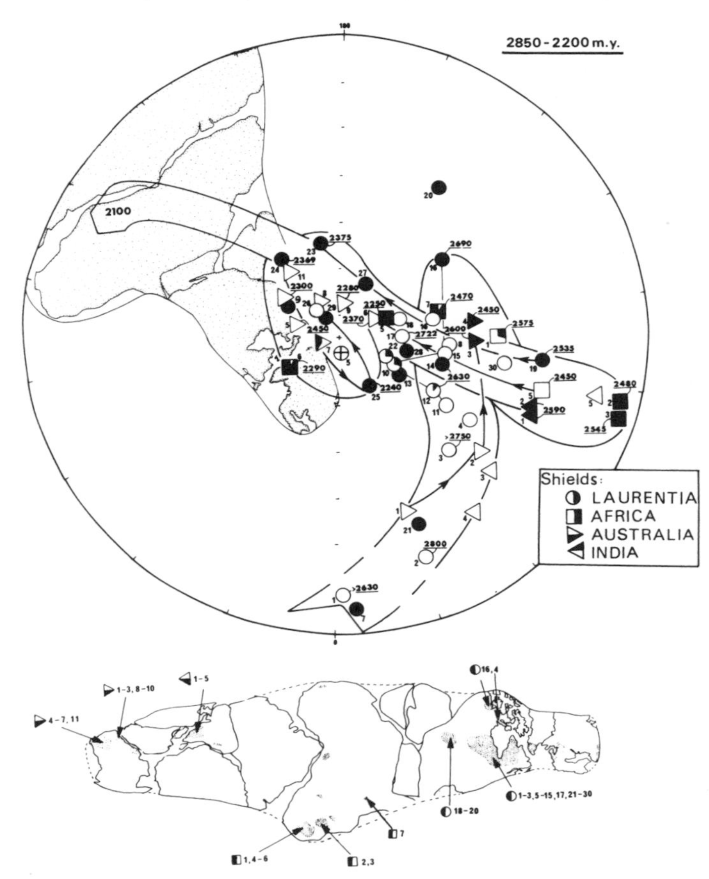

Figure 2. *Note:* The paleopoles utilized in this and subsequent diagrams are summarized in the Tables to number XVI of the *Geophysical Journal of the Royal Astronomical Society* or in references given in the text. All poles are plotted after the rotations listed in Table 1, retaining the Laurentian Shield in present-day coordinates. In figures 2 to 7 and 9 and 10, closed symbols are poles, open symbols are antipoles, mixed symbols are divided according to the ratio of poles to antipoles; where this is not known, symbols are crossed or divided 50:50 if reversals are present. The method of age determination where known is given as: $^{+}$K-Ar, $^{++39}$Ar/^{40}Ar or K-Ar isochron age; *Rb-Sr mineral or isochron age; **U-Pb. For clarity only some of these ages are shown on the figures. The lines link paleopoles from the same rock unit, and the arrows illustrate the older to younger age relationships indicated by the field relationships or suggested by the blocking temperature spectra.

Tests in the Laurentian Shield confirming a pre-2200-Ma remanence apply to the Kamiskotia Complex (1), the Matachewan dikes (11–15), Archean gabbro (6) (Irving and Naldrett, 1977; Schutts and Dunlop, 1981), and the Gowganda 'A' component (25) (Morris, 1977a). Morris proposed the double anticlockwise loop to incorporate the Chibougamau greenstones (17, 2722 Ma, Superior Province), the Matachewan dikes (11–15, 2630 Ma, Superior Province), the Dogrib dikes (16, 2690 Ma, Slave Province), and the Thessalon and Mugford volcanics (23, 24, 2325 Ma and 2320 Ma, Superior Province), with the path retracing to incorporate the Gowganda 'A' component (2240 Ma), the Gowganda 'B' component, and the 2200- to 2100-Ma data plotted in Figure 3. The path between pre-Matachewan and Matachewan poles is identical to that between Australia poles 2 and 3 linked to 3000- to 2600-Ma metamorphic events and post-2450-Ma poles. Part of the Laurentian APW identified by Morris (1977a) and Irving and Naldrett (1977) is incorporated by the motion between African poles 2 and 3 (2540–2480 Ma), the Lower and Upper Ventersdorp lavas (2450–2250 Ma), and the Gaberones granite (6, 2290 Ma). Dike swarms from Australia assigned to the interval 2450 to 2280 fall along the post-2400-Ma loop as defined by Morris.

Paleomagnetic poles assigned to pre-2200-Ma times in approximate order of age (where known) are:

LAURENTIAN SHIELD: 1, Kamiskotia Complex (>2630*); 2, Dundonald Sill (~2800); 3, Skead Group (>2750**); 4, unmetamorphosed Kaminak dikes (2370*); 5, Frechville greenstone; 6, Archean gabbro; 7, Archean basalt-gabbro; 8, Pike's Hill lava; 9, Archean gneiss; 10, Poohbah alkaline complex (2706–2556^{+}); 11–15, Matachewan dikes (2630**); 16, Dogrib dikes (2690**); 17, Chibougamau greenstone sills (2722*); 18, Stillwater Complex (2690*'**); 19, 20, Beartooth dikes (2765* 2450*); 21, 22, Shelley Lake granite, group 1 and group 2 (2595^{++}); 23, Thessalon volcan-

at 2200 to 2100 Ma B.P. (Fig. 3) comprises "Track 5" of Roy and Lapointe (1976). The magnitude of this motion is defined (Fig. 3) by positive contact tests on both the westerly and southerly directions present in the Nipissing diabase and Abitibi dikes (Roy and Lapointe, 1976; Irving and Naldrett, 1977; Morris, 1979), although the sense of this motion is not yet resolved (cf. Symons, 1971, and Morris, 1979) and Figure 2 illustrates only one possible interpretation. The southerly directions are coincident with ca 2100-Ma data from Africa.

The scale of APW motion between 2000 and 1750 Ma B.P. is defined approximately by the stratigraphic sequence of poles from the Coronation Geosyncline and Authapuscow Aulacogen as an elongate loop (Fig. 4) that incorporates the sequence of poles from the Sudbury Complex, a probable Hudsonian overprint in the Superior Province, as well as the highest blocking temperature components from the Hudsonian-age mobile terrain in northwest Scotland at its ca 1800-Ma apex. The ca 1900 to 1800-Ma-old swathe is identically defined by the sequence of poles from intrusive complexes, the Mashonaland dolerites and the Waterberg Sandstones of southern Africa as well as by a range of poles from Australia. Data points from India and South America also fall within this loop, although their age control is not as good. Magnetizations from the highest levels of the Authapuscow Geosyncline, together with a prominent overprint in these formations (Evans and others, 1980), define the hairpin at 1800 to 1750 ma B.P., and the subsequent southeast-northwest motion is recognized both in the sequence of post-Hudsonian magnetizations in the metamorphic terrains of the Laurentain and Fennoscandian Shields and in supracrustal suites in the former shield (Park, 1977, and Fig. 5). Data from other shields for the 1750 to 1320-Ma-old interval are rather few, but the single loop defined by the Laurentian and Fennoscandian paleopoles incorporates poles from South America and paleopole sequences from the Australian Shield. Subsequent data for the 1450-to 1200-Ma-old interval also define a single loop using the same unique reconstruction (Fig. 6), parts of which are defined by the sequences within Laurentian anorthosites and volcanic provinces. The rapid APW motion at 1150 to 1120 Ma B.P. identified from the late Gardar dike swarms and alkaline complexes links the paleopole record from the ca. 1200-Ma-old Jotnian and Mackenzie episodes with the Keweenawan paleopoles (1120–1040 Ma). The outward and return paths at ca. 1100 Ma B.P. are so close in time and space (cf. Figs. 6 and 7) that the assignment of some individual units such as the Logan diabases to either limb is in doubt. The return path at ca. 1120 to 1040 Ma B.P. is defined by the sequence of reversely to normally magnetized Keweenawan rocks terminating in the paleopole sequence from the Jacobsville Sandstone (Roy and Robertson, 1978) and from the Lower and Upper Torridonian sediments (Smith and others, 1983). This part of the track is precisely defined by a contemporaneous sequence of paleopoles from either side of the Damaran belt in South West Africa (Fig. 7).

The post-Jotnian dolerites (poles 9–14 in Fig. 6) dated 1290 to 1180 Ma B.P. are the youngest data from the Fennoscandian Shield to conform to the reconstruction of Figure 1 (Patchett and others, 1978). Post-1000-Ma poles conform to a reconstruction with the shields again in juxtaposition but with the Fennoscandian Shield rotated clockwise (Patchett and Bylund, 1977; Piper, 1980a). Breakup of this part of the supercontinent is thus constrained to the interval 1280 to 1050 Ma B.P., and a close genetic link with the Keweenawan rifting is implied. Precursors to final continental breakup are identified for nearly 100 Ma prior to this and include the earliest alkaline magmatism and basaltic volcanism association with the Gardar rifting in South Greenland at 1299 to 1280 Ma B.P., the intrusion right across the width of the shield of the Mackenzie (1257–1232 Ma), Sudbury (1205–1189 Ma) and mid-Gardar (1250–1210 Ma) dikes, intrusion at the northwest extremity of the Mackenzie swarm of the Muskox complex (1214 Ma) and Coppermine Group (1240 Ma), and the last alkaline complexes in the Gardar Province (Fig. 8) during the initial phases of the main Keweenawan magmatism (1160–1080 Ma). These last events, which define the apex of the Great Logan paleomagnetic loop (Figs. 6 and 7), were also coincident with the peak of the Grenville deformation (Baer, 1976). Thickening, remobilization, and deformation of the Grenville terraine were associated with dextral movement along the Grenville Front, which deformed the sediments of the Labrador Trough along *en enchelon* faults south of the front and opened the Keweenawan rift zone by pulling at a sub-block of the Laurentian Shield at the bulge south of the Great Lakes (Donaldson and Irving, 1972; McWilliams and Dunlop, 1978). The opening of the inverted L-shaped rift

ics (2325*); 24, Mugford basalts (2320*); 25, Gowganda prefolding 'A' remanence (2240*); 26, Gowganda Formation; 27, Firstbrook Formation; 28, Coleman Member (>2100*); 29, Gowganda post-folding 'B' remanence (~2200); 30, Cobalt Formation (2650–2100).

AFRICAN SHIELD: 1, Modipe gabbro, Botswana (2575*); 2, Great Dike of Zimbabwe (2480*); 3, satellite dikes of the Great Dike (2545*): 4, Lower Ventersdorp lavas (2450*); 5, Upper Ventersdorp lavas (2252*); 6, Gaberones Granite (2290*); 7, West Kenya granites (2470*–2580$^+$).

AUSTRALIAN SHIELD: 1, Duffer Formation (3452**); 2, Duffer Formation 'B'; 3, Duffer Formation 'C' (>2600); 4, YE dikes (2450*); 5, Ravensthorpe dikes (2450*); 6, Widgiemooltha dikes (2370*); 7, YA dikes (2500–1700*); 8, Mt. Goldsworthy lode ore MG3 (3000–2000); 9, BR dikes (2280*); 10, CD dikes (2300*); 11, Koolyanobbing–Dowd's Hill ore (2750–2200).

INDIAN SHIELD: 1, 2, quartz-magnetite metamorphic rocks (2590*); 3, 4, 5, metamorphosed dikes at Chitaldurg, Dharwar, and Hyderabab (~2500). Note that these poles come from a region also subjected to metamorphism at ca. 2000 Ma and may instead be applicable to the APW path illustrated in Figure 4.

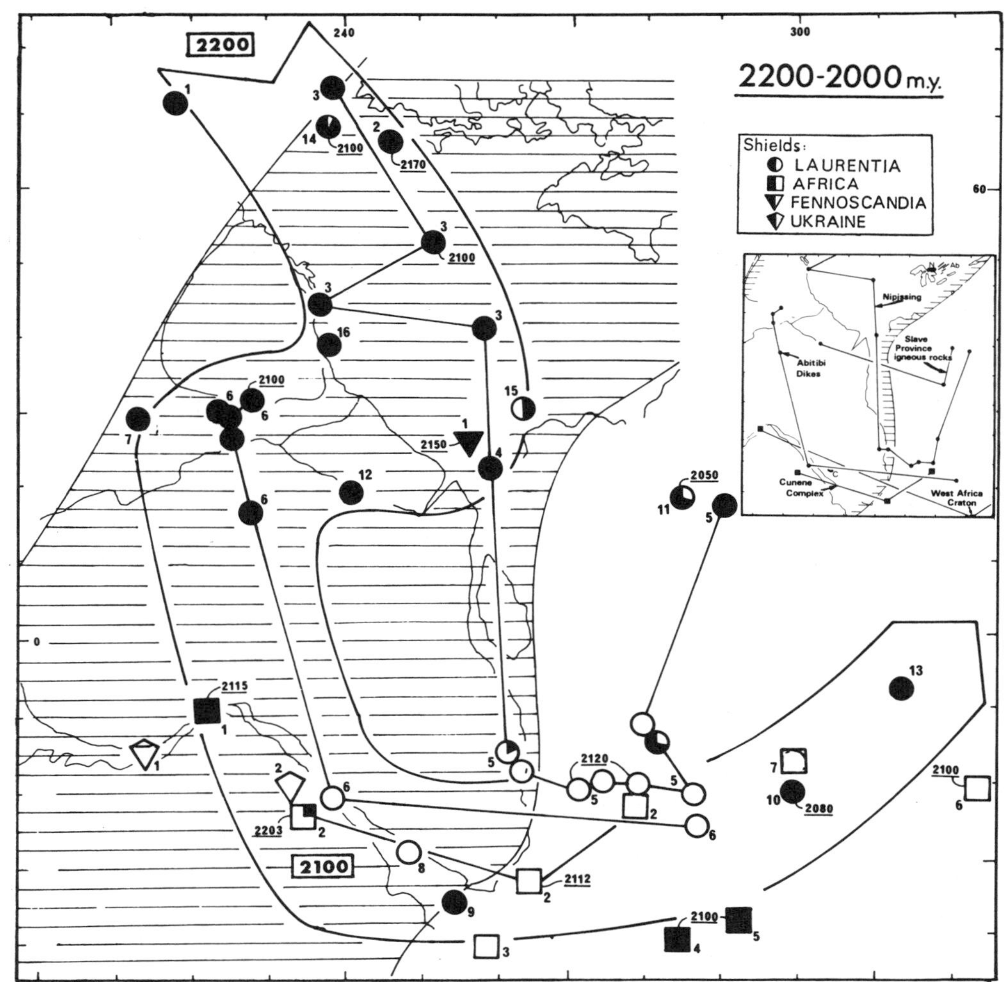

Figure 3. Paleomagnetic poles assigned to the interval 2200 to 2000 Ma B.P.
LAURENTIAN SHIELD: 1, Gowganda 'B'; 2, Big Spruce Complex 'D' (±2171*, 2067*); 3, Nipissing 'C' (2120*, 2110*); 4, Cobalt Formation, Nipissing Contact; 5, Nipissing 'D' (2120*, 2110*); 6, Abitibi dikes (2210*–2102*); 7, Marathon dikes (2172*); 8, Owl Creek dikes (2090⁺–1910⁺); 9, Sokoman iron-formation, pre-folding remanence (2200–2100); 10, Indian Harbour dikes (2080⁺); 11, Indin dikes (2050*); 12, 'X' dikes (2160⁺); 13, Duck Lake sill (2090⁺–1490⁺); 14, Otto Stock (2100**); 15, Gunflint Formation; 16, Soudan iron ores and volcanics.
AFRICAN SHIELD: 1, tonalites, NW Sahara (2115*); 2, Cunene anorthosite complex (2112*); 3, Transvaal System, lavas (~2203*); 4, syntectonic igneous rocks, NW Sahara (~2115*); 5, Tarkwaian intrusions, Ghana (~2100⁺'**); 6, Obuasi greenstone body (~2100⁺'**); 7, Orange River lavas (2100).
UKRAINIAN SHIELD: 1, amphibolitized diabases (2240⁺–2180⁺); 2, Taratash Complex (2080).
FENNOSCANDIAN SHIELD: 1, Jatulian igneous rocks (2150*).
This path may commence with the secondary remanence from the Huronian Supergroup (Gowganda 'B', which defines a major folding and remagnetization event prior to intrusion of the Nipissing diabase; Morris, 1977a) and the Big Spruce Complex (primary) in the Slave terrain. Two distinct directions of magnetization are derived from the Nipissing and Abitibi intrusions: a less common westerly direction (N1) yielding poles such as group 3 has one polarity, while the southerly direction (N2, pole group 5) has both polarities. Both of these groups of directions are now established as primary by contact tests and are indicative of appreciable APW motion and/or a protracted episode of intrusion at 2100 Ma. Evidence for the relative ages of N1 and N2 is currently ambiguous: polar path and stability data have been interpreted to indicate a sequence N1 → N2 (Roy and Lapointe, 1976), but Symons (1971) recognized N2 in Nipissing sills and N1 in cross-cutting dikes and suggested that the sequence N2 → N1 is applicable; until this point is resolved the polarity of the pre-2200-Ma path (Fig. 2) will remain in doubt. The N2 direction may be applicable to the ca. 1900-Ma path in Figure 4.

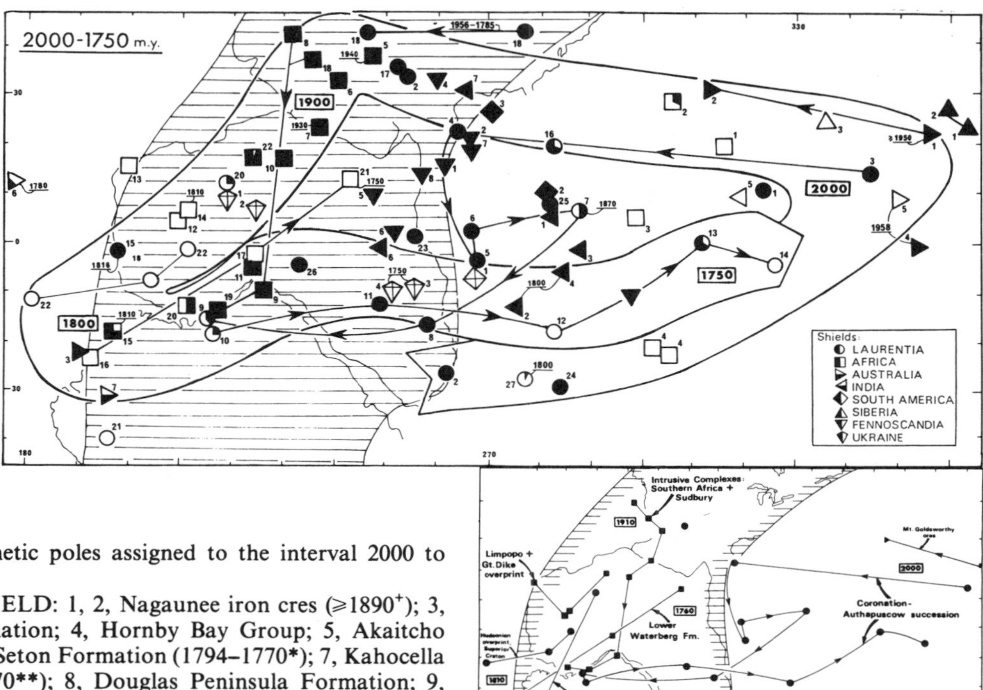

Figure 4. Paleomagnetic poles assigned to the interval 2000 to 1750 Ma B.P.
LAURENTIAN SHIELD: 1, 2, Nagaunee iron cres (≥1890⁺); 3, Western River Formation; 4, Hornby Bay Group; 5, Akaitcho River Formation; 6, Seton Formation (1794–1770*); 7, Kahocella Group, primary (1870**); 8, Douglas Peninsula Formation; 9, Stark Formation; 10, Tochatawi Formation; 11, Takiyuak Formation; 12, Pearson Formation 'A'; 13, Et-Then Group primary; 14, Pearson Formation 'B'; 15, Murdoch, Thompson Lake and Menihek Association (1816*); 16, Indin dikes (2050⁺); 17, Otish gabbro (1930⁺); 18, Sudbury Complex (1956–1785*); 19, Big Spruce 'X' (1900–1600); 20, late N2 diorites, West Greenland, high blocking temperature component (>1690*); 21, Laxfordian high blocking temperature component, NW Scotland; 22, Nipissing 'E' Hudsonian overprint; 23, Cameron Bay Group porphyry (1733*); 24, Retty peridotite, Labrador 'A'; 25, Slave craton overprint (SE directions); 26, Nordfjord gneisses, E. Greenland; 27, Peninsula Sill (1800**).
AFRICAN SHIELD: 1, dolerite intrusion, Ivory Coast (1730⁺); 2, Cunene anorthosite complex, younger facies (2030*); 3, Orange River lavas (2100–1850); 4, Aftout plutons (1940–1910*); 5, Aftout gabbro (1940–1910*); 6, Losberg intrusion (1910*); 7, Bushveld Complex (1910*); 8, Palabora Complex, pyroxenite + Vera Hill syenite; 9, Palabora Complex, eastern syenite, cross-cutting dike; 10, Vredefort ring complex (1930*); 11, diorite intrusions, NW Sahara (<1910*); 12, main dike swarm related to southerly extension of Great Dike, Limpopo overprint (ca. 1900–1800); 13, Great Dike extension, Ruri + Crystal Springs dike swarm, (overprint, ≤1810); 14, Sebanga dyke (~1810*); 15, Mashonaland dolerites (1810*); 16, 17, Waterberg Formation, lower sites (1910–1740*); 18–20, Palabora Complex groups 1–3; 21, Rust der Winter, acid volcanics (1752*); 22, Limpopo gneisses 'A'. Results 18 to 22 are listed by Morgan and Briden (1980).
SOUTH AMERICAN SHIELD: 1, Supamo-Pastara granite-greenstone terrain (2000–1900⁺); 2, 3, Imatuca granulite complex (2055–2000*).
AUSTRALIAN SHIELD: 1, 2, Mt. Goldworthy lode ores MG1 and MG2 (>1950); 3, Koolyanobbing 'A' deposit; 4, Mt. Tom Price ore (1958*–1800); 5, Mt. Newman ore (1958*–1800); 6, Hart dolerite (1780*); 7, YF dikes (~1700).
INDIAN SHIELD: 1–4, Gwalior Traps (1800*); 5, 6, Viskhapatnan charnockites (~1800); 7, Kondapalli Charnockites.
FENNOSCANDIAN SHIELD: 1, Central Karelia dolerites; 2, 3, Central Karelia sandstones (1870–1610); 4, Northern Karelia sandstones (1870–1610); 5, Kola Peninsula, gabbro-norite intrusions; 6, Omega gabbro-dolerite intrusions; 7, Shoksha Group, South Karelia; 8, Pedasel'sk and Pukhta Groups;
SIBERIAN SHIELD: 1, 2, Khapchan Series; 3, quartz-gabbro stock (2085–1850⁺).
UKRAINIAN SHIELD: 1, Bug-Podolia Series gneisses (2000⁺); 2, Oktyabr'sk alkaline massif (2060⁺); 3, Korosten Complex (1750); 4, Korosten granite (1750).

The APW path for this interval is defined in outline by the sequence of paleopoles from the Coronation Geosyncline and Authapuscow Aulacogen (1 → 14) and in Africa by 1900- to 1800-Ma intrusive events (6–10 and 15) with the Hart dolerite and Mt. Goldsworthy ores of Australia (6). It is further defined by overprint magnetizations related to a ca. 1800-Ma reheating event in the Limpopo mobile belt separating the Zimbabwe and Kaapvaal cratons (Jones and others, 1977, 12–14). A common change in ambient field polarity is observed here in the Laurentian, African, and Australian shields. The return path defined by the Authapuscow succession links the highest blocking temperature components in the Hudsonian terrains (20, 21, and probably 26), and a probable Hudsonian overprint in the Superior craton (the Nipissing 'E' magnetizations (23 in Fig. 4) of Roy and Lapointe (1976)) with the lower blocking temperature uplift-related magnetizations in the Hudsonian terrains and the overprinted magnetizations in the Coronation and related successions (plotted in detail in Fig. 5). A comparable movement is recorded in lower levels of the Waterberg red beds terminating in the Rus der Winter acid horizon dated 1750 Ma B.P. Figures 3 and 4 differ from earlier APW paths (e.g., Irving and McGlynn, 1976) which constrain all 2200- to 1700-Ma data into a single closed APW loop: the combined recognition of two sets of primary directions in the Nipissing and Abitibi, the earliest Hudsonian paleopoles at ca. 210° E, O° N, the sequence of magnetizations in the Authapuscow rocks, and possibly the Sudbury sequence, renders the case for a single APW loop between 2200 and 1700 Ma no longer tenable.

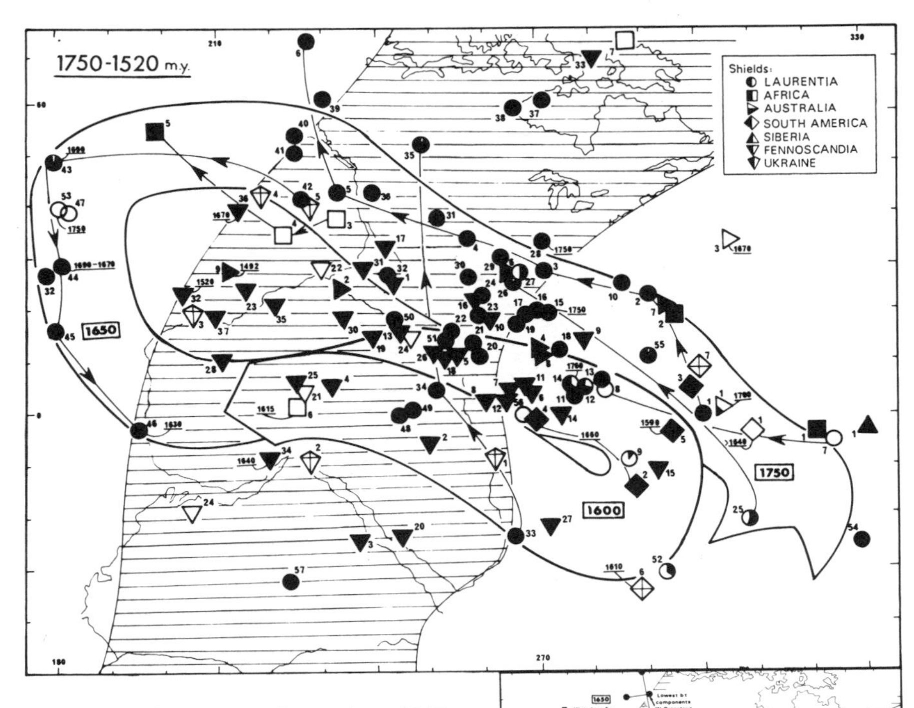

Figure 5. Paleomagnetic poles assigned to the interval ca. 1750 to 1500 Ma B.P.

LAURENTIAN SHIELD: 1–6, sequence of uplift magnetizations, Nagssugtoqidian terrain, W. Greenland (~1700$^+$); 7, Pearson Formation 'B'; 8, Pearson Formation 'C'; 9, Martin Formation (1830–1650$^+$); 10, Kaellinghaetten gneiss, W. Greenland; 11, Retty peridotite, Labrador 'B'; 12, Menihek Formation, Labrador 'B'; 13, Big Spruce Complex, 'Y'; 14, Dubawnt Group (1760*); 15, Itivdleq dikes (~1750$^+$); 16, Coronation geosyncline overprint; 17, Metamorphosed Kaminak dikes (1900–1620$^+$); 18, Nanacho Group (1850–1750$^+$); 19, Kahocella secondary; 20, Daly Bay metamorphics 'A' (1690–1590$^+$); 21, Sokoman iron-formation,-post-folding remanence; 22, Itivdleq dikes (1790–1650$^+$); 23, Kangamiut dikes south of Nagssugtoqidian Front; 24, Amitsôq gneisses; 25, Flin-Flon secondary (~1760*); 26, Flin-Flon Tertiary (1700–1600$^+$); 27, Gunflint Formation (≥1600*); 28, Spanish River Carbonatite (1750*); 29, Nordre Strφmfjord gneisses; 30, Angmagssalik gneisses (1800–1600$^+$); 31, 32, Molson dikes (1650–1280$^+$); 33, Seward Formation 'A'; 34, Seward Formation 'B'; 35, Seward Formation 'C'; 36, Wind River dikes (1880–1680$^+$); 37, Sagdlerssuaq dikes (1620^{++}); 38, 39, Ketilidian metavolcanics (1700–1600$^+$); 40, Amphibolitized dikes, north of Nagssugtoqidian Front; 41, Sarfanguaqland amphibolites; 42, Lewisian 'A2' (1650–1625$^+$); 43, Lewisian 'A3' (1690–1680$^+$); 44, Lewisian 'A4' (1690–1670$^+$); 45, Lewisian 'A5' (1500–1470$^+$); 46, Lewisian 'B' (1630*); 47, Eskimo Volcanics, (1750*–1625$^+$); 48 Flaherty Volcanics (<47, 1690$^+$–1640*); 49, Haig intrusions (1790*–1620$^+$); 50, Eskimo Volcanics, secondary; 51, Cape Smith Metavolcanics (1650–1450$^+$); 52, Lewisian Outer Hebrides (1720–1500*$^+$); 53, Richmond Gulf Volcanics, 54, Richmond Gulf–Manitounuk Island Volcanics; 55, Sparrow dikes (1550–1390$^+$, 1700^{++}); 56, Beartooth dikes, 7 and 8 (1500$^+$); 57, Iron Mountain ore.

It is possible that the lobe in the APW path at ca. 1750 m.y. should be extended 30° to the SE to accommodate the antipoles of 47 and 53.

AFRICAN SHIELD: 1, dikes intruding Gueld el Hadid Series (1760–1350$^+$); 2, Dikes intruding d'Akileb Deilel Series (1760–1350$^+$); 3–5, Waterberg Formation, higher sites (<1760**Ma); 6, Van dike Mine, dolerite dike, South Africa (1615*); 7, Limpopo overprint 'B'.

SOUTH AMERICAN SHIELD: 1, Cudivero-Caicara, acid metavolcanics (1960–1640*); 2, Roraima Sandstone (1660*); 3, 4, Roraima intrusive suite (1660*); 5, Parguaza pluton (1590*–1524**$^{,+}$); 6, Telles Pires (1610*); 7, Beneficente Group (1480*).

FENNOSCANDIAN SHIELD: 1, 2, Vuollerim gabbro; 3, Harads amphibolites; 4, Radmanso gabbro-diorite; 5, Tärendö Gabbro; 6, Tärendö acid rocks; 7, Ylivieska Gabbro; 8, Pohjanmaa gabbro-diorite; 9, Tammela gabbro-diorite; 10, Mikkeli gabbro-diorite, 11, Hyvinkää gabbro-diorite; 12, SW Finland gabbro-diorites; 13–16, Kallax Gabbro; 17, Korstrask Gabbro; 18, Niemisel Gabbro; 19, 20, Sangis Gabbro; 21–24, Gallivare basic rocks; 25, 26, Stora Lulevatten gabbro; 27–29, Jokkmokk basic rocks; 30, Loftahammar gabbro (1660–1470*$^+$); 31, Uppsala metabasites 'A' (≥1570*); 32, Hälleforsnäs giant dike 'A' (1520*); 33, Hame dolerites (1800–1640*); 34, Kumlinge dolerites (1640**); 35, Föglö dolerite; 36, Åva intrusive (1700–1670*); 37, Upper Dala Volcanics (≤1634*).

AUSTRALIAN SHIELD: 1, YD dikes (~1700); 2, YC dikes (≤1500, <YD); 3, GB dikes (1670*); 4, GA dikes (1470*); 5, Iron Monarch, positive group ore (1750–1510); 6, Iron Monarch, negative group ore (1750–1510); 7, Iron Prince ore (1750–1510); 8, Gawler Range Volcanics (1525*); 9, Lunch Creek lopolith (1492*).

SIBERIAN SHIELD: 1, Diabase and diorite, Aldan region (1590$^+$).

UKRAINIAN SHIELD: 1, Uman granite; 2, Turchinka gabbro;

(Fig. 8) was followed by infilling with lavas and sediments. The Torridonian sediments (paleomagnetic results summarized in Fig. 7) are related to the rift system along which the shield was ultimately dismembered: the lower part, deposited on an irregular surface, was folded prior to deposition of the Upper Torridonian as a fluviatile sequence derived from the northwest and gradually covered (rock units yielding poles 53 and 54 in Fig. 7) by a marine trough encroaching from the south (Williams, 1966).

The 1470- to 1125-Ma-old Australian poles 1–4 in Figure 6 and Indian poles 1–4 are the youngest poles from these shields to conform with the Proterozoic reconstruction of Figure 1, and continental breakup and relative movement to achieve the Gondwanaland configuration (Smith and Hallam, 1970) took place prior to 750 Ma B.P. Single poles from Antarctica and India (Fig. 7) and Australia (Fig. 9) conform closely with data from other shields on the Gondwanaland reconstruction and suggest relative motions restricted to a short interval at ca. 1100 Ma B.P., but this cannot be confirmed by the present data. This first breakup of the Proterozoic continental crust correlates closely with an important change in paleoenvironments as a sedimentation regime restricted largely to deep aulacogens gave way to transgressing circum-shield seas (Stewart, 1976).

The 1000- to 820-Ma-old APW path is a flattened loop (Fig. 9) with similar outward and return paths recognized by the sequence of uplift paleopoles from the Grenville Province (Buchan and Dunlop, 1976; Buchan, 1978; McWilliams and Dunlop, 1978; Roy and Blyth-Robertson, 1979; Berger and others, 1979) and the Sveconorwegian terrain in the southwestern parts of the Fennoscandian Shield (Poorter, 1975; Murthy and Deutsch, 1975; Stearn and Piper, 1983). Much of this path is also defined by supracrustal rocks of the Bukoban System in central Africa, and a part is probably represented by sediments of the Yenesei Ridge in the Siberian Shield (Fig. 9). A time gap in the paleomagnetic record at 820 to 740 Ma B.P. leaves this segment of the APW path in some doubt, but the subsequent path is identified by paleopoles from sedimentary formations in all the major shields (Fig. 10); many of these formations are specifically assigned to Upper Riphean and Vendian times, but since the 740- to 550-Ma-old segment of the path is dependent primarily on sediments where the primary or diagenetic natures of the magnetizations are not, in general, clear, this part of the analysis is correspondingly less satisfactory. However, the path does incorporate in correct sequence the few igneous magnetizations assigned to this interval (Fig. 10).

At about the beginning of Cambrian times the APW paths subdivide on the single reconstruction to follow independent paths (Fig. 10). Between the Precambrian-Cambrian transition and late Middle Cambrian times the Gondwanaland path executed a closed APW loop (McElhinny and others, 1974) taking northern Africa first across, and then back to, the South Pole; the size of this loop is currently disputed (Kirshvinck, 1978; McWilliams and McElhinny, 1980; Klootwyk, 1980). The APW paths for the Siberian, Fennoscandian, and Laurentian Shields moved rapidly across the present pole in Early Cambrian times and into low paleolatitudes by Middle Cambrian times when their respective paleopoles occupied radically different positions on the Proterozoic reconstruction. The analysis of Figure 10 thus demonstrates a breakup of these

---

3, Korosten gabbros (1550^{+}–1650^{+}); 4, Ukrainian diabases (1550^{+}-1650^{+}); 5, Olivine diabases and lamprophyres (1770^{+}); 6, Taratash Complex, secondary (1550^{+}).
The SE-NW APW motion is defined by post-Hudsonian uplift magnetizations (1 → 6, Piper, 1981) and the Seward and Menihek Formations of the Labrador Trough (33–35). Currently exposed levels of the Lewisian metamorphic terrain of NW Scotland, which also experienced rapid uplift (and magnetization) after the ca. 1800-Ma mobile episodes (Dickinson and Watson, 1976), exhibit a continuous sequence of magnetizations defined by the mean poles 42 → 46 → 52 linked to K-Ar hornblende ages mostly in the range 1690 to 1600 Ma. This path marginally overlaps with Greenlandic and North American data and is interpreted as a later extension (Smith and Piper, 1982). The oldest magnetization (47) from late Hudsonian rocks of the Circum-Ungava Geosyncline at Belcher Island lies on this path (Schmidt, 1980), but since field tests indicate that the Eskimo Volcanics (47) have a primary magnetization predating poles 48–50 and dated 1750 Ma and polarities are opposite to those in the Lewisian, it is likely that the Coronation Loop at ca. 1750 Ma should be extended 30° to the SE in this figure to incorporate this and poles 53 and 54 from the Circum-Ungava Geosyncline (Irving and McGlynn, 1979).
Another large body of data for this interval comes from the Svecokarelian terrain of Finland (Neuvonen, 1974) and the Svecofennian terrain of Sweden (Piper, 1980b). Both terrains were affected by Hudsonian age mobile episodes terminating at about 1750 Ma, and acquired their remanence during subsequent uplift and cooling. In northern Sweden Svecofennian poles 13–29 are broadly bracketed between intrusion of the Older and Younger Lina granites at 1780 to 1750 and 1530 Ma, respectively, but it is not yet possible to assign specific ages. Poles 19–24 and 27–29 are from syntectonic bodies, and 13–18, 25, and 26 are from late- to post-tectonic bodies. The areas experienced extensive volcanic activity between 1690 and 1605 Ma and granite and syenite intrusion between 1690 and 1530 Ma, and it is likely that most of the poles are applicable to this interval. The late- to post-tectonic Finnish gabbro-diorite poles 7–12 are close to poles for a range of post-tectonic dike swarms (39 and 40) in this part of the shield, which are similar in age or somewhat older than the type-Rapakivi granite (1640 Ma) in Finland (Neuvonen and Grundström, 1969); it is not yet clear whether their magnetizations postdate or predate the Rapakivi magmatism. The collective radiometric evidence suggests that the paleopoles from the Svecofennian and Svecokarelian terrains correlate with the younger part of the Laurentian loop, with which there is complete overlap, rather than the older (ca. 1750 Ma) part with which overlap is incomplete. The youngest part of the path illustrated here is probably the Hälleforsnäs giant dike dated 1520 Ma (32).

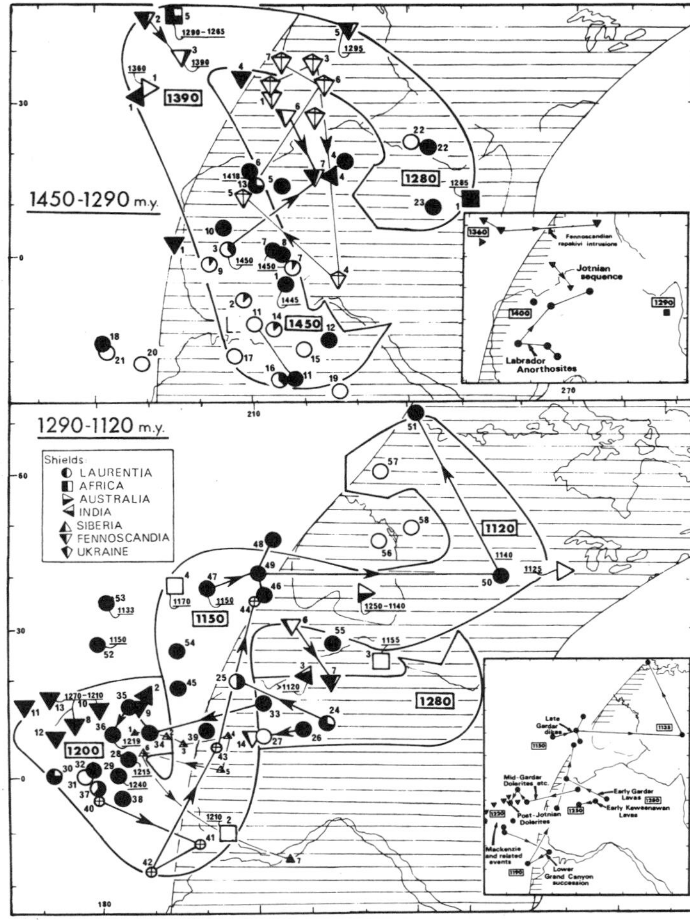

Figure 6. Paleomagnetic poles assigned to the interval 1450 to 1120 Ma B.P.

LAURENTIAN SHIELD: 1, Croker Island Complex (1445*); 2, Sherman granite (1380*); 3, Harp Complex (1450*); 4, Harp dikes (<3); 5, Harp country rocks; 6, Arbuckle granites (1400–1320*); 7, Michikamau anorthosite (1450–1400$^+$); 8, St. Francois rocks (1380–1250*); 9, Mistatin pluton (1310*); 10, Seal Lake Group redbeds (1320); 11, Sibley Group (1340*); 12, Spokane Formation argillites (1300?); 13, Nain anorthosite (1418*); 14–16, Upper Belt Supergroup, Klintla, Shepard, and Purcell Formations; 17, Missoula Group, Montana; 18, Grinnell argillite, Montana; 19, Pioneer shale, Apache Group, Arizona; 20, Uinta Mountain Group, Utah; 21, Big Cottonwood Formation, Utah; 22, Baron quartzite, Wisconsin, and Sioux quartzite, Minnesota; 23, Western Channel Diabase (1392*); 24, 25, Lower, Upper Gardar lavas (ca. 1283*); 26, 27, Lower, Upper Powdermill lavas (1220–1200); 28, Muskox intrusion (1214*); 29, Coppermine Group (1240*); 30, Mackenzie diabases (1250*–1230*); 31, Laramie Range anorthosite; 32, Rama diabase (1200–850$^+$); 33, BDO dikes (1251*–1212*); 34, 35, Mid-Gardar lamprophyre dikes (1249*–1228*), and Gardar NNW dolerite dikes (<34); 36, Kûngnât ring dike (1219*, <35); 37, Sudbury dikes (1205*–1189*); 38, Savage point sills; 39, South Trap Range lavas (1190*); 40–44, Grand Canyon Supergroup, stratigraphic succession of poles from lower formations; 45, Seal Group 'B'; 46, Narssaq gabbro; 47, Hviddal Giant Dike (1150*); 48, Gardar gabbro giant dikes; 49, NE dikes Tugtotôq (1150*–1140*); 50, 51, Ilímaussaq marginal syenites and fractionates (1140*, 1120*, <49); 52, Gila Country diabase sills (1140$^+$, 1150*); 53, Logan diabase (Canada, 1133); 54, Logan diabase (U.S.A.); 55, Aillik dikes; 56, Logan dikes reversed; 57, Alona Bay lavas; 58, Baraga County dikes.

INDIAN SHIELD: 1, Newer dolerites, Singbhum; 2, Bhima sediments (1300–1200); 3, Kaimur Sandstone (>1120*); 4, Cuddapah Traps (1400–1200).

AFRICAN SHIELD: 1, Pilanesberg dikes (1282*); 2, Kisii Series lavas (1210^{++}); 3, National kimberlite (1155*, 1140*); 4, Premier Mine kimberlite (1220–1170*); 5, Barby Formation lavas (≤1290*, 1265*).

FENNOSCANDIAN SHIELD: 1, Jotnian sediments, Finland; 2, Nordingrå gabbro-anorthosite (1385*); 3, Nordingrå granite (1385*); 4, Gavle granite; 5, Ragunda complex (1295*); 6, Jotnian (Dalarna) sediments; 7, Jotnian (Dalarna) lavas; 8, Nordingrå Complex, Jotnian remagnetization; 9, Vaasa dolerites, Finland (1270**, 1225*); 10, Satakunta dolerites, Finland (1236*, 1225*); 11, Market dolerites, Finland (1270**); 12, Post-Jotnian dolerites, East Sweden (1254^{++}); 13, Post-Jotnian dolerites, West Sweden (1290*–1210*); 14, Post-Ragunda complex dikes (<1295*). (More recent Rb-Sr dating of unit 2 (T. Lundqvist, 1981, personal commun.) suggests that it may be as old as 1500 Ma and relevant to the position of Australian pole 9 and Fennoscandian pole 32 in Fig. 5.)

UKRAINIAN SHIELD: 1, Avzyan Group, Malvinzer and Kataska sequences; 2, Avzyan Group, Green and Ushakovo sequences; 3, Avzyan Group, combined result; 4, Avzyan Group Revet sequence; 5, Zil' Merdak Group, combined result; 6, Katav and Zil' Merdata Groups; 7, Katavsh Group. (These sedimentary sequences are constrained by K-Ar ages in the range of 1350 to 940 Ma.)

AUSTRALIAN SHIELD: 1, Morowa lavas (1360*); 2, Giles Complex (1250$^+$–1140$^+$); 3, Lake View dolerite (1125*).

SIBERIAN SHIELD: 1, Oslgansk Series; 2–4, Tingusik Series; 5–7, Sukhopit Series. These sediments are constrained within a maximum age range of ca. 1300 to 930 Ma and may not belong to this sector of the path.)

A NE APW motion is defined by the Harp Complex, country rocks, and dikes (3–5) to the slightly younger Fennoscandian anorthosites (2–5), Australian pole 1 in Figure 6 with the extremity of the closed loop defined by the ca. 1295-Ma Ragunda Complex following in sequence to the 1285-Ma Pilanesberg dikes and the Jotnian lavas and sediments. The return path is defined by the stratigraphic sequence of poles in the Powdermill lavas (early Keweenawan 26 and 27) and the early Gardar lavas (24 → 25, 1280 Ma) in addition to the general trend between the 1290-Ma anorthosites and the ca. 1250- to 1200-Ma Jotnian-Gardar-Mackenzie magmatism and the sequence of Greenlandic dike swarms at 1250 to 1220 Ma (33 → 36). The stratigraphic sequence of poles from the lower part of the Grand Canyon Supergroup (Elston and Grommé, 1975) define the movement from the ca. 1200-Ma Mackenzie–mid Gardar-Jotnian paleopoles to 1220- to 1150-Ma African kimberlites and the later (ca. 1150 Ma) NE-SW dike swarms and giant dikes of the Gardar Province. These, in turn, predate the Ilímaussaq complex (50 and 51, 1140–1120 Ma) which defines a rapid APW movement towards the Laurentian Shield in common with Australian pole 4 (1125 Ma) and (?) certain Indian data.

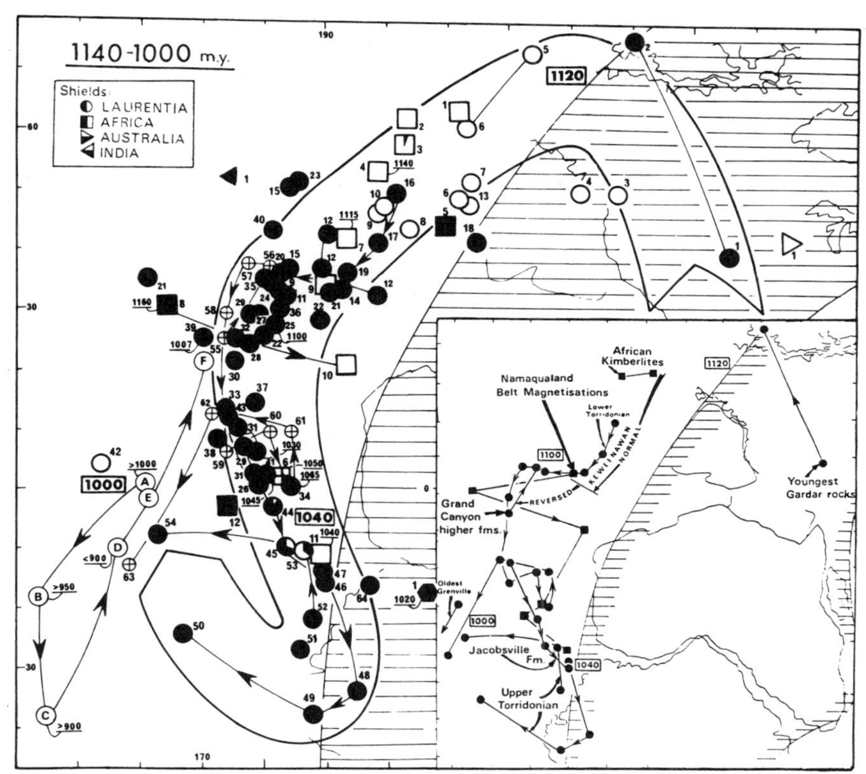

Figure 7. Paleomagnetic poles assigned to the interval 1120 to 1000 Ma B.P.
LAURENTIAN SHIELD: 1, 2, Ilímaussaq intrusion (1140*, 1120*); 3, Baraga County dikes; 4, Mamainse lavas (1040*); 5, Lower cape Gargantua volcanics; 6, Logan dikes (reversed group); 7, Marquette County dikes; 8, Duluth Complex (reversed sites); 9, Osler lavas (1115^+); 10, North Shore Volcanics (reversed group, 1135); 11, North Shore Volcanics (normal group, 1105); 12, Duluth Complex (three poles, normal group, 1115^+); 13, Thunder Bay dikes (reversed 1135^+, normal 1170–1150*); 14, Keweenawan intrusive (1120^+); 15, Keweenawan Gabbro, Wisconsin, Minnesota; 16–20, Stoer Group (in approximate stratigraphic order); 21, Endion Sill (1150^+) and Lester River Sill; 22, Beaver Bay Complex, basalts (1090^+); 23, Hazel Formation, New Mexico; 24, Upper Cape Gargantua Volcanics (1090^+); 25, Portage Lake lavas (1100^+); 26, Freda Sandstone; 27, Michipicoten Island lavas (952^+); 28, Copper Harbour lavas (1060*); 29, Pikes Peak granite (1030^+*); 30, Isle Royale lavas; 31, Nonesuch Shale (1065*–1025*); 32, Basalt dikes, Minnesota; 33, Nankoweap Formation (1000); 34, Cardenas lavas (1065*); 35, Logan dikes (normal group 1050^+); 36, Mamainse Lavas (1050*); 37, Copper Harbour conglomerate, secondary; 38, Fond du Lac Formation; 39, Kearsage rhyolite (1007); 40, Nemagonsenda carbonatite (1035^+); 41, Freda and Nonesuch Sandstone (1045*); 42, Seal and Croteau igneous suite (~950); 43–46, Jacobsville JIC, JIB, JIA, JISA; 47, Diabaig Formation; 48, Torridonian, Cape Wrath; 49, Applecross Formation, lower sites; 50, Applecross Formation, upper sites; 51, Applecross, basal sites, Loch Broom; 52, Applecross Formation, Loch Maree; 53, Aultbea Formation, lower part; 54, Aultbea Formation, higher part; 55–60, 34, 61–63, Grand Canyon Supergroup, poles from higher formations in stratigraphic order after Elston and Grommé (1975); 64, Bass Limestone is an earlier result from these rocks. A to F are mean thermochron poles from the Grenville Province (data for this interval are covered in detail in Fig. 9).
Note that the Keweenawan rocks defined as normal are reversed according to the interpretation of Figure 10 (see inset).
AFRICAN SHIELD: 1, Kanangono kimberlite, Ivory Coast; 2, Montrose kimberlite, South Africa; 3, Waterberg dolerites; 4, Umkondo dolerites (1140*); 5, Group de Char Formation, Mauretania (1019); 6, Chela Group Angola (1100–1050*); 7, Umkondo lavas (1090*); 8, Guperas lavas (1250**); 9, Koras Group, Kalkpunt Formation (1200–1000); 10, Auborus Formation (~1020, <8); 11, O'okiep intrusions (1020*, 1090–1050**); 12, Nosib Group (<1010**, >844*).
AUSTRALIAN SHIELD: 1, Lake View dolerite (1125*), (primitive reconstruction).
INDIAN SHIELD: 1, Mundwara Complex (1000–950) (Gondwanaland reconstruction).
ANTARCTICA SHIELD: 1, Vestfold Hills dikes (1020**) (Gondwanaland reconstruction).
Note that the Gardar rocks are reversely magnetized and are succeeded by normally magnetized lavas and dikes attributed to the Lower Keweenawan (Pesonen and Halls, 1979). The reversely magnetized Lower Torridonian straddles the N-R transition in the Keweenawan. In common with the Jacobsville Formation, which includes at least one reversal, polarity reversals are again encountered in the upper members of the Torridonian succession (where the stratigraphically highest poles define a migration towards the post-1050-Ma data from the Grenville terrain) and ca 1040-Ma African data. The last part of this path is defined both by the Applecross (49 → 50) and Aultbea Formations (53 → 54), probably because these are diachronous along the outcrop. A minimum age for the Keweenawan sequence is defined by the intrusive Bear Lake Rhyolite dated 986 Ma (data of Chaudhuri quoted in Henry and others, 1977). Parts of the APW path recorded by the Keweenawan and Torridonian rocks are also identified in the upper part of the Grand Canyon succession (poles 55–63, Elston and Grommé, 1975) including the Dox Sandstone, Cardenas Lavas, and Nankoweap Formations.

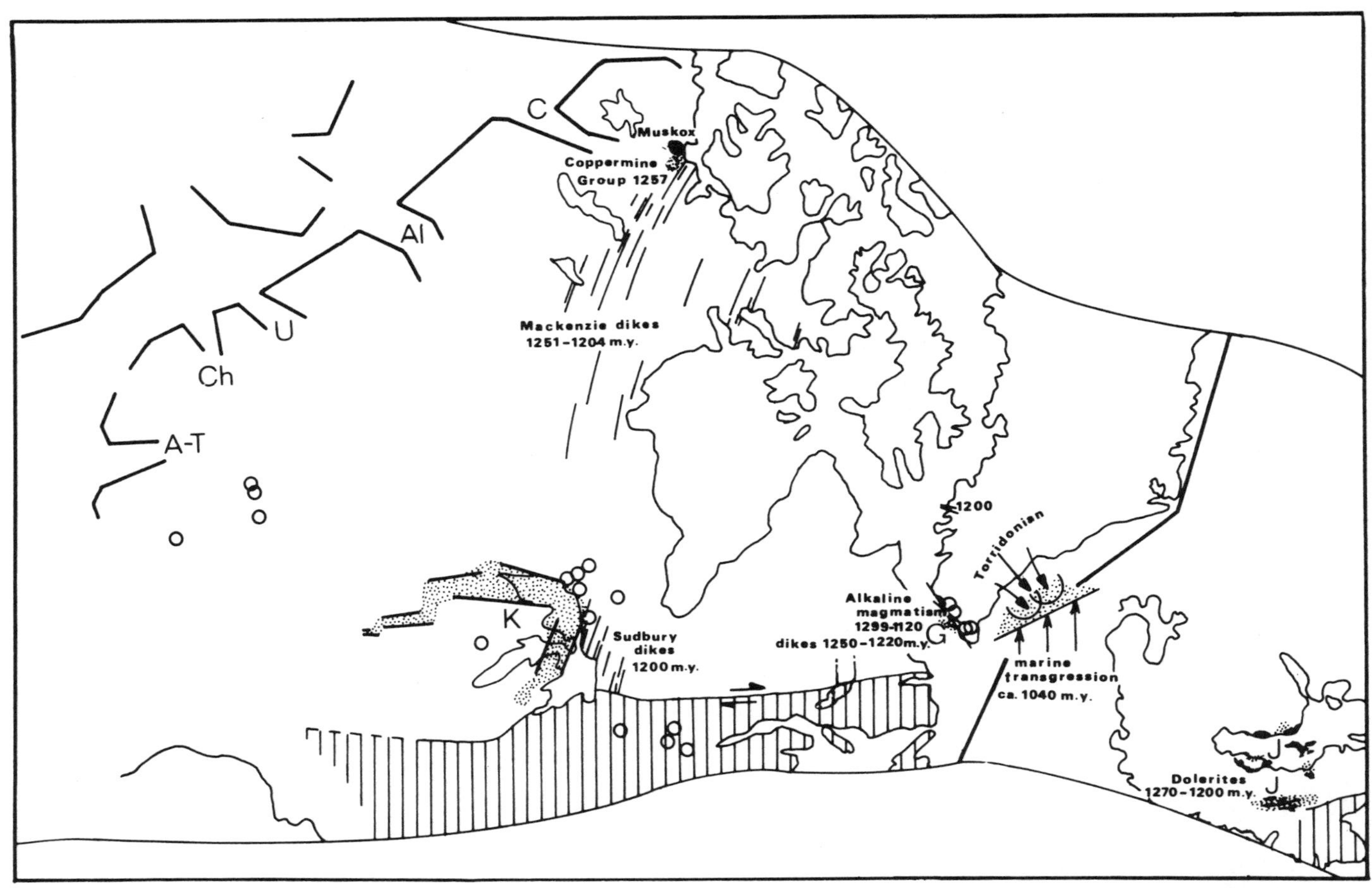

Figure 8. Features linked to fracturing and breakup of the Laurentian and Fennoscandian Shields at ca. 1100 Ma. Sediment-filled grabens (stippled in part) are lettered: A-T, Apache-Troy; Ch, Chuar; U, Uinta; Al, Alberta; C, Coppermine; K, Keweenawan; G, Gardar; J, Jotnian. Circles are ca. 1290 to 1050-Ma alkaline complexes. Vertical shaded areas are the Grenville and Sveconorwegian mobile episodes.

major shields at the base of the Cambrian with the rapid opening of ocean basins between the Laurentian, Fennoscandian, Siberian, and Gondwanaland Shields in Early Cambrian times.

ENVIRONMENTAL CHANGES AT THE PROTEROZOIC-PHANEROZOIC TRANSITION

Large-scale breakup of the Proterozoic supercontinent and development of new oceans near the base of the Cambrian terminated many of the conditions characteristic of the Proterozoic Era, and the paleomagnetic analysis now links faunal diversification with continental fragmentation and dispersal. This event is recorded by several chemical changes: the large increase in sulphur isotope ratio at the time (Holser, 1977) was probably achieved by the rapid release of brines accumulated in enclosed basins into the surface layer of the oceans. Later stages of this mixing cycle may have been associated with sulphide-sulphate transfers which restored nutrients to surface waters, increased the deposition of organic carbon, and raised phosphate levels (Holser, 1977). All of these effects would have combined with the increase in the length of the marine coastline to facilitate hard body secretion by the metazoa.

The progressive increase in the $Sr^{87}:Sr^{86}$ isotope ratio of seawater observed throughout Proterozoic times is interrupted at the beginning of the Phanerozoic and reflects a marked increase in the Upper Mantle contribution of strontium versus the continental contribution (Viezer, 1976). A sympathetic change in the $K_2O:Na_2O$ ratio of sedimentary and igneous rocks cannot be precisely linked to this transition, but it defines a return to values more typical of the Archean (Engel and others, 1974), reflecting increased incorporation of the products of sea-floor spreading and subduction-related processes into the continental crust.

LATE PRECAMBRIAN APW AND GLACIOGENIC DEPOSITS

Rocks of known or probable glaciogenic origin assigned to the late Precambrian are documented and discussed by a number of workers (Harland, 1964a, 1964b;

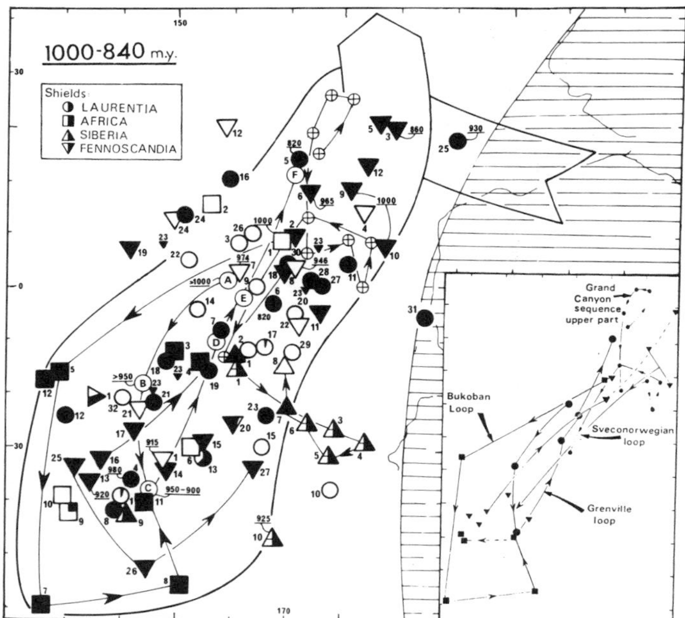

Figure 9. Paleomagnetic poles assigned to the interval 1000 to 800 Ma B.P.

LAURENTIAN SHIELD: (Paleomagnetic poles derived from the Grenville mobile belt and its margins are listed in alphabetic order because their ages are not directly known.) 1, Allard Lake anorthosite; 2, Frontenac dikes (this pole may belong to the APW path at ca. 650 Ma); 3, Grenville Front anorthosite; 4, 5, 6, Haliburton intrusion HA (960^{++}), HB, HC (820^{++}); 7, Indian Head anorthosite; 8, 9, Morin anorthosite M1, M2; 10, 11, Mealy Mountain E, NW; 12, Magnetawan metasediment; 13, Ottawa intrusions; 14, St. Urbain; 15, 16, Thanet gabbro complex, A, B; 17, Umfraville gabbro; 18, Wilberforce pyroxenite; 19, 20, 21, Whitestone anorthosite, W, Y, Z; 22, Seal-Croteau igneous suite (~950); A → F are the mean thermochron poles from the Grenville province as calculated by McWilliams and Dunlop (1978); 23, Keweenawan shock-induced remanence B; 24, Eileen Sandstone; 25, El Paso rocks (930*); 26, Michael Gabbro; 27, Orienta Sandstone, primary; 28, Rama diabase (935^{+}, 850^{+}); 29, Shabogamo gabbro; 30, Freda and Nonesuch Sandstone Formations, secondary; 31, Rapitan Formation 'X' component (900–825^{+}), 32, Steel Mountain anorthosite. Small open circles are the poles in stratigraphic order from the Grand Canyon succession.

FENNOSCANDIAN SHIELD: 1, Karlshamn dike (915*, 855*); 2, Tärnö dike (860*); 3, Bräkne-Hoby dike (860*); 4, Väby dike; 5, Fäjö dike; 6, Nilstorp dike (965*); 7, Arby dike (974*); 8, Falun dike (945*); 9, Bratton norite (1000^{+}); 10, Algon norite (1000^{+}); 11, Dolerite, Bratton; 12, Listed and Bolshavn "hyperites"; 13, Aana-Sira Massif (920^{+}*); 14, Rogaland Complex (900^{+}*); 15, Garsaknett body; 16, Rogaland Complex, north part; 17, Egersund-Ogna Massif; 18, Rogaland, 'Y' component; 19, amphibolites and hyperites, Bamble and Kongsberg (1100–950^{+}); 20, amphibolites, norites, and anorthosites, south Rogaland; 21, Hunnedalen dolerites; 22, Tuve dolerite, Gothenburg; 23, "Hyperite" dikes of south Sweden; 24, "Hyperites" of Kragero district; 25, Farsundite Complex; 26, Farsundite, south part; 27, Farsundite, north part.

AFRICAN SHIELD: 1, Bukoba Sandstone (>900–1000); 2, Abercorn Sandstone; 3, Klein Karas dikes (890^{+}); 4, Marico River intrusions; 5, Kigonero Flags (>890); 6, Florida Formation, secondary; 7, Gagwe amygdaloidal lavas (960^{+}, 820^{+}); 8, Manyovu Red Beds; 9, Bukoban dolerites (850^{+}, 810^{+}); 10, Mbala dolerites; 11, Malagarasi Sandstone; 12, Ikorongo Group.

SIBERIAN SHIELD: 1–8, Yenisei Ridge sedimentary sequences in stratigraphic order: 1, Gorbilok Group; 2, Udere Group; 3, Pogoryui Group; 4, Potoskui Group; 5, Shuntar Group; 6, Kirgitei Group; 7, 8, Nizhneangara Group; 9, Yenisei Group, Kuznets Alatau. (The maximum age range of these sediments is 1320–750 Ma.) 10, Burovaya Suite (925).

Single pole positions from the Grenville and Sveconorwegian terrains incorporate individual sites which often encompass the whole loop (Roy and Blyth-Robertson, 1979), and hematite poles from some units correspond with magnetite poles from others. For this reason a simple single-stage cooling model may not be applicable everywhere and the assessment based on thermochron zonations provides a useful, but oversimplified, summary. To derive mean paleopoles (A → F) McWilliams and Dunlop (1978) assumed (with a few exceptions) that the Grenville magnetizations are postmetamorphic in age and followed a cooling sequence as defined by the K-Ar mica ages, although they doubtless have somewhat older absolute ages. The Sveconorwegian Province is defined by mobilization events with comparable ages to the Grenville: mineral ages range from 1200 to 850 Ma, although Rb-Sr isochrons define earlier events in excess of 1600 Ma (Versteeve, 1975). The ca. 1500 km^2 Rogaland Complex intruded at depths of ca. 25 to 35 km (de Waard and others, 1974) includes the Egersund-Ogna body (17) followed by a range of noritic and monzonitic rocks, the Aana-Sira anorthosites (13), and finally the farsundite complex (25–27) at the end of the main deformational phases; zircon ages in the range 977 to 945 Ma date intrusion of these bodies while the metamorphic country rocks were undergoing granulite facies metamorphism at ca. 1000 to 950 Ma. Mineral ages in the range 900 to 850 Ma from the migmatites are less than 50 Ma younger than Rb-Sr isochron ages and imply uplift commencing during or shortly after the major intrusive episode. Paleomagnetic studies resolve steep directions of magnetization with limited evidence for an antiparallel reversed component. Mean paleopoles from the region lie along a swathe about 25° in length, and the two farsundite poles lie approximately at either end. As in the Grenville terrain, the distribution of site means is much greater than that of the group means and defines a swathe of about 70° of arc. Demagnetization trends and blocking temperature spectra suggest that the steepest directions (yielding poles 13, 14, 16, 25, and 26) are the oldest. Rates of APW movement inferred from blocking temperature spectra and mineral age data are 1.3–3°/Ma (Stearn and Piper, 1983). The majority of uplift magnetizations are ca. 900 Ma in age, while the total range of poles 13–18 is estimated to be 920 to 880 Ma.

Syn- to late-kinematic basic bodies ("hyperites") in the eastern sector of the Sveconorwegian mobile belt dated ca. 1080 to 1010 Ma B.P. and norite and anorthosite bodies at Bratton and Algon in east Sweden dated ca. 1000 Ma define the oldest magnetizations in this belt. The collective data fall along a closed loop defined firstly by the west Sweden anorthosite–norite poles (9, 10) plus the east Norway hyperites and other amphibolites (19), at ca. 1000 Ma, moving to the Rogaland high blocking temperature components (13–17) at ca. 900 Ma and to the Rogaland "Y" component (18) at ca. 840 Ma(?). In the Fennoscandian Shield this analysis is confirmed in part by Rb-Sr and paleomagnetic data from a dike swarm (Patchett and Bylund, 1977) intruded parallel to the Sveconorwegian Front into cold and stabilized Svecofennian terrain and along a fracture system apparently related to relative uplift of the evolving Sveconorwegian mobile belt. The dikes yield paleopoles falling along the swathe by the Rogaland data with ages ca. 860 Ma for dikes falling close to the Rogaland 'Y' pole (Patchett

(continued on following page)

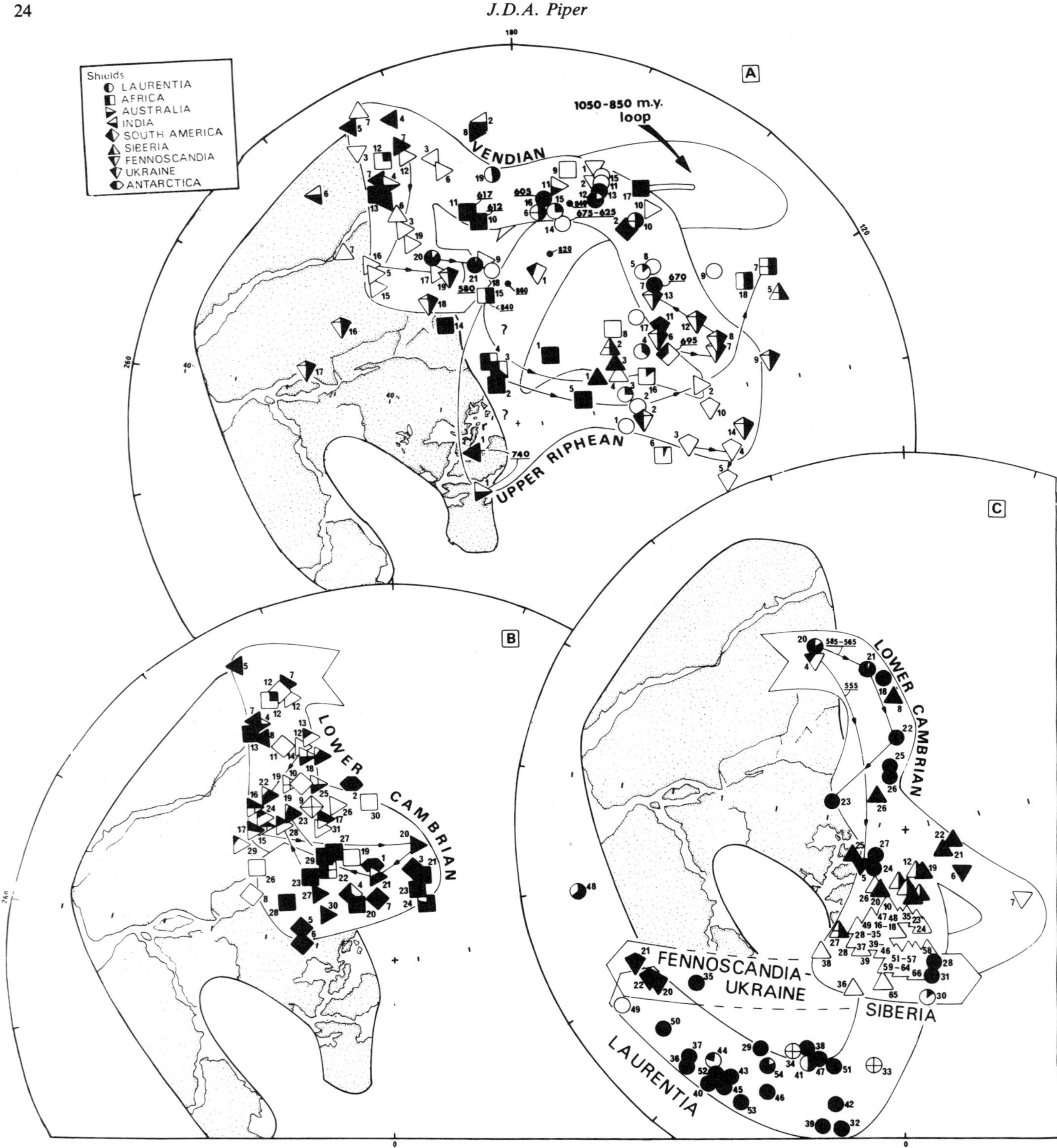

(continued from previous page)

and Bylund, 1977). The record from the Bukoban System commences with the ca. 1000-Ma Bukoba Sandstone (1) followed by the Kiganero Flags (5, 890 Ma), the Gagwe Lavas (pole 7, K-Ar dates of 960 and 820 Ma), and terminating with the Malagarasi Sandstone (11) and Bukoban dolerites (pole 9, K-Ar dates of 850 and 810 Ma).

Figure 10. Paleomagnetic poles from the major shields assigned to the interval 800 Ma B.P.—Early Paleozoic times.
LAURENTIAN SHIELD: 1, Cordova 'C' (7); 2–6, Colorado intrusives (LPc-C, 704–485^{+}); 7, Tudor Gabbro (670^{++}); 8, Iron Mountain–Maclure Mountain Complex (LPc-C); 9, Frontenac dikes (817–751^{+}); 10, Grenville dikes (LPc); 11, Franklin lavas and dikes (625^{++}); 12, Franklin diabases (675–625^{+}); 13, Aston Bay dikes; 14, Coronation sills (647^{+}); 15, Johnnie Formation (LPc);

16, Cloud Mountain basalt (615^+); 17, Lamotte Formation (1, LPc-C); 18, Lamotte Formation (E, LPc-C); 19, Quebec Lavas, A; 20, Ikertôq shear belt pseudotachylites (>23); 21–23, West Greenland alkaline province ($585–570^{+*}$); 24, Chequamegon Sandstone, secondary; 25, Rapitan Formation, 'Y' component; 26, Orienta Sandstone, secondary; 27, Jacobsville Sandstone, J2 component; 28, Lamotte Sandstone, 2a component (C); 29, Lamotte Sandstone, 2b component (C); 30, Lodore Formation (C); 31, Bonnetere Dolostone (C); 32, Bradore Sandstones (C_l); 33, 34, Quebec lavas, B and C components; 35, Ratcliffe Brook Formation (C_l); 36, Carrara-Bonanza King Formation ($C_{l\text{-}m}$); 37, Carrara Formation; 38, Wilberns formation ($C_{l\text{-}m}$); 39, Waynesboro Formation ($C_{l\text{-}m}$); 40, Rome Formation ($C_{l\text{-}m}$); 41, Tapeats Sandstone ($C_{l\text{-}m}$); 42, Ophiolite Complex, Quebec (550^+); 43, Hickory Sandstone ($C_{m\text{-}u}$); 44, Cap Mountain Limestone ($C_{m\text{-}u}$); 45, Lion Mountain Limestone ($C_{m\text{-}u}$); 46, Welge Sandstone/Morgan Creek Limestone ($C_{m\text{-}u}$); 47, Point Peak Shale ($C_{m\text{-}u}$); 48, 49, Colorado intrusives (525^+); 50–54, Wichita granites (525); 55, Quebec dykes (497^+).

FENNOSCANDIAN SHIELD: 1, 2, Egersund dikes (LPc); 3, Batsfjord dikes (650^+; 4, 5, Alnö Complex, A (553*, 554^+), B; 6, Fen Rϕdberg ($600–530^{+*}$); 7, Nexo Sandstone (LPc-C).

UKRAINIAN SHIELD: 1, Lower Katav Group (LPc); 2, Katavsk Group (LPc); 3–5, Kuk-Karauk Group (LPc(V)); 6–8, Basinsk Group (LPc(V)); 9, Inzer Group (LPc); 10, Katav Group, Podinzer sequence; 11, M-U Katav Group (LPc); 12, 13, Basinsk Group, higher formations (LPc(V)), Man' Insk Nyorovei and Kokpel Groups (LPc(V)); 20, Middle Urals intrusions ($O_{m\text{-}u}$); 21, Karachan Group sediments (O_l); 22, Bardym Group.

SIBERIAN SHIELD: 1, Omninsk Group (LPc); 2, Malginsk Group (LPc); 3, Tsipanda Group (LPc); 4, Lakhanda Group (LPc); 5, Ust' Kunda Group (LPc-C_l); 6, Podkrasno tsvetnaya Group (C_l); 7, Karagasski Suite (LPc(V)); 8, East Aldan sediments (C_l; 9, Charsk Group (C_l); 10, Ust' Agul'sk Group (C_l); 11, Emyaksa Group (C_l); 12, Chernoles Group (C_m); 13–15 Ust'-Maisk and Amga Groups (C_m); 16, 17, Olenek River Groups (C_m); 18, Silisir Dzhakhtar Groups; 19, 20, Ust' Maya Group (C_m); 21, Amga River sediments (C_m); 22, Ust'Botoma Group (C_m); 23, Dzakhtar Group (C_m); 24, Siligir Group (C_m); 25, Akcha Group volcanics (C_m); 26, Nadak Group (C_m-C_u); 27–29, Upper Lena Group (C_u); 30–34, 37, 38, 42–45, Verkholensk Group (C_u); 35, Evenkiisk Group (C_u-O_l); 36, Gornaya Altai Group (C_u-O_l); 39, Chukuk and Markha Groups (C_u); 40, Lena River Sills (C_u); 41, Iglinsk Group (C_u); 46, Lena River sills (O_l); 47, Ust' Kut Group (O_l); 48, Ahakit River Limestones (O_l); 49, Ust'Kutsk Group (O_l); 50, Ust'Kutsk and Kazimirovsh Groups (O_l); 51, Chertovsk Group (O_m); 52, Lena River sandstones and clays (O_m); 53–56, Lena River sediments; 57, Lower Makarovsk Group ($O_{m\text{-}u}$); 58, 59, Makarovsk Group (O_u); 60, River Nepa, combined result (O_u); 61, Makarovsk Group and Chertovsk horizon (O_u); 62, Bratsk and Makarovsk Groups (O_u); 63 Bratsk Group, combined result (O_u); 64, Taratash Complex (Ou); 65, Lower Bratsk Group (Ou); 66, Lena River sediments (Ou).

AFRICAN SHIELD: 1, Pre-Nama dikes (640 ±70*); 2, Blaubeker Formation (≤670*); 3, Mbozi Complex (750^+); 4, Lower Nama Group, N1 (<2); 5, Plateau Series A (LPc); 6, Dokhan Volcanics ($665–605^+$); 7, Upper Nama Group N2 (LPc); 8, Group de Char Formation, secondary; 9, Klipheuval Formation (LPc-C); 10, Adma diorite (610–590); 11, Ntonya ring structure (617 ±24*); 12, Nama Group, N3 (LPc); 13, Sijarira Group (LPc-C); 14, Nosib Group, NQ2 (679–660*); 15, Otavi Group, DC1 (<840, >651, 684–618*); 16, Otavi Group DC2-3 (<DC1); 17, Nosib Group, NQ3 (<NQ2); 18, Mulden Group (560–550*); 19, Plateau Series, B (LPc-C); 20, Nama Group, secondary; 21, Sabaloka ring structure (530*); 22, Moroccan lavas ($C_{l\text{-}m}$); 23, Ben Azzer volcanic sediments (520*); 24, QS dikes ($530–480^+$); 25, Dokhan Volcanics ($500–465^+$); 26, Doornpoort Formation (550–500); 27, 28, Adras de Mauretainie CO_{10}, CO_8 (C-O); 29, Tassili sediments (C-O); 30, Table Mountain series (O).

AUSTRALIAN SHIELD: 1, YB dikes (735*); 2, Wooltana Volcanics (≤900–850); 3, Copley Quartzite (LPc); 4, Merinjina Tillite (LPc); 5, Tapley Hill Formation (LPc); 6, Angepena Formation (LPc); 7, 8, Brachina Formation (LPc); 9, Bunyeroo Formation (LPc); 10, Arumbera Sandstone (LPc-C); 11, Antrim Plateau Volcanics (LPc-C_l); 12, Lower Arumbera sediments (LPc-C_l); 13, Upper Arumbera sediments (LPc-C_l); 14, Todd River sediments (C_l); 15, Aroona Dam sediments (C_l); 16, Basal Lake Froome Group (C_m); 17, Lake Froome Group, lower (C_m); 18, Hawker Group (C); 19, Red beds, Kangaroo Island (C_l); 20, Hudson Formation (C_l); 21, Hugh River Shale ($C_{l\text{-}m}$); 22, Billy Creek Formation ($C_{l\text{-}m}$); 23, Lake Froome Group, upper ($C_{m\text{-}u}$); 24, Pantapinna Formation (C_m); 25, Dundas Group (C_u); 26, Jinduckin Formation (O_l); 27, Stairway sandstone (O_m); 28, Tumblegooda Sandstone (O); 29, Mereenie Sandstone (S-D); 30 Merinjina Tillite, secondary; 31, Brachina Formation, secondary.

INDIAN SHIELD: 1, Malani rhyolites (730*); 2, 6, Rewa Sandstone (LPc-C); 3–5, Bhander Sandstone (LPc-C); 7, Khewra Sandstone (C_l); 8, Baghanwala Formation (C_m).

SOUTH AMERICAN SHIELD: 1, La Tinta Formation (695*); 2, 5, Purmamarca sediments (C); 3, North Tilcara sediments (C); 4, South Tilcara sediments (C); 6, Abra de Cajas sediments (C); 7, Salta sediments (O); 8, Suri Formation (O); 9, Urucum Formation (O); 10, 11, Salta and Jujuy sediments (O); 12, Bolivian sediments (O).

ANTARCTICA SHIELD: 1, Mirnyy Station charnockites (495*); 2, Sϕr Rondale intrusions ($O_{l\text{-}m}$, 485).

Stratigraphic age assignments are: LPc, late Precambrian; C, Cambrian; O, Ordovician; l, m, u = lower, middle, upper divisions.

The youngest poles defining the loop in Figure 9 are the Haliburton 'C' (820 Ma), Sveconorwegian Front–parallel dykes (860 Ma), and Rogaland 'Y' (ca. 840 Ma) components and indicate a northerly motion of the APW path at this time. Ca 750 to 700-Ma poles from India, Africa, and Australia lie close to the present pole, and a sequence (1, 2, 4, 7, 14, 15 → 16) is defined by the Pre-Nama dikes unconformably overlying sediments of the Blaubeker Formation, Nama, Nosib, and Otavi Groups. A single path incorporates sedimentary magnetizations from the Ukrainian Shield (western Urals), the Siberian Shield, and the Adelaide Geosyncline of Australia on a path incorporating dated magnetization in sequence from the La Tinta Formation of Argentina (695 ± 24 Ma), the Tudor Gabbro (670 Ma) and Franklin igneous province (ca. 650 Ma), possibly the Cordova 'C' magnetization and Coronation sills, the Franklin lavas (625 Ma), Ntonya Ring Structure (617 Ma), and Adma diorite (610 Ma). The hairpin at ca. 600 Ma is constrained by magnetizations from a number of sedimentary rocks of latest Precambrian age (African poles 9 and 13, Australian poles 12 → 15, and Indian pole 2) plus 620- to 610-Ma igneous magnetizations 10 and 11 from Africa. The longitudinal motion is defined by the sequence of poles from sedimentary successions of central Australia (12 → 14 → 15 + 19) which span the late Precambrian to Lower Cambrian boundary. They link directly with the sequence of poles from pseudotachylites and kimberlite dikes of the ca. 585- to 570- Ma West Greenland alkaline province, and the 'A' and 'B' magnetizations from the Alnö Complex (555 Ma) of the Fennoscandian Shield. The same APW motion is defined by Australian sedimentary succession of Lower or early Middle Cam-

(continued on following page)

Steiner and Grillmair, 1973; Williams, 1975). It is not possible to allocate a specific paleolatitude location to these occurrences in the context of the late Precambrian APW path of Figure 10 because the radiometric ages may date diagenetic events not directly related to deposition and they have age uncertainties incorporating appreciable APW movement. Furthermore, it is difficult to link the magnetizations in these drab sediments with primary depositional events (see Morris, 1977b), and with one exception (McElhinny and Embleton, 1976) predominantly shallow inclination directions of magnetization have been determined from these sediments to date. Published ages of late Precambrian glaciogenic sequences fall into several groups (Williams, 1975, and Fig. 11) concentrated in the intervals 960 to 940, 820 to 760, 740 to 680, and 640 to 580 Ma B.P. when the continental crust drifted near the poles (Fig. 10), and there is a paucity of occurrances when most or all of the crust lay in low paleolatitudes at 680 to 640 Ma B.P. Glacial deposits of the Windermere System of British Columbia (800 ± 50 Ma) and a variety of other locations falling between California and the Yukon assigned to the interval 850 to 750 Ma B.P. all passed within 30° of the pole between ca. 820 and 750 Ma; the same path would incorporate Siberian localities dated 810 to 750 Ma B.P. Glaciogenic rocks from central Africa assigned to this interval include localities in Gabon, the Congo, Angola (740 ± 50 Ma), and Zaire (840–710 Ma) and do not, however, appear to have drifted farther than 40° from the paleoequator during this interval. The movement of the pole to present high latitudes at ca. 750 Ma B.P. (Fig. 10) could accommodate localities in European Russia (810–715 Ma) and the Appalachians (<820 Ma) which moved within 30° of the pole at this time and the Varangian tillites of northern Norway, although the Rb-Sr isochron on the latter (650 ± 23 Ma) is too young to positively support this interpretation.

After 750 Ma B.P., the continental crust moved rapidly away from the South Pole such that the North Pole (Fig. 11) moved across Antarctica and Australia at ca. 700 Ma B.P. where the Moonlight Valley–Sturtian tillite is dated 720 Ma B.P. (Dunn and others, 1971). This position would also fit the stratigraphic location of the Numees (<720 Ma) and Nama tillites of Namibia and tillites of the Adelaide Geosyncline (see Fig. 10 and caption) which moved within 30° of the pole at this time; paleomagnetic studies, however, have currently been unable to establish this with certainty (McWilliams and McElhinny, 1980; Kröner and others, 1980).

With the exception of this brief excursion, the continental crust remained in low latitudes (Fig. 10) until Africa moved back to the vicinity of the South Poles at ca. 620 Ma B.P. It is over the subsequent interval 620 to 570 Ma that glaciogenic deposits can specifically be assigned to migration of the continental crust within 30° of the South Pole commencing in central Africa and finishing at the Fennoscandian Shield: the earliest part of the path accommodates tillites of Brazil (⩾600 ± 25 Ma), Ghana (⩾620 Ma), Algeria and Mauretania (650–610 Ma), Siberia (675–570 Ma), east and northern Greenland (600 Ma), Spitsbergen (ca. 620 Ma), Norway (ca. 600 Ma), European Russia (640–620 Ma), Scotland (ca. 570 Ma), and Newfoundland (600–570 Ma).

The 980- to 570-Ma-old glaciogenic deposits are indicative of a general global cooling because few older deposits of this kind are recorded, although much of the continental crust lay near the South Pole in earlier times (Figs. 2–7). Now that APW motions during late Precambrian times are better understood, it is clear that most of these deposits could be interpreted in the context of movement of the continental crust across a polar ice cap. This conclusion does not exclude more complicated and nonuniformitarian models because not all the age data are accommodated, but it does make them less attractive.

ALKALINE PROVINCES AND CONTINENTAL BREAKUP

The paleomagnetic analysis identifies episodes of continental breakup and relative movements at ca. 1100 Ma B.P. affecting peripheral parts of the supercontinent and at ca. 560 Ma B.P. leading to breakup of the axial parts (Fig. 1). Continental rifting is genetically associated with alkaline magmatism (Bailey, 1974), and most occurrences of Precambrian alkaline rocks are accommodated by these two episodes of rifting (MacIntyre, 1970). Examples from Laurentia and Gondwanaland have been noted previously, and other examples assigned to the interval 1290 to 1010 Ma B.P. are listed by MacIntyre (1970) and Barker (1975).

Rifting and alkaline magmatism at 590 to 560 Ma B.P. took place extensively within those shields (Siberian, Laurentian, Fennoscandian-Ukrainian) dismembered by the ca. 570-Ma-old event (Doig, 1970); the magmatism is defined in different areas by carbonatite, syenite, and alkali-granite plutons, together with kimberlite, lamprophyre, and alnöite dike swarms. In addition to the rifts along which separation ultimately took place at this time, of which the south mar-

(continued from previous page)
brian age (13-15 → 19-20) and African rocks of the same age (9-13 → 16-20). Close to the present North Pole the APW paths become clearly divergent: poles from Australia (20, 21), Africa (14, 18, 19), and South America (3) carry the Gondwanaland path to the west, after which it retraces a path to poles of Middle (Australia poles 16, 23, 14; Africa pole 21; and India pole 8) and Late (Australia pole 25) Cambrian age; the same path is outlined by Cambrian poles from South America (2–6), Antarctica (1, 2), and Africa (22–24) for which no specific age assignments are possible. The APW paths for the Siberian, Laurentian, and Fennoscandian-Ukrainian Shields move rapidly across the North Pole to mean poles of late Early-Middle Cambrian age.

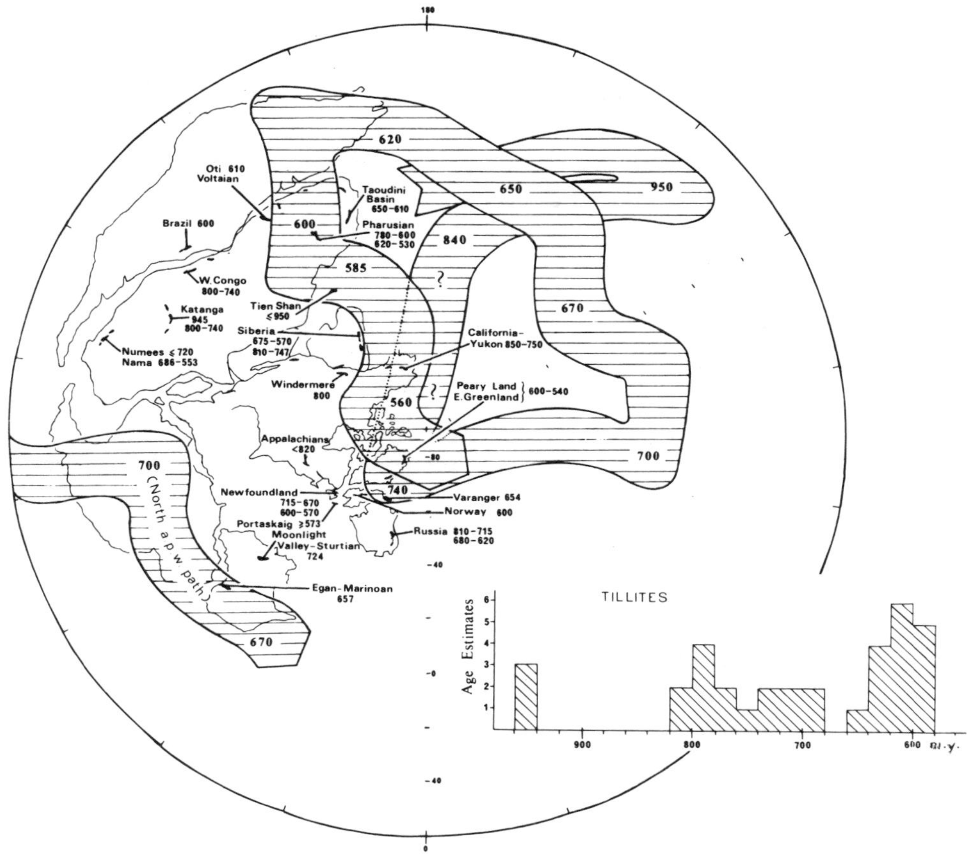

Figure 11. The APW path for the interval 850 to 560 Ma with best age estimates defined by the paleomagnetic data and the distribution of Late Precambrian glacial deposits based on Harland (1964a, 1964b). Age estimates for these deposits are based mainly on summaries by Williams (1975) and Deynoux and Clauer (1978). The histogram of age estimates for the glaciogenic deposits is slightly updated from Williams (1975).

gin of the Siberian Shield is a notable example of rift-associated alkaline magmatism (Butakova, 1975), rifts initiated at this time have been the loci for later continental separation (Labrador Sea–Davis Strait), or later rifting and volcanism without separation (Oslo graben), or they have remained dormant (the Superior–Hudson Bay lineament and the western Baltic).

RATES OF APW MOTION AND CHANGE IN PALEOLATITUDE

The APW paths of Figures 2–7, 9, and 10 are converted into equivalent rates of APW movement in Figure 12. These rates were notably slower (~0.5° Ma^{-1}) prior to 2200 Ma than in later Proterozoic times when they were both variable and intermittently rapid, exceeding 3° Ma for short periods. After Early Cambrian times this pattern was replaced by quasi-static intervals separated by short episodes of movement with rates of up to about 1° Ma^{-1} (e.g., Briden, 1967). Between 2100 and 1100 Ma B.P. the continental crust was concentrated in the Southern Hemisphere. The oscillatory motions that produced the APW loops of Figures 2–10 had the resultant effect of returning the continental crust periodically to an equilibrium position (Dunlop, 1980). This is now seen to be a position with the geometrical centre of the continental crust at the south geographic pole and presumably reflects episodic stability and overturn of the mantle convection system containing and driving the continental plate. Return motion to the stable configuration suggests a control by the geoid shape. After the ca. 1100-Ma-old mobile episodes the crust was fractured and redistributed with the result that the long axis of the supercontinent was reduced in arc length from 220° to 180°. In later Proterozoic times movements were less systematic (Figs. 9, 10), and a drift of the crust from the South Pole to the North Pole and back to the South Pole culminated in further breakup and separation at the base of the Cambrian.

The distinctive signature of the Proterozoic APW paths, comprising sequences of closed loops, has been rec-

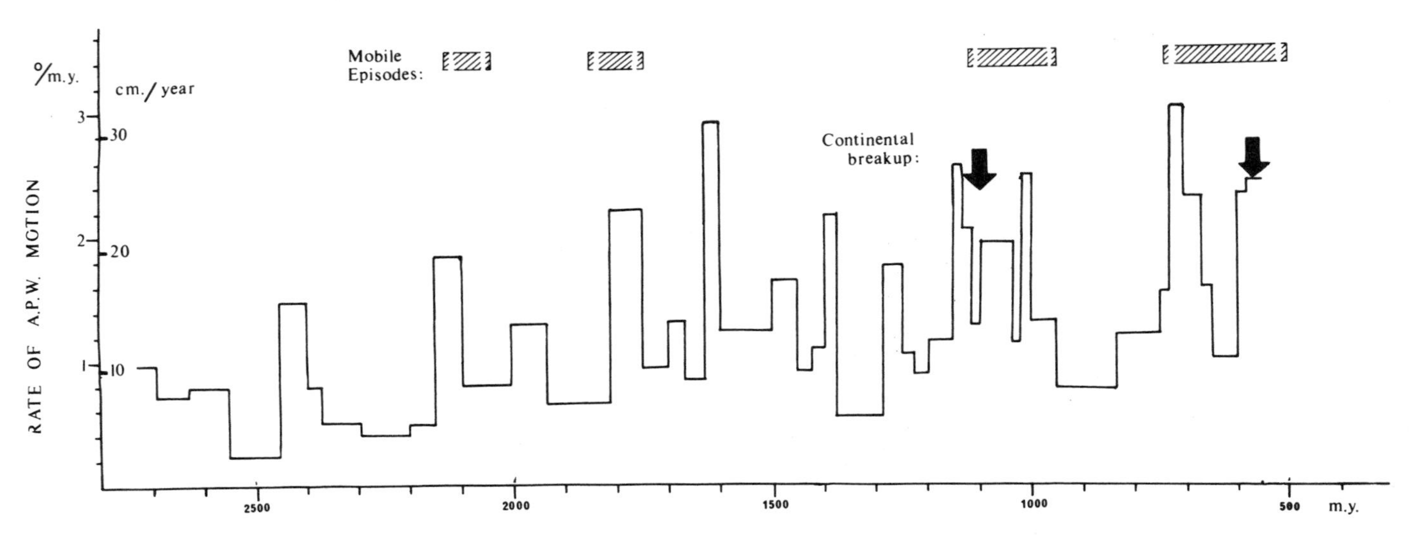

Figure 12. The rate of APW motion derived from the APW paths of Figures 2–7, 9, and 10 plotted as a function of time. The main intervals characterized by mobile activity and the two intervals of continental breakup at 1100 and 570 Ma are also indicated.

ognized for more than a decade (Spall, 1971; Irving and Park, 1972), and the acute changes in direction, or hairpins, at each extremity have been interpreted in a tectonic context and linked to mobile episodes and/or continental collision (Irving and Park, 1972; Piper, 1974). However, now that Proterozoic APW is better understood, it is clear that no such correlation exists; a number of loops are present that are not contemporaneous with any recognized mobile episode, and these episodes are also known to be more time-distributed events (e.g., Baer, 1981). In fact, Figure 12 suggests that the reverse is true: the major mobile episodes are preceded by 100- to 200-Ma intervals of relatively slow APW movement and are either contemporaneous with, or are followed by, the very rapid motions executing APW loops. This is unlikely to be an artefact of the data because APW is well defined prior to a number of mobile episodes, notably at ca. 1100 Ma B.P. A cause for the mobile activity is therefore most likely to be found in a thermal blanketing effect of the continental crust analogous to the phenomenon observed in Africa during Phanerozoic times (Briden and Gass, 1974) where quasi-static intervals correlate with the development of intraplate magmatism

TECTONIC MAGMATIC EVENTS IN PROTEROZOIC TIMES

Models for the transition in global tectonics from Archean to Proterozoic regimes consider this in the context of the exponential decline in radiogenic heat production (Lambert, 1976) and have become progressively more specific over the past decade. Fyfe (1976) linked the thickness of the granitoid crust to heat production and concluded that early sialic material, concentrated by convection mechanisms at several levels, was distributed over the globe but aggregated together as larger convection cells took over from smaller ones (Fyfe, 1974) with descent of the melting zone into the mantle. Strong and Stevens (1974) linked the change from small-scale to large-scale convection to the decline of the geothermal gradient accompanying a degassing of the mantle and upward migration of the peridotite solidus until mantle-wide melting ceased and crustal fractionation was greatly reduced. The declining geothermal gradient would eventually intersect the granulite stability field (Tarling, 1980) and permit stabilization of large segments of thickening sialic crust. During this permobile phase, greenstone belts evolved in a situation somewhat analogous to sea-floor spreading and consumption (Windley, 1977); their root zones appear to be oceanic crust and mantle emplaced between preexisting, rifted, sialic scum (Engel and others, 1974). The oldest greenstone belts (3400 to 2900 Ma) of South Africa and Zimbabwe are essentially isotropic, but younger belts (2800 to 2200 Ma) have high length to width ratios. The consistency of these trends between a number of isolated greenstone terrains noted by Engel and Kelm (1972) is enhanced on the supercontinent reconstruction (Fig. 13), and the greenstones are collectively oriented parallel to the long axis of the crust; they link the geometry of small-scale sub-crustal convection systems responsible for this permobile regime to the large-scale convection beneath the oceanic lithosphere responsible for aggregating the continental crust. (The noteworthy exception is the deflection of these belts around the ancient stable nucleus of South Greenland, Fig. 13).

Conformable and elongate layers of calcic anorthosites formed in late Archean–early Proterozoic times are a major and distinctive component of several high-grade Archean

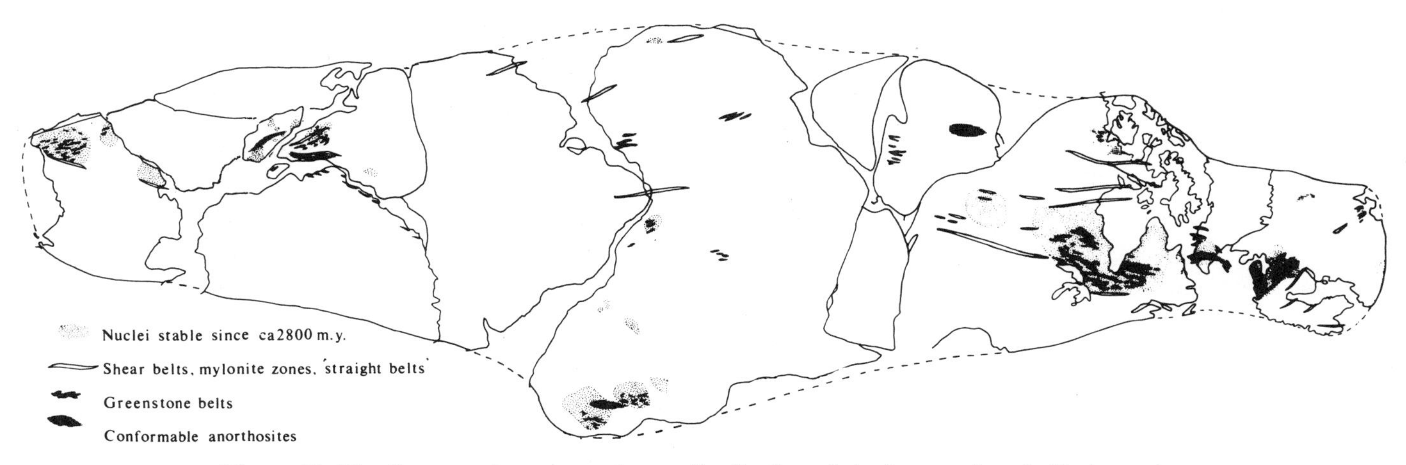

Figure 13. The Proterozoic supercontinent: distribution of Archean and early Proterozoic tectonic and magmatic features.

terrains (Windley and Bridgwater, 1971). Localities where they are at present recognized are parallel to the long axis of the Proterozoic continental crust (Fig. 13) in eastern India, the Kaapvaal craton to Madagascar, the northwest Laurentian Shield (Queen Maud block), Greenland to northwest Scotland, and the western Ukraine; they define an axis along which later massive anorthosites developed between ca. 1100 and 950 Ma B.P. and have individual trends close to this lineament (Sutton, 1971). In general, the relict Archean crust exhibits weak anisotropy, and reconstitution by Proterozoic tectonism has only occurred freely where accession of volatiles has taken place (Watson, 1973). A distinctive feature of early Proterozoic times is the development of straight belts (Watson, 1973) into which Archean structures are deflected and aligned into well-developed planar zones and along which relative movement took place between adjacent blocks. They are the oldest pure lineaments in the continental crust and range from zones of ductile shear, several tens of kilometres in width of which examples are well documented in Greenland (Bak and others, 1975), to long mylonite zones in West Africa, South America, and the northwest part of the Laurentian Shield (Heywood and Schau, 1978). Examples in Australia and the Laurentian Shield separate Archean provinces from Proterozoic mobile terrains. Other lineaments at deeper levels are recognized from aeromagnetic anomalies (Watson, 1973), and parallel trends have controlled many later tectonic/magmatic events. There is again an alignment of most of these lineaments between the shields and parallel to the long axis of the continental crust (Fig. 13, Watson, 1973; Sutton and Watson, 1974). They run for distances of up to several thousands of kilometres between already stabilized divisions of the continental crust with predominantly isotropic fabrics (Sutton, 1971; Watson, 1973). Because this alignment is such a prominent feature of the early Proterozoic crust, it may reflect localization in the accession of heat and volatiles from linear convection rolls in the sub-continental asthenosphere.

The mobile belts formed after 2200 Ma B.P. are an order and more wider than the earlier greenstone belts and lineaments, although distribution of the latter seems to have controlled subdivision of the crust into stable nucleii and zones of later mobility by controlling the accession of volatiles (Watson, 1973). The broad zone incorporating the ca. 1800-Ma-old "Hudsonian" episodes extends from the Ukraine via Greenland and the Laurentian Shield to the Siberian Shield (Sears and Price, 1978, and Fig. 14). Similar belts follow in general alignment through the West Africa, South America, India, China, and Australian Shields; many structures incorporated in this wide zone are aligned along this axial trend.

It is generally inferred that the angle of subduction beneath the continental crust in Proterozoic times was appreciably shallower than at the present time (Tarling, 1980), both because the thickness of accreted and modified mantle would have been less and because the subducting slab would not retain a physical identity to the depths at which major phase changes occurred. For this reason and because intermittently active subcontinental convection was in progress, margin-related subduction would have been less prominent during the Proterozoic, but notable examples of magmatic activity with a chemical variation interpretable in this context include the ca. 1800-Ma-old Penokean belt (Van Schmus, 1976) and the ca. 1700-Ma-old Svecofennide arc (Hietanen, 1975, and Fig. 14), and the Coronation Geosyncline formed in a comparable situation at the other margin of the continental crust after ca. 2100 Ma (Hoffman, 1973). The Sveconorwegian zone of southwest Norway has been linked to a Cordilleran model at ca. 1000 Ma B.P. (Torske, 1977). The direction of subduction inferred from each of these models was beneath the continental crust (Fig. 14).

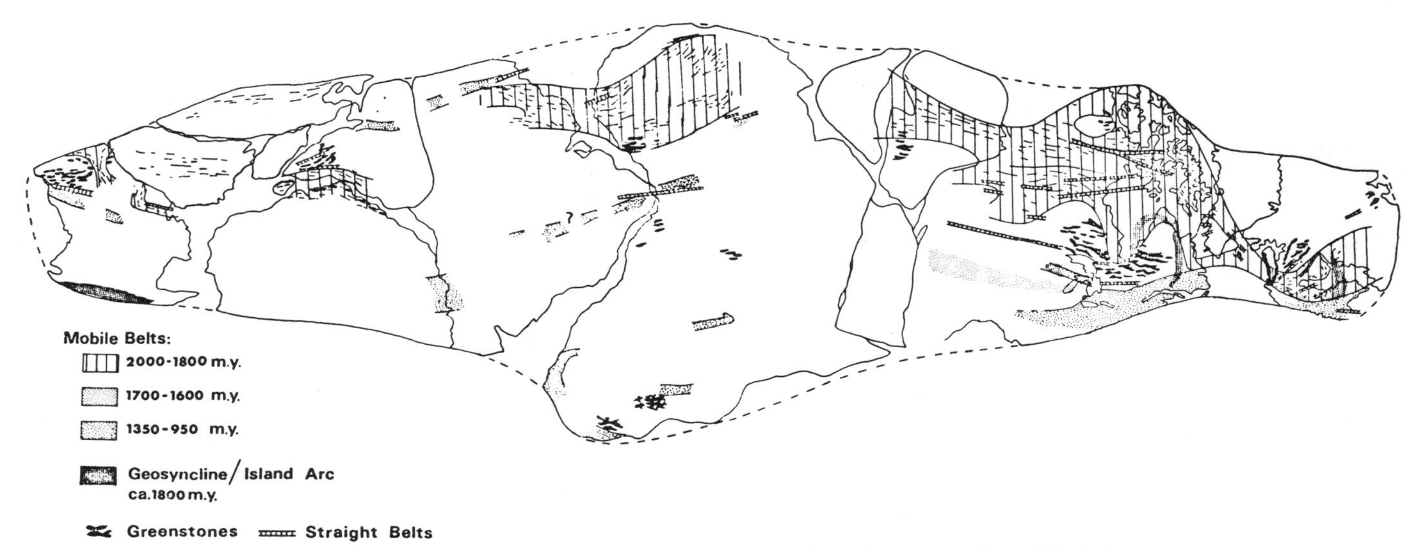

Figure 14. The Proterozoic supercontinent: distribution of Proterozoic mobile belts.

The massive anorthosite plutons (Fig. 15) were intruded approximately between 2100 and 950 Ma B.P. under conditions of high thermal gradients (Bridgwater and others, 1974) and are concentrated in those areas that remained zones of high thermal activity after the end of regional mobility. Although the anorthosites tend to lie along an axial trend (Fig. 15 and Herz, 1969), the most important information they yield to evaluating crustal conditions is the latest date at which intrusion of this kind was still possible at present crustal levels. The "chrontours" of Figure 15 are plotted from information documented by Bridgwater and Windley (1973), Bickford and Mose (1975), and Windley (1977) for the Laurentian and Ukrainian Shields and Piper (1980a) for the Fennoscandian Shield; they indicate that the high temperature gradients under which these bodies could be intruded to high crustal levels retreated towards one margin of the continental crust between the ca. 1800- and 1100-Ma episodes. The age data for the other shields are much more fragmentary and have been discussed by Fudao and Guanghong (1978). It appears that intrusion was largely complete here by 1550 Ma B.P., and a possible continuation of the chrontours incorporating these data is illustrated in Figure 15; probably only in the Musgrave belt of Australia were conditions still appropriate to anorthosite intrusion at high crustal levels during the 1350- to 950-Ma mobile episodes. The massive anorthosites are associated with a range of other intrusions, notably rapakivi granites. Bridgwater and others (1974) further linked the intrusion of these mushroom-shaped plutons to a range of high-level phenomena, notably graben faulting with accumulation of arkosic sandstones, basaltic magmatism, and the massive extrusion of acid volcanics. These events are

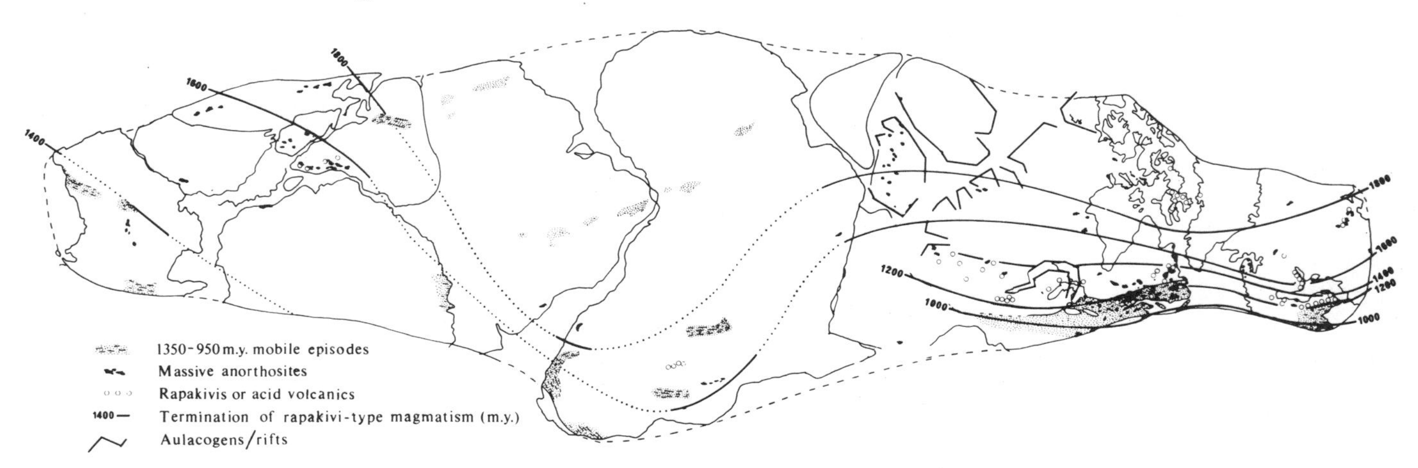

Figure 15. The Proterozoic supercontinent: distribution of the massive anorthosite-rapakivi suite, some upper Proterozoic rift systems, and the younger (1350–950 m.y.) mobile belts. The 'chrontours' illustrate the approximate time of termination of anorthosite and related magmatism in the continental crust.

concentrated within the anorthosite belts and suggest a similar temporal contraction with time (Fig. 15 and Bridgwater and Windley, 1973).

Consistent with the contraction of this magmatism to one margin of the continental crust is the observation that large-scale brittle fracturing at triple junctions, possibly related to mantle-generated plumes (Burke and Dewey, 1973), commenced on a large scale at ca. 1500 Ma B.P. along the opposite margin of the supercontinent. The resulting aulacogens were the locations of episodic deposition after this time and ultimately were the sites of continental separation.

The belts mobilized between ca. 1350 and 950 Ma B.P. are narrower than the older 1800-Ma zones but are remarkably linear in trend and are aligned close to the long axis of the supercontinent in common with the older lineaments noted above. With the exception of the Grenville and Sveconorwegian belts, mobile activity of this age was not concentrated within a single zone. In Africa there are several parallel trends: in addition to the Kibaran and Irumide trends, Grant and others (1972) recognized a zone of this age in West Africa which forms a lineament with locations in Brazil (Hurley and Rand, 1969); in common with a number of other areas, however, the thermal and/or tectonic nature of this zone is not clear from present data. The Albany-Frazer-Musgrave belt of Australia and the Aravalli belt of India are now identified as part of the same system of mobile belts. If the ca. 2200- to 1000-Ma-old mobile belts are to be linked to sublithosphere convection (Runcorn, 1962; Fyfe, 1976), it is clear from comparison of Figures 13, 14, and 15 that the scale of such a process must have increased in size rather suddenly at about 2200 Ma. A transition at this time coincides with an increase in APW rates: prior to 2200 Ma B.P., the small-scale greenstone belt, straight belt, and convection(?) systems correlate with low APW rates (Fig. 2) with the exception of a single rapid movement at ca. 2450 Ma. After 2200 Ma, APW motions (and hence displacements of the continental plate) were larger and intermittently very rapid after mobile episodes. There is provisional evidence here for a changeover from a small-scale to a large-scale sub-crustal mantle convection system at about 2200 Ma, an event that correlates broadly with an important crustal accretion event (e.g., Windley, 1977). The consistent axial alignment of the main tectonic elements indicates that a form of large-scale roll convection pertains until the base of the Cambrian when some kind of subdivision or reorganization was presumably required to achieve dispersal of the continental shields (Fig. 9).

The trends of dike swarms, giant dikes, and lopolithic plutons have not been used in this assessment because they are highly variable in trend (e.g., Windley, 1977) and evidently related to localized stress systems; furthermore, in zones such as the Gardar Province, between 1250 and 1200 Ma they exhibit rapid temporal changes. Sutton (1971), however, has made the observation that they increase in both extent and continuity through Proterozoic times as larger areas of terrain became stabilized. Paradoxically, it is during the late Proterozoic times (800 to 570 Ma. B.P.) that this analysis is least satisfactory, both because the paleomagnetic evidence comes mostly from sedimentary rocks where the nature and age of the remanence is frequently not clear and because there are no obvious geologic lineaments to check the reconstruction. During earlier times, however, the evidence that possible suture zones provide for relative movements between divisions of the Proterozoic crust (Burke and others, 1976) must be outweighed by the alignment of the major tectonic elements on the paleomagnetic reconstruction, because geologic evidence alone cannot decide whether movements across these possible sutures are to be gauged in kilometres or thousands of kilometres. Indeed, the strengths of the supercontinental model developed here are, firstly, that it accommodates the whole Proterozoic paleomagnetic record without severe selection while using a rigid reconstruction and, secondly, that the derived reconstruction independently brings into alignment the bulk of the major tectonic elements formed during this interval. This combined integration of geologic and geophysical evidence is unique in the tectonic models proposed for Proterozoic times.

ACKNOWLEDGMENTS

Precambrian paleomagnetic studies are supported by NERC grants GR3/2398 and GR3/4495. I am grateful to R. L. Wilson and anonymous reviewers for criticism of this paper.

REFERENCES CITED

Baer, A. J., 1981, Two orogenies in the Grenville Belt?: Nature, v. 290, p. 129–131.

Bailey, D. K., 1974, Continental rifting and alkaline magmatism, *in* Sorensen, H., ed., The alkaline rocks: London, John Wiley, p. 148–159.

Bak, J., Sorensen, K., Grocott, J., Kortsgaard, J. A., Nash, D., Watterson, J., 1975, Tectonic implications of Precambrian shear belts in western Greenland: Nature, v. 254, p. 566–569.

Barker, D. S., 1975, Alkaline rocks of North America, *in* Sorensen, H., ed., The alkaline rocks: London, John Wiley, p. 160–171.

Berger, G. W., York, D., and Dunlop, D. J., 1979, Calibration of Grenvillian paleopoles by $^{40}Ar/^{39}Ar$ dating: Nature, v. 277, p. 46–47.

Bickford, M. E., and Mose, D. G., 1975, Geochronology of Precambrian rocks in the St. Francois Mountains, southeastern Missouri: Geology, v. 3, p. 537–540.

Briden, J. C., 1967, Recurrent continental drift of Gondwanaland: Nature, v. 215, p. 1334–1339.

Briden, J. C., and Gass, I. G., 1974, Plate movement and continental magmatism: Nature, v. 248, p. 650–653.

Bridgwater, D., and Windley, B. F., 1973, Anorthosites, post-orogenic granites, acid volcanic rocks, and crustal development in the North Atlantic Shield during the mid-Proterozoic, *in* Lister, L. A., ed., Symposium on granite, gneisses and related rocks: Geological Society of South Africa, Special Publication No. 3, p. 307–318.

Bridgwater, D., Sutton, J., and Watterson, J., 1974, Crustal downfolding associated with igneous activity: Tectonophysics, v. 21, p. 57–77.

Buchan, K. L., 1978, Magnetic overprinting in the Thanet gabbro complex, Ontario: Canadian Journal of Earth Sciences, v. 15, p. 1407–1421.

Buchan, K. L., and Dunlop, D. J., 1976, Paleomagnetism of the Haliburton intrusions: Superimposed magnetisations, metamorphism and tectonics in the Late Precambrian: Journal of Geophysical Research, v. 81, p. 2951–2967.

Burke, K., and Dewey, J. F., 1973, Plume generated Triple Junctions: Key indicators in applying plate tectonics to old rocks: Journal of Geology, v. 81, p. 406–433.

Burke, K., Dewey, J. F., and Kidd, W.S.F., 1976, Precambrian paleomagnetic results compatible with contemporary operation of the Wilson Cycle: Tectonophysics, v. 33, p. 287–299.

Butakova, E. L., 1975, Regional distribution and tectonic relations of the alkaline rocks of Siberia, *in* Sorensen, H., ed. The alkaline rocks: London, John Wiley, p. 172–183.

Cavanaugh, M. D., and Seyfert, C. K., 1977, Apparent polar wander paths and the joining of the Superior and Slave Provinces during Proterozoic time: Geology, v. 5, p. 207–211.

Crawford, A. R., 1974, A greater Gondwanaland: Science, v. 184, p. 1179–1181.

Dalrymple, G. B., 1980, Critical tables for conversion of K-Ar ages from old to new constants: Geology, v. 7, p. 558–560.

Davies, F. B., and Windley, B. F., 1976, The significance of major Proterozoic high-grade linear belts in continental evolution: Nature, v. 263, p. 383–385.

de Waard, D., Deuchesne, J. C., and Michot, J., 1974, Anorthosites and their new environment, *in* Geologie des domaines cristallins: Liege, Geological Society of Belgium, p. 323–346.

Deynoux, M., and Clauer, N., 1978, Upper Precambrian and lowermost Paleozoic correlations in West Africa and in the western part of Central Africa. Probable diachronism of the late Precambrian tillite: Geologischen Rundschau, v. 67, p. 615–630.

Dickinson, B. B., and Watson, J. V., 1976, Variations in crustal level and geothermal gradient during the evolution of the Lewisian Complex of northwest Scotland: Precambrian Research, v. 3, p. 363–374.

Doig, R., 1970, An alkaline rock province linking Europe and North America: Canadian Journal of Earth Sciences, v. 7, p. 22–28.

Donaldson, J. A., and Irving, E., 1972, Grenville Front and rifting of the Canadian Shield: Nature (Physical Science), v. 237, p. 139–140.

Dunlop, D. J., 1980, Paleomagnetic evidence for Proterozoic continental development: Philosophical Transactions of the Royal Society of London A301, p. 265–277.

Dunn, P. R., Thomson, B. P., and Rankama, K., 1971, Late Precambrian glaciation in Australia as a stratigraphic boundary: Nature, v. 231, p. 498–502.

Elston, D. P., and Grommé, C. S., 1975, Precambrian polar wandering from Unkar Group and Nankoweap Formation, eastern Grand Canyon, Arizona: Geological Society of America, Rocky Mountain Section Meeting, p. 97–117.

Engel, A.E.J., and Kelm, D. L., 1972, Pre-Permian global tectonics: A tectonic test: Geological Society of America Bulletin, v. 83, p. 2325–2340.

Engel, A.E.J., Itson, S. P., Engel, C. G., Stickney, D. H., and Cray, E. J., Jr., 1974, Crustal evolution and global tectonics: A petrogenic view: Geological Society of America Bulletin, v. 85, p. 843–858.

Evans, M. E., Haye, G. S., and Bingham, D. K., 1980, The paleomagnetism of the Great Slave Supergroup: The Akaitcho River Formation: Canadian Journal of Earth Sciences, v. 17, p. 1389–1395.

Fudao, X., and Guanghong, X., 1978, The age of the anorthosite event and its geological implications: Geochimica, v. 3, p. 202–208 (in Chinese).

Fyfe, W. S., 1974, Archean tectonics: Nature, v. 249, p. 338.

—— 1976, Heat flow and magmatic activity in the Proterozoic: Philosophical Transactions of the Royal Society of London, v. A280, p. 655–660.

Grant, N. K., Hickmann, M. H., Burkholder, F. R., and Powell, J. L., 1972, Kibaran metamorphic belt in Pan-African domain of West Africa: Nature (Physical Sciences), v. 238, p. 90–91.

Harland, W. B., 1964a, Critical evidence for a great Infra-Cambrian glaciation: Geologischen Rundschau, v. 54, p. 45–61.

—— 1964b, Evidence of late Precambrian glaciation and its significance, *in* Nairn, A.E.M., ed., Problems in paleoclimatology: London, Interscience Publishers, p. 119–149.

Henry, S. G., Mauk, F. J., and Van der Voo, R., 1977, Paleomagnetism of the Upper Keweenawan sediments: The Nonesuch shale and Freda sandstone: Canadian Journal of Earth Sciences, v. 14, p. 1128–1138.

Herz, N., 1969, Anorthosite belts, continental drift and the anorthosite event: Science, v. 164, p. 944–947.

Heywood, W. W., and Schau, M., 1978, A subdivision of the Northern Churchill Structural Province: Geological Survey of Canada, Paper 78-1A, p. 139–143.

Hietanan, A., 1975, Generation of potassium-poor magmas in the northern Sierra Nevada and the Svecofennian of Finland: Journal of Research, U.S. Geological Survey, v. 3, p. 631–645.

Hoffman, P., 1973, Evolution of an early Proterozoic continental margin: The Coronation Geosyncline and associated aulacogens of the northwestern Canadian Shield: Philosophical Transactions of the Royal Society of London, v. A273, p. 547–581.

Holser, W. T., 1977. Catastrophic chemical events in the history of the ocean: Nature, 167, p. 403–408.

Hurley, P. H., and Rand, J. R., 1969, Pre-drift continental nucleii: Science, v. 164, p. 1229–1242.

Hurley, P. M., Lee, J. H., Fairbairn, A. W., and Pinson, W. H., 1971, 19th Annual Progress Report: Massachusetts Institute of Technology, p. 5–13.

Irving, E., and Hastie, J., 1975, Catalogue of paleomagnetic directions and poles: Geomagnetic Service of Canada, Publication 3, 42 p.

Irving, E., and McGlynn, J. C., 1976, Proterozoic magnetostratigraphy and the tectonic evolution of Laurentia: Philosophical Transactions of the Royal Society of London, v. A280, p. 433–468.

—— 1979, Paleomagnetism of the Coronation Geosyncline and its bearing on the arrangement of the continents in the mid-Proterozoic: Geophysical Journal of the Royal Astronomical Society, v. 58, p. 309–336.

Irving, E., and Naldrett, A. J., 1977, Paleomagnetism in Abitibi Greenstone Belt, and Abitibi and Matachewan diabase dikes: Evidence of the Archean geomagnetic field: Journal of Geology, v. 85, p. 157–176.

Irving, E., and Park, J. K., 1972, Hairpins and super-intervals: Canadian Journal of Earth Sciences, v. 9, p. 1318–1324.

Jones, D. L., Robertson, I.D.M., and McFadden, P. L., 1977, A paleomagnetic study of Precambrian dike swarms associated with the Great Dyke of Rhodesia: Transactions of the Geological Society of South Africa, v. 78, p. 57–65.

Kirschvinck, J. L., 1978, The Precambrian-Cambrian boundary problem: Paleomagnetic directions from the Amadeus Basin, Central Australia: Earth and Planetary Science Letters, v. 40, p. 91–100.

Klootwyk, J. L., 1980, Early Palaeozoic paleomagnetism in Australia: Tectonophysics, v. 64, p. 249–332.

Kröner, A., 1976, Precambrian mobile belts of southern and eastern Africa—ancient sutures or sites of ensialic mobility? A case for crustal evolution towards plate tectonics: Tectonophysics, v. 40, p. 101–135.

Kröner, A., McWilliams, M. O., Germs, G.J.B., Reid, A. B., and Schalk, K.E.L., 1980, Paleomagnetism of the Late Precambrian early Paleozoic mixtite-bearing formations in Namibia (South West Africa): The Nama Group and Blaubecker Formation: American Journal of Science, v. 280, p. 942–968.

Lambert, R. St. J., 1976, Archean thermal regimes, crustal and upper mantle temperatures and a progressive evolutionary model for the Earth, *in* Windley, B. F., ed., The early history of the Earth: London, John Wiley, p. 363–387.

MacIntyre, R., 1970, Apparent periodicity of carbonatite emplacement in Canada: Nature, v. 230, p. 79–81.

McElhinny, M. W., 1973, Paleomagnetism and plate tectonics: Cambridge University Press, 358 p.

McElhinny, M. W., and Embleton, B.J.J., 1976, Precambrian and early Paleozoic paleomagnetism in Australia: Philosophical Transactions of the Royal Society of London, v. A280, p. 417–432.

McElhinny, M. W., and McWilliams, M. O., 1977, Precambrian geodynamics—A paleomagnetic view: Tectonophysics, v. 40, p. 137–159.

McElhinny, M. W., Giddings, J. W., and Embleton, B.J.J., 1974, Paleomagnetic results and late Precambrian glaciations: Nature, v. 248, p. 557–561.

McElhinny, M. W., Cowley, J. A., Brown, D. A., and Wirubov, N., 1977, Palaeomagnetic results from the U.S.S.R.: Australian National University, Research School of Earth Sciences, Publication No. 1268, 78 p.

McElhinny, M. W., Cowley, J. A., and Brown, D. A., 1979, Paleomagnetic results from the U.S.S.R., Supplement No. 1: Australian National University, Research School of Earth Sciences, Publication No. 1377, 23 p.

McWilliams, M. O., and Dunlop, D. J., 1978, Grenville paleomagnetism and Tectonics: Canadian Journal of Earth Sciences, v. 15, p. 687–695.

McWilliams, M. O., and McElhinny, M. W., 1980, Late Precambrian paleomagnetism of Australia: The Adelaide Geosyncline: Journal of Geology, v. 88, p. 1–26.

Morgan, G. E. and Briden, J. C., 1981, Aspects of Precambrian paleomagnetism with new data from the Limpopo Mobile Belt and Kaapraal craton in Southern Africa: Physics of the Earth and Planetary Interiors, v. 24, p. 142–168.

Morris, W. A., 1977a, Paleolatitude of glaciogenic upper Precambrian Rapitan Group and the use of tillites as chronostratigraphic marker horizons: Geology, v. 5, p. 85–88.

—— 1977b, Paleomagnetism of the Gowganda and Chibougamau Formations: Evidence for 2200 m.y. folding and remagnetisation event of the Southern Province: Geology, v. 5, p. 137–140.

—— 1979, A positive contact between Nipissing diabase and Gowganda argillites: Canadian Journal of Earth Sciences, v. 16, p. 607–611.

Morris, W. A., and Roy, J. L., 1977, Discovery of the Hadrynian Track and further study of the Grenville problem: Nature, v. 266, p. 689–692.

Murthy, G. S., and Deutsch, E. R., 1975, A new Precambrian paleomagnetic pole for northern Europe: Physics of the Earth and Planetary Interiors, v. 11, p. 91–96.

Neuvonen, K. J., 1974, Paleolatitude and cause of Svecokarelian orogeny: Bulletin of the Geological Society of Finland, v. 46, p. 75–79.

Neuvonen, K. J., and Grundström, L., 1969, Paleomagnetism of the dike systems in Finland, IV. Remanent magnetisations of the dolerites and related dikes in the Aland Archipelago: Bulletin of the Geological Society of Finland, v. 41, p. 57–63.

Onstott, T. C., and Hargraves, R. B., 1981, Proterozoic transcurrent tectonics: Paleomagnetic evidence from Venezuela and Africa: Nature, v. 289, p. 131–136.

Park, J. K., 1977, A reconnaissance paleomagnetic study of the Central Labrador Trough, Quebec: Canadian Journal of Earth Sciences: v. 14, p. 159–174.

Patchett, P. J., and Bylund, G., 1977, Age of Grenville Belt magnetisations: Rb-Sr and paleomagnetic evidence from Swedish dolerites: Earth and Planetary Science Letters, v. 35, p. 92–104.

Patchett, P. J., Bylund, G., and Upton, B.G.J., 1978, Paleomagnetism and the Grenville orogeny: New Rb-Sr ages from dolerites in Canada and Greenland: Earth and Planetary Science Letters, v. 40, p. 349–364.

Perry, E. A., and Turekian, K. K., 1973, The effects of diagenesis on the redistribution of strontium isotopes in shales: Geochimica et Cosmochimica Acta, v. 38, p. 929–935.

Pesonen, L. J., and Halls, H. C., 1979, The paleomagnetism of Keweenawan dikes from Baraga and Marquette Counties, northern Michigan: Canadian Journal of Earth Sciences, v. 16, p. 2136–2149.

Piper, J.D.A., 1974, Proterozoic crustal distribution, mobile belts and apparent polar movements: Nature, v. 251, p. 381–384.

—— 1976a, Paleomagnetic evidence for a Proterozoic Supercontinent: Philosophical Transactions of the Royal Society of London, v. A280, p. 469–490.

—— 1976b, Definition of pre-2000 m.y. apparent polar wander movements: Earth and Planetary Science Letters, v. 28, p. 470–478.

—— 1980a, Paleomagnetism of the Swedish rapakivi suite: Proterozoic tectonics of the Baltic Shield: Earth and Planetary Science Letters, v. 46, p. 443–461.

—— 1980b, Paleomagnetic study of Svecofennian basic rocks: Proterozoic configuration of the Fennoscandian, Laurentian and Siberian Shields: Physics of the Earth and Planetary Interiors, v. 23, p. 165–187.

—— 1981, The altitude dependence of magnetic remanence in the slowly cooled Precambrian plutonic terrain of Central-West Greenland: Earth and Planetary Science Letters, v. 54, p. 449–466.

Piper, J.D.A., Bridan, J. C., and Lomax, K., 1973, Precambrian Africa and South America as a single continent: Nature, v. 245, p. 244–248.

Poorter, R.P.E., 1975, Paleomagnetism of Precambrian rocks from southeast Norway and south Sweden: Physics of the Earth and Planetary Interiors, v. 10, p. 74–87.

—— 1976, Paleomagnetism of the Svecofennian Loftahammar gabbro and some Jotnian dolerites in the Swedish part of the Baltic Shield: Physics of the Earth and Planetary Interiors, v. 12, p. 51–64.

Roy, J. L., and Blyth-Robertson, P., 1979, An assessment of the St. Urban and other Grenville paleopoles: Canadian Journal of Earth Sciences, v. 16, p. 1857–1865.

Roy, J. L., and Lapointe, P. L., 1976, The paleomagnetism of Huronian redbeds and Nipissing diabase; post-Huronian igneous events and apparent polar path for the interval -2300 to -1500 Ma for Laurentia: Canadian Journal of Earth Sciences, v. 13, p. 749–779.

Roy, J. L., and Robertson, W. A., 1978, Paleomagnetism of the Jacobsville Formation and the apparent polar path for the interval -1100 to -670 m.y. for North America: Journal of Geophysical Research, v. 83, p. 1289–1304.

Roy, J. L., Morris, W. A., Lapointe, P. L., Irving, E., Park, J. K., and Schmidt, P. W., 1978, Apparent polar wander paths and the joining of the Superior and Slave provinces during early Proterozoic time: Comment and reply: Geology, v. 6, p. 132–133.

Runcorn, J. L., and Blyth-Robertson, P., 1979, An assessment of the St. Urban and other Grenville paleopoles: Canadian Journal of Earth Sciences, v. 16, p. 1857–1865.

Runcorn, S. K., 1962, Towards a theory of continental drift: Nature, v. 193, p. 311–314.

Schmidt, P. W., 1980, Paleomagnetism of igneous rocks from the Belcher Island, Northwest Territories, Canada: Canadian Journal of Earth Sciences, v. 17, p. 807–829.

Schutts, L. D., and Dunlop, D. J., 1981, Proterozoic magnetic overprinting of Archean rocks in the Canadian Superior Province:

Nature, v. 29, p. 642–644.
Sears, J. W., and Price, R. A., 1978, The Siberian connection: A case for Precambrian separation of the North American and Siberian cratons: Geology, v. 6, p. 267–270.
Shackleton, R. M., 1973, Correlation of structures across Precambrian orogenic belts in Africa, *in* Tarling, D. H., and Runcorn, S. K., eds., Implications of continental drift to the earth sciences: London, Academic Press, p. 1091–1095.
Smith, A. G., and Hallam, A., 1970, The fit of the southern continents: Nature, v. 225, p. 139–144.
Smith, R. L., and Piper, J.D.A., 1982, The paleomagnetism of the Southern Zone of the Lewisian (Precambrian) Foreland, NW Scotland: Geophysical Journal of the Royal Astronomical Society, v. 68, p. 325–347.
Smith, R. L., Stearn, J.E.F., and Piper, J.D.A., 1983, Palaeomagnetic studies of the Torridonian sediments, NW Scotland: Scottish Journal of Geology, v. 19, p. 29–45.
Spall, H., 1971, Precambrian apparent polar wandering: Evidence from North America: Earth and Planetary Science Letters, v. 10, p. 273–280.
——1972, Paleomagnetism and Precambrian continental drift: International Geological Congress, 24th, Montreal, Section 3, p. 172–179.
——1973, Review of Precambrian paleomagnetic data for Europe: Earth and Planetary Science Letters, v. 18, p. 1–8.
Stearn, J.E.F., and Piper, J.D.A., 1983, Paleomagnetism of the Sveconorwegian mobile belt, of the fennoscandian Shield: Precambrian Research (in press).
Steiger, R. H., and Jäger, E., 1977, Subcommission on geochronology: Convention on the use of the decay constants in geo- and cosmochronology: Earth and Planetary Science Letters, v. 36, p. 356–362.
Steiner, J., and Grillmair, E., 1973, Possible galactic causes of periodic and episodic glaciations: Geological Society of America Bulletin, v. 84, p. 1003–1018.
Stewart, J. H., 1976, Late Precambrian evolution of North America: Plate Tectonic implications: Geology, v. 4, p. 11–15.
Strong, D. F., and Stevens, R. K., 1974, Possible thermal explanation of contrasting Archean and Proterozoic geological regimes: Nature, v. 248, p. 37–39.
Sutton, J., 1971, Some developments in the crust: Special Publications of the Geological Society of Australia, v. 3, p. 1–10.
Sutton, J., and Watson, J. V., 1974, Tectonic evolution of continents in early Proterozoic times: Nature, v. 247, p. 433–435.
Symons, D.T.A., 1971, A paleomagnetic study of the Nipissing diabase, Blind River, Elliot Lake area, Ontario: Geological Survey of Canada, Paper 70-63, p. 18–30.
Tarling, D. H., 1979, Paleomagnetic reconstructions and the Variscan Orogeny: Proceedings of the Ussher Society, v. 4, p. 233–261.
——1980, Lithosphere evolution and changing tectonic regimes: Journal of the Geological Society of London, v. 137, p. 459–467.
Torske, T., 1977, The south Norway Precambrian region—a Proterozoic Cordilleran-type orogenic segment: Norsk Geologisk Tidskrift, v. 57, p. 97–150.
Van Schmus, W. R., 1976, Early and Middle Proterozoic history of the Great Lakes area, North America: Philosophical Transactions of the Royal Society of London, v. A280, p. 605–628.
Versteeve, A. J., 1975, Isotope geochronology in the high grade metamorphic Precambrian of south western Norway: Norsk Geologiska Undersokning, v. 318, p. 1–50.
Viezer, J., 1976. ^{87}Sr:^{86}Sr evolution of seawater during geological history and its significance as an index of crustal evolution, *in* Windley, B. F., ed., The early history of the Earth: London, John Wiley, p. 569–578.
Watson, J. V., 1973, Effects of reworking on high-grade gneiss complexes: Philosophical Transactions of the Royal Society of London, v. A273, p. 443–456.
Williams, G. E., 1966, Paleogeography of the Torridon Applecross Group: Nature, v. 209, p. 1303–1306.
——, 1975, Late Precambrian glacial climate and the Earth's obliquity: Geological Magazine, v. 112, p. 441–544.
Windley, B. F., 1977, The evolving continents: London, John Wiley, 385 p.
Windley, B. F., and Bridgwater, D., 1971, The evolution of Archean low- and high-grade terrains: Geological Society of Australia, Special Publication 3, p. 33–46.

MANUSCRIPT ACCEPTED BY THE SOCIETY APRIL 14, 1983

Printed in U.S.A.

Geological Society of America
Memoir 161
1983

Proterozoic magnetic overprinting and tectonics of the Laurentian Shield

David J. Dunlop
Larry D. Schutts
Geophysics Division
Departments of Physics and Geology
University of Toronto
Toronto, Ontario M5S 1A7
Canada

ABSTRACT

The NRM (natural remanent magnetization) of a metamorphic rock is the vector sum of primary NRM and one or more secondary overprints. Magnetic overprinting is a thermal or chemical effect resulting from (1) burial and uplift (regional heating), (2) intrusive activity (local heating), or (3) hydrothermal supercritical solutions (local heating and/or alteration. We present a number of examples drawn from the Proterozoic of North America illustrating how paleomagnetists decipher magnetic overprints and use them to date and interpret tectonic events. Granites from the western Superior Province record the 2600 Ma Kenoran orogeny and an event at 1250 Ma, perhaps related to Mackenzie dike intrusion elsewhere in the Shield. Diabase dikes and country rocks in the Abitibi subprovince, particularly those near incoherent dike contacts and fault zones, bear thermal overprints whose probable ages are 1900 to 1700 Ma. The overprints agree in direction with primary NRMs of similar ages from the Churchill Province, implying that the Hudsonian orogeny involved little relative motion of Superior and Churchill cratons. Multiple overprints dating from slow uplift and cooling of the Grenville orogen between 1050 and 800 Ma postdate the collisional phase of the Grenvillian orogeny, but 1100-Ma-old surviving primary NRM of the Tudor gabbro appears to record precollisional divergence between "Grenvillia" and the rest of the Shield.

INTRODUCTION

Proterozoic time was characterized by a sequence of great orogenies of continental extent. In the Laurentian Shield (Fig. 1) during the early and middle Proterozoic (Proterozoic X and Y), the last pervasive regional metamorphism of the Superior, Slave, and Wyoming Provinces occurred during the 2700-2600 Ma Kenoran orogeny. The Churchill, Bear, and Southern Provinces and much of Greenland and northwest Scotland were affected by the 1900-1650 Ma Hudsonian/Penokean/Nagssugtoqidian/Laxfordian event or events. Keweenawan rifting (1150-1050 Ma) of the Southern Province and the Grenvillian orogeny (1100-850 Ma) of the Grenville Province and its equivalent in Fennoscandia may be causally or only temporally related. On a regional rather than a continental scale, widespread tensional regimes prevailed around 2600 Ma (just post-Kenoran), 2150 Ma and 1250 Ma, resulting in the intrusion of Matachewan, Abitibi/Nipissing, and Mackenzie/Sudbury dike swarms.

Paleomagnetism has enormous potential for deciphering metamorphic and tectonic histories. Local to regional thermal or hydrothermal events leave their mark on the natural remanent magnetization (NRM) of a rock in the form of thermal or chemical "overprints." The age of each event is deduced from the position of the paleomagnetic

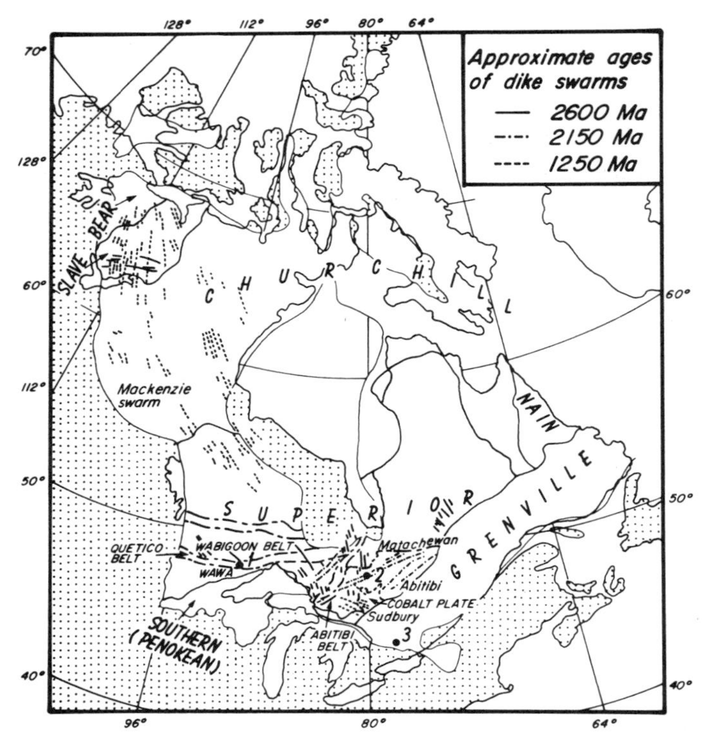

Figure 1. Structural provinces and selected subprovinces of the Laurentian Shield with locations of early and middle Proterozoic diabase dike swarms (based on Stockwell and others, 1970, Figs. IV-1 and 30). Locations 1, 2, and 3 are the sites of paleomagnetic studies described in sections 2, 3, and 4 of the text.

pole of the NRM overprint on a time-calibrated section of the apparent polar wander path (APWP) for the continent or continental block. If the APWP is incompletely known or its time calibration is in doubt—a frequent situation for Proterozoic time—thermal NRM overprints can be dated by comparison with $^{40}Ar/^{39}Ar$ mineral ages and closure temperatures (Buchan and others, 1977; Berger and others, 1979), a method referred to as "thermochronometry." Slow cooling of orogens is recorded by a set of K/Ar or $^{40}Ar/^{39}Ar$ uplift mineral ages and the related set of magnetic overprints (Beckmann and Mitchell, 1976; Morgan, 1976; McWilliams and Dunlop, 1978).

Dated paleomagnetic poles derived from NRM overprints specify the paleolatitudes and paleorotations of tectonic blocks within continents. The signature of intracratonic orogeny, involving no major (⩾1000 km) ocean opening or closing, is a common APWP for all cratonic elements concerned (following paleogeographical reconstruction) over the time span of the orogeny and 50-100 Ma preceding it. Continental collision is marked by convergence of independent precollisional APWPs. In principle, the kinematics of collision can be determined from the precollisional data; but in practice, sufficiently complete data rarely survive in the interior of an active orogen.

Exhaustive reviews of Proterozoic paleomagnetic data and global tectonic interpretations can be found in the literature (e.g., Beckmann, 1979; Briden, 1976; Dunlop, 1981; Irving, 1979; Irving and McGlynn, 1976, 1981; McElhinny and McWilliams, 1977; McWilliams, 1981; Morris and others, 1979; Piper, 1976a, b, 1983). We shall confine ourselves to a few well-documented examples showing the extent and nature of Proterozoic tectonism in the Superior and Grenville Provinces of Laurentia.

SUPERIOR PROVINCE: QUETICO, WAWA AND WABIGOON BELTS

Resolving multivectorial NRMs

Preliminary paleomagnetic results for mafic and intermediate metavolcanics, gabbros, an alkaline complex, syenites, granites, gneisses, and an iron formation from the Quetico, Wawa, and Wabigoon Subprovinces (see Fig. 1) have been summarized by Dunlop (1979a). The results shown in Figure 2 for a sample of the Shelley Lake granite from the Quetico gneiss belt typify the behaviour of most units. The NRM is a sum of vectors belonging to two distinct populations. The first population (group 1) comprises vectors with northward declinations and downwards or positive inclinations averaging about 55° below the horizontal, or the reverse of these directions, southward-pointing with intermediate negative inclinations. In the second population (group 2) are vectors with WSW declinations and shallow positive inclinations or the reverse of these directions. The sample illustrated possesses group 1 NRM vectors of both "normal" and "reverse" polarities and group 2 NRM of a single polarity. [True polarities relative to the present geomagnetic field are unknown because the Proterozoic paleomagnetic record is incomplete and the forward connection with Phanerozoic data remains uncertain.]

Only the pure group 1 and group 2 vectors have fundamental significance. The paleomagnetist's first task is therefore to decompose the composite NRM into its component parts. In any study, it will usually happen that a certain number of samples completely or almost completely lack one or other of the component NRMs. In other samples, one type of NRM will display much lower resistance to stepwise alternating field (AF) or thermal demagnetization than the other, allowing the more resistant vector to be isolated as a stable "endpoint." In Figure 2(a), for example, the normalized resultant NRM vector swings progressively along a great circle (the trace of the plane defined by group 1 and group 2 vectors on the unit sphere) towards the pure group 1 direction in the course of stepwise AF cleaning and towards the group 1 "reverse" direction during thermal cleaning. In either case, group 2 NRM is preferentially erased. The "normal" group 1 direction is reached as a stable endpoint in AF cleaning but a "reverse" group 1

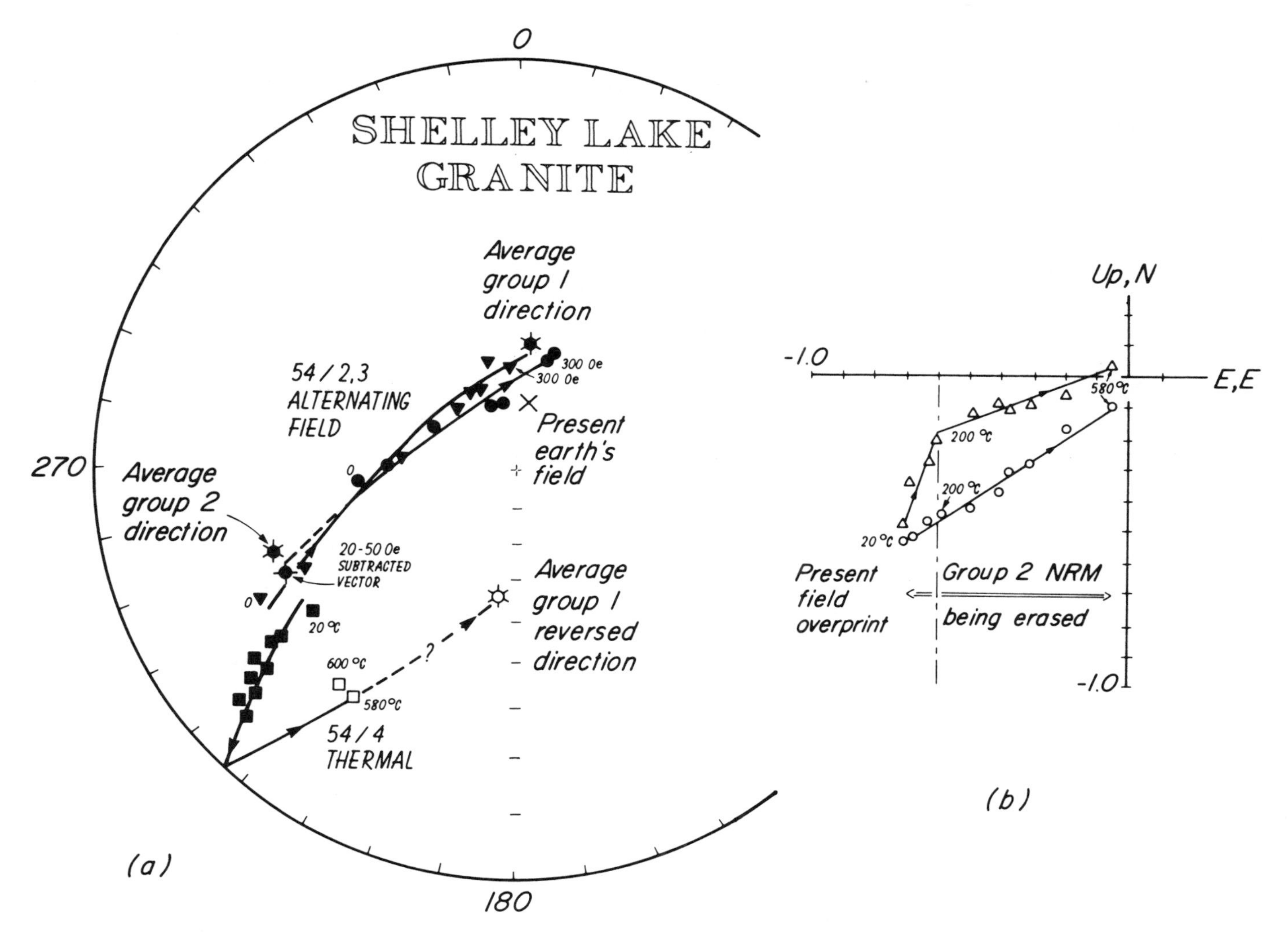

Figure 2. (a) Stereographic projection of the direction of the normalized NRM vector in three specimens of Shelley Lake granite, sample 54 during the course of stepwise AF or thermal demagnetization. Solid/open symbols denote downward/upward vectors, respectively. The NRM is the sum of group 1, reversed group 1, and group 2 vectors (mean group directions for isolated vectors from all samples are shown as asterisks). (b) Vector diagram showing the vertical-plane (triangles) and horizontal-plane (circles) projections of the unnormalized NRM vector of specimen 54/4 during thermal demagnetization. A steep downward vector is erased between 20°C and 200°C, and a shallower, southwestward vector belonging to group 2 is erased between 200°C and 580°C.

thermal endpoint is not reached by 600°C. The "reverse" group 1 direction must be obtained by other means.

If the more resistant NRM is not erased at all at low AF or thermal steps, the vector subtracted between successive steps defines the direction of the less resistant NRM. In Figure 2(a), the resultant NRM of specimen 54/3 before AF cleaning is close to the average group 2 direction, but the initial NRM of specimen 54/2 contains a higher proportion of group 1 NRM. Its direction is therefore displaced along the great circle towards the group 1 direction. However, the vector subtracted between 20 Oe and 50 Oe lies near the group 2 mean direction.

To test whether one component vector or both are demagnetized over given AF or temperature ranges, paleomagnetists use vector diagrams (Zijderveld, 1967; Wilson, 1961), simultaneous horizontal-plane and vertical-plane projections of the (unnormalized) resultant vector. Linear segments in both projections over the same AF or temperature range indicate removal of a single vector, whose direction can be obtained from the slopes of the segments (Dunlop, 1979b) or by vector subtraction. In the example of Figure 2(b), a steeply-inclined vector (probably a present field overprint) is removed between 20°C and 200°C; a group 2 NRM is largely but not completely

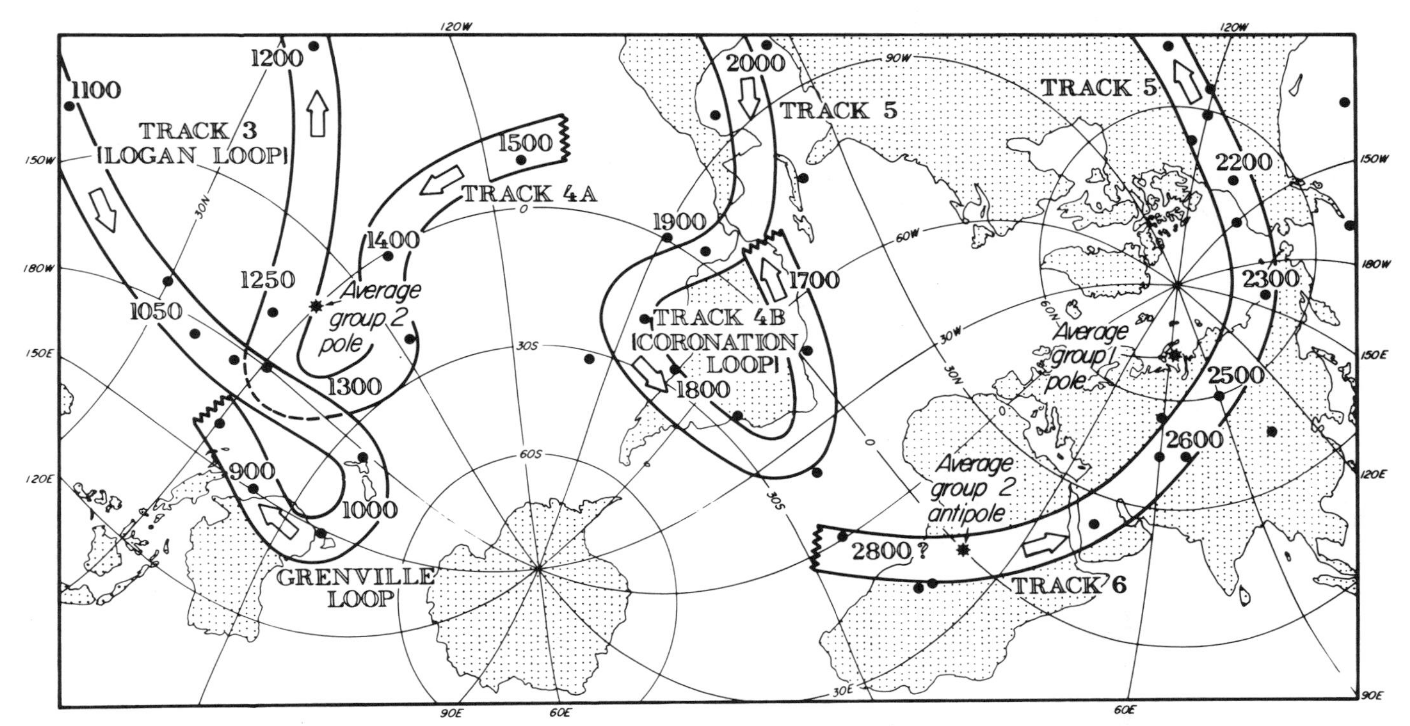

Figure 3. Apparent polar wander path (APWP) for Laurentia over the time interval 2800 Ma to 850 Ma, with selected tie-point poles (based on Irving, 1979, Figs. 9, 10, and 11 and Irving & McGlynn, 1979; Track numbers follow Irving and McGlynn, 1976). As a result of the gaps in the APWP between 1700 and 1500 Ma and after 850 Ma, the polarity of paleopoles is ambiguous. Both "pole" and "antipole" for group 2 results fall on the APWP but at widely differing ages.

erased between 200° C and 600° C; and the "reverse" group 1 NRM is not attacked at all and evidently has no blocking temperatures below 580° C.

Ideal behaviour (component vectors erased in mutually exclusive AF or temperature ranges) is the exception rather than the rule. When both vectors are attacked simultaneously but to different extents, it is sometimes possible to estimate the direction of one vector from the intersection of great circle traces for different samples or units (Halls, 1976). A related technique can resolve the vector with intermediate AF or thermal resistance in a three-vector resultant (Hoffmann and Day, 1978; Halls, 1979).

Paleopoles and tectonic interpretations

Having isolated the fundamental NRM vectors, the paleomagnetist next seeks to determine their ages and origins. Assuming a geocentric axial dipole paleomagnetic field, the average direction of each isolated vector specifies a position for the ancient north or south pole in present-day geographic coordinates. The simplest means of dating an NRM vector is by comparing its paleomagnetic pole to the apparent polar wander path (APWP) traced out by well-dated paleopoles from previous studies in the same continent or continental block.

In Figure 3, the late Archean and early and middle Proterozoic APWP for Laurentia is shown. The path is a swathe ≈20° wide, a reflection of the uncertainty in the positions and ages of paleopoles. The paleopole corresponding to the mean group 1 NRM of the Shelley Lake granite falls near the APWP between 2600 and 2500 Ma. It also falls near the present-day north pole, but the group 1 NRM cannot be a present-field overprint because reverse as well as normal vectors are present (Fig. 2a).

The age of the group 2 NRM is more problematic. Its paleopole is consistent with a magnetization age of either ≈2800 Ma or 1250 Ma. If the former age is correct, the group 2 NRM is a primary Archean magnetization that has survived the Kenoran orogeny. If the latter age is correct, the group 1 NRM is either primary or a Kenoran overprint, and the group 2 NRM is a middle Proterozoic overprint.

Contact tests were carried out in a number of intrusions in an attempt to prove or disprove the primary nature of group 1 or group 2 NRMs. The Shelley Lake body has no clear intrusive contact with surrounding lithologically similar but weakly magnetic granites, but the nearby Poohbah Lake alkaline complex has a well-exposed contact with Archean schists. The result was ambiguous. Schists in the baked contact zone were remagnetized to the same group 1 reversed direction exhibited by the Poohbah intrusion. However, schists outside the baked zone possessed neither an intrusion overprint nor any identifiable preintrusion NRM. Their NRM was exclusively a present-field overprint.

Thus it is not clear whether the baked schists were overprinted at the time the intrusion acquired a primary thermal NRM (a positive contact test) or whether intrusion and country rock alike suffered subsequent Kenoran remagnetization, the unbaked schists having since lost this overprint because their physical properties, e.g., grain size, render them poor magnetic recorders compared to the baked schists. Contact tests on intrusions with a dominant group 2 NRM were likewise inconclusive because the unbaked country rock tended to be unstably magnetized.

It is often assumed (e.g., Dunlop and Buchan, 1977) that of coexisting NRMs with mutually exclusive blocking temperature ranges, the one with higher blocking temperatures is surviving primary NRM and the lower blocking temperature NRM is a later thermal overprint. In the Shelley Lake study, this test failed because group 2 NRM possesses blocking temperatures up to 580°C, the Curie temperature of magnetite (Fig. 2a). Group 1 NRM is carried exclusively by hematite (Curie temperature 670°C) and could be a later chemical overprint acquired at low temperatures. Thus the possibility remained that group 2 NRM was a primary Archean magnetization, as had been demonstrated by positive contact tests for similar remanences in Archean country rocks of the Abitibi subprovince (Irving and Naldrett, 1977; Schutts and Dunlop, 1981).

The question was settled conclusively by $^{40}Ar/^{39}Ar$ step-heating mineral ages (Berger and York, 1979; G. W. Berger, written communication, 1979). Biotite and hornblende plateau ages were 2595 and 2560 Ma, respectively. Since hornblende usually has a high Ar closure temperature, of the order of 600-700°C, and the regional grade of metamorphism is greenschist, implying reheating to no more than 500°C, the Shelley Lake granite must have been intruded near the close of the Kenoran orogeny, acquiring its group 1 NRM during initial cooling. Nothing can be deduced about the nature of the Kenoran event since no pre-Kenoran magnetization is recorded.

Plagioclase $^{40}Ar/^{39}Ar$ data indicate a mild heating event at approximately 1100 Ma (Berger and York, 1979). Since blocking temperatures as high as 580°C could not have been reactivated in this event, the group 2 NRM must be a chemical overprint carried by secondary magnetite. Because of the large amount of apparent polar wander between 1300 and 1100 Ma (Fig. 3), the paleomagnetic date of 1250 Ma for the event has less uncertainty than the $^{40}Ar/^{39}Ar$ age. It is, of course, possible that two separate heating events affected these rocks: the 1250 Ma event contemporaneous with intrusion of the Mackenzie and Sudbury dike swarms to the north and east and an 1100 Ma event related to Keweenawan rifting and volcanism to the south.

The extent of Mackenzie-age igneous activity and mild regional heating appears to have been much greater than the surficial evidence of mapped dike swarms would suggest. Paleomagnetism, preferably supported by $^{40}Ar/^{39}Ar$ dating, is the only means by which one can hope to map the extent of the Mackenzie episode in the western Superior Province or elsewhere.

SUPERIOR PROVINCE: ABITIBI SUBPROVINCE AND COBALT PLATE

Previous studies of Archean country rocks, 2630 Ma Matachewan and 2150 Ma Abitibi diabase dikes of the Abitibi subprovince (Larochelle, 1966; Irving and Naldrett, 1977; Schutts and Dunlop, 1981) and of 2160 Ma Nipissing diabase sills of the Cobalt Plate (summary in Irving, 1979, Fig. 10), have established tie points for Tracks 5 and 6 of the Laurentian APWP, based on proven primary NRMs. A number of these paleopoles appear in Figure 3. Although the question is not completely resolved (Irving and McGlynn, 1981), it is interesting to note that ≈2150-Ma-old paleopoles for formations from the Nain and Slave Provinces seem to agree with Abitibi and Nipissing primary paleopoles. It is probable that the Superior, Slave, and Nain Provinces were assembled in approximately their present-day relative positions (although not in their present latitudes and orientations) at least 200 Ma before the onset of the 1900-1650 Ma Hudsonian orogeny. There are no proven preorogenic paleopoles for rocks of the Churchill, Bear, Southern, or Greenland Provinces to prove or disprove pre-Hudsonian integrity of the entire Shield, but it is probable that the Churchill orogen was then, as now, encircled by the Superior, Slave, and Nain cratons.

Although the last major metamorphism of the Superior Province was Kenoran, the Abitibi subprovince and Cobalt Plate (and perhaps other regions as well) did not altogether escape Hudsonian/Penokean reactivation. A post-2150 Ma NRM overprint is seen locally in Nipissing sills (see summary in Roy and Lapointe, 1976) and regionally in Abitibi and Matachewan dikes and country rocks of the Abitibi Belt (Schutts and Dunlop, 1981). Although sporadic in our samples, the overprint is believed to be thermal, not chemical. One of the lines of evidence is illustrated in Figure 4(a). Those Matachewan dike samples possessing a large proportion of low blocking temperatures exhibit significant overprinting. Samples with only high blocking temperatures (>~500°C) generally have unreset NRMs.

Low blocking temperatures are frequently a result of fine grain size and as such may well be encountered more often near the chilled margin of a dike than in the interior. Grain size is not the only factor favouring remagnetization near dike contacts, however. The peak temperature experienced during remagnetization seems to be significantly

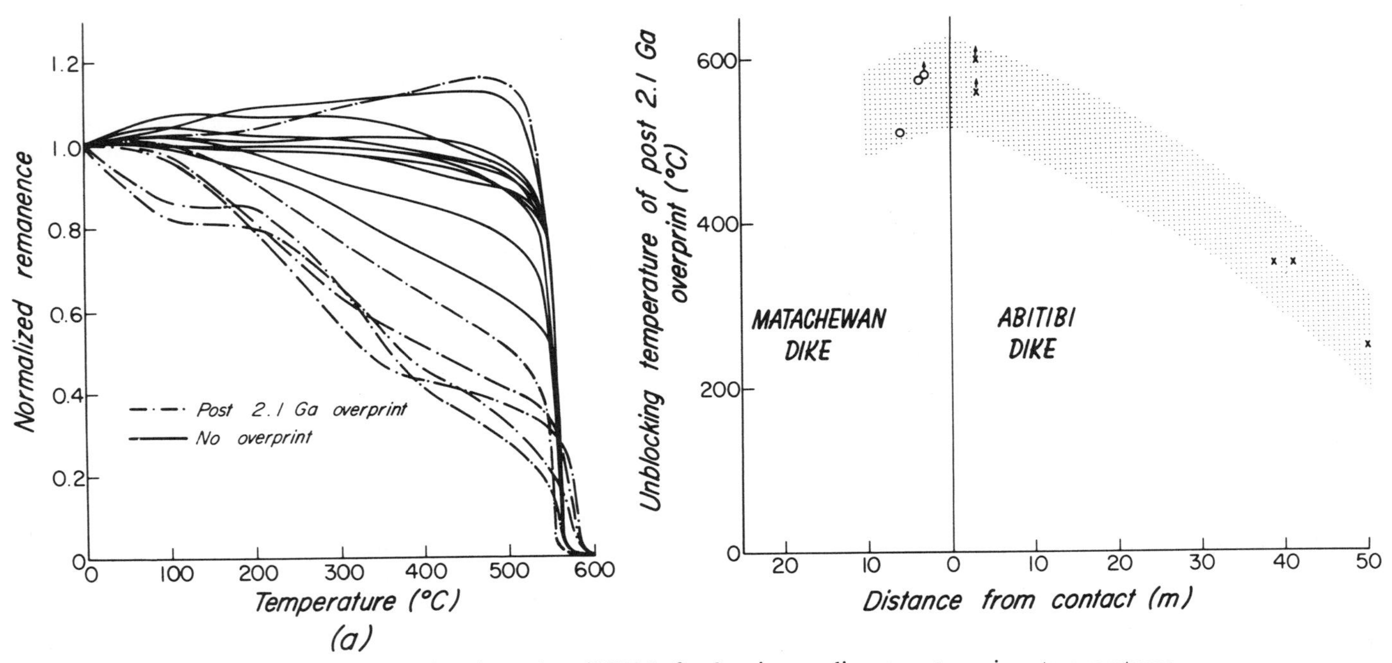

Figure 4. (a) Normalized intensity of NRM after heating-cooling steps to various temperatures for samples from a single 30 m wide Matachewan dike in Munro Township, Ontario. A post-2.1 Ga NRM overprint is generally present in samples with a large fraction of low blocking temperatures and absent from samples with only high blocking temperatures. (b) Maximum temperature of magnetic overprinting as a function of distance from the contact between a 100m wide Abitibi dike and the Matachewan dike of (a).

higher near the margin of an Abitibi dike (Fig. 4(b) than in its interior, an effect we attribute to heating by hot fluids channeled along the dike contact. Overall, 70% of our overprinted samples, whether dikes or country rocks, were in proximity to mapped faults or intrusive contact zones of weakness.

Hanes and York (1979), in a $^{40}Ar/^{39}Ar$ study of the same Abitibi dike illustrated in Figure 4(b), discovered an updating of isotopic ages near the dike contact that parallels the pattern of magnetic overprinting. They appealed to chemical resetting, but we have observed in samples taken within a few meters of the contact (where remagnetization was prominent) that the magnetic oxides have remained essentially pristine. We therefore attribute the magnetic overprinting, at least, to mild regional heating, with local heat concentrations near faults and physically incoherent contact zones that channelled supercritical solutions.

The principal tie-points for Tracks 4B and 4C of the Laurentian APWP (the Coronation Loop of Irving and McGlynn, 1979) between 1850 and 1700 Ma are paleopoles from Churchill and Bear Province rocks magnetized at the time of the Hudsonian orogeny. These paleopoles were shown in Figure 3 but are omitted from Figure 5 to highlight secondary overprint paleopoles from Superior Province rocks. Our interpretation of the direction of motion on Tracks 4 and 5 is the conventional one (Roy and Lapointe, 1976; Irving, 1979), although apparently primary contact tests for both NRM components of the Nipissing diabase (Morris, 1979) throw some doubt on the question (Irving and McGlynn, 1981; Piper, 1983). However, only the direction of motion we assume is consistent with the demonstrated primary/secondary sequence of our Abitibi dike poles (Schutts and Dunlop, 1981).

Many of our Abitibi Belt formations have been overprinted, but the number of overprint vectors per site is not large enough to calculate a statistically confident average paleopole for each unit. In Figure 5, therefore, we have plotted virtual geomagnetic poles (VGPs) for individual overprint vectors regardless of formation, and a single mean paleopole for the entire region.

The VGPs have large uncertainties compared to those of the paleopoles, but they do illustrate the fact that the overprints were likely acquired at times throughout the 1900–1700 Ma interval, rather than at a single time. Hanes and York (1979) obtained a similar range of updated $^{40}Ar/^{39}Ar$ ages for felsic and mafic mineral separates from samples near the margin of the Abitibi dike of Figure 4(b). Some of our overprint VGPs are therefore independently dated within broad limits.

Our regional mean paleopole falls in an ambiguous position on the Coronation Loop. It could indicate either early (≈1900 Ma) or late-stage (≈1700 Ma) "Hudsonian" overprinting. The tectonic implications of these alternatives are very different. If our paleopole is ≈1900 Ma old, its

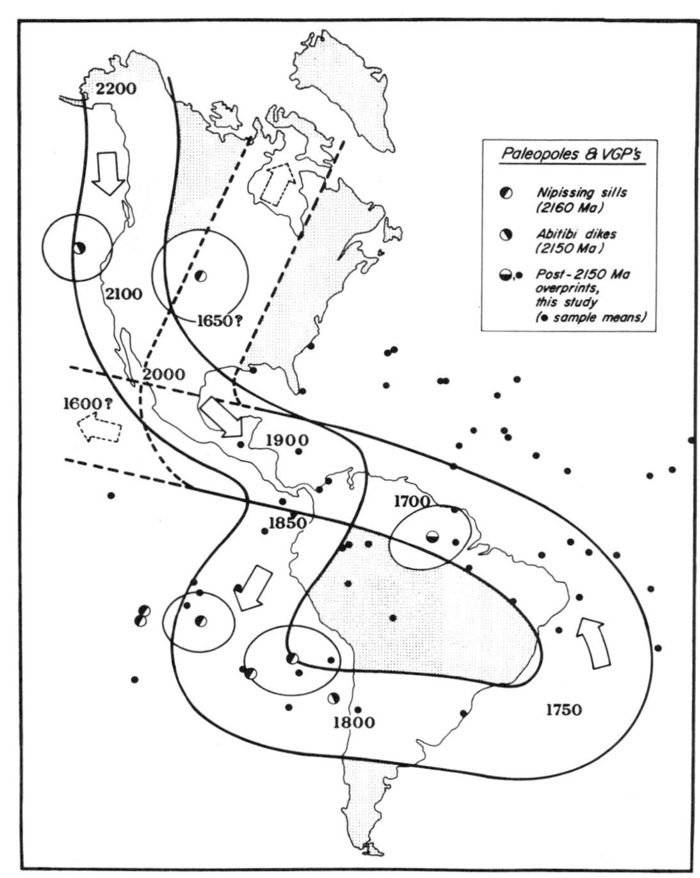

Figure 5. Enlargement of part of Tracks 4 and 5 of Figure 3. The trend of the APWP after 1700 Ma is uncertain. Paleopoles shown (all from Superior Province rocks) are derived from primary and secondary NRMs of Nipissing sills and Abitibi dikes and from regional secondary overprints of Abitibi and Matachewan dikes and country rocks of the Abitibi Subprovince. VGPs corresponding to sample mean NRMs from the latter study are shown as small solid dots. Ovals of 95 percent confidence are given for the primary and some of the overprint paleopoles. Secondary paleopoles and VGPs are consistent with time-correlative paleopoles from the Churchill and Bear orogens.

agreement with the APWP defined by Churchill and Bear Province poles implies integrity of much of the Shield from the earliest stages of the Hudsonian event. If our paleopole is ≈1700 Ma old, it could be merely recording the final stage of cooling following Hudsonian-age collision of Superior and Churchill cratons. [The tendency of our VGPs to fall in southwesterly and northeasterly concentrations leaves open the possibility that both early and late overprinting occurred.]

Paleopoles for Nipissing diabase overprints and an Abitibi dike secondary paleopole of Larochelle (1966) fall between 1850 and 1800 Ma on the APWP, favouring a largely intracratonic model of orogeny for the Churchill and Superior, rather than a collision between the two. This view also fits the evidence cited earlier that most cratonic elements were assembled in their present configuration by

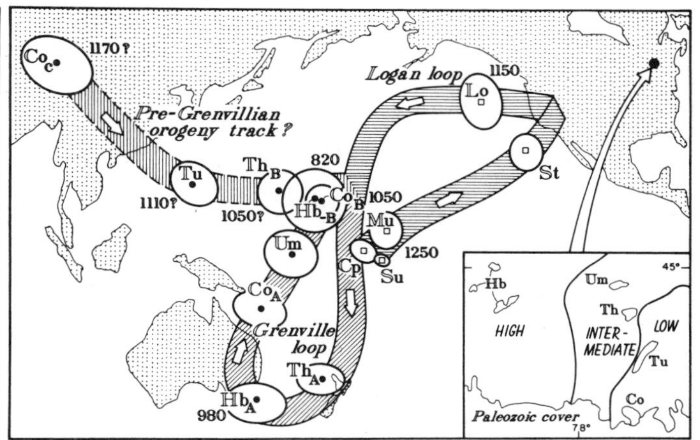

Figure 6. Enlargement of part of the middle Proterozoic APWP for Laurentia (Fig. 3), with the addition of a possible pre-Grenvillian orogeny track, defined by Grenville Province paleopoles Co_C, Tu, and Th_B, that converges with the time-correlative APWP for the rest of Laurentia (the Logan Loop) around 1050 Ma. Such a convergence is the signature of continental collision. Tie-point poles Cp, Mu, Su, St, and Lo are referenced in Dunlop (1981, Fig. 5). The remaining paleopoles, from the Haliburton-Hastings area, Ontario (inset map), are discussed in the text.

2150 Ma because of the geometric difficulty of inserting the Churchill within encircling stable cratons after that time.

GRENVILLE PROVINCE: THE HASTINGS BASIN

Rocks of the Grenville Province (Fig. 1) have been profoundly affected by deep burial during the 1100-850 Ma Grenvillian orogeny. At the crustal level presently exposed by uplift and erosion, little pre-Grenvillian magnetic record survived, except perhaps in the Hastings Basin of Central Ontario (see Fig. 6, inset) where the metamorphic grade is locally "low" (greenschist) compared to the regional amphibolite to granulite grade.

Dating synorogenic paleopoles from most of the Grenville has been a severe problem (Dunlop and others, 1980). Uplift and cooling were extremely slow and different isotopic clocks record entirely different ages. The most appropriate way of dating paleopoles is $^{40}Ar/^{39}Ar$ "thermochronometry" (Buchan and others, 1977; Berger and others, 1979) because Ar closure temperatures for hornblende, biotite, and feldspars span the usual blocking temperature ranges of hematite and magnetite.

Argon release patterns during step heating provide specific mineral closure temperatures (which can differ from one sample to another by as much as 200° C) as well as mineral ages. Using the regional cooling curve derived from $^{40}Ar/^{39}Ar$ data, NRM overprints of *thermal* origin can be dated through their characteristic blocking temperatures. A *chemical* overprint often has laboratory blocking temperatures greatly exceeding the temperature at which it was produced in nature, and so it cannot be dated by thermoch-

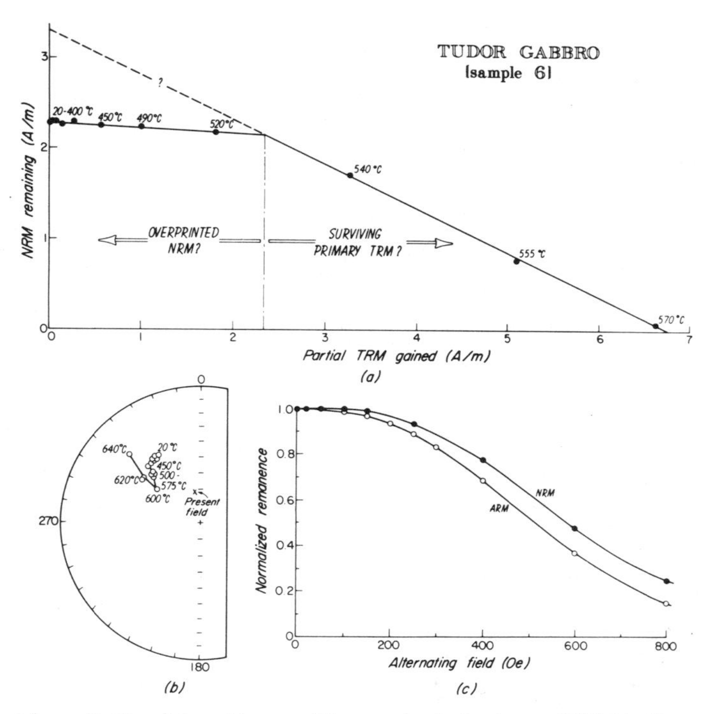

Figure 7. Possible evidence of the survival of primary TRM in the Tudor gabbro. (a) A comparison of the reciprocal thermal decay of NRM and acquisition of partial TRM (the Thellier paleointensity experiment). Above 520° C, the linear relation implies that the NRM originated as TRM in a field about one-half (the slope of the line) the present field strength. The dashed line below 520° C depicts original NRM that has been overprinted and effectively demagnetized. (b) The direction of NRM during thermal demagnetization of a companion specimen of the same sample, showing directional stability over the inferred blocking temperature range (500–575° C) of primary TRM and lower stability in other ranges. Equal-area projection; all vectors are upward. (c) Comparisons of normalized intensity decay curves during AF demagnetization, showing the similar behaviour of NRM and ARM (an analog of TRM).

ronometry. It is therefore of paramount importance to demonstrate the thermal nature or otherwise of all component NRM vectors.

The earliest Grenville paleopoles to be dated by thermochronometry (Berger and others, 1979) were Hb_A and Hb_B (Fig. 6), corresponding to the high-temperature A and low-temperature B NRMs of the Haliburton intrusions (Buchan and Dunlop, 1976). A and B NRMs were shown to have adjacent, nonoverlapping blocking temperature ranges (500–650° C and 20–400° C, respectively) and were inferred to be successive thermal overprints of the primary NRM, none of which has survived. The average ages determined were 980 Ma for Hb_A and 820 Ma for Hb_B.

Berger and York (1981) have recently determined the cooling history of the Thanet gabbro and surrounding area. Buchan (1978) in his paleomagnetic study of the Thanet body found two superimposed NRM vectors with generally similar directions to the Haliburton NRMs; but in this case the B NRM had the higher blocking temperatures and, if of thermal origin, must be older than the A component. In fact, the B NRM could be primary thermal remanent magnetization (TRM) that survived the Grenvillian event, since the B blocking temperature range of 550–600° C exceeds the probable metamorphic reheating temperature of the Thanet and surrounding amphibolite-grade terrain. The primary TRM hypothesis is all the more attractive in that Berger and York (1981) found a pre-Grenvillian $^{40}Ar/^{39}Ar$ hornblende age of 1200 Ma, the first ever for the Grenville.

Proving that the highest blocking temperature component in a multivectorial NRM is of thermal origin, and thus datable by $^{40}Ar/^{39}Ar$ thermochronometry, presents some difficulties. One can be reasonably confident that lower blocking temperature components with discrete blocking temperature ranges are successively younger thermal overprints of preexisting NRM or NRMs; but the earliest NRM could be of thermal, chemical, or some other origin. A positive contact test (§2.2) would demonstrate primary TRM in the intrusion, but a high-temperature regional thermal overprint of intrusion and country rock would not be distinguishable from a chemical overprint: both would yield negative contact tests.

The best test of the thermal nature of an NRM component, either primary or overprint, is a positive result of the Thellier and Thellier (1959) paleointensity experiment, in which NRM and laboratory TRM are compared in companion heating steps that span the entire blocking temperature range. In Figure 7(a), the single-component NRM of a sample of the Tudor gabbro is tested in this manner. The Tudor body is located in the low-grade centre of the Hastings Basin (Fig. 6, inset), where survival of primary NRM is more plausible than elsewhere. The Thellier plot has a striking form. From 20° C to about 500° C, laboratory TRM is gained but no NRM is lost. Between 520° C and 570° C, the NRM is completely replaced by laboratory TRM.

The linear plot over the 520–570° C interval indicates matching NRM and laboratory TRM blocking temperature spectra and is evidence that the NRM had a thermal origin. Supporting evidence is the reasonable value indicated for paleofield intensity (about one-half the present field intensity at the same latitude) and the similar AF demagnetization curves (Fig. 7(c)) of NRM and anhysteretic remanent magnetization or ARM, a frequently used TRM analog (Levi and Merrill, 1976). Since the minimum NRM blocking temperatures of ≈500° C for this sample and two others that pass the Thellier test exceed the probable reheating temperature in this area (≤500° C, greenschist facies), the NRM is probably a primary TRM rather than a later thermal overprint.

The Tudor gabbro paleopole (Palmer and Carmichael, 1973) falls well to the west of the paleopoles that define the Grenville Loop (Fig. 6). Hayatsu and Palmer (1975) obtained a K/Ar isochron age of 675 Ma for the Tudor and considered the NRM to be a late Proterozoic overprint. Baksi (1982) has reexamined the question, using $^{40}Ar/^{39}Ar$ stepheating. His hornblende and plagioclase separates, respectively, recorded cooling through ≈550°C at 1110 Ma and through 200–250°C at ≈700 Ma. Since the Tudor NRM is likely high-temperature (500–580°C) primary TRM, not low-temperature CRM, we tentatively assign an age of 1110 Ma rather than ≈700 Ma to the Tudor paleopole.

The Cordova gabbro, like the Tudor gabbro, is located in the lowest-grade part of the Hastings Basin (Fig. 6, inset). Unlike the Tudor, which yielded one NRM vector, the Cordova possesses three NRMs. Paleopoles for the A and B NRMs resemble the corresponding paleopoles from the Haliburton and Thanet intrusions, but the C paleopole is unique. It lies far to the west of other Grenville poles in the general area of upper Ordovician and Silurian paleopoles for North America. From $^{40}Ar/^{39}Ar$ thermochronometry on the Cordova, Lopez-Martinez and York (1983) find very different ages for hornblende and plagioclase separates. Since the Cordova C NRM usually has rather low blocking temperatures, it is likely a young (i.e., Paleozoic) overprint. A pre-Grenvillian age for pole Co_C, as hypothesized in Figure 6, is not ruled out but is less probable.

The Thanet B NRM *may* be a ≥580°C hematite TRM, but it may equally well be a CRM. No Thellier test has been attempted and the choice is subjective. Berger and York (1981) preferred a CRM origin and considered Th_B to be an overprint dating from late-stage Grenvillian uplift and cooling. If instead Th_B is a thermal overprint, its age, according to the Thanet cooling curve (Berger and York, 1981, Fig. 5; Dunlop and others, 1980, Fig. 8), must be ≈1100 Ma.

Even in the Hastings Basin, little of the paleomagnetic record predates the Grenvillian orogeny. Penetrating the Grenvillian metamorphic veil are $^{40}Ar/^{39}Ar$ hornblende ages from the Thanet, Tudor, and Cordova gabbros; but only in the case of the Tudor can one be at all confident that the high-temperature NRM likewise sees through the Grenvillian event.

The Logan Loop, defined by data from cratonic North America excluding the Grenville, and the Grenville Loop, defined by Grenville data only, are consecutive APWP segments. They imply no disruption of the Laurentian craton. However, if Tu and perhaps Th_B (conceivably also Co_C) are either primary NRMs or thermal overprints, their paleopoles define a 1200–1100 Ma Grenville APWP segment concurrent with the Logan Loop but divergent from it.

If this view proves to be correct, convergence of the two tracks between 1100 and 1050 Ma (Fig. 6) would mark the collision of "Grenvillia" (Irving and others, 1974) and "Interior Laurentia." The Grenvillian orogeny would then represent a collisional reactivation of Himalayan style, followed by slow unroofing and cooling during the subsequent 200 or 300 Ma. A continental reconstruction using the data of Figure 6 (see Dunlop, 1981, Fig. 6) leads to an acceptable collisional configuration, in which a Proterozoic "Atlantic" ocean closed scissors-style about a pole of rotation near Newfoundland. Subsequently, between 1050 and 820 Ma, the united Laurentian continent drifted from the paleoequator to high latitudes and back to the equator at a minimum rate of 60 mm/a.

DISCUSSION

The analysis and interpretation of Proterozoic paleomagnetic data require subtlety and a certain degree of dedication. A production-line approach—blanket AF cleaning and the like—is entirely inappropriate. Every sample must be fully AF or thermally demagnetized and the spacing of steps may need adjustment to suit individual distributions of demagnetizing fields or blocking temperatures. Unresolved multivectorial NRMs are insidious sources of noise in the paleomagnetic record. Every effort must be made, using vector diagrams and analysis of great circle trends, to identify and isolate all the NRM vectors.

There are both associative and interpretative approaches to dating the resolved NRMs. Associative dates, from matching paleopoles to existing APWPs, are only as reliable as the least confidently dated neighbouring paleopole anchoring the APWP. Furthermore, associative dates are sometimes ambiguous. In the Shelley Lake granite (§2, Fig. 3), the group 2 pole and antipole both fell on the Laurentian APWP, the dates and resulting tectonic interpretations being very different in the two cases. Abitibi subprovince overprint poles (§3, Fig. 5) lie near a loop intersection and could date from either the onset or the conclusion of Hudsonian reactivation. The difference is crucial to tectonic interpretation. In the case of the Grenville Province, the existence of a pre-Grenvillian track (§4, Fig. 6) is not established with certainty, but paleopole Th_B certainly falls at a loop intersection and could either predate or largely postdate Grenvillian metamorphism. As with the Abitibi study, the tectonic choice is between intracratonic reactivation and the collision of cratonic elements.

The tectonic indeterminacy can often be lifted by determining relative ages of NRM components, one of which can be confidently dated. The first step is usually to demonstrate the thermal origin of one or more of the NRMs by means of contact tests, comparison of NRM and TRM characteristics (AF or thermal demagnetization curves, Thellier experiment), or the existence of discrete blocking temperature intervals in a single mineral carrier (cf. Figs. 2b, 4a, 7a, 7c). Primary TRM is clearly the oldest component NRM. Thermal overprints with successively lower blocking temperatures are successively younger.

It frequently happens that all the wiles of the paleomagnetist's art fail to date an NRM component conclusively; $^{40}Ar/^{39}Ar$ dating by step-heating of mineral separates is then indispensable. The examples in this paper attest to the power of the $^{40}Ar/^{39}Ar$ method. The Shelley Lake group 1 NRM is shown to be a Kenoran-age component acquired during fairly rapid cooling and the group 2 NRM, a middle Proterozoic overprint (§2). Abitibi overprints are shown to be unquestionably of Hudsonian age (§3). Likewise, $^{40}Ar/^{39}Ar$ thermochronometry (mineral ages *and* Ar closure temperatures) is central to the interpretation of Grenvillian reactivation, uplift, and cooling. Until the advent of thermochronometry, ages of Grenville paleopoles were uncertain by 100–200 Ma—an uncertainty that was only appreciated in hindsight, when a number of tectonic hypotheses were shown to be untenable (e.g., Dunlop and others, 1980).

A capsule summary of Laurentian tectonic events whose nature and extent are clarified by paleomagnetism would omit the Kenoran orogeny (whose record outside the Superior Province has yet to be discovered) but would include the Hudsonian/Penokean orogeny (1900–1650 Ma), the Mackenzie igneous episode (1250 Ma), Keweenawan rifting (1150–1050 Ma; for a paleomagnetic summary, see Halls and Pesonen, 1982), and the Grenvillian orogeny (1100–850 Ma). Hudsonian deformation of the Churchill Province and reactivation of the Superior Province (Abitibi subprovince and Cobalt Plate) appear to have involved no paleomagnetically detectable relative motion of the two provinces (§3). The extent of Mackenzie-age reactivation is greater than the extent of mapped Mackenzie and Sudbury dike swarms. Mild thermal overprinting of this age was detected in rocks of the Quetico, Wawa, and Wabigoon Subprovinces (§2). $^{40}Ar/^{39}Ar$ dating of one of these formations suggests possible additional Keweenawan overprinting.

The Grenvillian orogeny may have been initiated by collision of "Grenvillia" and "Interior Laurentia" between 1100 and 1050 Ma, but the evidence is not overwhelmingly in favour of this model. Much depends on the survival of primary, preorogenic NRM in the Hastings Basin metamorphic "window," a question that is not yet settled beyond doubt. An alternative model (Dewey and Burke, 1973) is reactivation through marginal accretion of a third cratonic element, no longer preserved.

ACKNOWLEDGMENTS

We thank an anonymous reviewer for useful comments. The research described here has been supported by Energy, Mines and Resources Canada research agreements and by a Natural Sciences and Engineering Research Council operating grant to DJD.

REFERENCES CITED

Baksi, A. K., 1982, $^{40}Ar/^{39}Ar$ incremental heating study on the Tudor gabbro, Grenville Province, Ontario; its bearing on the North American apparent-polar-wander path in late Proterozoic times: Royal Astronomical Society, Geophysical Journal, v. 70, p. 545–562.

Beckmann, G.E.J., 1979, A review of Nagssugtoqidian palaeomagnetism: Rapp. Grønlands Geol. Unders., v. 89, p. 115–124.

Beckmann, G.E.J., and Mitchell, J. G., 1976, Palaeomagnetic and geochronological work in central West Greenland: Earth and Planetary Science Letters, v. 30, p. 269–280.

Berger, G. W., and York, D., 1979, ^{40}Ar-^{39}Ar dating of multicomponent magnetizations in the Archean Shelley Lake granite, northwestern Ontario: Canadian Journal of Earth Sciences, v. 16, p. 1933–1941.

——1981, ^{40}Ar-^{39}Ar dating of the Thanet gabbro, Ontario: looking through the Grenvillian metamorphic veil and implications for paleomagnetism: Canadian Journal of Earth Sciences, v. 18, p. 266–273.

Berger, G. W., York, D., and Dunlop, D. J., 1979, Calibration of Grenvillian paleopoles by $^{40}Ar/^{39}Ar$ dating: Nature, v. 277, p. 46–47.

Briden, J. C., 1971, Application of palaeomagnetism to Proterozoic tectonics: Royal Society of London, Philosophical Transactions, ser. A, v. 280, p. 405–416.

Buchan, K. L., 1978, Magnetic overprinting in the Thanet gabbro complex, Ontario: Canadian Journal of Earth Sciences, v. 15, p. 1407–1421.

Buchan, K. L., and Dunlop, D. J., 1976, Paleomagnetism of the Haliburton intrusions: superimposed magnetizations, metamorphism and tectonics in the late Precambrian: Journal of Geophysical Research, v. 81, p. 2951–2967.

Buchan, K. L., Berger, G. W., McWilliams, M. O., York, D., and Dunlop, D. J., 1977, Thermal overprinting of natural remanent magnetization and K/Ar ages in metamorphic rocks: Journal of Geomagnetism and Geoelectricity, v. 29, p. 401–410.

Dewey, J. F., and Burke, K.C.A., 1973, Tibetan, Variscan and Precambrian basement reactivation: products of continental collision: Journal of Geology, v. 81, p. 683–692.

Dunlop, D. J., 1979a, A regional paleomagnetic study of Archean rocks from the Superior Geotraverse area, northwestern Ontario: Canadian Journal of Earth Sciences, v. 16, p. 1906–1919.

——1979b, On the use of Zijderveld vector diagrams in multicomponent paleomagnetic studies: Physics of the Earth and Planetary Interiors, v. 20, p. 12–24.

——1981, Palaeomagnetic evidence for Proterozoic continental development: Royal Society of London, Philosophical Transactions, ser. A, v. 301, p. 265–277.

Dunlop, D. J., and Buchan, K. L., 1977, Thermal remagnetization and the paleointensity record of metamorphic rocks: Physics of the Earth and Planetary Interiors, v. 13, p. 325–331.

Dunlop, D. J., York, D., Berger, G. W., Buchan, K. L., and Stirling, J. M., 1980, The Grenville Province: a paleomagnetic case-study of Precambrian continental drift, *in* Strangway, D. W., ed., The continental crust and its mineral deposits: Geological Association of Canada Special Paper 20, p. 487–502.

Halls, H. C., 1976, A least-squares method to find a remanence direction from converging remagnetization circles: Royal Astronomical Society, Geophysical Journal, v. 45, p. 297–304.

——1979, Separation of multicomponent NRM; combined use of difference and resultant magnetization vectors: Earth Planetary Science Letters, v. 43, p. 303–308.

Halls, H. C., and Pesonen, L. J., 1982, Paleomagnetism of Keweenawan rocks: Geological Society of America, Memoir 156, p. 173–201.

Hanes, J. A., and York, D., 1979, A detailed $^{40}Ar/^{39}Ar$ age study of an Abitibi dike from the Canadian Superior Province: Canadian Journal of Earth Sciences, v. 16, p. 1060–1070.

Hayatsu, A., and Palmer, H. C., 1975, K-Ar isochron study of the Tudor gabbro, Grenville Province, Ontario: Earth Planetary Science Letters, v. 25, p. 208–212.

Hoffmann, K. A., and Day, R., 1978, Separation of multicomponent NRM: a general method: Earth Planetary Science Letters, v. 40, p. 433–438.

Irving, E., 1979, Paleopoles and paleolatitudes of North America and speculations about displaced terrains: Canadian Journal of Earth Sciences, v. 16, p. 669–694.

Irving, E., and McGlynn, J. C., 1976, Proterozoic magnetostratigraphy and the tectonic evolution of Laurentia: Royal Society of London, Philosophical Transactions, ser. A, v. 280, p. 433–468.

—— 1979, Palaeomagnetism in the Coronation Geosyncline and arrangement of the continents in the middle Proterozoic: Royal Astronomical Society, Geophysical Journal, v. 58, p. 309–336.

—— 1981, On the coherence, rotation and palaeolatitude of Laurentia in the Proterozoic, *in* Kroner, A., ed., Precambrian plate tectonics: Amsterdam, Elsevier, p. 561–598.

Irving, E., and Naldrett, A. J., 1977, Paleomagnetism in Abitibi greenstone belt and Abitibi and Matachewan dikes: evidence of the Archean geomagnetic field: Journal of Geology, v. 85, p. 157–176.

Irving, E., Emslie, R. F., and Ueno, H., 1974, Upper Proterozoic paleomagnetic poles from Laurentia and the history of the Grenville Structural Province: Journal of Geophysical Research, v. 79, p. 5491–5502.

Larochelle, A., 1966, Paleomagnetism of the Abitibi dike swarm: Canadian Journal of Earth Sciences, v. 3, p. 671–683.

Levi, S., and Merrill, R. T., 1976, A comparison of ARM and TRM in magnetite: Earth and Planetary Science Letters, v. 32, p. 171–184.

Lopez-Martinez, M., and York, D., 1983, Further unravelling of the age and paleomagnetic record of the southwest Grenville Province: Canadian Journal of Earth Sciences, v. 20 (in press).

McElhinny, M. W., and McWilliams, M. O., 1977, Precambrian geodynamics— a palaeomagnetic view: Tectonophysics, v. 40, p. 137–159.

McWilliams, M. O., 1981, Palaeomagnetic and tectonic evolution of Gondwana, *in* Kroner, A., ed., Precambrian plate tectonics: Amsterdam, Elsevier, p. 649–688.

McWilliams, M. O., and Dunlop, D. J., 1978, Grenville paleomagnetism and tectonics: Canadian Journal of Earth Sciences, v. 15, p. 687–695.

Morgan, G. E., 1976, Palaeomagnetism of a slowly cooled plutonic terrain in Western Greenland: Nature, v. 259, p. 382–385.

Morris, W. A., 1979, A positive contact test between Nipissing diabase and Gowganda argillites: Canadian Journal of Earth Sciences, v. 16, p. 607–611.

Morris, W. A., Schmidt, P. W., and Roy, J. L., 1979, A graphical approach to polar paths: paleomagnetic cycles and global tectonics: Physics of the Earth and Planetary Interiors, v. 19, p. 85–99.

Palmer, H. C., and Carmichael, C. M., 1973, Paleomagnetism of some Grenville Province rocks: Canadian Journal of Earth Sciences, v. 10, p. 1175–1190.

Patel, J. P., and Palmer, H. C., 1974, Magnetic and paleomagnetic studies of the Nipissing diabase, Lake Matinenda area, Ontario: Canadian Journal of Earth Sciences, v. 11, p. 353–361.

Piper, J.D.A., 1976a, Palaeomagnetic evidence for a Proterozoic supercontinent: Royal Society of London, Philosophical Transactions, ser. A, v. 280, p. 469–490.

—— 1976b, Definition of pre-2000 m.y. apparent polar movements: Earth Planetary Science Letters, v. 28, p. 470–478.

—— 1983, The dynamics of the continental crust in Proterozoic times: Geological Society of America, Memoir 161 (this volume).

Roy, J. L., and Lapointe, P. L., 1976, The paleomagnetism of Huronian red beds and Nipissing diabase: post-Huronian igneous events and apparent polar path for the interval -2300 to -1500 Ma for Laurentia: Canadian Journal of Earth Sciences, v. 13, p. 749–773.

Schutts, L. D., and Dunlop, D. J., 1981, Proterozoic magnetic overprinting of Archean rocks in the Canadian Superior Province: Nature, v. 291, p. 642–645.

Stockwell, C. H., McGlynn, J. C., Emslie, R. F., Sanford, B. V., Norris, A. W., Donaldson, J. A., Fahrig, W. F., and Currie, K. L., 1970, Geology of the Canadian Shield, *in* Douglas, R.J.W., ed., Geology and economic minerals of Canada (fifth edition): Ottawa, Geological Survey of Canada, Department of Energy, Mines and Resources, Economic Geology Report 1, p. 43–150.

Symons, D.T.A., and Londry, J. W., 1975, Tectonic results from paleomagnetism of the Aphebian Nipissing diabase at Gowganda, Ontario: Canadian Journal of Earth Sciences, v. 12, p. 940–948.

Thellier, E., and Thellier, O., 1959, Sur l'intensité du champ terrestre dans le passé historique et géologique: Annales de Géophysique, v. 15, p. 285–376.

Wilson, R. L., 1961, Paleomagnetism in Northern Ireland, I. The thermal demagnetization of natural magnetic moments in rocks: Royal Astronomical Society, Geophysical Journal, v. 5, p. 45–69.

Zijderveld, J.D.A., 1967, A. C. demagnetization of rocks: analysis of results, *in* Collinson, D. W., and others, eds., Methods in palaeomagnetism: Amsterdam, Elsevier, p. 254–286.

Manuscript Accepted by the Society April 14, 1983

Printed in U.S.A.

Geological Society of America
Memoir 161
1983

Proterozoic orogenies and crustal evolution

A. J. Baer
University of Ottawa
Ottawa, Ontario K1N 6N5
Canada

ABSTRACT

A brief review of secular trends of Proterozoic sedimentation, volcanism, K_2O/Na_2O ratio of supracrustal rocks, massive sulfide mineral deposits, isotopic Sr ratio in seawater, geochronology, and paleomagnetism clearly shows the episodic nature of orogenic activity. Brief episodes of deformation and generation of continental crust, around −1800 Ma and around −1000 Ma were separated by long (800 Ma) periods of limited continental growth. Rapid thickening of continental lithosphere and growing instability of oceanic lithosphere led to the start of subduction around −800 Ma. Subduction-controlled plate tectonics has dominated orogenic evolution ever since. A theory of unsteady mantle convection limited to the upper mantle (Tozer, 1965) can explain Proterozoic orogenies as the consequence of convective over-turns separated by "warm-up" periods. Present plate motions would control the distribution and motions of mantle currents rather than vice versa. Proterozoic plate motions of limited lateral amplitude led to formation of ensialic orogens. Paleomagnetic polar wander paths suggest that local crustal extension preceded phases of compression responsible for orogenies. The change-over from the Archean to the Proterozoic would correspond to a change in convection regime of the upper mantle from steady to unsteady convection.

INTRODUCTION

Subduction-driven plate tectonics and the Wilson cycle have been particularly successful in unraveling recent tectonics. This model can be safely extrapolated back to about −800 Ma, when the first typical ophiolites appeared in the geological record (Leblanc, 1976).

Whereas a sharp change distinguishes Archean from younger orogens, the transition from Proterozoic orogens to Phanerozoic ones appears to be more gradual. The question has arisen therefore about the nature of Proterozoic orogenies. Are they controlled by plate tectonics or are they not (Dewey and Spall, 1975)? This paper attempts to review the evidence and to establish what constraints apply to all models of Proterozoic crustal evolution. The narrower the constraints, the more confident the models that will accommodate them. It is important to establish boundary conditions even though it may be premature to propose any specific model of Proterozoic crustal evolution.

Conveniently, if somewhat arbitrarily, constraints are considered to fall in three groups: geological, geochemical, and geophysical. They shall then be integrated in the last section of the paper.

GEOLOGICAL CONSTRAINTS

In spite of some overlap, data relevant to the problem at hand can be associated with each of the three groups of sedimentary, igneous, and metamorphic rocks.

Data from Sedimentary Rocks

Historically, the abundance of platform sediments in the Proterozoic and their scarcity in the Archean had been recognized very early by geologists of the last century. Recent compilations (Condie, 1982) show that the Proterozoic of all continents has an abundance of such shelf sediments (Fig. 1a) up to about -1300 Ma. In contrast, greywacke is scarce except in the interval -1800 to -1600 Ma. In fact, the relative abundance of greywackes is so small, volume-wise,

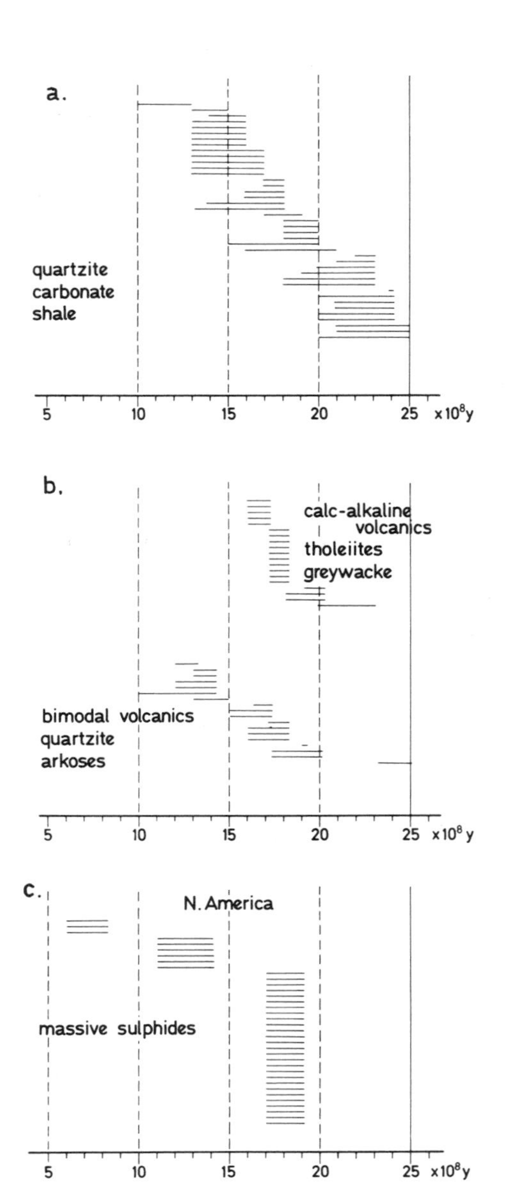

Figure 1. Distribution through time of various rock-types. (a) quartzite, carbonate, and shale world-wide between –2500 Ma and –1000 Ma (data from Condie, 1982); (b) bimodal volcanic assemblages and tholeiitic, calc-alkaline volcanic and greywacke assemblages, world-wide, between –2500 Ma and –1000 Ma (data from Condie, 1982); (c) Proterozoic massive sulphide deposits of North America (data from Sangster, 1980). Each line corresponds to one particular rock sequence (Condie, 1982). In each of the four major assemblages represented, individual sequences are plotted in order of decreasing age, from bottom to top. The vertical scale only corresponds to a number of sequences in each assemblage.

that it does not appear to affect the K_2O/Na_2O ratio of all sedimentary rocks (Engel et al., 1974) (Fig. 2), unless the slight drop in that ratio between -1700 and -1500 Ma indicates their presence. If scarcity of greywacke reflects stability, comparison of the two graphs of Figure 2 shows that Proterozoic continents were dominantly stable until at least -1300 Ma ago, with a short period of greywacke deposition around -1700 Ma. The late Proterozoic was marked by a rapid change to less K_2O-rich sediments after -1100 Ma and a sharp reversal of this trend around -700 Ma. This analysis rests on the assumption that preserved sequences tabulated by Condie (1982) faithfully reflect the proportion of deposited sediments. It also assumes that the lack of sedimentary differentiation in greywackes controls their K_2O/Na_2O ratio.

Data from Igneous Rocks

Figure 1b shows that the distribution of greywacke matches that of tholeiitic and calc-alkaline volcanics because of their well-known spatial and temporal association. Bimodal volcanics do occur later than -1600 Ma, however, until about-1200 Ma. The quasi-absence of any well-developed volcanic suite from -2500 Ma to -2000 Ma has important implications for crustal evolution. Large volumes of andesitic volcanics are known from the Archean (Glikson, 1980a). Except for the 2000-1600 Ma interval, they only reappear in the geological record after about -900 Ma in West Africa (Bertrand and Caby, 1978), Saudi Arabia (Engel et al., 1980; Greenwood et al., 1976), and the North American cordillera (Douglas, 1970), for instance. The oldest known *ophiolites* are upper Proterozoic (640 Ma at Bou-Azzer, Leblanc, 1976), and their advent coincides approximately with the reappearance of andesites.

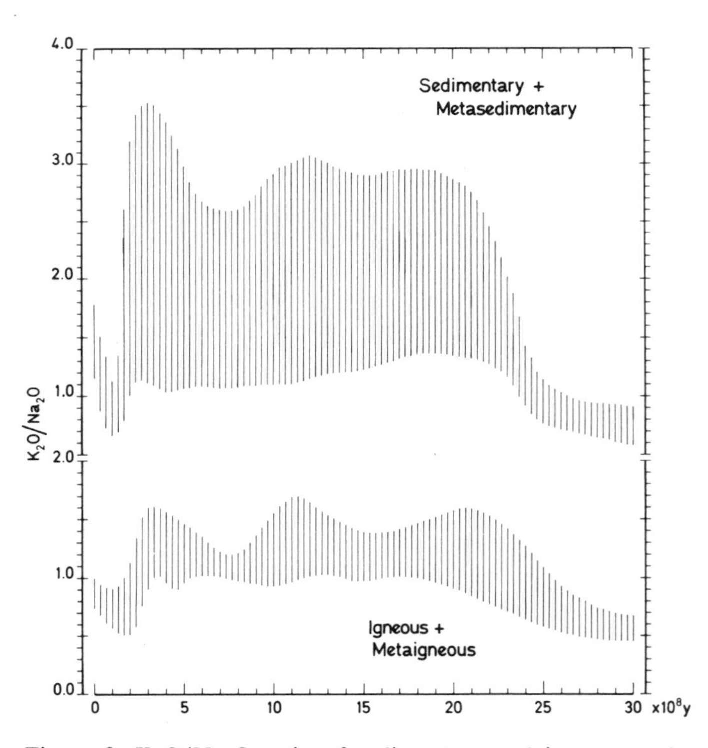

Figure 2. K_2O/Na_2O ratio of sedimentary and igneous rocks through time (after Engel et al., 1974).

"Ophiolites" is used here to mean a complex of zoned ultramafic to gabbroic rocks underlying sheeted dykes and pillow lavas with marine sediments. The K_2O/Na_2O ratio of igneous rocks, plutonic and volcanic (Engel et al., 1974) (Fig. 2), reflects the geological record and should not increase abruptly unless large amounts of granitic rocks are brought up to surface and weathered away (as in orogenies). The averaging effect of sedimentation presumably means that rapid changes in shape in the upper graph of Figure 2 must have world-wide importance.

A recent compilation by Sangster (1980) further shows a strong correlation between the abundance of North American massive sulfide deposits and the -1900 to -1700 Ma interval (Fig. 1c). Since it appears reasonable to associate the genesis of massive sulfides to some volcanic activity, the absence of calc-alkaline volcanism in the -2500 to -2000 Ma interval is thus corroborated, in contrast to the abundance of such activity during the Archean.

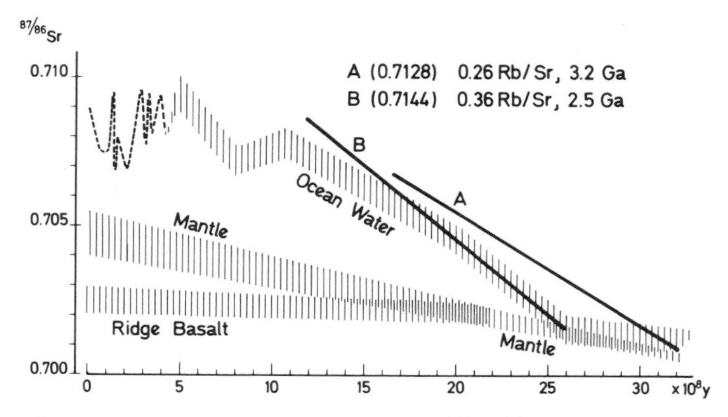

Figure 3. Evolution of isotopic ratio of $^{87}Sr/^{86}Sr$. Mantle envelope and ridge basalt envelope from Sun and Hanson (1975); Precambrian ocean water from Veizer and Compston (1976); Phanerozoic ocean water from Veizer and Compston (1974). A and B, two possible lines of evolution for continental crust (see text).

Data from Metamorphic Rocks

Various authors have noted that two "signatures" of subduction, glaucophane schists and paired metamorphic belts, are absent from all but the latest Proterozoic (Shackleton, 1973; Windley, 1977). More often than not, regional metamorphism in Proterozoic orogens is of a high-temperature, low-pressure type (Fraser and Heywood, 1978).

GEOCHEMICAL CONSTRAINTS

The two most powerful tools are here the isotopic evolution of the mantle and that of seawater (Veizer and Compston, 1976) (Fig. 3). The modern upper mantle comprises two distinct reservoirs, one that appears to be the source of magmas of oceanic islands and the other, relatively depleted, that is the source of mid-ocean ridge magmas (Carmichael et al., 1974). Studies of Sr, Pb, and Nd isotopes all indicate that these two reservoirs have not been mixing since some time in the Precambrian. This time can be roughly approximated at around -2000 to -1000 Ma. Other geochemical evidence indicates that if, as is probable, the depleted mantle source represents the residue left by the formation of the earth's crust, its volume cannot exceed half the total volume of the mantle (O'Nions et al., 1979).

The Phanerozoic and Precambrian isotopic evolution of Sr in seawater has been studied by Veizer and Compston (1974, 1976) (Fig. 3). The evolution curve itself shows knick-points that correspond well with the events discussed above. Major changes happen at -2500, -2000, -1100, and -800 Ma. The apparent absence of an event around -1700 Ma may have two causes. It may reflect the relatively minor importance of the 1700 Ma event, or, more probably, it may be due to the worrisome paucity of data points in this part of the curve. Even if the -1700 Ma event represented ensialic anatexis, the crustal differentiation that would necessarily follow should be reflected in the Sr ratio of seawater. By contrast, had significant segments of oceanic crust opened up at that time, a drop in $^{87}Sr/^{86}Sr$ of seawater should have occurred. The rapid variations shown in the Phanerozoic record are in part an artifact of the abundance of data but also a genuine contrast in the rates of evolution of $^{87}Sr/^{86}Sr$ ratio in seawater.

Primary sources of seawater Sr are mafic, mantle-derived materials and continental crust. The seawater curve must therefore plot somewhere between the other two. This means that for continental crust formed from the mantle around -3200 Ma ago and having at present an average $^{87}Sr/^{86}Sr$ ratio of 0.716 the average evolution line (line A, Fig. 3) corresponds to an Rb/Sr ratio of 0.26. If this continent had been supplying Sr to the oceans since that time, however, the seawater curve should show some evidence of it; but it does not and remains parallel with the mantle curve up to the end of the Archean. The assumption, instead, that most continents formed from the mantle around -2500 Ma requires that their Rb/Sr ratio be at least 0.36, corresponding to a granite sensu stricto (line B, Fig. 3). The geological evidence is that the Archean continents were closer to tonalite in composition and did form in part prior to -2500 Ma. Line B of Figure 3 is thus inconsistent with the geological record and represents an incorrect assumption. Line A is also incorrect, and probable explanations shall be dealt with later in this paper.

Note finally that slope changes in lines of Figure 3 show close similarities to those of Figure 2 and that all geological and geochemical data reviewed appear to show positive correlations with each other.

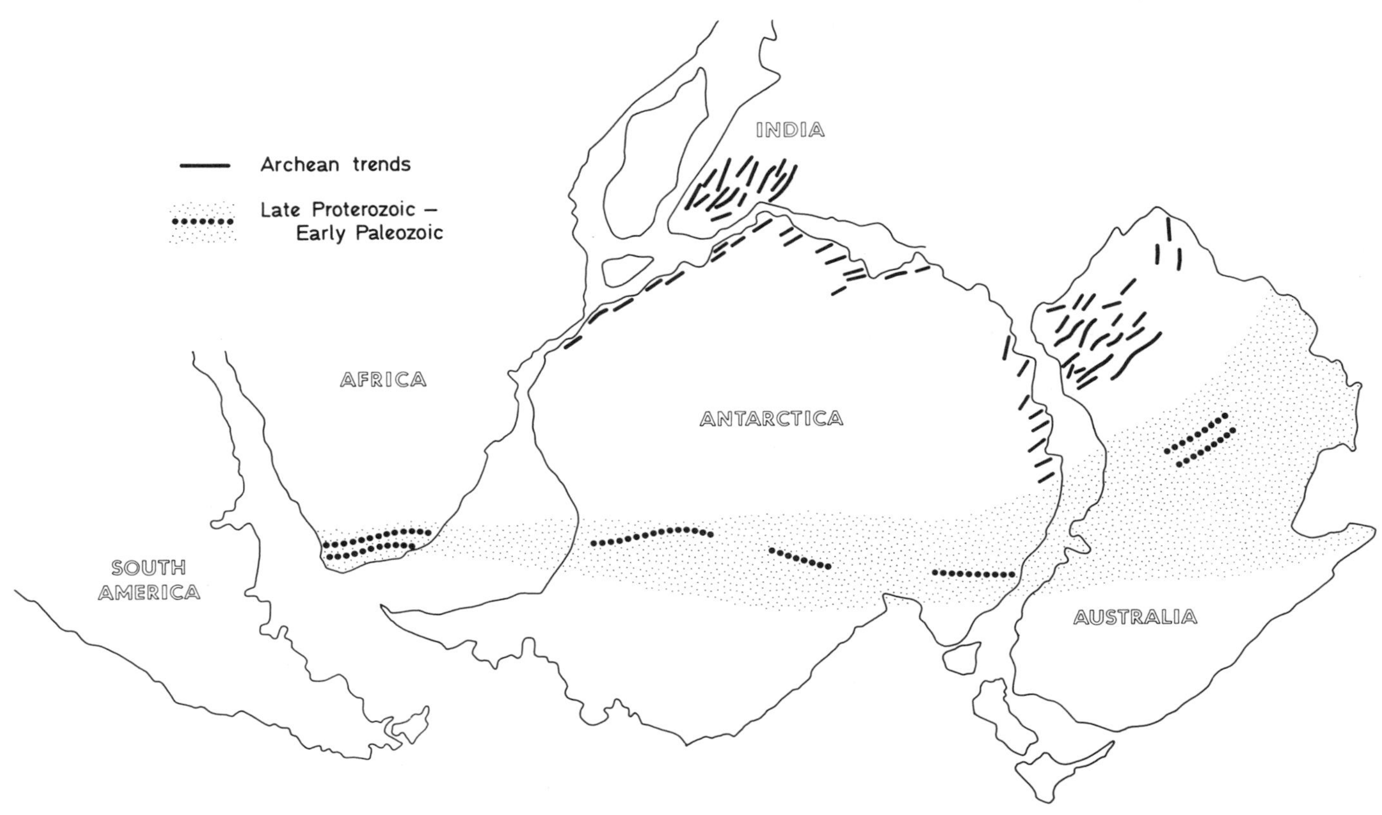

Figure 4. Continuity of Precambrian structural trends in Permian Gondwana (after Engel et al., 1974).

GEOPHYSICAL CONSTRAINTS

Tectonic Data

In the last 200 Ma, continents have drifted far and wide across the face of the earth, in apparent contrast to their behaviour during the previous 2300 Ma. Evidence for this derives from considerations of geometry first expressed by Engel (Engel and Kelm, 1972) and by Davies and Windley (1976) (Figs. 4, 5). On a reconstruction of Permian Gondwana, structural trends of Archean and even early Paleozoic belts are continuous from continent to continent, indicating that they did not rotate much relative to each other. So from the Archean to the early Paleozoic, relative motions of continents involved little or no relative rotation. If chances of such rotations increase with the distance between continents, this implies that they remained clustered close to each other during most of the Precambrian.

Paleomagnetic Data

The overall drift of Proterozoic sial relative to the poles is proven by the existence of apparent paleowander paths for all of them. Furthermore, far from being random, this drift is closely related to episodes of orogenic activity (Irving and Park, 1972; Morris et al., 1979; Baer, 1979). The presence of sharp changes in direction of drift ("hairpins") corresponds to abrupt motions of continents, as is well shown for North America (Irving, 1979). Because of restrictions inherent to the method itself, paleomagnetism cannot detect the presence of motions parallel to lines of latitude, however, or that of relative motions of less than 800–1000 km. However, a comparison of APW curves for North America, Greenland, Africa, and Australia (Embleton and Schmidt, 1979) strongly suggests that cratons which comprise the individual continents retained their relationships for much of Precambrian time. These data reinforce observations on the distribution of orogenic belts and speak against large-scale continental motions in the Proterozoic.

Heat Generation Data

Given the rates of radiogenic decay of ^{40}K, ^{235}U, ^{238}U, and ^{232}Th, the earth is now generating about half as much heat as at the end of the Archean (Lambert, 1976; Shackleton, 1973). This presumably implies that past geothermal gradients were steeper than now. If it is assumed that

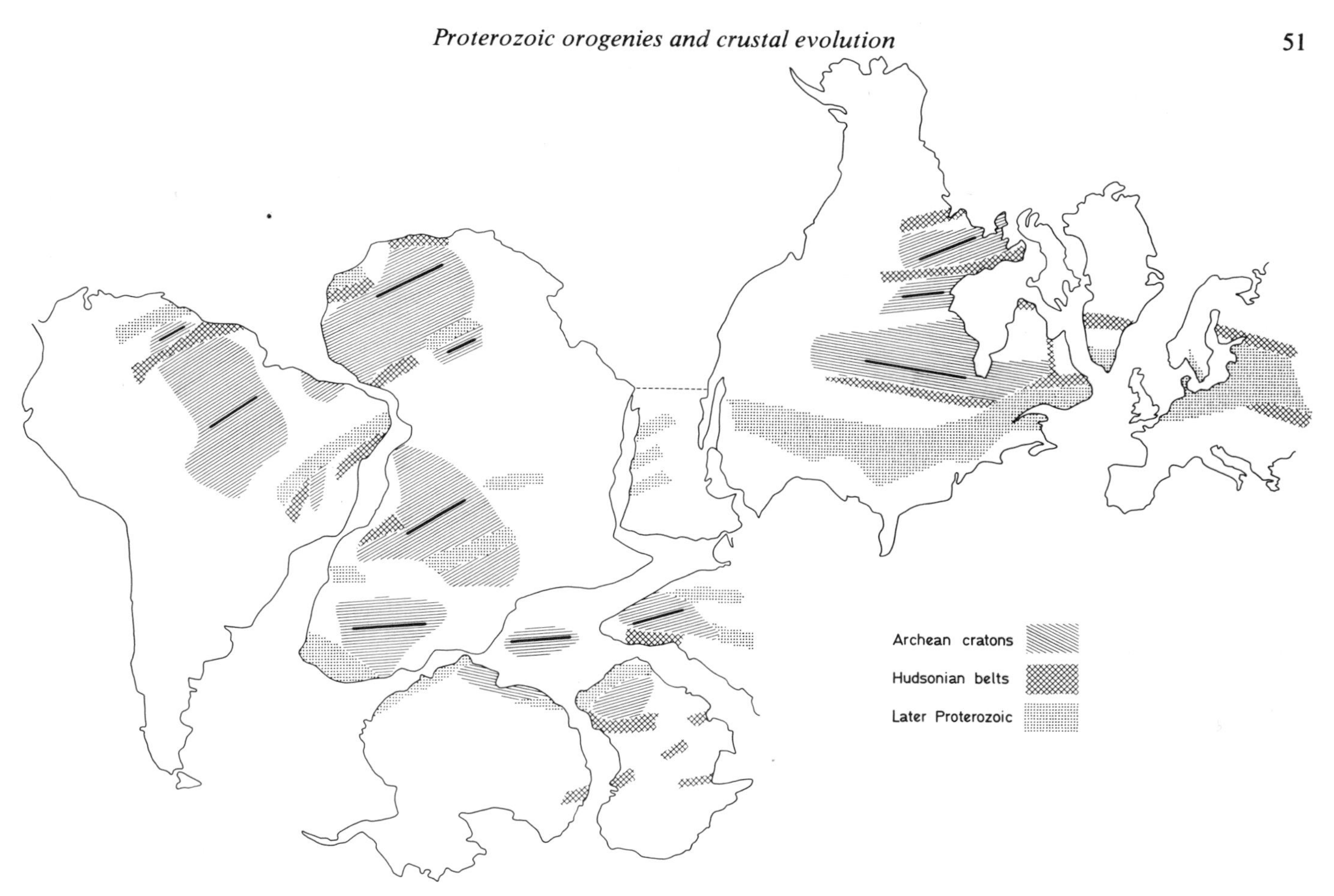

Figure 5. Distribution of Precambrian structural trends on a presumed supercontinent (Piper, 1976). Archean cratons are lined; heavier lines indicate structural trends where known (After Davies and Windley, 1976; and Engel et al. 1974, modified).

the base of the lithosphere corresponds to the beginning of melting (solidus) in the mantle, this has a series of important consequences (Baer, 1981c). (Fig. 6, 7). Lithospheric plates (i.e., upper mantle plus crust) are thicker now than in the past, and continental plates are now also considerably thicker than oceanic ones. Accelerated thickening of continental plates started around -1100 Ma. This must have profoundly affected plate motions.

In a Wilson cycle, oceanic plates sink into the asthenosphere by gravity. Thinner plates would be less dense since basalt is considerably lighter than peridotite and since the thickening process adds peridotite to the bottom of the plates. Estimates of the time at which oceanic plates of a cooling earth started sinking give an earliest time of -1600 Ma and a probable time of -900 Ma (Baer, 1981c).

Relation of Heat Generation to Heat Loss

It has been assumed that present heat generation balances heat loss (McKenzie and Weiss, 1975). This is incorrect (Davies, 1980; Schubert et al., 1980). Depending upon the model chosen, present heat generation is at least 45 percent but at most 85 percent of heat loss. Although heat generation decreases regularly with time, heat flow may vary independently. Now, it depends upon the rate of accretion at diverging plate margins and upon the total length of ridges. It would also vary with changes in patterns of mantle convection. The ratio of heat generation to heat loss need not be constant. This relation appears instinctively to be correct but may be quantified in the case of Upper Cretaceous events, as follows.

Sealevel has fluctuated through time, and shows a major rise in the Upper Cretaceous (Vail and Mitchum, 1979) (Fig. 8c). It has been postulated (Hurley, 1968; Wise, 1974) and demonstrated (Pitman, 1978) that this change of sealevel was caused by an upsurge of activity of mid-oceanic ridges leading to a greater volume of ridges and to flooding of continents. The time-lag between the beginning of accelerated ridge activity and the maximum sealevel is about 70 Ma. Leg 76 of the Deep Sea Drilling Project (DSDP) showed that the North Atlantic probably opened around 145 Ma ago when spreading rates were about 5 cm/yr as opposed to 2 cm/yr now (Geotimes, 1981). According to Pitman (1978), this difference of 3 cm/yr would

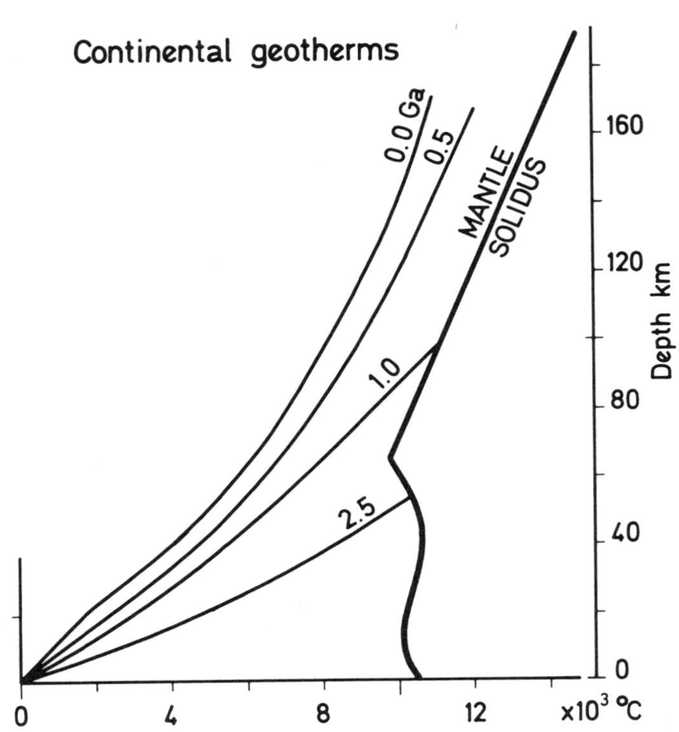

Figure 6. Continental geotherms for a continent with 42 mWm^{-2} heat flow at present (After Baer, 1981c).

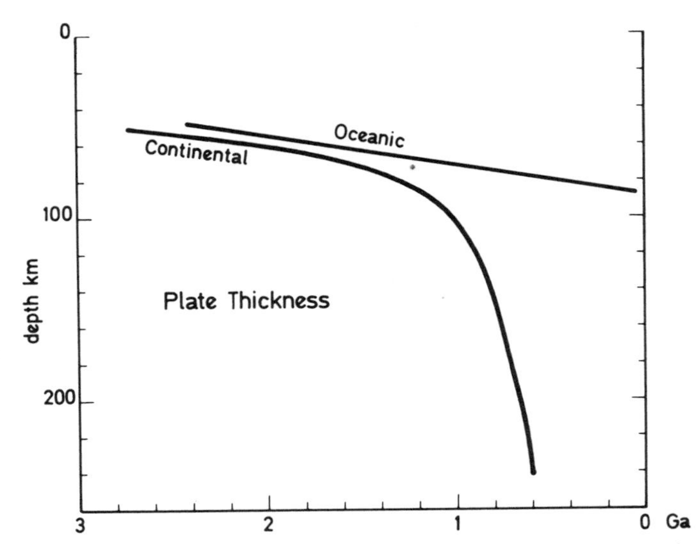

Figure 7. Thicknesses of oceanic and continental lithospheres calculated from geotherms (From Baer, 1981c).

cause an ultimate rise of 339 m in sealevel, 70 Ma later. Actual estimates are about 350 m around 75 Ma ago (Vail and Mitchum, 1979).

The activity of ridges of a constant length is readily measured from the amount of new crust formed. This is estimated to be about 1.1 km^2yr^{-1} at present (for a 55.000-km-long ridge system spreading at an average double spreading rate of 2 cm/yr) and thus would have been 2.5 times greater for spreading rates of 5 cm/yr. Heat loss is presumably proportional to the amount of new crust formed at ridges and was therefore over twice the present values. Ridges and subduction zones contribute at least half the earth's total heat loss at present (Williams and von Herzen, 1974). The total heat loss from earth was therefore at least 1.5 times greater than it is now, but evidently heat generation was hardly different from the present (Fig. 8a). Heat loss therefore may vary independently from heat generation (Turcotte and Burke, 1978).

It stands to reason that greater volcanic activity on oceanic ridges must mean accelerated supply of mantle Sr to seawater. The evolution curve of $^{87}Sr/^{86}Sr$ should reflect this change (Fig. 8b). With the required shift of 70 Ma, the sharp drop of the isotopic ratio to about 0.707 corresponds well to the peak of the marine transgression. This correlation confirms that $^{87}Sr/^{86}Sr$ ratio of seawater faithfully and instantly reflects changes in the source areas. Mesozoic evolution of the earth shows that an increase of volcanic activity in oceans may cause major flooding of continents.

The Strength (S) of the Lithosphere

The question of lithospheric strength is relevant to a discussion of ensialic (intraplate) versus periplate orogenies. Does the existence of ensialic Proterozoic orogenies imply that plates were considerably weaker? Some conclusions may be drawn from analogy with the strength of known crustal materials. "S" is defined here as the maximum stress that the rock will sustain before it yields, at any given depth. The mantle lithosphere probably follows the deformation pattern of olivine, and this mineral may be a reasonable substitute. Theoretical and experimental data (Kirby, 1980) (Fig. 9) show not only that S is strongly temperature-dependent but also that it decreases rapidly below about 35-40 km depth. At greater depths, the material presumably creeps under low differential stresses. Continental lower crust is assumed here to be formed of granulites. Despite mineralogical differences, their mechanical behaviour is probably closely comparable to that of anhydrous granite. Experimental data on dry Westerly granite (Tullis and Yund, 1977) have been used to extrapolate lower crustal curves. The upper continental crust will contain varying amounts of water which will considerably decrease its strength. A general "guesstimate" is that S may be only about 60 percent of S under dry conditions (Fyfe, Price, and Thompson, 1978). This value has been shown in Figure 9. Thus, to a first approximation, the S of oceanic and continental plates is about the same (Fig. 10). Both are quite sensitive to thermal gradients and decrease drastically around 40 km depth. At depths greater than 40-50 km, the lithosphere is expected to creep under diffential stresses σ_1-σ_2 of less than 1 kbar. This would imply that under comparable temperatures, a thick (200 km) lithosphere is just as deformable as a thin one (80 km).

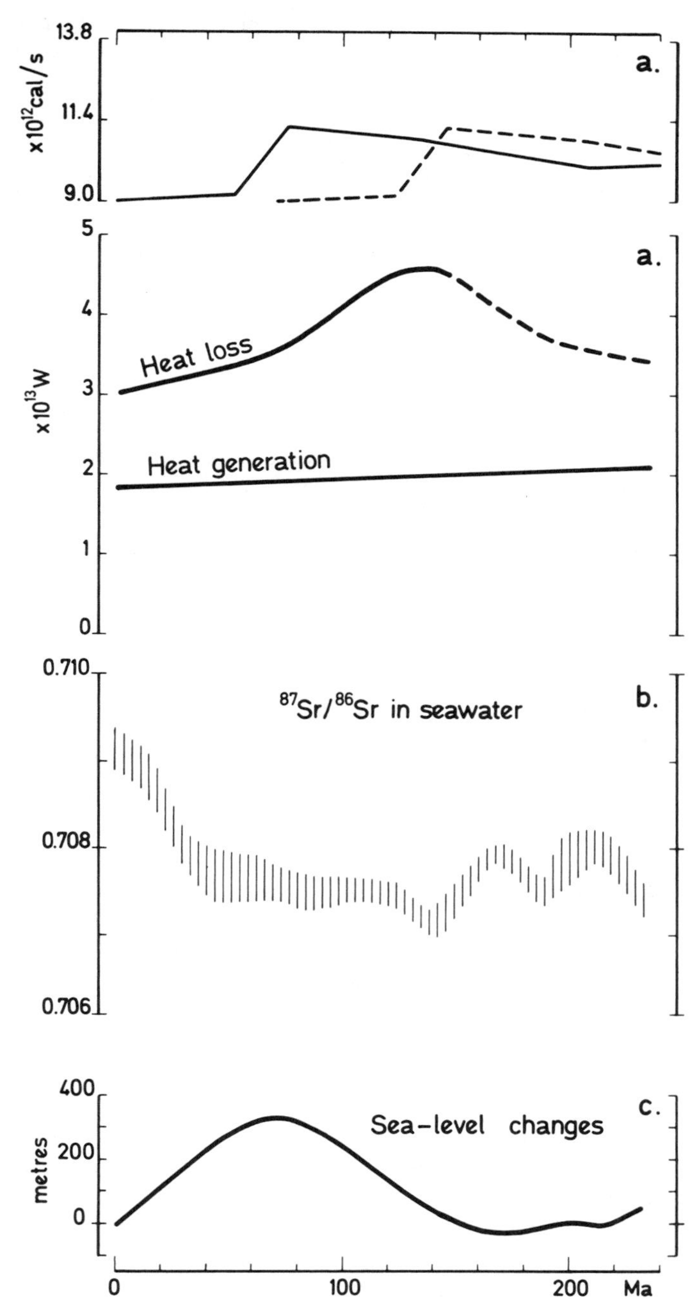

Figure 8. Correlation between rise of sealevel, heat loss of the earth, and isotopic ratio of Sr in seawater in the last 200 Ma. (a) heat loss, top curve from Turcotte and Burke (1978); next curve, estimated, this paper; (b) $^{87}Sr/^{86}Sr$ ratio of seawater, from Veizer and Compston (1974); (c) sealevel changes, from Vail and Mitchum (1979). Note the shift of 70 Ma calculated by Pitman (1978) (see text).

INTEGRATION OF AVAILABLE DATA

Data reviewed above determine conditions under which the Proterozoic crust evolved and place limits on acceptable models. Integration of constraints imposed by

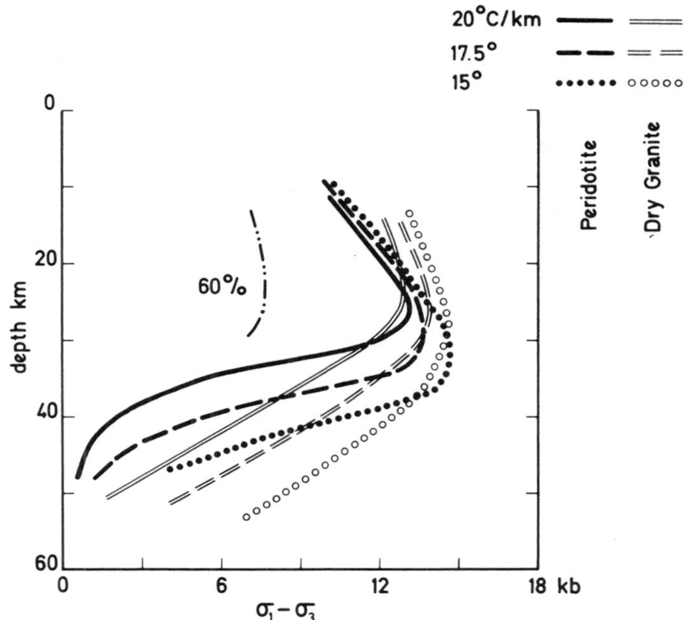

Figure 9. Comparison of strength curves for lithospheric materials. Full lines: data for peridotite (Kirby, 1980); open lines: data for dry Westerly granite (Tullis and Yund, 1977) see text.

geological, geochemical, and geophysical data is therefore necessary. Because Proterozoic orogenies were clearly episodic, it is also important to integrate available information over time. This will now be done as an extended "timetable" of crustal evolution from -2500 Ma to -500 Ma.

Prior to -2500 Ma: Continental and oceanic crust form from the mantle through one or more stages of partial melting. Volcanic activity is intense and may or may not display periodicity (Glikson 1980a, and personal communication, 1981).

Some crust is possibly recycled in the mantle, but the total amount of preserved continental crust may be estimated at somewhat more than half the present amount and possibly as much as 80 percent (Wise, 1974).

Around -2500 Ma: Volcanism stops abruptly. Neither continents nor oceans (ocean water) show evidence of significant volcanic activity from -2500 Ma to -2000 Ma. By analogy with Cretaceous events, the abrupt cessation of volcanic activity in oceans must necessarily lead to a major marine regression.

As a consequence, large areas of continents that were previously flooded (i.e., shunted out of the seawater Sr system) are now being weathered. The rest of them are under shallow water and form the platforms where deposits are being accumulated. This interpretation explains the discordance between seawater Sr evolution and continental growth in the Archean, without having to call upon extreme crustal recycling prior to -2500 Ma. It is to be expected that denudation of late Archean potassic granites

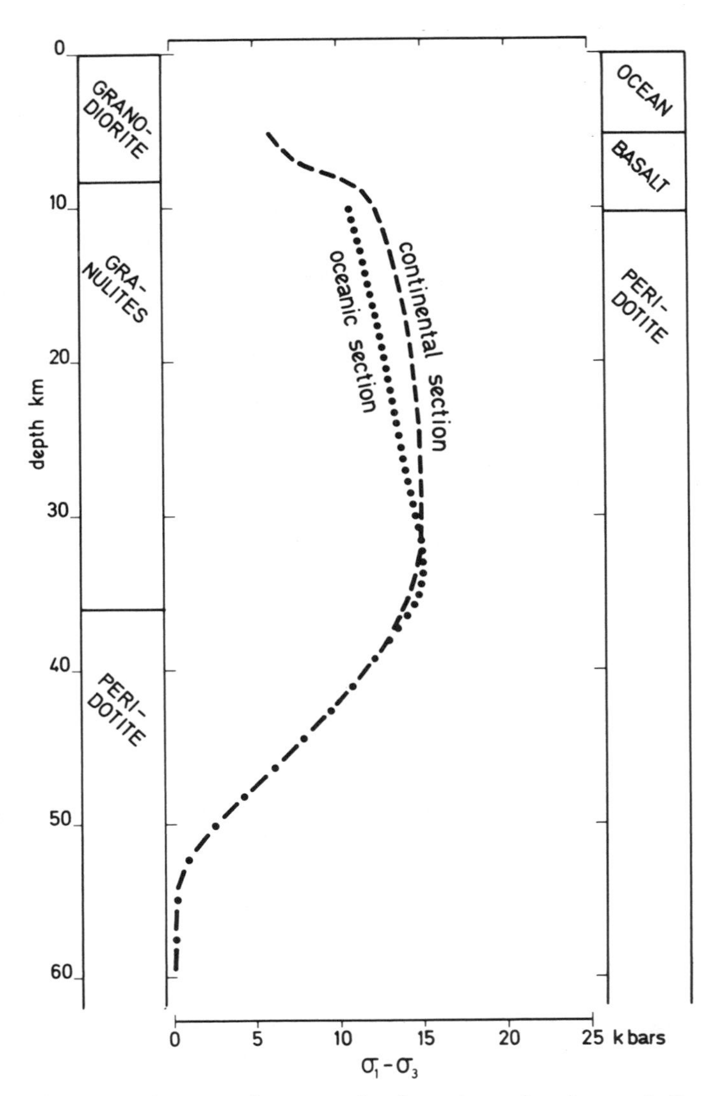

Figure 10. Comparative strength of continental and oceanic lithosphere, assumed from data in Figure 9, for a geothermal gradient of 15° C/kbar.

would also contribute to increase sharply the $^{87}Sr/^{86}Sr$ ratio of sediments.

From -2500 Ma to -1800 Ma: A remarkable stability of oceans and continents is maintained. In particular, no evidence exists for the formation of large amounts of crust, continental and oceanic. This means that the mantle is not being depleted. Since the separation of a depleted and an undepleted mantle reservoir goes back to at least that period (Sun and Hanson, 1975), and since depletion (manifested by formation of crust) ended around -2500 Ma, it can be confidently assumed that the events that led to the segregation of the two reservoirs occurred in the Archean. The separation was achieved by -2500 Ma.

From -1800 ± 50 Ma to -1700 ± 50 Ma: A brief episode of volcanism and plutonism brings more mantle-derived material into the crust. It is accompanied by a violent readjustment of plate geometry (the hairpins of paleomagnetic APW paths) and by orogenies. The overall coherence of Archean structural trends in Permian Gondwana indicates that this Hudsonian event was not accompanied by the closure of large (thousands of km) oceans.

From -1700 ± 50 Ma to -1000 ± Ma: Continents recover a great deal of stability. However, rifting and bimodal volcanism are not rare, and towards the end of the period, platform-type sedimentation is uncommon. Major rift systems appear in North America after -1300 Ma (Mackenzie dykes, Gardar dykes, Keweenawan graben, for instance).

From -1000 Ma to -800 Ma: Mantle input into oceanic crust is intense, but little new material appears in the continents. Plate geometry is once again strongly modified. During this time, lithospheric roots of continents thicken considerably (Fig. 7), a condition that must slow down their ability to drift around. It will then tend to create zones of stress at the continent-ocean boundary.

Around -800 Ma: The first genuine ophiolites appear in the geological record and well-developed island arcs show that subduction is now operating (for instance, in Saudi Arabia; Greenwood et al., 1976) and in the Hoggar (Bertrand and Caby, 1978).

From -800 Ma to -500 Ma: A consequence of the onset of subduction is that large amounts of continental crust are now uplifted and eroded, and their erosion products reach the ocean. Orogenic belts are not episodic any more, so that the averaging effect of seawater and of K_2O/Na_2O graphs makes it very difficult to assess specific results of any one factor. Sealevel rises and will continue to rise in the lower Paleozoic, a probable sign of increased activity on oceanic ridges that are beginning to form a world-wide network.

FURTHER CONSTRAINTS ON PROTEROZOIC OROGENIC EVENTS

If orogenic events operated within the framework described above, a number of important consequences arise from the lack of subduction (Baer, 1981c). In particular, "unsinkable" plates will move relative to each other in one of three ways: along steep shear-zones or straight belts (Watson, 1973); along steep extension fractures (dykes or graben); and along shallow-dipping thrusts.

Orogenic belts, however, result from crustal thickening through the action of tectonic forces. In most Proterozoic belts, this thickening is only partly accomplished by input of new material derived from the mantle. Thickening in one region therefore implies thinning or rifting of continental crust in another. As the values of shortening across mountain belts are measured in tens of kilometers or at the most in a few hundreds of kilometers, corresponding rifting of the crust is of the same order of magnitude unless subduction takes place. Large oceans cannot open by this process, and continents keep their overall cohesion.

It would appear that little thickening of oceanic crust took place in the Proterozoic. Thick piles of basalt would melt from the base, causing formation of tonalites, trondhjemites, and dacites; such materials should have been preserved in the geological record (Glikson, 1980b). Their relative scarcity suggests that oceanic lithosphere was possibly slightly stronger than continental lithosphere, so that deformation was concentrated on the continents. This would lead to formation of ensialic (intraplate) orogens. In the Phanerozoic, subduction requires that mountain belts form along the edges of plates, but this restriction would not have applied to intraplate Proterozoic orogens.

The episodicity of Precambrian orogenies has been recognized for years (Gastil, 1960; Stockwell, 1961), and major dyke swarms commonly formed during quiet periods between orogenies. In terms of lithospheric strength, this could mean one of three things:

If thermal gradients remained constant, stresses applied to the lithosphere exceeded 12 kbars during short periods (orogenies) but remained around 3-4 kbars at other times (Fig. 10). To break a plate in extension requires at most 30 percent of the yield stress in compression (Kirby, 1980); and since basic dykes did form, stresses were up to 4 kbars.

If stresses remained constant, considerable rise in the temperature of one region could presumably lower the strength of a plate below the yield point.

If stresses and temperature both increased during orogenies, the required stress would be lowered to somewhere below 12 kbars and above 4 kbars. This last option is the most probable because paleomagnetic "hairpins" strongly suggest an increase in stresses and intrusive plutonic activity implies increased temperature during orogeny.

EXAMPLES OF PROTEROZOIC OROGENS

The Wopmay (Coronation) Belt

This orogenic belt has been well described in recent years (Hoffman, 1973, 1980), and its evolution is reasonably well known. It started with a rifting phase that allowed formation of a continental margin sedimentary prism similar to Phanerozoic ones (Hoffman, 1973). Farther west, the sedimentary pile was intruded by granitic batholiths of probable "S-type." Still farther west, a bimodal succession of minor tholeiitic basalts and dominant rhyolites, ignimbrites, and dacites represents the westernmost visible part of the belt. The rifting phase was followed by a compressional phase, during which the western regions were presumably considerably thickened, which led to the generation of felsic volcanics by melting of continental crust. It is possible that oceanic crust did separate the eastern and western sides of the orogen. The slightly weaker continental lithosphere would thus have deformed prior to and against the slab of oceanic lithosphere separating it from the eastern edge of the belt. Further tightening finally eliminated all remnant of ocean floor and did thrust the western hinterland on and over the eastern foreland. The apparent lack of any remnant of oceanic crust may militate, however, against the existence of an ocean.

Drifting motions of the region during this period are closely related to its deformation history (Irving, 1979). Around -1900 Ma, the belt (future belt?) trends northeast at 35° latitude. By -1850 Ma, it has drifted by about 10° to a lower latitude but its orientation is the same. Around -1800 Ma, latitude is again 10° lower, but the area swings clockwise to a more ENE orientation. In the next 50 Ma, the clockwise rotation accelerates and the belt is now SE at a latitude of about 25°. From -1750 Ma, it swings back in the opposite direction and drifts away from the equator to about 25° latitude. This drift away from the equator accelerates in the next 50 Ma where the area reaches almost 70° latitude around -1650 Ma. It is tempting to correlate the clockwise rotation with an episode of rifting and crustal extension. The anticlockwise rotation beginning around -1750 Ma would correspond to a time of compression and folding. In other words, the first arm of the APW hairpin would correspond to an extension, and the second to a compression phase (the orogeny).

The Grenville Belt

The poorly known Grenville belt developed in two phases (Baer, 1981a). A first, more intense event of restricted distribution affected the central part of the Grenville Province and the Sveco-Norwegian belt of Scandinavia around -1100 Ma. A second, less intense but far-reaching event closed the K-Ar isotopic system around -900 Ma. The Grenville belt represents an ensialic orogen considerably thickened along southeasterly or easterly dipping shallow thrusts. Inasmuch as trends of rifts and dykes and those of folds and reverse faults may be used to estimate orientation of principal stresses, the evolution of the province was more complex than that of the Wopmay belt (Baer, 1981b). Assuming that dates attributed to paleomagnetic poles are correct, the record indicates four phases of drift between -1400 Ma and -800 Ma (Irving, 1979). From -1400 Ma to -1150 Ma, the Grenville Province progressively rotates anticlockwise by about 70°. After -1150 Ma, the rotation becomes clockwise until -1100 Ma (40° in 150 Ma); from -1000 Ma to -950 Ma, it is anticlockwise again (80° in 50 Ma); and after -950 Ma, it is once more clockwise (110° in 150 Ma).

Comparison of this data with geological and geochronological information suggests that periods of clockwise rotation correspond to compression across the belts, and anticlockwise motion means extension. The evolution of the region would then read this way: (a) -1400 Ma to -1150

Ma, extension, rifting (Seal Lake, Gardar, Keweenawan); (b) -1150 Ma to -1000 Ma, compression, first Grenvillian deformation in North America and Scandinavia; (c) -1000 Ma to -950 Ma, brief period of extension, indicated by Keweenawan late eruptions (Baragar, 1978) and dolerites in southern Sweden (Patchett and Bylund, 1977); (d) -950 Ma to -800 Ma, compression causing final uplift of the province.

In the case of belts as different as the Grenville and the Wopmay orogens, the motion of plates, reflected in paleomagnetic wanderings, would appear to correlate reasonably closely with tectonic events in the plates. When the latter are under compression, if stresses increase beyond their yield strength, they shorten and thicken and orogenic belts form. If plates yield in extension, rifts and dykes develop.

ULTIMATE CAUSES

The origin of plate motions must reside in the mantle. Mantle convection leads to formation of crust by depletion of LIL elements but also contributes to cooling of the mantle in transferring heat-producing K, Th, and U to the continental crust. Mantle depletion and formation of crust must always accompany each other. If convection did not operate, formation of crust would only proceed from some possible localized mantle diapirism and would be considerably hampered.

An important body of geological and geochemical data shows that formation of continental crust was a common feature of the Archean but was strongly episodic in the Proterozoic, with a peak around 1700 Ma and another around 1000 Ma. These data suggest therefore that mantle convection is episodic.

A thorough analysis of mantle convection (Tozer, 1965) shows that physical parameters require that convection be limited to the upper mantle (above 700 km) and that it be episodic, short half-turns of cells being separated by long "warm-up" intervals. The question of whole mantle convection or shallow mantle convection has been and still is extensively debated, and geophysical arguments alone may be unable to solve it. However, the need to have kept two mantle reservoirs separated for the last 2500 Ma favours convection cells that would not reach below the 680 km discontinuity. Geochemical modeling (O'Nions et al., 1979) suggests that formation of all existing crust partially depleted no more than 50 percent of the mantle. This partially depleted mantle is the source of MORB basalt. As 33 percent of the volume of the mantle is a shell reaching down to about 700 km depth, mantle depletion and thus convection may not have reached deeper than that.

If Tozer's analysis (1965) is valid, adjusting parameters to geologically meaningful values indicates that the upper mantle is in a regime of unsteady convection in cells 580 km high with a velocity of 0.9 10^{-7} cms^{-1} (2.9 cm/yr). The periods of turn-over are 20 Ma long, and the quiet intervals are 790 Ma long. Assuming a 100 km thick lithospheric slab, convection cells reach down to the 680 km discontinuity. The times of over-turn coincide evidently with -1760 Ma, -950 Ma, and -140 Ma.

If a convecting medium heated from inside is cooling, it will pass a critical point, determined by the Péclet number (Tozer, 1965) where it will change over from steady (continuous) to unsteady convection. If the earth is now in an unsteady convection pattern, it must have passed such a limit. As convection currents slowed down, they would have switched rapidly from steady to unsteady convection. Geological and geochemical evidence suggests that this critical point in time was about -2500 Ma.

CONCLUSIONS

To conclude and summarize, I believe that geological, geochemical, and geophysical data all point to the following causes for Proterozoic orogenies.

During the Archean, the upper mantle was in steady convection, in cells 580 km high. Convection caused mantle depletion and formation of crust. Around -2500 Ma, the upper mantle went into unsteady convection. Volcanic activity stopped in oceans, causing a drop of the sea floor and a generalized emergence of continents. Crust stopped forming and the earth cooled only by conduction for the next 800 Ma. Around -1700 Ma, a convective over-turn caused a burst of crust generation and violent drift of plates. Orogenies formed by intraplate deformation; and in most if not all cases, a brief period of rifting preceeded crustal shortening in the orogen. Basic volcanism is, for instance, characteristic of the basal part of most Proterozoic orogens in the Canadian Shield (e.g., Thessalon volcanics of Lake Huron, Seward Formation of Labrador, Fox River belt of northern Manitoba). A second interval of 800 Ma was similar to the first, followed by another over-turn around -900 Ma.

This time, however, two other factors complicated the picture. One is the rapid thickening of continental plates at about that time. The other is the growing instability of oceanic lithosphere. It is probable that the convective over-turn triggered the beginning of subduction. From that time onward, plate tectonics with subduction has controlled world tectonics. However, the next convective over-turn may be responsible for the sudden increase in ridge activity about 140 Ma ago.

A necessary consequence of this model is that convection currents do not drive the plates, except at 800 Ma intervals. Subducting plates are driven by gravity, as analysed by Jacoby (1970). Subduction is only an artifact of the cooling of the earth in the last 700 Ma, but it is superposed on more fundamental convective processes.

ACKNOWLEDGMENTS

I thank K. C. Condie for permission to use his paper prior to publication. This work was supported by NSERC grant A-8531. D. F. Sangster drew my attention to the distribution of massive sulphide deposits in the Proterozoic. Thanks to C. Pride and S. Reed for helpful comments. Critical suggestions by A. Y. Glikson and an anonymous reviewer helped improve the manuscript.

REFERENCES CITED

Baer, A. J., 1979, An unconventional paleomagnetic polar wander path for North America and its advantages: Physics of Earth Planetary Interiors 19, 100–105.

——1981a, Two orogenies in the Grenville belt?, Nature 290, 129–131.

——1981b, A Grenvillian model of Proterozoic plate tectonics, p. 353–386, *in*, Kröner, A., ed., Precambrian plate tectonics: Eslevier, Amsterdam, 775 p.

——1981c, Geotherms, evolution of the lithosphere and plate tectonics: Tectonophysics 72, 203–227.

Baragar, W.R.A., 1978, Michipicoten Island, Ontario, *in* Wanless, R. K., and Loveridge, W. D., Rb-Sr isotopic age studies report 2: Geol. Survey Canada Paper 77–14, 40–43.

Bertrand, J.M.C., and Caby, R., 1978, Geodynamic evolution of the Pan-African orogenic belt: a new interpretation of the Hoggar shield (Algerian Sahara): Geol. Rundsch. 67, 357–388.

Carmichael, I.S.E., Turner, F. J., Verhoogen, J., 1974, Igneous petrology: New York, McGraw-Hill, XIII, 739 p.

Condie, K. C., 1982, Early and Middle Proterozoic supracrustal successions and their tectonic settings: Am. J. of Science 282, 341–357.

Davis, F. B., and Windley, B. F., 1976, Significance of major Proterozoic high grade linear belts in continental evolution: Nature 263, Sept. 30, 1976, 383–385.

Davies, G. F., 1980, Thermal histories of convective earth models and constraints on radiogenic heat production in the earth: J. Geophys. Res. 85, B5, 2517–2530.

Dewey, J., and Spall, H., 1975, Pre-Mesozoic plate tectonics: how far back in earth history can the Wilson cycle be extended? Geology 3 (8), 422–424.

Douglas, R.J.W., 1970, Geology of Western Canada, Precambrian *in*: Douglas, R.J.W., ed.: Geology and Mineral Deposits of Canada, Geol. Survey Canada, Ec. Geo. Ser. 1, 369–375.

Embleton, B.J.J., and Schmidt, P. W., 1979, Recognition of common Precambrian polar wandering reveals a conflict with plate tectonics: Nature 282, 705–707.

Engel, A.E.J., Dixon, T. H., Stern, R. J., 1980, Late Precambrian evolution of Afro-Arabian crust from ocean arc to craton: Geol. Soc. America Bull. I, v. 91, 699–706.

Engel, A.E.J., Itson, S. P., Engel, C. G., Stickney, D. M., Crax, E. J., 1974, Crustal evolution and global tectonics: a petrogenic view: Geol. Soc. America Bull. 85, 843–858.

Engel, A.E.J., and Kelm, D. L., 1972, Pre-Permian global tectonics: a tectonic test: Geol. Soc. America Bull. 83, 2325–2340.

Fraser, J. A., and Heywood, W. W., eds., 1978, Metamorphism in the Canadian Shield: Geol. Survey Canada Paper 78–10, 367 p.

Fyfe, W. S., Price, N. J., Thompson, A. B., 1978, Fluids in the earth's crust: Amsterdam, Elsevier, XVIII, 838 p.

Gastil, R. G., 1960, The distribution of mineral dates in time and space: Amer. Jour. Science 258, 1–34.

Geotimes, 1981, Mid-Jurassic rocks cored off Florida: Geotimes, April 1981, 15–16.

Glikson, A. Y., 1980a, Precambrian Sial-Sima relations: evidence for earth expansion: Tectonophysics 63, 193–234.

——1980b, The missing Precambrian crust: reply: Geology 8 (3), 114–117.

Greenwood, W. R., Hadley, D. G., Anderson, R. E., Fleck, R. S., and Schmidt, D. L., 1976, Late Proterozoic cratonization in southwestern Saudi Arabia: Phil. Trans. Roy. Soc. London, A280, 429–442.

Hoffman, P. F., 1973, Evolution of an early Proterozoic continental margin: the Coronation geosyncline and associated aulacogens of the northwestern Canadian Shield: Phil. Trans. Roy. Soc. London, A273, 547–581.

——1980, Wopmay orogen: a Wilson cycle of early Proterozoic age in the northwest of the Canadian Shield: Geol. Assoc. Canada Spec. Paper 20, 523–549.

Hurley, P. M., 1968, Absolute abundance and distribution of Rb, K and Sr in the earth: Geochim. Cosmochim. Acta 32, 273–283.

Irving, E., 1979, Paleopoles and paleolatitudes of North America and speculations about displaced terrains: Can. J. Earth Sciences 16 (3), 669–694.

Irving, E., and Park, J. K., 1972, Hairpins and superintervals: Can. J. Earth Sciences 9-10, 1318–1324.

Jacoby, W. R., 1970, Instability in the upper mantle and global plate movements: J. Geophys. Res. 75, 29, 5671–5680.

Kirby, S. H., 1980, Tectonic stresses in the lithosphere: constraints provided by the experimental deformation of rocks: J. Geophys. Res. 85, B11, 6353–6363.

Lambert, R. St. J., 1976, Archean crustal regimes, crustal and upper mantle temperatures and a progressive evolutionary model for the earth, *in*, Windley, B. F., ed., The early history of the earth: London, Wiley and Sons, 363–373.

Leblanc, M., 1976, Proterozoic oceanic crust at Bou Azzer (Morocco): Nature 261, 5555, 34–35.

McKenzie, D. P., and Weiss, N. O., 1975, Speculations on the thermal and tectonic history of the earth: Geophys. J. Roy. Astron. Soc. 42, 131–174.

Morris, W. A., Schmidt, P. W., and Roy, J. L., 1979, A graphical approach to polar paths; paleomagnetic cycles and global tectonics, Physics of Earth Planetary Interiors 19, 85–99.

O'Nions, R. K., Evensen, N. M., and Hamilton, P. J., 1979, Geochemical modeling of mantle differentiation and crustal growth: J. Geophys. Res. 84, B11, 6091–6101.

Patchett, P. J., and Bylund, G., 1977, Age of Grenville belt magnetisation: Rb-Sr and paleomagnetic evidence from Swedish dolerites: Earth and Planetary Science Letters 35, 92–104.

Piper, J.D.A., 1976, Paleomagnetic evidence for a Proterozoic supercontinent: Phil. Trans. Roy. Soc. London, A280, 469–490.

Pitman, W. C., 1978, Relationship between eustacy and stratigraphic sequences of passive margins: Geol. Soc. America Bull. 89, 1389–1403.

Sangster, D. F., 1980, Distribution and origin of Precambrian massive sulphide deposits of North America: Geol. Assoc. Canada Spec. Paper 20, 723–739.

Schubert, G., Stevenson, D., Cassen, P., 1980, Whole planet cooling and the radiogenic heat source contents of the earth and moon: J. Geophys. Res. 85, B5, 2531–2538.

Shackleton, R. M., 1973, Problems of the evolution of the continental crust: Phil. Trans. Roy. Soc. London, A273, 317–320.

Stockwell, C. H., 1961, Structural provinces, orogenies and time-classification of rocks of the Canadian Precambrian Shield: Geol. Survey Canada Paper 61–17, 108–118.

Sun, S. S., and Hanson, G. N., 1975, Evolution of the mantle: geochemical evidence from alkali basalt: Geology 3, 297–302.

Tozer, D. C., 1965, Heat transfer and convection currents: Phil. Trans. Roy. Soc. London, A258, 252–271.

Tullis, J., and Yund, R. A., 1977, Experimental deformation of dry Westerly granite: J. Geophys. Res. 82, 36, 5705–5718.

Turcotte, D. L., and Burke, K., 1978, Global sea-level changes and the thermal structure of the earth: Earth and Planetary Science Letters 41, 341–346.
Vail, P. R., and Mitchum, R. M., 1979, Global cycles of relative changes in sealevel from seismic stratigraphy, *in* Amer. Assoc. of Petrol. Geol., Memoir 29, 469–472.
Veizer, J., and Compston, W., 1974, $^{87}Sr/^{86}Sr$ composition of seawater during the Phanerozoic; Geochim. Cosmochim. Acta 38, 1461–1484.
—— 1976, $^{87}Sr/^{86}Sr$ in Precambrian carbonates as an index of crustal evolution: Geochim. Cosmochim. Acta 40, 905–914.
Watson, J. V., 1973, Effects of reworking on high-grade gneiss complexes: Phil. Trans. Roy. Soc. London, A273, 443–455.
Williams, D. L., and von Herzen, R. P., 1974, Heat loss from the Earth: new estimate: Geology 2 (7), 327–328.
Windley, B. F., 1977, The evolving continents: New York, John Wiley and Sons, XVIII, 385 p.
Wise, D. U., 1974, Continental margins, freeboard and volume of continents and oceans through time, p. 45–58, *in* Burke, C. A., and Drake, C. L., eds., The geology of continental margins: New-York, Springer Verlag, 1009 p.

Manuscript Accepted by the Society April 14, 1983

Printed in U.S.A.

Geological Society of America
Memoir 161
1983

Proterozoic mobile belts compatible with the plate tectonic concept

A. Kröner
Institut für Geowissenschaften
Johannes-Gutenberg-Universität
Postfach 3980
6500 Mainz
West Germany

ABSTRACT

Proterozoic foldbelts older than about 1 Ga lack the distinctive signatures of the contemporary Wilson cycle although they frequently contain thick sedimentary assemblages that resemble those in Phanerozoic orogens. Mafic volcanic rocks are rare, however, and occur intestratified with sedimentary strata; they are not layered and contain no sheeted dikes and can therefore not be interpreted as ophiolites.

These characteristics as well as paleomagnetic and isotopic constraints preclude an evolution of these belts during closure of extensive oceans and subduction of significant amounts of oceanic lithosphere.

An alternative plate tectonic model is developed that invokes rifting, heating, and stretching of the crust as a result of lithospheric thinning over a mantle plume. This mechanism eventually leads to a "geosynclinal" basin entirely floored by continental crust. The rise of asthenosphere enhances gravitational instabilities in the old and dense subcrustal lithosphere that, on fracturing after crustal stretching, may delaminate spontaneously. Hot asthenospheric material rises to take the place of the detached and sinking lithospheric slab, thereby inducing A-subduction and interstacking of continental crust. The much thickenend crust is partially melted at depth, intruded by synorogenic and postorogenic granites, and finally uplifted and eroded to its present level of exposure. Episodic thermal anomalies during orogeny are caused by the rise of asthenospheric magmas to the base of the crust and by radioactive self-heating after crustal interstacking.

The model is entirely compatible with the concept of horizontally moving plates but differs from the Wilson cycle in that no wet oceanic crust is generated during basin formation and none is consumed during orogeny. Instead, dry subcrustal lithosphere sinks down but does not cause calc-alkalic magmatism.

Towards the end of the Proterozoic, Wilson cycle signatures become widespread in the global rock record and signify a worldwide change from predominantly intraplate orogeny to predominantly plate margin orogeny that characterizes the Phanerozoic geodynamic pattern. Plate tectonics, therefore, is a nonuniformitarian process.

INTRODUCTION

The Proterozoic record on virtually all continents contains rock assemblages whose distribution, composition, and tectonic setting is broadly comparable with that of Phanerozoic orogenic belts. In pre-plate tectonic days all these domains were regarded as the result of intracontinental "geosynclinal" and "orogenic" evolution, leading to linear foldbelts and mountain ranges of varying proportions.

A reconsideration of these terranes and their development in view of the currently accepted framework of global plate tectonics has led to a controversy that has been going on in the literature for the past 10 to 15 years. One school proposes that processes of ocean opening and closing in terms of the post-Mesozoic Wilson cycle have operated since the early Archean (Burke and others, 1976a; Windley, 1981). Others, however, argue that, for various geophysical and geochemical reasons, oceanic plate consumption was virtually impossible until about 1,000 Ma ago (for example, Baer, 1977, 1981; Lambert, 1981; D. H. Green, 1981), that the available paleomagnetic record favors the existence of a few large continental plates since early Proterozoic times (Dunlop, 1981; McWilliams, 1981), and that many Precambrian mobile belts lack the distinctive signature of the modern Wilson cycle (Kröner, 1977b; Rutland, 1976).

Plate tectonic supporters have rejected most of the above arguments as incorrect or unproven and argue that the superficial difference between Phanerozoic orogens and Precambrian mobile belts is largely due to different erosion levels (for example, Burke and others, 1977), that typical collision signatures such as sutures, ophiolites, and melanges are present but have not been recognized in most Precambrian terranes (Shackleton, 1976; Shackleton and others, 1980), and that ensialic models are incompatible with the paleomagnetic record of moving continental plates since the Archean (for example, Burke and others 1976b; Windley, 1981) and with geochemical concepts of crustal growth (Moorbath, 1977).

For many earth scientists unfamiliar with the Precambrian rock record the "mobile belt debate" may have created the impression that "ensialic orogeny" is a non-plate tectonic process and that those favoring this mechanism reject the concept of plate tectonics for Precambrian crustal evolution.

This paper does not provide a uniform model for the evolution of all Precambrian belts. However, it draws attention to the fact that numerous Proterozoic belts have apparently evolved through intense horizontal shortening of "geosynclinal" basins in which there is no convincing evidence for plate separation and generation of oceanic crust. It is contended that orogeny in these terranes was not caused by subduction and continental collision processes but by the closure of intracontinental basins through inter-stacking of crust and possible delamination of subcrustal mantle lithosphere (Kröner, 1981a; McWilliams and Kröner, 1981). This model represents a variation of the plate tectonic concept that is compatible with constraints imposed by paleomagnetism, field geology, and isotope geochemistry.

WILSON CYCLE SIGNATURES IN PRECAMBRIAN TERRANES

The process of ocean opening and closing with subduction of oceanic crust and eventual continental or island arc collision leaves a characteristic signature in the rock record, which has so far enabled most Phanerozoic orogenic belts to be recognized as the result of Wilson cycle evolution. The Appalachian and Himalaya belts are cited as examples of continental collision, while the Andean belt is due to subduction of oceanic crust and the opening and closing of minor marginal basins. The origin, evolution, and collision of ensimatic island arcs and marginal basins can be studied in the present West Pacific.

The rock types and tectonics produced in these settings are well studied and provide a basis for comparison with Precambrian terranes. If good agreement is found, the conclusion is generally that similar processes had operated in the past. However, if the Precambrian setup differs markedly from the modern model, the conclusion is frequently that the difference in erosion level does not permit direct comparisons but that geochemical parameters nevertheless favor a Wilson cycle evolution. This way of reasoning has led to the deplorable practice of ignoring many field relationships in Precambrian belts in favor of geochemical criteria; that is, the identification of basaltic rocks as "tholeiites of oceanic affinity" according to currently popular discrimination diagrams immediately leads to their interpretation as ocean floor, regardless of the *geological* environment, and the same applies to the classification of volcanic and granitoid rocks as "calc-alkalic," thereby automatically implying the operation of subduction processes.

Detailed work in Precambrian terranes of virtually all continents has demonstrated over the past 10 years that there appear to be fundamental differences in the evolution of regions commonly referred to as "orogenic" if compared with Phanerozoic orogens. This is particularly evident in Africa and Australia or, more generally, in the continents previously constituting Gondwanaland.

One of the major reasons for not considering these belts as the result of Wilson cycle processes is the apparent continuity of older structures on either side (Hurley, 1972; Shackleton, 1973), their spectacular cross-cutting relationships (Wynne-Edwards and Hasan, 1970; Kröner, 1977a, b) (see Fig. 3) and the longevity and episodic character of orogenic and magmatic activity, in some cases exceeding

Figure 1. Sheeted dike complex of a late Precambrian ophiolite in Wadi Ghadir, Eastern Desert of Egypt.

1,000 Ma (Kröner, 1981b). The latter, if due to contemporary plate tectonics, would demand extremely large relative motions between bordering cratons for which there is no paleomagnetic evidence (Dunlop, 1981; McWilliams, 1981). Furthermore, it has been suggested that uplift following orogeny was an order of magnitude less in many Precambrian belts if compared to Phanerozoic orogens, that is, only 2 to 3 mm per 100 years as also supported by K-Ar cooling ages (Sutton, 1977), and that such slow vertical motion is incompatible with crustal thickening through Himalaya-type continental collision.

Terranes revealing close analogies with Phanerozoic tectonics appear to become widespread in the global rock record during the so-called Pan-African event since about 1,000 Ma ago and have led to the suggestion that this signifies the onset of present-day tectonics (Baer, 1977; Kröner, 1977b, 1979b, 1981a, 1981b). The most spectacular example is provided by the evolution of the Arabian-Nubian shield where excellent exposures and the low degree of metamorphism reveal a complex history of island arc formation, ocean closure, and collision between about 1,200 Ma and 500 Ma ago (Greenwood and others, 1976; Gass, 1981). Geological evidence supporting this model is the large amounts of calc-alkalic, island arc–type volcanic material and associated granitoid batholiths, nearly all with isotopic systematics favoring an ensimatic origin (Fleck and others, 1979), the ubiquitous presence of arc-derived volcanogenic sedimentary rocks (Schmidt and others, 1979), and, above all, the undoubted presence of tectonically emplaced ophiolites containing rock units identical to those found in present oceanic crust (Frisch and Al-Shanti, 1977; Hussein and others, 1982).

El-Bayoumi (1980) has discovered what must be regarded as one of the best preserved and most complete segments of late Precambrian ocean crust in the Wadi Ghadir complex of the Eastern Desert of Egypt. This unit is about 800 to 900 Ma old and reveals a complete sequence from chert through tholeiitic pillow lava, sheeted dikes, layered gabbro with minor trondhjemite, dunite with chromite lenses, and harzburgite. The sheeted dike complex is particularly well preserved (Fig. 1) and provides convincing evidence that ocean-floor spreading was an important crust-forming process since at least late Precambrian times. The association of the Wadi Ghadir ophiolite with extensive and tectonically emplaced mélanges that appear to have been thrust over shallow-water metasedimentary sequences of a former continental margin reveals an evolutionary scenario that suggests horizontal accretion of juvenile crust through subduction-related island arc generation, arc collision, and obduction of oceanic crust. Although individual models differ in detail (for example, Garson and Shalaby, 1976; Gass, 1981; Kröner, 1979a; Schmidt and others, 1979; Engel and others, 1980) and paleomagnetic data of the region are not availalbe, few investigators contest the accretion model since virtually all the decisive elements of the Wilson cycle are preserved except for blueschist assemblages.

Other late Precambrian mafic to ultramafic complexes with strong ophiolitic affinities occur in Pan-African terranes of southern Morocco (Leblanc, 1981), in the southern Hoggar Mountains of Mali (Black and others, 1979), in the Gariep belt of southwestern Namibia (Kröner, 1979a), and in the Mozambique belt of Kenya (Shackleton and others, 1981) and Ethiopia (Kazmin and others, 1978). However, these units are now tectonically dismembered, contain no positively identified sheeted dike complex, and their relationship to neighboring domains is largely unknown.

It seems significant that, at least in the Arabian-Nubian shield, Precambrian Wilson cycle signatures are often well preserved despite the fact that some segments of the shield are deeply eroded and now expose upper amphibolite grade assemblages (Ramsay and others, 1979).

Other Pan-African and older Proterozoic belts lack the voluminous igneous rock associations characteristic of plate margin orogeny and consist largely of metasedimentary strata. It is particularly this type of belt that has given rise to controversy as to its origin. These belts often contain great thicknesses of psammitic and pelitic sediments with intercalated subordinate amounts of volcanic rocks, and in many cases, deposition has taken place in miogeosynclinal and eugeosynclinal domains that are strikingly similar to those reconstructed from Phanerozoic orogens such as the Alps.

In Africa, belts of this type include the approximately 1,100 to 1,400 Ma old Irumides and Kibarides (for detailed literature see Kröner, 1977a, 1977b) and the Pan-African Damara, Katanga, West Congo, and Dahomey belts bordering the Kalahari, Congo, and West African cratons, respectively (Martin and Porada, 1977; Kröner, 1979b, 1980). Similar zones in other continents include the Uruaçu and Brazilian belts of Brazil (de Almeida and others, 1981), the Labrador Trough of Canada (Dimroth, 1981), almost all Proterozoic belts of Australia (Plumb, 1979a, 1979b; Rutland and others, 1981), and the late Precambrian Grampian belt of Scotland (Harris and others, 1978).

All these belts have in common that orogeny was preceded by deposition of thick sedimentary strata, first in graben-like basins which subsequently widened and deepened into well-defined linear troughs that received large amounts of clastic to pelitic sediments. It is also characteristic of these basins that mafic volcanic rocks are either absent or appear *late* in the depositional history (Fig. 2), that calc-alkalic volcanic assemblages are absent or are almost totally lacking, and that the outline and geometry of the troughs are often inconsistent with plate separation and subsequent collision. In the Labrador Trough of Canada, for example, Dimroth (1981) has shown that tholeiitic volcanics are *interstratified* with sediments and have internal structures unlike those found in spreading ocean crust. The same applies to the volcanics in the Grampian belt (Harris and others, 1978).

Sr-isotopic data, where available, consistently indicate that pretectonic and early syntectonic intrusives such as syenites, alkaline granites, and granodiorites have comparatively low $^{87}Sr/^{86}Sr$ initial ratios between 0.703 and 0.707, suggesting a lower crustal and/or upper mantle derivation, while granitoid rocks of the main orogenic phases have considerably higher ratios between 0.706 and 0.720. Post-tectonic high level granites have ratios above 0.714 and up to 0.759 (for example, Kibaran-Burundian belt of central Africa, Vernon-Chamberlain and Snelling, 1972; Cahen and others, 1972; Australian belts, see Plumb, 1979b; Damara belt of Namibia, see Kröner, 1982; Hawkesworth and others, 1983). All these data indicate that crustal melting has dominated virtually the entire orogenic histories of these belts.

Direct field evidence for an intracratonic development is often more difficult to demonstrate since basement/cover relationships are mostly concealed or have been obliterated during orogenic deformation. However, there are regions where continuity of basement from one side of a belt to the other can be shown. For example, in the 1,100- to 1,300-Ma-old Irumide belt of northern Malawi the sialic floor is exposed over the entire width of the mobile zone and no suture is evident (see references in Kröner, 1977b). Farther southwest, in Zambia, the late Precambrian Katanga belt crosses the Irumides (Fig. 3), but apart from Pan-African metamorphic overprinting there is little effect of the younger event on the older structures, that is, the Irumide belt disappears under the younger Katanga belt and reappears on the other side to continue into Zimbabwe (Drysdall and others, 1972).

In Australia, Horwitz and Smith (1978) have presented a detailed account of the Gascoyne-Median belt separating the Archean Yilgarn and Pilbara blocks in Western Australia. Here the early Proterozoic sedimentary and volcanic successions of the Hamersley and Nabberu basins were clearly deposited on a continuous Archean substratum, and intense deformation and metamorphism have affected both basement and cover.

Some of the belts discussed here contain mafic volcanic assemblages that have been interpreted as dismembered ophiolites and therefore as evidence for ocean closure and continental collision (Burke and others, 1977). However, *none* of these mafic complexes contains the full range of rock types found in post-Mesozoic ocean floor and, apart from the Arabian-Nubian shield discussed above, there is no recorded case of a sheeted dike system, the prerequisite for ocean-floor spreading. In most places the so-called ophiolite consists of tholeiitic lava flows that are frequently *interbedded* with clastic sedimentary strata and not tectonically emplaced as the ocean closure model would require. For example, Dimroth (1981) has shown that the basalts of the Labrador Trough in Canada form a horizontally stratified sequence that cannot have originated through lateral accretion, and De Paepe and others (1975) found tholeiitic pillow lavas and hyaloclastites *interstratified* with a shallow marine tillite in the West Congo belt of Zaire. Similarly, tholeiitic metavolcanics are interbedded with greywacke and shale in the upper sequence of the Damara belt of Namibia (Sawyer, 1978; Kröner, 1977b,

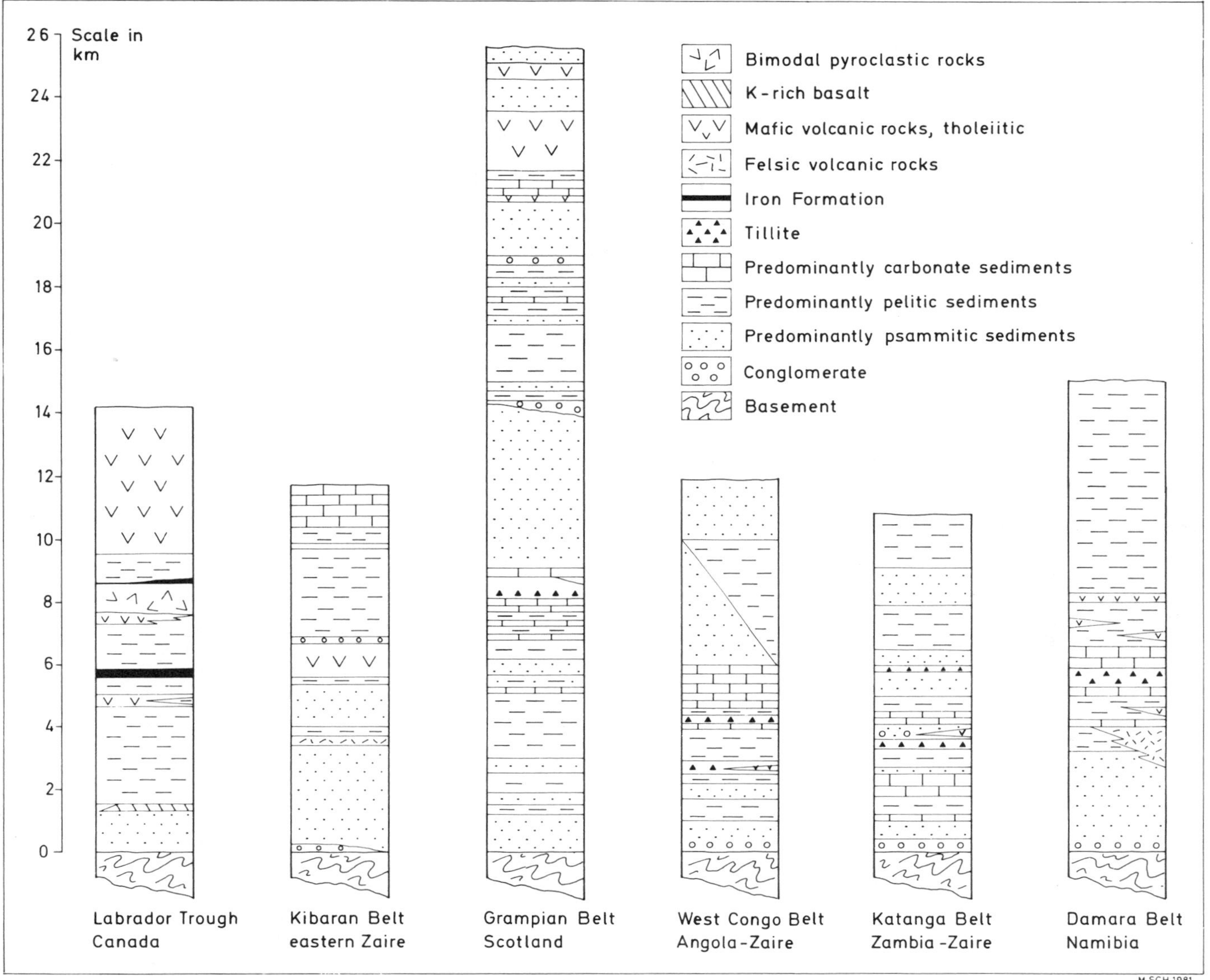

Figure 2. Simplified stratigraphic sections of typical ensialic Proterozoic basins that evolved into foldbelts. The thickness of individual units represents an average or maximum. Aggregate thicknesses, therefore, are not necessarily representative of any given section. Source of information are: Labrador Trough (Baragar and Scoates, 1981), Kibaran belt (Cahen and Lepersonne, 1967), Grampian belt (Harris and others, 1978), West Congo belt (Stanton and others, 1972; Cahen, 1980), Katanga belt (Cahen and Lepersonne, 1967; Cahen, 1970), Damara belt (Martin, 1965).

1982) and in the upper part of the Dalradian sequence of the Grampian belt in Scotland (Harris and others, 1978). Currently popular discrimination diagrams and chemical characteristics classify these rocks as ocean-floor basalts, yet field relationships clearly contradict such interpretations. It is relevant in this context that the Tertiary tholeiitic basalts of Baffin Island in northeastern Canada rest on Precambrian sialic basement, yet they are chemically indistinguishable from mid-ocean ridge basalts (O'Nions and Clarke, 1972). Also, the late Precambrian to Cambrian Oklahoma aulacogen of the United States contains subalkaline volcanic rocks such as basalt and andesite that are apparently neither related to ocean formation or subduction but to intracontinental rifting (Hanson and Al-Shaieb, 1980).

One of the best studied regions for which an intracratonic development is proposed is the Pan-African Damara belt of Namibia, and the evolutionary model proposed below is largely based on studies in this belt. Detailed fieldwork, geochronology, and paleomagnetism have revealed an exceptionally long depositional history from about 1,000 to 750 Ma ago, followed by several episodes of

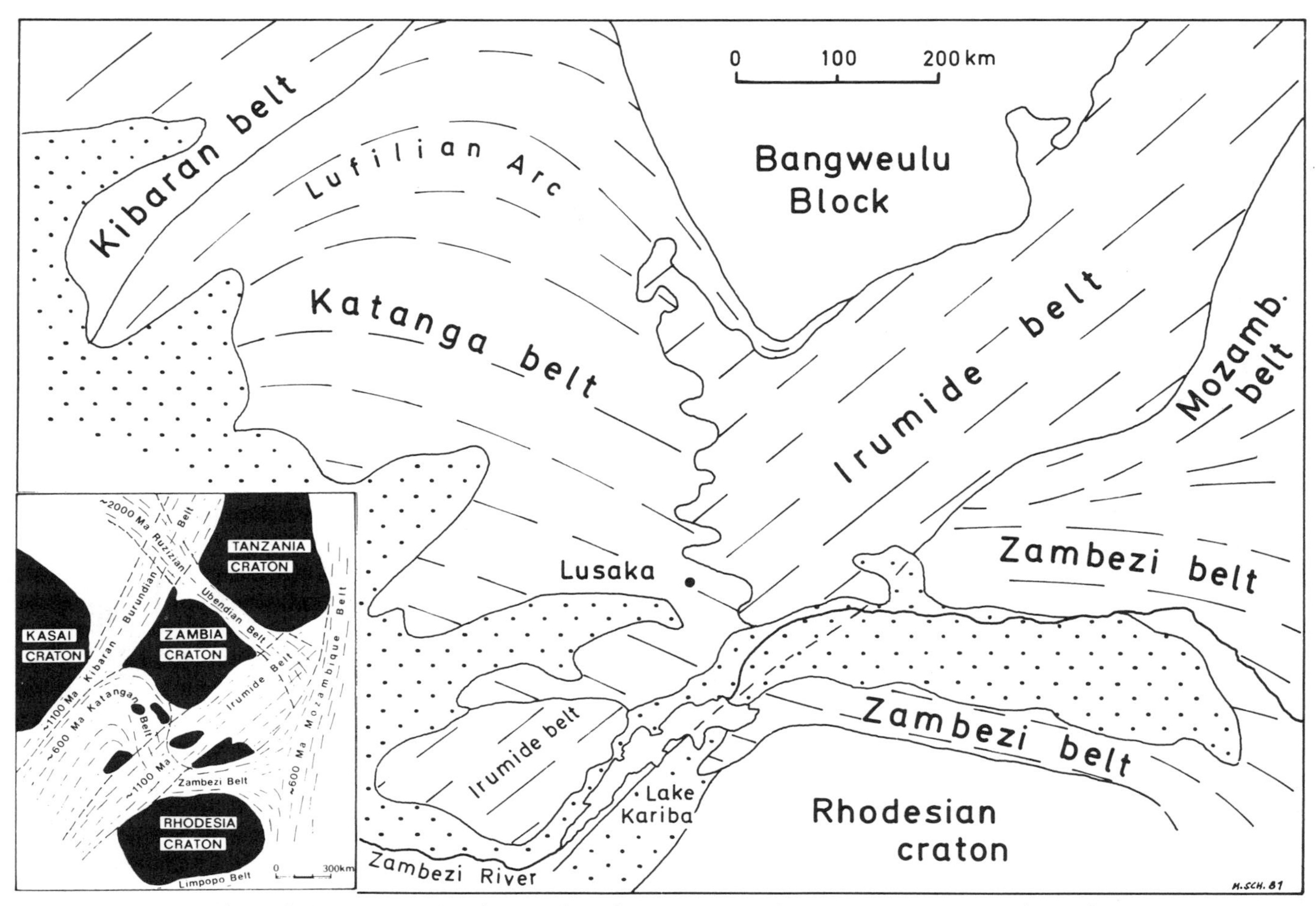

Figure 3. Sketch map showing relationship between Irumide and Katanga-Zambezi belts in Zambia, based on Drysdall and others (1972). Inset map (Kröner, 1977b) illustrates cross-cutting relationship of Proterozoic mobile belts in east-central Africa.

deformation, metamorphism, and magmatism between 750 and 450 Ma ago (Martin and Porada, 1977; Kröner, 1982). Paleomagnetic data indicate that no large-scale relative motions between the Congo and Kalahari cratons have occurred during the evolution of this belt (McWilliams and Krömer, 1981), and the lack of characteristic Wilson cycle evidence such as ophiolites, sutures, calc-alkalic volcanism, and blueschist assemblages support this contention.

Deposition in the Damara basin began in several rift-induced graben structures, which later widened to a "geosynclinal" trough some 600 km wide and floored by 1.1- to 2-Ga-old sialic basement. A pronounced deepening in the southern part of this basin at about 760 to 800 Ma ago produced the Khomas flysch trough that was filled with a thick turbidite assemblage. Tholeiitic lavas and tuffs were repeatedly emplaced during this period, the most extensive of which are known as the Matchless amphibolite belt. Field relations show these rocks to be interbedded with the turbidite sequence (Kröner, 1977b). Occasional gabbroic intrusives and serpentinites have also been found in this belt and elsewhere in the Khomas trough. The mafic rocks and pretectonic diorite-granodiorite intrusives with low $^{87}Sr/^{86}Sr$ ratios indicate that the geosynclinal basin reached its greatest width at about 750 to 770 Ma ago, and a lower crustal/upper mantle thermal anomaly must have existed at that time (Kröner, 1982).

Subsequent orogeny reflects closure of this oceanic intracontinental basin as revealed by early recumbent folding and thrusting involving both basement and cover slices (Downing and Coward, 1981). Strong thermal events at about 650 Ma and 530 to 550 Ma ago caused high-grade metamorphism in the central belt and widespread granite intrusion, induced largely by melting in the ca. 2-Ga-old basement. This was accompanied by further horizontal shortening and uplift, deposition of molasse sequences in the forelands, and intense thrusting as well as nappe emplacement along the southern margin of the belt. A final thermal event at about 500 to 460 Ma ago produced high-level granites and spectacular U-bearing alaskitic pegmatites by further melting of basement gneisses (Kröner, 1982; Hawkesworth and others, 1983).

A model for this and the other belts ennumerated above must therefore explain the process of rifting and basin formation through crustal thinning without continental separation, followed by intracontinental orogeny characterized by polyphase deformation, metamorphism, and crustal melting.

RIFTING, DELAMINATION, AND A-SUBDUCTION: A MODEL FOR THE EVOLUTION OF PROTEROZOIC FOLDBELTS

The stratigraphic record in almost all Proterozoic foldbelts shows that geosynclinal development started with crustal extension and deposition of clastic sediments in grabenlike basins (Fig. 2). This phase is probably similar to the beginning of continental breakup as shown in Phanerozoic graben systems such as the early stage of the Red Sea, the Baikal Rift, or the East African Rift System.

There has been some debate in the literature on what mechanism causes this extension and faulting. Some authors consider intraplate stresses arising from continental collisions or small differences in the absolute velocities of plates (for example, Molnar and Tapponier, 1975; Charpal and others, 1978) that may be strong enough to eventually tear continents apart. Others suggested that the prime cause is lithospheric thinning as a result of convective heat transfer by magma intrusion from the asthenosphere (Zorin, 1981; Withjack, 1979) or through a combination of convection and conduction (Spohn and Schubert, 1982). The latter authors have calculated that the lithosphere may be convectively thinned to half its initial thickness in less than 100 Ma.

Since continental rift zones are generally characterized by anomalously high heat flow, negative Bouguer anomalies, and initial updoming, the model of lithospheric thinning and upward advection of asthenosphere is preferred here for the initiation of rifting in the evolving Proterozoic basins.

Extension through upper crustal rifting may amount to several tens of kilometres but does not account for all of the crustal thinning observed under presently active rift zones. It has therefore been suggested that extension occurs by brittle fracture in the upper crust and by ductile flow in the lower crust, a variation of the original Vening Meinesz model proposed by Bott (1971). Such fundamentally different rheological properties of the crust have recently been confirmed by seismic profiling in the Bay of Biscay where listric faults bordering rifted blocks do not continue below a depth of 9 km where they curve and flatten (Charpal and others, 1978). Flow within the ductile layer below is considered by these authors to accommodate the balance of the thinning required by geological and geophysical data. Evidence for considerable plastic extension of the lower crust during faulting and basin subsidence has also been reported from the Basin and Range province in the western United States (Eaton, 1979). Here an annual extension rate in the range 0.3 to 3 mm/year has been calculated for the last 26 Ma (Woodward, 1977; Stewart, 1971), yet crustal failure has not taken place. Seismic imaging of the deep crust in many Phanerozoic and Precambrian terranes has revealed the presence of marked reflection zones beginning in about 18- to 20-km depth that are interpreted as the result of large-scale banding and layering caused by ductile flow (Smithson and Brown, 1977; Phinney and Jurdy, 1979).

A significant heat source, probably a thermal plume, is required to enable rapid lithospheric thinning, while the general ductility of the crust below some 20-km-depth, together with the additional plume-generated heat, will facilitate subsequent crustal spreading. In situations where the lower crust is too cool or too thin or where extension is too fast, complete crustal rupture ensues early in the rifting phase. For example, the southern Gulf of California developed through rapid ocean opening after rotation of Baja California towards the west. Plate separation has been estimated at 60 mm/year during the past 4 Ma (Niemitz and Bischoff, 1981), 20 to 200 times faster than crustal extension in the Rio Grande Rift.

Returning to our scenario for the development of Proterozoic basins, I suggest, from the above observations, that initial graben systems can develop into a wide and deep intracontinental trough through a process of slow lower crustal attenuation. This process causes further thinning of the crustal layer, and after ductile spreading, the subcrustal thermal anomaly initially located under the rift now also extends horizontally and heats a continuously increasing part of the lower crust. Evidence for crustal heating during the early graben stage comes from alkaline intrusives with low $^{87}Sr/^{86}Sr$ initial ratios that intrude the clastic sediments in many Proterozoic belts.

Zorin (1981) has shown that subcrustal lithospheric thinning, graben formation, and lower crustal flow in the Baikal Rift have brought the asthenosphere to depths of only 50 to 60 km. The length of the zone where the asthenosphere has almost reached the lower crust exceeds 2,000 km, and its width is as much as 250 to 300 km. This situation has been adopted in Figure 4, which shows a simplified section across a possible Proterozoic graben system some 100 to 200 Ma after initiation of rifting and just before evolution into a wide intracontinental oceanic basin (the example is the proposed setting in the Damara basin some 850 Ma ago).

The situation is now that a broad section of the mantle lithosphere under the evolving basin has been thinned to considerably less than its original thickness, perhaps even to only a few kilometres, thus exposing the remaining part

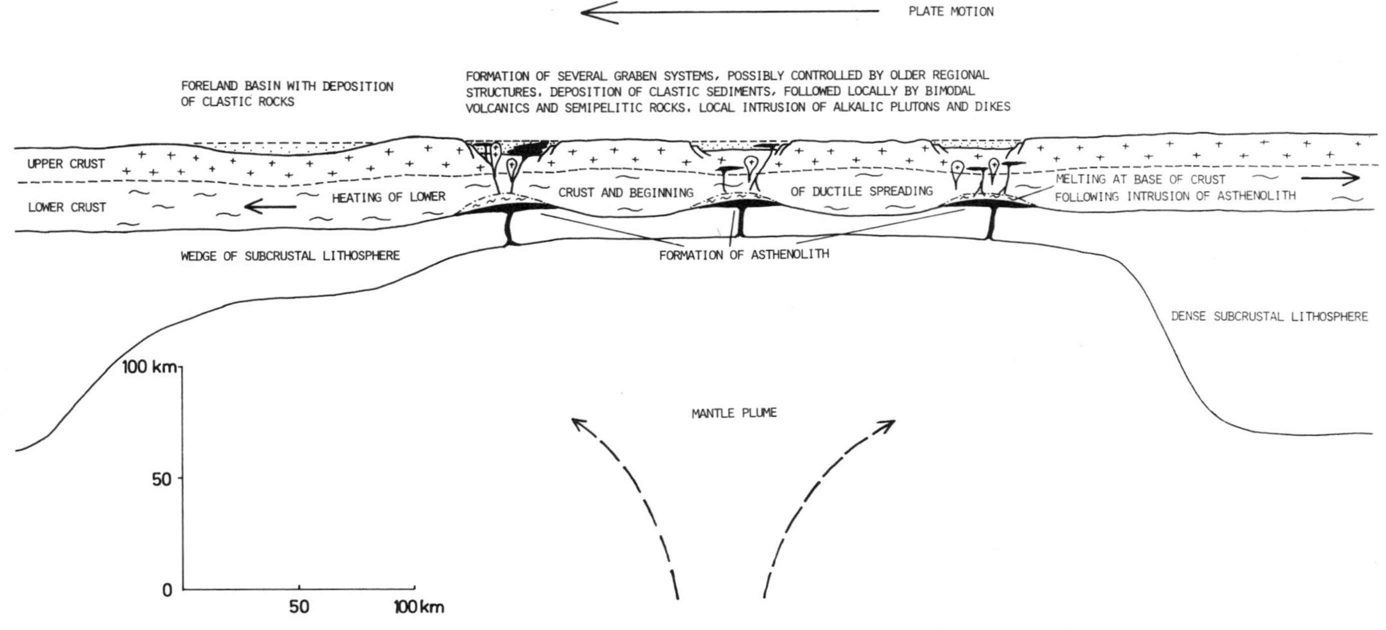

Figure 4. Simplified and schematic cross section showing suggested evolution of graben system after lithospheric thinning (based on Damara belt, Namibia, and modified after Kröner, 1980).

as well as the overlying crust to a significant increase in heat flow from the convecting asthenosphere below. On either side of the basin the lithosphere resumes its original instantaneous thickness of about 80 to 100 km or more. However, the shape and thickness of the lithosphere under the evolving basin will vary because it is assumed that the plate on which the basin develops is itself in motion relative to the asthenospheric thermal anomaly below. Withjack (1979) has shown that the curvature of the lithosphere/asthenosphere boundary depends on the rate of magma entry and plate velocity. As the plate moves, the thermal anomaly trails behind and a long subcrustal lithospheric wedge develops (Fig. 4).

It has been suggested that isotopic heterogeneities in the upper mantle below continents are long-lived, as shown by so-called mantle isochrons (Brooks and Hart, 1978), and that mantle lithosphere has therefore been attached to overlying continental crust for very long periods of time. Jordan (1979) has proposed that this phenomenon is caused by basalt-depletion of the subcrustal upper mantle during intracontinental mafic volcanism and that this basalt-depleted rigid segment, which he named tectosphere, has thickened through time. Seismic refraction profiling indeed indicates that the tectosphere is exceptionally thick under old Precambrian cratons such as the Canadian Shield and Australia (Jordan, 1979).

The important implication of this model is that at least the upper part of mantle lithosphere below ancient cratonic crust is older, cooler, and therefore also denser than "normal" mantle lithosphere under oceanic or Phanerozoic terranes. The calculations of Molnar and Gray (1979), Bird (1979), and Hargraves (1981) show that old subcrustal lithosphere is negatively buoyant with respect to the underlying asthenosphere and would therefore begin to sink if it were not for the light continental crustal segment above that keeps the plate "afloat." Using an average density difference of 0.08 g/gm^3 between asthenosphere and old subcrustal mantle lithosphere (asthenosphere $\rho = 3.22$, mantle lithosphere $\rho = 3.30$, see Hargraves, 1981), Hargrave (1981) has shown that for an average crustal density of 2.85 g/cm^3 a lithospheric plate with 30-km-thick continental crust and a 140-km-thick cool mantle segment would be in isostatic equilibrium with the asthenosphere (Fig. 5). If crustal thickness were considerably less, negative buoyancy of the entire plate would ensue, perhaps triggering subduction.

Crustal stretching during basin formation causes considerable thinning and may render the lithosphere gravitationally unstable under the basin, but this would be counteracted by rapid thinning of the subcrustal lithosphere during asthenospheric ascent as argued above and as shown in Figures 4 and 6. Spontaneous instability can be produced, however, if mantle lithosphere, alone or together with a substantial fraction of the lower continental crust, is detached from the upper part (Molnar and Gray, 1979). Bird (1978) has shown that normal continental lithosphere probably has a weak, creeping layer at the base of the crust that is subjected to vertical deviatoric tension due to positive buoyancy of the crust and negative buoyancy of the mantle below. Such tensional stress could amount to 350

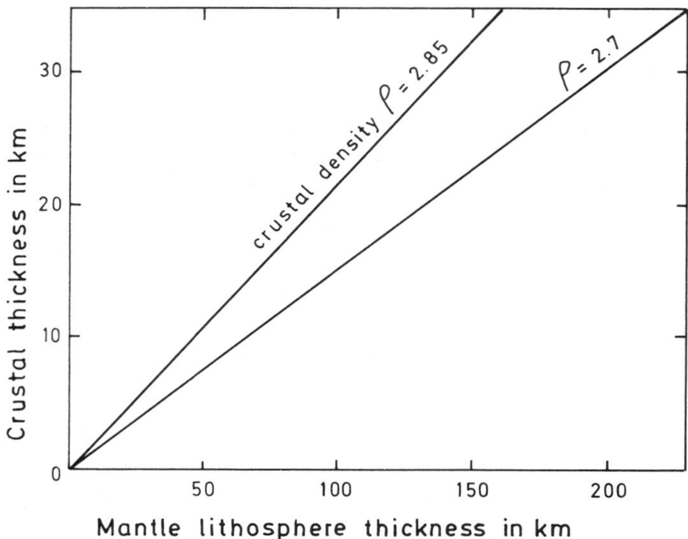

Figure 5. Diagram showing isostatic equilibrium conditions for lithospheric plate consisting of positively buoyant continental crust ($\rho \sim 2.85$) and negatively buoyant mantle lithosphere ($\rho \sim 3.30$) relative to asthenosphere ($\rho \sim 3.22$). A 140-km-thick mantle lithosphere requires 30 km of continental crust to remain in isostatic equilibrium with asthenosphere. Lighter crust ($\rho \sim 2.7$) requires even greater mantle lithospheric thickness; after Hargraves (1981).

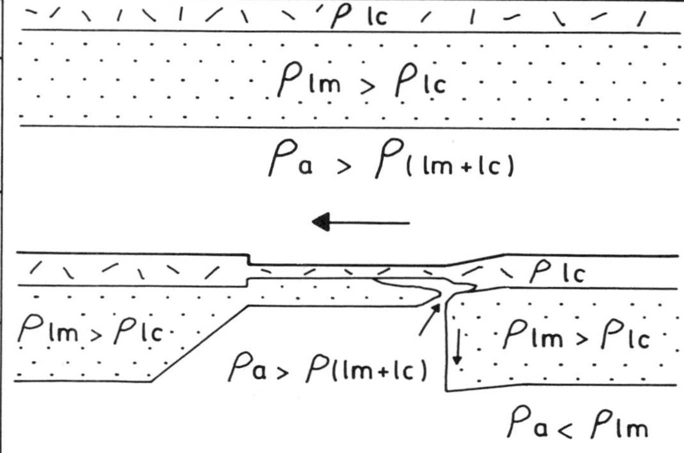

Figure 6. Mechanism causing delamination of thick and dense mantle lithosphere under intracontinental basin (modified after Bird, 1978). Spontaneous gravitational instability results from crustal necking, lithosphere rupture, and spreading of rising asthenosphere near crust/mantle boundary. Note that shape of asthenospheric intrusion results form motion of the entire plate relative to stationary plume.

bars at the bottom of the crust, assuming a 120-km-thick continental lithosphere (Toksöz and others, 1967).

Applied to the scenario of lithospheric behavior during crustal stretching and basin formation above a mantle plume, as shown in Figure 4, the region of greatest differential stress in the subcrustal lithosphere would be where lithospheric thickness changes rapidly from only a few kilometres under the evolving basin to more than 100 km under the adjoining cratonic domains. This is the most likely portion of the mantle lithosphere to fracture. Bird (1979) demonstrated that density differences between mantle lithosphere and asthenosphere would allow asthenospheric melts to rise along the fractures to the base of the crust where large differences in static pressure would favor horizontal spreading of these melts along the mechanically weak crust/mantle boundary (Fig. 6).

It is now suggested that mantle-derived mafic volcanic activity in the geosynclinal basin reflects this stage of lithospheric fracturing (Fig. 7). This would explain the chemical affinity of such extrusive and intrusive rocks with oceanic crust, the lack of sheeted dikes and other evidence

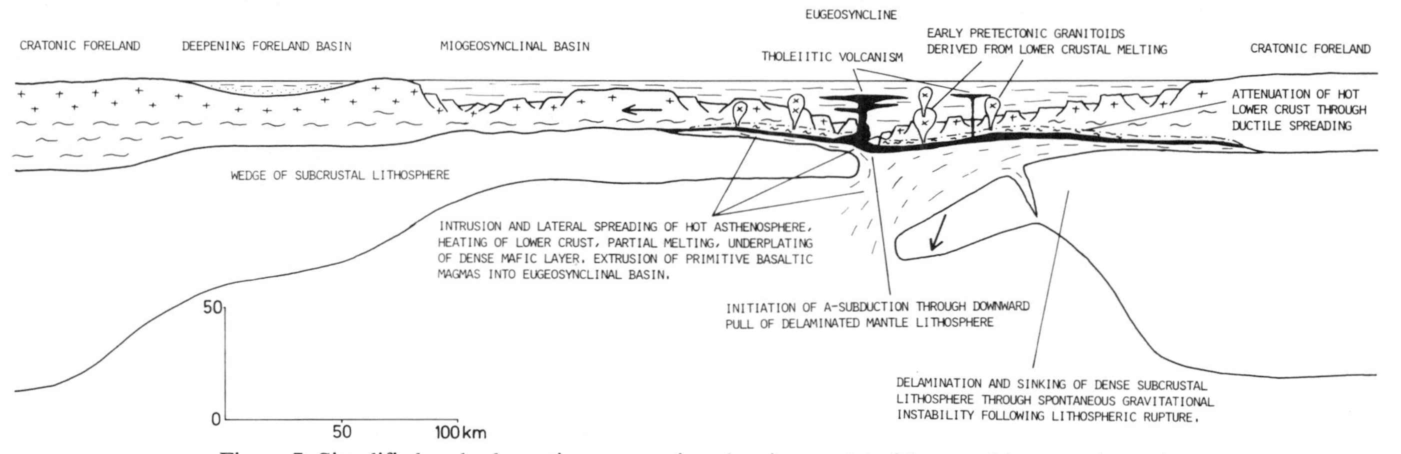

Figure 7. Simplified and schematic cross-section showing model of "mature" intracontinental geosynclinal basin with mafic volcanism and pretectonic granitoid magmatism. Underthrusting of one extremely attenuated basin margin under the other (A-subduction) is induced through downward pull of gravitationally unstable lithosphere after rupture and delamination. Note mafic underplating at base of crust stripped of its rigid base (based on Damara belt, Namibia, and modified after Kröner, 1980).

of lateral spreading, and the interbedding with continent-derived sedimentary strata. It also explains why such mafic rocks were emplaced relatively late in the depositional history of most Proterozoic geosynclinal basins as demonstrated above.

Depending on the rate of lithospheric extension, mafic magmatism may be of variable intensity. In some places of very slow spreading the lithospheric fracture zone may remain very narrow, and most of the mafic melts may never reach the surface of the basin but rather end as gabbroic or ultramafic intrusives within the lower crust because of their high densities. In other places, such as the Labrador, Damara, West Congo, and Grampian basins, basaltic lava flows occur as shown in Figure 7. In still other places such as the Pan-African Pharusian basin of the western Hoggar, lithospheric fractures must have penetrated the entire crust in an early stage of continental fragmentation, since large amounts of basic to ultrabasic rocks were intruded as sills, laccoliths, and stocks over wide areas into quartzites and limestones. These rocks, as in the example above, display geochemical affinity with modern oceanic crust but are clearly not ophiolites but mantle-derived complexes intruded into shallow water sediments (Caby and others, 1981).

Returning to the horizontally spreading asthenospheric wedge of Figure 6, spontaneous delamination of the dense and thick mantle segment under the cratonic block would now be made possible along the thermally weakened crust/mantle boundary and the mantle segment would sink thereby gradually and successively "peeling off" from the overlying crust and allowing further hot asthenospheric material to fill the gap (Fig. 7). Delamination may propagate at rates to the order of 5 cm/year, consistent with expected rates of plate motion (Bird, 1979). It will stop whenever the front of the asthenospheric wedge freezes through cooling, where the crust/mantle boundary strength increases away from the original mantle plume, or when the free end of the subsiding mantle lithosphere stops sinking.

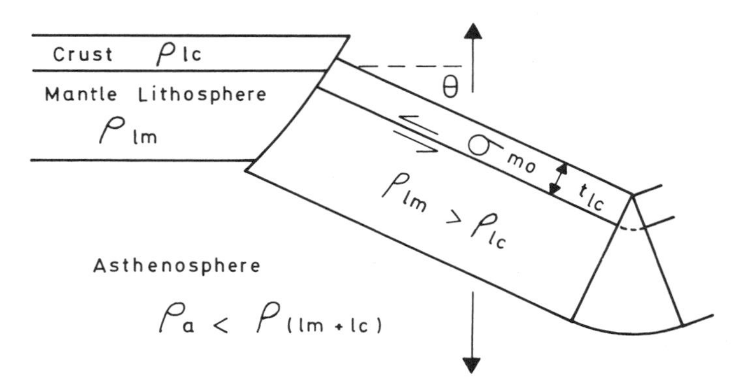

Figure 8. Model illustrating dependence of shear stress at crust/mantle boundary on inclination of lithospheric segment consisting of positively buoyant continental crust and negatively buoyant mantle lithosphere. Shear stress increases rapidly with increasing angle θ; after Hargraves (1981).

It is possible that fracturing of the mantle lithosphere propagates through part or through the entire crust above and that asthenospheric material rises above the crust/-mantle boundary. In this case a significant portion of the lower crust may initially be dragged down together with the subsiding mantle slab if gravitational instability prevails. This motion causes the crust/mantle boundary to become inclined, thereby reducing the critical shear stress for decoupling (Hargraves, 1981; see Fig. 8). The result on the overlying crust is a sudden deepening of part of the geosynclinal basin and the formation of a "eugeosyncline" with deposition of thick flysch-type sequences and interbedded volcanic rocks (Fig. 7). On the other hand, Bird and Baumgardner (1981) have calculated that subcrustal delamination produces a deep trough about 100 km in width, and it is therefore possible that the eugeosynclinal basin is largely the result of this process.

The onset of delamination, the weakness of the remaining continental lithosphere below the wide sedimentary basin, or other parameters may be responsible for the beginning of orogenic deformation as a result of crustal shortening and basin closure. At the same time extensive heating of the lower crust through rising asthenospheric magma triggers melting both in the crust and in the amphibolitic layer that has been underplated during the first phase of lithospheric fracturing. Such mafic layers can be expected at the base of the crust and result from the inability of the dense ($>3 g/cm^3$) partial melt fractions in the upper mantle to penetrate the overlying continental segment (Condie, 1981; Hanson, 1981; Kröner, 1981b). The lower crustal or subcrustal "juvenile" amphibolite may be the source of calc-alkalic diorite, granodiorite, and trondhjemite with low $^{87}Sr/^{86}Sr$ initial ratios that characterize the early stage of orogenic development.

The major difference between the above scenario and the conventional Wilson cycle model is that in the first case crustal spreading, if sufficiently slow, is entirely accommodated by laminar flow and stretching, therefore limiting intracontinental "ocean opening" to several hundred kilometres at most. No ocean floor is created if the continental crust remains intact or if the fractures are filled by mafic intrusions from below. However, if extension continues beyond the plastic yield strength of the crust through further thinning or through faster spreading, the crust may react by brittle failure, and ocean opening with formation of laterally spreading ocean crust ensues. Delamination of cool and dense subcrustal mantle and subsequent subduction of this material does *not* trigger calc-alkalic volcanism of island-arc type as in the Wilson cycle model, since the subducted mantle is *dry* whereas normal oceanic crust is wet and, during subduction, releases water that lowers the melting temperature in the overlying mantle wedge. This fundamental difference between subcrustal delamination and ocean crust subduction may explain why calc-alkalic volcanic arc assemblages are rare or absent in virtually all Precambrian belts discussed in this paper. The lack of these subduction-related rocks in Phanerozoic belts such as the Alps and the Hercynian orogen may suggest that similar mechanisms operated during their evolution.

Houseman and others (1981) have suggested an alternative situation to trigger delamination of subcrustal lithosphere. In their model, delamination occurs during the stage of intracontinental crustal shortening where crustal thickening is accompanied by an equal amount of subcrustal lithospheric thickening. The relatively cold lower lithosphere is therefore pushed downward into warmer asthenosphere, thereby enhancing the gravitational instability between these two layers. This may eventually lead to rapid detachment and sinking of the thickened cold mantle layer with concomitant rise of asthenospheric material and subsequent heating of the lower crust now stripped from its insulating base. Although the starting conditions in the model of Houseman and others are different from those in the "geosynclinal" model proposed above, the effects are broadly comparable. In particular, the calculations and experiments of the above authors suggest that, for parameters typical of the earth, the entire process of delamination of subcrustal lithosphere and replacing it with hotter asthenosphere from below may occur in a time span of less than 50 Ma. Houseman and others (1981) have also shown that the descending dense mantle lithosphere is likely to draw neighboring portions of it into the asthenosphere, thereby exerting a pull on the entire lithospheric segment above and enhancing crustal shortening.

The effect of crustal shortening on the attenuated margins of the mature basin and its floor stripped of its strong mantle foundation enhances the likelihood of underthrusting and crustal interstacking during the following period of basin closure and orogeny (see Fig. 7). As argued above no oceanic crust is subducted and mantle-derived calc-alkalic arc magmatism does not occur. Instead, limited subduction of lower continental crust, still attached to the sinking subcrustal mantle lithosphere, may lead to crustal thickening and a first phase of orogenic uplift.

Subduction of continental crust (A- or Ampferer-subduction) has been rejected for many years as an unlikely process during orogeny (for example, Dewey and Bird, 1970; Burke and others, 1977), but it has now been demonstrated in the Himalayas (Bird, 1978) and in the Alps (Hsü, 1979). Molnar and Gray (1979) calculated that significant fractions of the lower continental crust up to several hundred kilometres in length may be subducted if lithospheric instability prevails (Fig. 5) and if they can become detached from the upper crust. Such detachment is likely during the delamination process proposed above, and A-subduction has now been accepted in principle, since it explains the apparent disappearance in depth of continental lithosphere under Phanerozoic and Precambrian fold-belts (Bally, 1981).

Crustal thickening through horizontal interstacking and thrusting involving both the basement and its overlying sediments has been reported from many Precambrian belts, and particularly convincing examples have been documented from the Labrador Trough of Canada (Dimroth, 1981) and the Pan-African Damara belt (Downing and Coward, 1981). Similar crustal shortening or thin-skinned tectonics in the Alps and in the Apennines has produced low-velocity channels that are interpreted as decoupling horizons (Hsü, 1979; Reutter and others, 1980). It is no surprise, therefore, that such low-velocity layers have now also been detected under part of the Damara belt of Namibia (Paier and Green, 1983). A schematic interpretation of basin closure through A-subduction is presented in Figure 9.

A prominent feature of many Precambrian belts is the polycyclic tectonothermal nature and long duration of orogenic evolution. In the Damara belt detailed geochronology suggests three thermal events over a period of 200 Ma (Kröner, 1982), revealing successively higher levels of crustal melting as crustal shortening proceeds (Hawkesworth and others, 1983). Such episodic heating and melting is in accord with the proposed intracontinental development. The early and often most intense periods of metamorphism and granite formation are probably still related to lower crustal heating after mantle delamination and asthenospheric spreading, since the total crust under the evolving orogen is still relatively thin when the attenuated crustal wedges of the former geosynclinal basin are now thrust under each other. Later, when shortening proceeds, the lower crust thickens and becomes increasingly isolated from the asthenospheric heat source below (Fig. 9), which also decays as the mantle plume degenerates or is left behind by the moving plate. Upper crustal temperatures are therefore likely to decline after the first thermal event. The later thermal events are likely to be caused by radioactive self-heating after crustal thickening during the earlier stage. Toksöz and Bird (1977) have calculated a minimum time of 40 Ma before self-heating due to tectonic thickening of continental crust significantly elevates the heat flow. In the Damara belt the second thermal event during orogeny occurred some 60 to 80 Ma after the first event and produced voluminous crustal-derived granitoid batholiths.

The geosynclinal sediments are subjected to compressive deformation during basin closure and crustal shortening, finally leading to high-level thrusting, imbrication, and nappe tectonics as observed in many Precambrian belts (Fig. 9). This evolution is comparable to Phanerozoic continental collision belts and may produce high-pressure metamorphic assemblages in zones of exceptionally high strain (Fig. 9). Crustal thickening has now reached a maximum and mountain building ensues. It is possible that

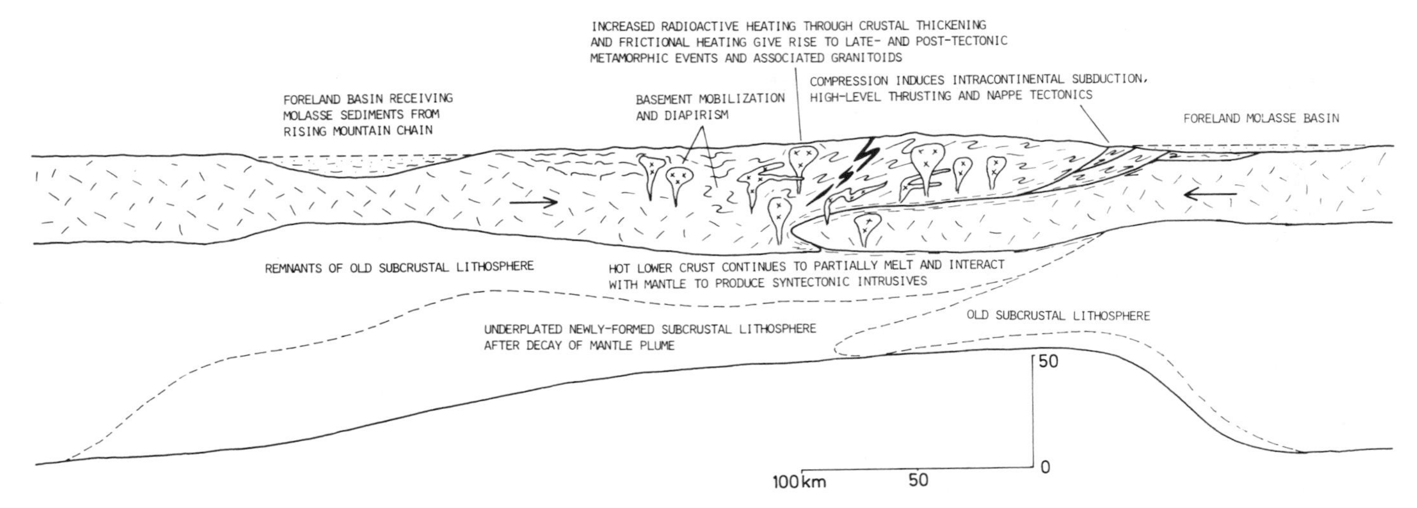

Figure 9. Simplified and schematic cross-section showing model of Proterozoic "ensialic" foldbelt resulting from horizontal crustal shortening, crustal interstacking, and closure of intracontinental geosynclinal basin. Note that no oceanic crust is subducted. Crustal thickening induces metamorphic events through radioactive self-heating. Fossil mantle lithosphere is underplated by juvenile lithosphere resulting from cooling of asthenosphere after decay of mantle plume or forward motion of plate. New mantle lithosphere under the foldbelt is thinner and less dense than old "cratonic" lithosphere, therefore keeping the region of the foldbelt mechanically weak and susceptible for further deformation.

continued horizontal shortening produces new intracrustal thrust zones similar to those developed in the Himalayas (Toksöz and Bird, 1977).

Radioactive self-heating reaches a maximum when maximum crustal thickness is attained and elevates the isotherms to the extent that surface heat flow is increased (Toksöz and Bird, 1977). If the rise of isotherms is fast compared with the rate of crustal uplift or erosion of the mountains, successively higher levels of the belt will be subjected to a further thermal event and to high crustal melting. This is again well documented in the Damara belt where widespread alaskitic granites and pegmatites with exceptionally high $^{87}Sr/^{86}Sr$ initial ratios attest to a final phase of upper crustal metamorphism and melting (Kröner, 1982; Hawkesworth and others, 1983).

The above discussion has shown that the entire complex depositional and orogenic evolution of many Precambrian foldbelts can be explained by the model of crustal thinning, subcrustal lithospheric delamination, and A-subduction and is therefore consistent with the limitations imposed by the paleomagnetic data and the observed rock record. A cartoon showing the graben-, delamination-, and A-subduction-stages is presented in Figure 10.

CONCLUSIONS

Proterozoic foldbelts older than about 1,000 Ma lack many of the distinctive signatures of the Wilson cycle, although many have been interpreted in terms of continental collision. Evolutionary models interpreting mafic volcanic rocks as remnants of ocean crust and calc-alkalic magmatic assemblages as the result of subduction-induced arc generation are persuasive on the basis of chemical data (for example, Hietanen, 1975) but are often either in disagreement with field relationships or cannot be proven on the basis of geological or geophysical criteria. There is no single recorded case of a sheeted dike complex older than about 800 Ma, thus direct evidence for ocean-floor spreading and concomitant subduction of oceanic crust is lacking. Even the often-cited mid-Proterozoic Wopmay orogen of the Canadian Shield (better known as the Coronation geosyncline, Hoffman, 1980) does not provide *geological* evidence for the operation of the Wilson cycle, that is, consumption of ocean floor, since it has been demonstrated above that both tholeiitic lavas as well as andesites and other calc-alkalic rocks can be generated in an ensialic environment.

It seems to be no coincidence that the evidence for Proterozoic ensialic orogeny, perhaps along the lines as suggested in this paper, is supported by the available paleomagnetic data (Dunlop, 1981; McWilliams, 1981), by the thermal history of the lithosphere (Baer, 1977; 1981; Lambert, 1981), and by isotopic results (Glikson, 1979).

The pattern of intraplate orogeny appears to change to an evolution dominated by plate margin processes towards the end of the Proterozoic, that is, the Wilson cycle of ocean opening and closing began operating at about 1,000 to 1,100 Ma ago and began to leave its characteristic signature in the rock record. Ophiolites with sheeted dike complexes appear, Andean-type and ensimatic volcanic arcs are clearly recognizable, glaucophane schists are found, and

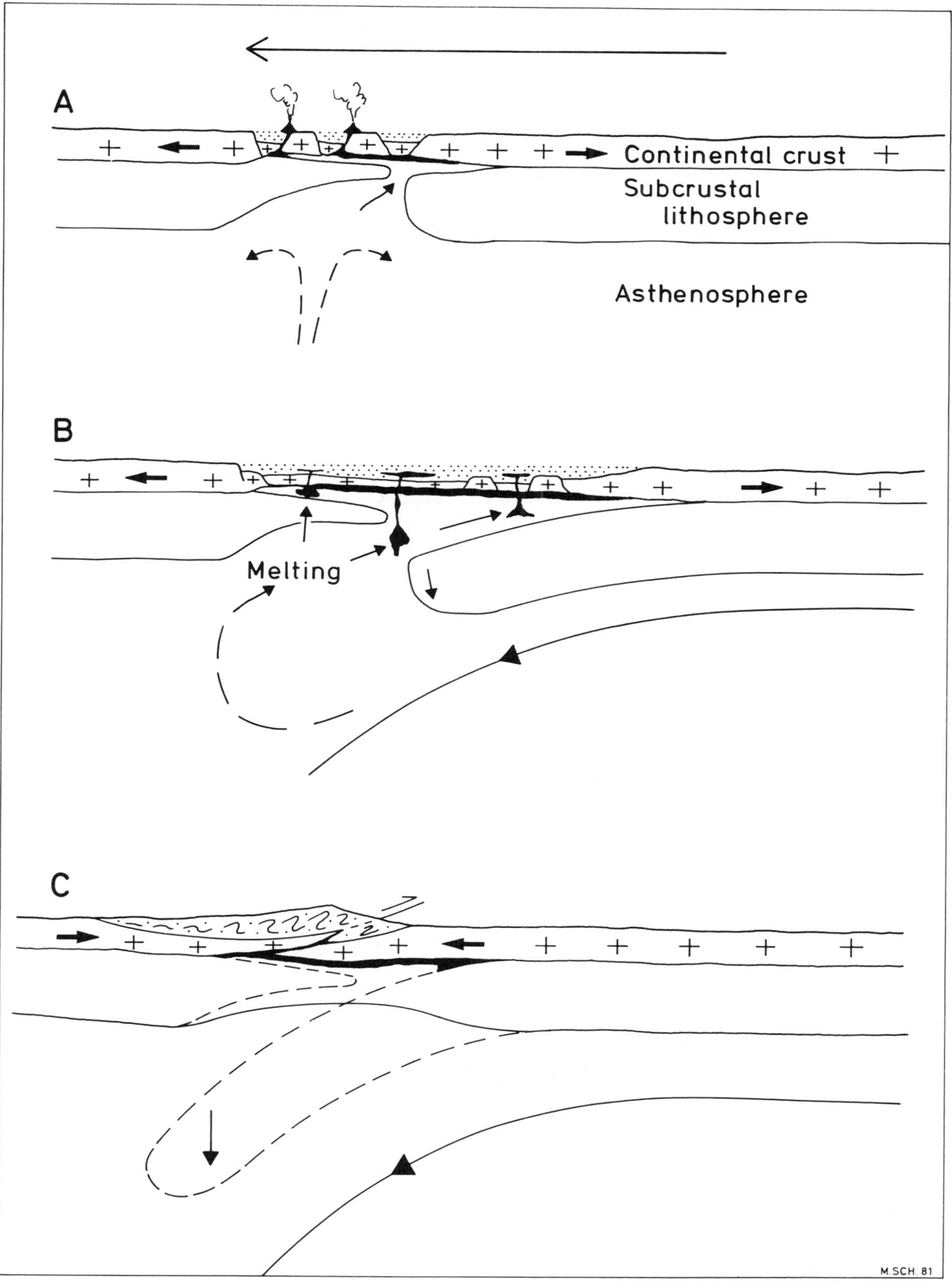

Figure 10. Cartoon depicting three stages in the evolution of an "ensialic" foldbelt through rifting, crustal stretching, delamination of mantle lithosphere, and crustal interstacking or A-subduction causing horizontal shortening and orogeny; modified after Kröner (1981a).

apparent polar wander paths begin to reveal continental collision events (Kröner, 1981b). These changes are accompanied by an apparent sharp increase in worldwide maximum metamorphic geotherms and a corresponding decrease in the minimum metamorphic geotherms (Grambling, 1981).

However, despite the increasing horizontal mobility, ensialic orogeny still continues in late Precambrian to Early Paleozoic times as shown by the evolution of the Damara belt in Africa and the Adelaide and Amadeus basins of Australia (McWilliams and Kröner, 1981), and it is contended that the model of delamination and A-subduction may also be appropriate to explain the evolution of Phanerozoic orogens such as the Pyrenees (Den Tex, 1979), the Hercynian belt (Zwart and Barnslepen, 1978), and the Alps (Hsü, 1979).

The model is entirely consistent with the concept of plate tectonics, that is, with the interaction of rigid lithospheric plates moving over a layer of viscous asthenosphere, since it explains ensialic orogenic belts as the result of limited horizontal motion but not involving entire plate separation and subsequent destruction of ocean crust by subduction. The fundamental difference to the modern Wilson cycle is that *dry* subcrustal lithosphere, as well as some continental crust, is subducted during orogeny rather than *wet* oceanic lithosphere, and that this results in a rock assemblage strikingly different from that of conventional plate collision. Ensialic orogeny and A-subduction, therefore, constitute one important variation of the plate tectonic scheme that may have dominated crustal evolution up to late Precambrian times. The increasing evidence for changes in the global style of plate interaction since Archean times (Kröner, 1981b; Goodwin, 1981) should help to combat the uniformitarian dogma that all orogenic belts are a direct consequence of Wilson cycle evolution and that the chemical result should be the formation of a new piece of continental crust (Allègre and Othman, 1980).

ACKNOWLEDGMENTS

This work was largely funded by the German Research Council. I thank P. Bird, C. Burchfiel, K. Burke (who strongly disagrees with the conclusions of the paper), W. Jacoby, and E. M. Moores for constructive criticism of the manuscript.

REFERENCES CITED

Allègre, C. J., and Ben Othman, D., 1980, Nd-Sr isotopic relationship in granitoid rocks and a continental crust development: A chemical approach to orogenesis: Nature, v. 286, p. 335–342.

Almeida, F.F.M., de, Hasui, Y., Brito-Neves, B. B. de, and Fuck, R. A., 1981, Brazilian structural provinces: An introduction: Earth-Science Reviews, v. 17, p. 1–30.

Baer, A. J., 1977, Speculations on the evolution of the lithosphere: Precambrian Research, v. 5, p. 249–260.

——— 1981, Geotherms, evolution of the lithosphere and plate tectonics: Tectonophysics, v. 72, p. 203–227.

Bally, A. W., 1981, Thoughts on the tectonics of folded belts, *in* McClay, K., and Price, N. J., eds., Trust and nappe tectonics: Geological Society of London, Special Publication 9, p. 13–32.

Baragar, W.R.A., and Scoates, R.F.J., 1981, The Circum-Superior belt: A Proterozoic plate margin? *in* Kröner, A., ed., Precambrian plate tectonics: Amsterdam, Elsevier, p. 297–330.

Bird, P., 1978, Initiation of intracontinental subduction in the Himalaya: Journal of Geophysical Research, v. 83, p. 4975–4987.

—— 1979, Continental delamination and the Colorado Plateau: Journal of Geophysical Research, v. 84, p. 7561–7571.

Bird, P., and Baumgardner, J., 1981, Steady propagation of delamination events: Journal of Geophysical Research, v. 86, p. 4891–4903.

Black, R., Bamako, H. B., Bertrand, J. M., Boullier, A. M., Caby, R., Davison, I., Fabre, J., Leblanc, M., and Wright, L., 1979, Outline of the Pan-African geology of Adrar des Iforas (Republic of Mali): Geologische Rundschau, v. 68, p. 543–564.

Bott, M.H.P., 1971, Evolution of young continental margins and formation of shelf basins: Tectonophysics, v. 11, p. 319–327.

Brooks, C., and Hart, S. R., 1978, Rb-Sr mantle isochrons and variations in the chemistry of Gondwanaland's lithosphere: Nature, v. 271, p. 220–223.

Burke, L., Dewey, J. F., and Kidd, W.S.F., 1976a, Precambrian palaeomagnetic results compatible with contemporary operation of the Wilson cycle: Tectonophysics, v. 33, p. 287–299.

—— 1976b, Dominance of horizontal movements, arc and microcontinental collisions during the later permobile regime, *in* Windley, B. F., ed., The early history of the Earth: London, Wiley & Sons, p. 113–129.

—— 1977, World distribution of sutures—the sites of former oceans: Tectonophysics, v. 40, p. 69–100.

Caby, R., Bertrand, J.M.L., and Black, R., 1981, Pan-African ocean closure and continental collision in the Hoggar-Iforas segment, central Sahara, *in* Kröner, A., ed., Precambrian plate tectonics: Amsterdam, Elsevier, p. 407–434.

Cahen, L., 1970, Igneous activity and mineralization episodes in the evolution of the Kibaride and Katangide orogenic belts of central Africa, *in* Clifford, T. N., and Gass, I. G., eds., African magmatism and tectonics: Edinburgh, Oliver & Boyd, p. 97–117.

—— 1980, La stratigraphie et la tectonique du Supergroupe Ouest-Congolien dans les zones mediane et externe de l'orogène Ouest-Congolien (Pan-Africain) au Bas-Zaire et dans les regions voisines: Tervuren, Belgium, Annales du Musée Royal de l'Afriue Centrale, Série in-8, Sciences Geologiques, no. 83, 150 p.

Cahen, L., and Lepersonne, J., 1967, The Precambrian of the Congo, Ruanda, and Burundi, *in* Rankama, K., ed., The Precambrian, v. 3: London, Interscience Publications, p. 143–290.

Cahen, L., Delhal, J., and Deutsch, S., 1972, A comparison of the ages of granites of S. W. Uganda with those of the Kibaran of central Shaba: Tervuren, Belgium, Annales du Musée Royal de l'Afrique Centrale, Série in-8, Sciences Géologiques, no. 73, p. 45–67.

Charpal, O. de, Guennoc, P., Montadert, L., and Roberts, D. G., 1978, Rifting, crustal attenuation and subsidence in the Bay of Biscay: Nature, v. 275, p. 706–711.

Condie, K. C., 1981, Archean greenstone belts: Amsterdam, Elsevier, 550 p.

Den Tex, E., 1979, A pre-Variscan continental rift system in NW Spain: Krystallinikum, v. 14, p. 19–31.

De Paepe, P., Hertogen, J., and Tack, L., 1975, Mise en évidence de laves en coussins dans les faciès volcaniques basiques du massif de Kimbungu (Bas Zaire) et implications pour le magmatisme Ouest-Congolien: Annales de la Société Géologique de Belgique, v. 98, p. 251–270.

Dewey, J. F., and Bird, J. M., 1970, Mountain belts and the new global tectonics: Journal of Geophysical Research, v. 75, p. 2625–2647.

Dimroth, E., 1981, Labrador geosyncline: Type example of early Proterozoic cratonic reactivation, *in* Kröner, A., ed., Precambrian plate tectonics: Amsterdam, Elsevier, p. 331–352.

Downing, K., and Coward, M. P., 1981, The Okahandja lineament and its significance for Damaran tectonics in Namibia: Geologische Rundschau, v. 70, 972–1000.

Drysdall, A. R., Johnson, R. L., Moore, T. A., and Thieme, J. G., 1972, Outline of the geology of Zambia: Geologie en Mijnbouw, v. 51, p. 265–276.

Dunlop, D. J., 1981, Palaeomagnetic evidence for Proterozoic continental development: Royal Society of London Philosophical Transactions, v. A301, p. 265–277.

Eaton, G. P., 1979, A plate-tectonic model for late Cenozoic crustal spreading in the western United States, *in* Riecker, R. E., ed., Rio Grande Rift: Tectonics and magmatism: American Geophysical Union, p. 7–32.

El-Bayoumi, R. M., 1980, Ophiolites and associated rocks of Wadi Ghadir, east of Gebel Zabara, Eastern Desert, Egypt [Ph.D. thesis]: University of Cairo, Egypt, 227 p.

Engel, A.E.J., Dixon, T. H., and Stern, R. J., 1980, Late Precambrian evolution of Afro-Arabian crust from ocean arc to craton: Geological Society of America Bulletin, Part I, v. 91, p. 699–706.

Fleck, R. J., Greenwood, W. R., Hadley, D. G., Anderson, R. E., and Schmidt, D. L., 1979, Rubidium-strontium geochronology and plate tectonic evolution of the southern part of the Arabian shield: U.S. Geological Survey Saudi Arabian Project Report 245, 105 p.

Frisch, W., and Al-Shanti, A., 1977, Ophiolite belts and the collision of island arcs in the Arabian shield: Tectonophysics, v. 43, p. 293–306.

Garson, M. S., and Shalaby, I. M., 1976, Precambrian-Lower Paleozoic plate tectonics and metallogenesis in the Red Sea region: Geological Association of Canada, Special Paper 14, p. 573–596.

Gass, I. G., 1981, Pan-African (Upper Proterozoic) plate tectonics of the Arabian-Nubian shield, *in* Kröner, A., ed., Precambrian plate tectonics: Amsterdam, Elsevier, p. 387–405.

Glikson, A. Y., 1979, The missing Precambrian crust: Geology, v. 7, p. 449–454.

Goodwin, A. M., 1981, Precambrian perspectives: Science, v. 213, p. 55–61.

Grambling, J. A., 1981, Pressures and temperatures in Precambrian metamorphic rocks: Earth and Planetary Science Letters, v. 53, p. 63–68.

Green, A. G., 1981, Results of a seismic reflection survey across the fault zone between the Thompson nickel belt and the Churchill tectonic province, northern Manitoba: Canadian Journal of Earth Sciences, v. 18, p. 13–25.

Green, D. H., 1981, Petrogenesis of Archaean ultramafic magmas and implications for Archaean tectonics, *in* Kröner, A., ed., Precambrian plate tectonics: Amsterdam, Elsevier, p. 469–489.

Greenwood, W. R., Hadley, D. G., Anderson, R. E., Fleck, R. J., and Schmidt, D. L., 1976, Late Proterozoic cratonization in southwestern Saudi Arabia: Royal Society of London Philosophical Transactions, ser. A, v. 280, p. 517–527.

Hanson, G. N., 1981, Geochemical constraints for early crustal development: Royal Society of London Philosophical Transactions, ser. A, v. 301, p. 423–442.

Hanson, R. E., and Al-Shaieb, Z., 1980, Voluminous subalkaline silicic magmas related to intracontinental rifting in the southern Oklahoma aulacogen: Geology, v. 8, p. 180–184.

Hargraves, R. B., 1981, Precambrian tectonic style: A liberal uniformitarian interpretation, *in* Kröner, A., ed., Precambrian plate tectonics: Amsterdam, Elsevier, p. 21–56.

Harris, A. L., Baldwin, C. T., Bradbury, H. J., Johnson, H. D., and Smith, R. A., 1978, Ensialic basin sedimentation: The Dalradian Supergroup, *in* Bowes, D. R., and Leake, B. E., eds., Crustal evolution in northwestern Britain and adjacent regions: Liverpool, Geological Journal Special Issue 10, Seel House Press, p. 115–138.

Hawkesworth, C. J., Gledhill, A. R., Roddick, J. C., Miller, R. McG., and Kröner, A., 1983, Rb/Sr and $^{40}Ar/^{39}Ar$ studies bearing on models for the thermal evolution of the Damara belt, Namibia, *in* Miller, R. McG. ed., Geodynamic evolution of the Damara orogen: Geological Society of South Africa, Special volume (in press).

Hietanen, A., 1975, Generation of potassium-poor magmas in the southern Sierra Nevada and the Svecofennian of Finland: U.S. Geological Survey Journal of Research, v. 3, p. 631–645.

Hoffmann, P. F., 1980, Wopmay orogen: A Wilson cycle of early Proterozoic age in the northwest of the Canadian shield: Geological Association of Canada, Special Paper 20, p. 523–549.

Horwitz, R. C., and Smith, R. E., 1978, Bridging the Yilgarn and Pilbara blocks, Western Australia: Precambrian Research, v. 6, p. 293–322.

Houseman, G. A., McKenzie, D. P., and Molnar, P., 1981, Convective instability of a thickened boundary layer and its relevance for the thermal evolution of continental convergent belts: Journal of Geophysical Research, v. 86, p. 6115–6123.

Hsü, K., 1979, Thin-skinned plate tectonics during neo-alpine orogenesis: American Journal of Science, v. 279, p. 353–366.

Hurley, P. M., 1972, Can the subduction process of mountain building be extended to Pan-African and similar orogenic belts?: Earth and Planetary Science Letters, v. 15, p. 305–314.

Hussein, I. M., Kröner, A., and Dürr, S., 1982, Wadi Onib—a dismembered Pan-African ophiolite in the Red Sea Hills of the Sudan [abs.]: Precambrian Research, v. 17, p. 49.

Jordan, T. H., 1979, The deep structure of the continents: Scientific American, v. 240, p. 70–82.

Kazmin, V., Shifferaw, A., and Balcha, T., 1978, The Ethiopian basement: Stratigraphy and possible manner of evolution: Geologische Rundschau, v. 67, p. 531–546.

Kröner, A., 1977a, The Precambrian geotectonic evolution of Africa: Plate accretion versus plate destruction: Precambrian Research, v. 4, p. 163–213.

——1977b, Precambrian mobile belts of southern and eastern Africa—ancient sutures or sites of ensialic mobility? A case for crustal evolution towards plate tectonics: Tectonophysics, v. 40, p. 101–135.

——1979a, Pan African plate tectonics and its repercussions on the crust of northeast Africa: Geologische Rundschau, v. 68, p. 565–583.

——1979b, Pan African mobile belts as evidence for a transitional tectonic regime from intraplate orogeny to plate margin orogeny, *in* Tahoun, S. A., ed., Evolution and mineralization of the Arabian-Nubian shield, Volume 1: Oxford, Pergamon Press, p. 21–27.

——1980, Pan African crustal evolution: Episodes, v. 1980, no. 2, p. 3–8.

——1981a, Precambrian crustal evolution and continental drift: Geologische Rundschau, v. 70, p. 412–428.

——1981b, Precambrian plate tectonics, in Kröner, A., ed., Precambrian plate tectonics: Amsterdam, Elsevier, p. 57–90.

——1982, Rb-Sr geochronology and tectonic evolution of the Pan-African Damara belt of Namibia, southwestern Africa: American Journal of Science, v. 282, p. 1471–1507.

Lambert, R. St. J., 1981, Earth tectonics and thermal history: Review and a hot-spot model for the Archaean, *in* Kröner, A., ed., Precambrian plate tectonics: Amsterdam, Elsevier, p. 453–467.

Leblanc, M., 1981, The late Proterozoic ophiolites of Bou Azzer (Morocco): Evidence for Pan-African plate tectonics, *in* Kröner, A., ed.,

Precambrian plate tectonics: Amsterdam, Elsevier, p. 435–451.
Martin, H., 1965, The Precambrian geology of South West Africa and Namaqualand: Precambrian Research Unit, University of Cape Town, 159 p.
Martin, H., and Porada, H., 1977, The intracratonic branch of the Damara orogen in South West Africa: Precambrian Research, v. 5, p. 311–357.
McWilliams, M. O., 1981, Palaeomagnetism and Precambrian tectonic evolution of Gondwana, *in* Kröner, A., ed., Precambrian plate tectonics: Amsterdam, Elsevier, p. 649–687.
McWilliams, M. O., and Kröner, A., 1981, Paleomagnetism and tectonic evolution of the Pan-African Damara belt, southern Africa: Journal of Geophysical Research, v. 86, p. 5147–5162.
Molnar, P., and Gray, D., 1979, Subduction of continental lithosphere: Some constraints and uncertainties: Geology, v. 7, p. 58–62.
Molnar, P., and Tapponier, P., 1975, Cenozoic tectonics of Asia: Effects of a continental collision: Science, v. 189, p. 419–426.
Moorbath, S., 1977, Ages, isotopes and evolution of Precambrian continental crust: Chemical Geology, v. 20, p. 151–187.
Niemitz, J. W., and Bischoff, J. L., 1981, Tectonic elements of the southern part of the Gulf of California: Summary: Geological Society of America Bulletin, Part I, v. 92, p. 101–104.
O'Nions, R. K., and Clarke, D. B., 1972, Comparative trace element geochemistry of Tertiary basalts from Baffin Bay: Earth and Planetary Science Letters, v. 15, p. 436–446.
Paier, B., and Green, R., 1983, Crustal structure studies in central South West Africa, *in* Miller, R. McG., ed., Geodynamic evolution of the Damara orogen: Geological-Society of South Africa, Special volume (in press).
Phinney, R. A., and Jurdy, D. M., 1979, Seismic imaging of deep crust: Geophysics, v. 44, p. 1637–1660.
Plumb, K. A., 1979a, The tectonic evolution of Australia: Earth-Science Reviews, v. 14, p. 205–249.
—— 1979b, Structure and tectonic style of the Precambrian shields and platforms of northern Australia: Tectonophysics, v. 58, p. 291–325.
Ramsay, C. R., Jackson, N. J., and Roobol, M. J., 1979, Structural/lithological provinces in a Saudi Arabian shield geotraverse, *in* Tahoun, S. A., ed., Evolution and mineralization of the Arabian-Nubian shield, Volume 1: Oxford, Pergamon Press, p. 64–84.
Reutter, K.-J., Giese, P., and Closs, H., 1980, Lithospheric split in the descending plate: Observations from the northern Apennines: Tectonophysics, v. 64, p. T1–T9.
Rutland, R.W.R., 1976, Orogenic evolution of Australia: Earth-Science Reviews, v. 12, p. 161–196.
Rutland, R.W.R., Parker, A. J., Pitt, G. M., Preiss, W. V., and Murrell, B., 1981, The Precambrian of South Australia, *in* Hunter, D. R., ed., Precambrian of the southern hemisphere: Amsterdam, Elsevier, p. 169–187.
Sawyer, E., 1978, Damara structural and metamorphic geology of an area southeast of Walvis Bay, South West Africa/Namibia [M.Sc. thesis]: University of Cape Town, South Africa, 205 p.
Schmidt, D. L., Hadley, D. G., and Stoeser, D. B., 1979, Late Proterozoic crustal history of the Arabian shield, southern Najd Province, Kingdom of Saudi Arabia, *in* Tahoun, S. A., ed., Evolution and mineralization of the Arabian-Nubian shield, Volume 2: Oxford, Pergamon Press, p. 41–58.
Shackleton, R. M., 1973, Correlation of structures across Precambrian orogenic belts in Africa, *in* Tarling, D. H., and Runcorn, S. K., eds., Implications of continental drift to the earth sciences, Volume 2: London, Academic Press, p. 1091–1095.
—— 1976, Possible late Precambrian ophiolites in Africa and Brazil: 20th Annual Report, Research Institute of African Geology, University of Leeds, p. 3–7.
Shackleton, R. M., Ries, A. C., Graham, R. H., and Fitches, W. R., 1980, Late Precambrian ophiolitic mélange in the Eastern Desert of Egypt: Nature, v. 285, p. 472–474.
Shackleton, R. M., Ries, A. C., Fitches, W. R., and Graham, R. H., 1981, Late Proterozoic tectonics of NE Africa: Abstract-volume, 11th Collection of African Geology, Open University, Milton Keynes, p. 13.
Spohn, T., and Schubert, G., 1982, Convective thinning of the lithosphere: A mechanism for the initiation of continental rifting: Journal of Geophysical Research, v. 87, p. 4669–4681.
Smithson, S. B., and Brown, S. K., 1977, A model for lower continental crust: Earth and Planetary Science Letters, v. 35, p. 134–144.
Stanton, W. I., Schermerhorn, L.J.G., and Korpershoek, H. R., 1972, The West Congo System: Boletim dos Servicas de Geologia e Minas de Angola, no. 8, p. 69–78.
Stewart, J. H., 1971, Basin and Range structure: A system of horsts and grabens produced by deep-seated extension: Geological Society of America Bulletin, v. 82, p. 1019–1044.
Sutton, J., 1977, Some consequences of horizontal displacements in the Precambrian: Tectonophysics, v. 40, p. 161–181.
Toksöz, M. N., and Bird, P., 1977, Modelling of temperatures in continental convergence zones: Tectonophysics, v. 41, p. 181–193.
Toksöz, M. N., Chinnery, M. A., and Anderson, D. L., 1967, Inhomogeneities in the Earth's mantle: Geophysical Journal of the Royal Astronomical Society, v. 13, p. 13–59.
Vernon-Chamberlain, V. E., and Snelling, N. J., 1972, Age and isotopic studies on the Arena granites of S.W. Uganda: Tervuren, Belgium, Annales du Musée Royal de l'Afrique Centrale, Série in-8, Sciences Géologiques, no. 73, p. 1–44.
Windley, B. F., 1981, Precambrian rocks in the light of the plate-tectonic concept, *in* Kröner, A., ed., Precambrian plate tectonics: Amsterdam, Elsevier, p. 1–20.
Withjack, M., 1979, A convective heat transfer model for lithospheric thinning and crustal uplift: Journal of Geophysical Research, v. 84, p. 3008–3022.
Woodward, L. A., 1977, Rate of crustal extension across the Rio Grande Rift near Albuquerque, New Mexico: Geology, v. 5, p. 269–272.
Wynne-Edwards, H. R., and Hasan, Z., 1970, Intersecting orogenic belts across the North Atlantic: American Journal of Science, v. 268, p. 189–208.
Zorin, Y. A., 1981, The Baikal rift: An example of the intrusion of asthenospheric material into the lithosphere as the cause of disruption of lithospheric plates: Tectonophysics, v. 73, p. 91–104.
Zwart, H. J., and Dornsiepen, U. F., 1978, The tectonic framework of central and western Europe: Geologie en Mijnbouw, v. 57, p. 627–654.

Manuscript Accepted by the Society April 14, 1983

Printed in U.S.A.

Geological Society of America
Memoir 161
1983

A Wilson Cycle approach to some Proterozoic problems in eastern North America

Susan L. Anderson*
Kevin Burke**
Department of Geological Sciences
State University of New York at Albany
1400 Washington Avenue
Albany, New York 12222

ABSTRACT

Plate tectonic interpretations are commonly used for Phanerozoic tectonic features, but there are still differences of opinion regarding the best model for Proterozoic tectonic features. We suggest that it will be more fruitful to apply the plate model as used in Phanerozoic examples than to build a special model based only on Proterozoic data, or to decide *ad hoc* what modifications of the plate model may be necessary. As a stimulus for discussion and further work we present plate tectonic interpretations for three widely discussed problems in the Proterozoic terranes of eastern North America: the search for a Grenville suture, the relationship between the Grenville orogeny and Keweenawan rifting, and possible relationships between the Labrador Fold Belt and the Canadian Southern Province. We emphasize the separate stages of the Wilson Cycle of ocean opening and closing; examine some of the available data appropriate for plate tectonic interpretations, particularly isotopic dates; and point out new avenues of investigation suggested by the model.

INTRODUCTION

The Proterozoic Era (approximately 600 to 2600 m.y. ago) is intermediate between the Archean, in which the major tectonic features are greeenstone and gneiss belts, and the Phanerozoic, in which tectonic activity is primarily confined to the margins of large continents. The plate tectonic model has been widely applied to the Phanerozoic Era, and explains major tectonic features as the results of the Wilson Cycle (Dewey and Burke, 1974) of ocean opening and closing. Because of the conspicuous large-scale differences between Archean and Phanerozoic terranes and because of expected differences in the thermal budget and internal structure of the Earth earlier in its history, other tectonic models have been used for the Archean. Unfortunately, these models have included some that were originally developed using Phanerozoic evidence and then rejected for that era in favor of the plate model. However, some geologists have successfully adapted the plate tectonic model even to Archean examples, emphasizing the role of subduction and the formation and collision of island arcs (see, for example, Burke and others, 1976a; Tarney and others, 1976).

As a result of the differences of opinion regarding the best model for the tectonics of the Archean, the choice of models for the Proterozoic is rather broad. If a nonplate model is selected for the Archean, then for the Proterozoic one could use the same plate tectonic model used for the Phanerozoic, or the nonplate model chosen for the Archean, or a transitional model between these two. If a version of the plate model is used for the Archean, then one could also use that for the Proterozoic or use a transitional model between that and the Phanerozoic plate model.

We suggest that the most fruitful approach to the tec-

*Current address: New York State Geological Survey, Room 3136, CEC, Albany, NY 12230.
**Current address: Lunar and Planetary Institute, 3303 NASA Road 1, Houston, TX 77058.

tonics of the Proterozoic would be to test the plate model by beginning with the same form of the model used for the Phanerozoic. This approach would provide maximum access to analogies with Phanerozoic examples, where the plate model has been tested extensively on a broad variety of tectonic features. These include many that have not been truncated, overprinted, or disrupted by later tectonic events, as is unfortunately the case for most Proterozoic and Archean tectonic features. The alternatives are to build from scratch a special model based only on tectonic features in Archean and Proterozoic regions, or to make *ad hoc* assumptions about what modifications of the plate model might be required. We believe that it may actually be easier to detect weaknesses of the plate model for the Proterozoic, or modifications that might be needed, by applying the model directly and seeing whether this produces consistent analyses.

As a stimulus for discussion and further work, we suggest plate tectonic interpretations, emphasizing the Wilson Cycle of ocean opening and closing, for three widely discussed problems in the Proterozoic terranes of eastern North America:

1. The search for a Grenville suture;
2. The relationship between the Grenville orogeny and Keweenawan rifting; and
3. Possible relationships between the Labrador Fold Belt and the Canadian Southern Province.

We examine some of the available data appropriate for a plate model analysis, particularly isotopic dates, and point out some questions and approaches that are suggested by the plate model.

SEARCH FOR A GRENVILLE SUTURE

Introduction

The Canadian Grenville Province as defined by Stockwell (1964) is that part of eastern Canada dominated by isotopic dates of approximately 950 ± 150 m.y. This area was strongly affected by ductile deformation, intermediate to acidic igneous intrusion, and high-grade regional mettamorphism, all attributed to the Grenville orogeny; it constitutes nearly all of the exposed area in North America where that orogenic event has been recognized. Additional portions of the presumed Grenville orogenic belt include the Adirondack massif and several linear zones within the Appalachian orogenic belt, such as the Long Range of Newfoundland and the Blue Ridge of the southern Appalachians. In addition, correlations have been suggested between the Grenville rocks of Canada and the Late Precambrian rocks of the Llano uplift of Texas (Zartman, 1964); the Gardar province of southern Greenland (Bridgewater, 1965); rocks in the Moine of Scotland (Brook and others, 1976); northwest Ireland (Max, 1979); the Rockall Bank (Miller and others, 1973); parts of the Baltic, Ukranian, and Aldan shields (see summaries by Burwash, 1969; Max, 1979); and rocks in southern Europe and North Africa (Young, 1980). These correlations are made almost exclusively on the basis of isotopic dates. Because of repeated Phanerozoic rifting and orogeny in and near many of these areas, the full extent of the presumed Grenville orogenic belt is not known, nor are the relative positions in the late Proterozoic of all the smaller areas that have been correlated with Canadian Grenville rocks.

Some geologists have used Stockwell's (1964) date range as the time of the Grenville orogeny, but the dates on which that range was based are nearly all K-Ar dates, primarily from biotite and whole-rock samples. These are now understood to be cooling ages, set well after the peak of the period of deformation and regional metamorphism; so Rb-Sr and U-Pb dates have more recently been used to date the thermal peak of metamorphism and the time of widespread igneous activity. Wynne Edwards (1972) suggested that a reasonable mean date for the peak of the Grenville orogeny is 1200 m.y., with a range from 1170 to 1250 m.y. Recently, there have been several suggestions that deformation, igneous activity, and regional metamorphism previously attributed to a single Grenville event may be the product of at least two separate tectonic events. Some of these suggestions are based on statistical studies of available dates (Baer, 1981; Douglas, 1980), but these present no general agreement on the times or geographic extents of these events. Moore and Thompson (1980) combined geologic field evidence and U-Pb zircon concordia and Rb-Sr whole-rock isochron dates to suggest that two events can be distinguished in southern Ontario: the Elzevirian Orogeny (1225 to 1100 m.y. ago) and the Ottawan Orogeny (1050 to 1000 m.y. ago).

In terms of the Phanerozoic Wilson Cycle model, large regions of intermediate to acidic igneous intrusions into older continental crust, ductile deformation, and high-grade regional metamorphism can be generated in two large-scale tectonic settings: continental margins under which subduction of oceanic crust takes place (Andes and Altiplano of South America) and zones of continent-continent collision (Himalaya and Tibetan Plateau). Both settings are dominated by convergent structural style, with strong folding, development of foliation, and zones of thrusting. In both settings it is possible to develop continental crust as much as 60 km thick, as was apparently the case in parts of the Grenville Province in Canada and the Adirondacks, judging from paleopressure estimates obtained from peak metamorphic mineral assemblages in rocks now exposed at the surface (Brown and others, 1978; Putman and Sullivan, 1979; Bohlen and Boettcher, 1980; Klein, 1980).

Dewey and Burke (1973) suggested that Grenville-age igneous activity, deformation, and metamorphism were results of continent-continent collision, and that the synorogenic high-potash plutons in the Adirondacks and Canadian Grenville Province are tectonically analogous with the high-potash volcanic rocks of Tibet. They suggested that the suture between the tectonically reactivated edge of Archean Laurentia and the other continent involved in the collision would be southeast of the Tibet-like region, and possibly overprinted by Paleozoic orogenic events or even removed by rifting from present North America.

Following the discussion by Dewey and Burke (1973), several attempts have been made to define the location of the expected Grenville suture. Some of these candidate sutures have been based on regional-scale data, usually geophysical, and others extrapolated from or interpolated between small areas containing geologic or geophysical information. Still others have been defined only for small areas; this modest objective may be the most reasonable at this time considering the shortage of detailed mapping, disagreement about the applicability of the continent-continent collision model, and disagreement about how many sutures to expect.

It is important to consider how a Grenville suture, if it exists, could be recognized. The question actually consists of two parts:

1. How to recognize a suture; and
2. How to demonstrate that it was formed during the Grenville tectonic event.

A suture is the boundary surface or zone between two continental blocks that were once separated by oceanic lithosphere and which had separate geologic histories before the events leading up to their collision. It should not be possible to trace any precollision geologic feature from one block across the suture and into the other block. Ideally, isotopic dates within the blocks, away from the suture, will be distinctly different, but this may not always be true. The suture will lie within the belt of deformation and metamorphism generated during the approach and collision of the two continents. The ductile deformation, igneous activity, and metamorphism developed during this orogeny can be expected to obscure features that might be used to determine the extent of each continental block into the orogenic belt up to the suture.

The suture surface itself may not be a major feature in terms of thickness, or unique structures or lithologies, and can be expected to vary in character and orientation along the strike and dip of the surface. The surface will probably not be a smooth plane, and its map trace may not be a straight line, in part because of the expected initial irregular outlines of the continental blocks. Because of mechanical contrasts between the two continental blocks, the suture surface will probably be a zone of high strain; but not every mylonitic or cataclastic zone in an orogenic belt must represent a suture. Because the suture occupies a position between the two continental blocks that was once occupied by oceanic lithosphere, remnants of that oceanic material may be found in the suture zone, in the form of an ophiolite sequence or deformed and metamorphosed mafic and ultramafic rocks derived from fragments of oceanic crust and mantle, possibly visible only as a smear of fuchsite (Burke and others, 1977). Well-preserved, intact ophiolite sequences are rare even in documented Phanerozoic zones of continent-continent collision, and a thin band of deformed and metamorphosed remnants could have been overlooked in the Grenville orogenic belt, considering that most of the Canadian Grenville Province has been mapped only on reconnaissance scale (Davidson and others, 1979).

It may be possible to define a broad zone in which the suture must exist, by independently determining the extent of one of the continents into the orogenic belt, as by tracing some precollision structure, lithology, or characteristic isotopic date range into the belt from one side. It may also be possible to define the edge of one or both blocks at some stage before the collision, for example, by recognizing metamorphosed rocks derived from continental shelf, slope and rise sediments deposited on the precollision continental margin at a time when it was a passive, Atlantic-type rifted margin. It may also be possible to recognize an island arc or Andean arc developed along one side of the ocean during subduction that consumed the intervening oceanic lithosphere and preceded the continent-continent collision.

One point that deserves emphasis is that a suture should not be proclaimed on the basis of a single criterion. The geological character of the candidate suture and its surroundings should be consistent with the effects on facing continental margins of the whole sequence of Wilson Cycle stages preceding and including the continent-continent collision.

The second part of the question regarding a candidate Grenville suture is how to prove that it formed as a result of the Grenville orogeny, rather than during some earlier collision. One approach is to ask how many pre-Grenville sutures, or features that might resemble sutures, might be expected within the Grenville orogenic belt. Another is to ask how many "Grenville" sutures might exist, considering the recent proposals of more than one episode of deformation and metamorphism within the time range previously assigned to a single Grenville event. For several reasons, it will be difficult to answer these questions. One serious problem is that, as shown in the India-Asia collision, deformation and metamorphism associated with a continent-continent collision do not terminate in any one part of the orogenic belt when all of the oceanic lithosphere in that sector has been subducted or obducted. Deformation, crustal thickening, igneous activity, and metamorphism continue after initial establishment of the suture. As a result, even a Grenville suture would have been further deformed by the Grenville orogeny. Pre-Grenville sutures overprinted by Grenville-age deformation and metamorphism might not appear to be significantly more deformed than a Grenville suture.

Pre-Grenville sutures might well exist inside the Grenville orogenic belt. At least two areas affected by middle Proterozoic deformation, igneous activity, and metamorphism, perhaps also due to continent-continent collisions, can be traced into the Grenville Province from the northwest: the Southern Province and the Labrador Fold Belt. Their extent into the Grenville Province is not well established, and the positions for candidate sutures for these presumed orogenies have not been defined. In addition, Archean rocks of the Superior Province, including greenstone belts, have been traced into the Grenville Province. Dalziel, among others, has proposed that many of the features of Archean terranes are the result of successive island arc collisions, so these areas can be expected to also contain some of the characteristics found in continent-continent collision zones. Any candidate for a Grenville suture should be carefully examined to determine whether it can be traced into a possible pre-Grenville suture zone.

Another problem is that the absence of chronologically useful fossils in Precambrian rocks leads to a greater dependence on isotopic dates than in Phanerozoic terranes. Numerous isotopic dates are available from the Grenville orogenic belt in North America, but they are sparse in some critical areas and not always appropriate for dating a particular stage of the Wilson Cycle. K-Ar mineral dates were set during late-Grenville cooling, as were Rb-Sr mineral isochron dates. Rb-Sr whole-rock isochron dates might give the time of the peak of Grenville metamorphism but might also represent partially reset dates of some previous metamorphic or igneous event. U-Pb zircon concordia dates provide the time of original crystallization but would date the Grenville orogeny only if obtained from synorogenic igneous rocks. Zircons are sparse in the mafic and ultramafic rocks of oceanic lithosphere and island arcs, so this method might not be feasible for some of the rock types of greatest interest in or near a candidate suture zone.

Proposed Sutures Based on Large-Scale Data

Irving and others (1974) found that a path of apparent polar wander derived from several sites in the Canadian Grenville Province did not match the path for the main body of North America from 1300 to 1000 m.y. ago. They proposed that "Grenvillia" and "Interior Laurentia" rifted apart 1300 m.y. ago, Keweenawan volcanism and Grenville regional metamorphism took place while they were apart, and "Grenvillia" rejoined North America 1000 m.y. ago. The suture marking that reunion ought to lie between sample sites that defined the two paths for the time that the regions were apart, in the broad zone down the middle of the Canadian Grenville Province shown in Figure 1A. This scenario was revised by Irving and McGlynn (1976), who recognized that the "Grenvillia" magnetizations and the isotopic dates used to assign them positions in the polar wander path were probably set during cooling, after the peak of regional metamorphism that resulted from the postulated collision. Given that, it seems even odder that these magnetizations indicate a wide separation between "Grenvillia" and "Interior Laurentia" *after* the collision. The problem may be due to a shortage of pole positions from "Interior Laurentia" for the critical time interval, so that ". . .the Grenville poles may record the geomagnetic field for an interval that is not represented in the existing paleomagnetic record for Interior Laurentia, and form a part of the general path for Laurentia" (Irving and McGlynn, 1976, p. 459). In any case, as pointed out by Burke and others (1976b) and McWilliams and Dunlop (1978), rocks affected by high-grade metamorphism during the Grenville orogeny cannot be expected to record precollision polar wander paths, so they cannot be used to define the location of a Grenville suture.

Following the lead of Irving and others (1974), Thomas and Tanner (1975) sought the Grenville suture northwest of the sample sites for the "Grenvillia" polar wander path. Their candidate, shown in Figure 1B, lies along the southeast edge of a negative Bouguer gravity anomaly that is mainly inside the Grenville Province and follows the Grenville Front for 1200 km, from Lake Mistassini to the Labrador coast. They explained the anomaly as the result of downwarping of the edge of the Superior Province crust, and the steep gradient on the southeast side of the anomaly as the signature of a sharp contact with Grenville crust of higher density and greater thickness. Unfortunately, as shown in their own Figure 1(a), this line cuts through an area that Irving and others (1974) considered out of bounds for the Grenville suture because Superior Province lithologies can be recognized at least that far beyond the Grenville Front. The line also passes through an area in which Gastil and Knowles (1960) and Dimroth and others (1970) were able to trace Labrador Fold Belt lithologies into the Grenville Province, as shown in Figure 1B. These problems could be alleviated by moving the line a few kilometers to the southeast, but that might prove to be only a temporary solution as further detailed mapping can be expected to trace the lithologies farther into the Grenville Province. What is needed is positive evidence that this line divides distinct lithologies and that the suture was made by a Grenville collision rather than some earlier event. In this regard, it may be significant that the line separates the anorthosite massifs of Labrador from similar bodies within the Grenville Province, many of which give Rb-Sr whole-rock isochron dates in the range 1300 to 1500 m.y.

Sutures Constructed by Interpolation or Extrapolation

Dorr and Laurin (1971) mapped the locations of sev-

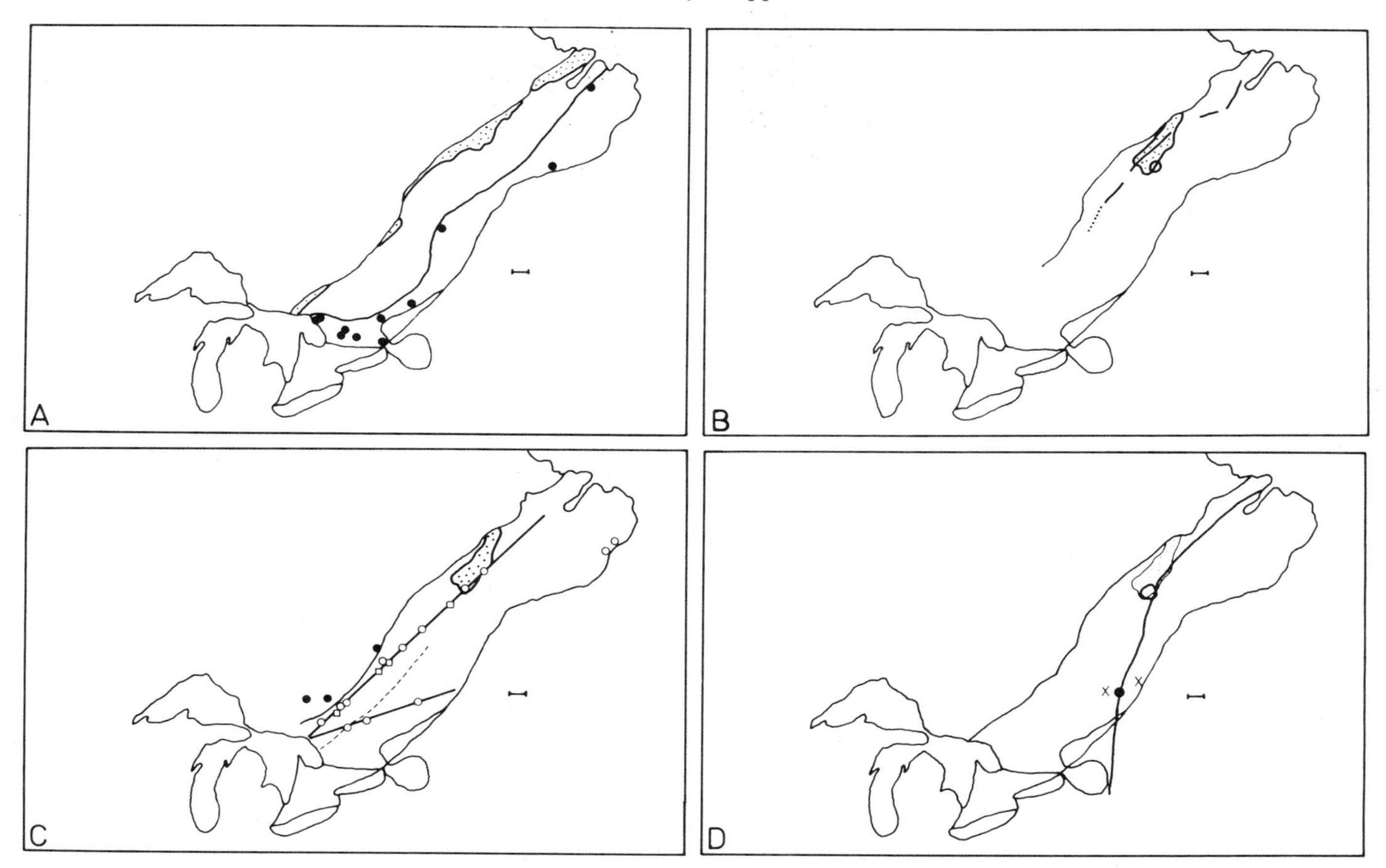

Figure 1. Proposed Grenville sutures. The Grenville Front is as shown in each reference. The scale bar is 100 km long. (A): Irving and others (1974). Stippled areas show the extent of older rocks southeast of the Grenville Front; solid circles are sample sites for "Grenvillia" paleopoles. The suture must be in the blank area. (B): Thomas and Tanner (1975). Line segments are along the southeast edge of a negative Bouguer gravity anomaly. The dotted extension to the southwest is based on aeromagnetic anomaly patterns. The circle is the Manicouagan impact feature. The stippled area is the extension of Labrador Trough lithologies into the Grenville orogen, after Dimroth and others (1970). (C): Dorr and Laurin (1971). Open circles are deposits associated with circular structures; open squares are deposits not associated with such structures; solid circles, northeast to southwest, are Chibougamau, Val d'Or, and Noranda-Rouyn. Stippled area is the same as in B. Dashed line is the southeast limit of Rb-Sr whole-rock isochron dates greater than 2000 m.y. (D): Rondot (1978). Solid circle is the proposed ophiolite at Saint-Maurice. Two X's are anorthosite bodies with apparently different strain histories. Large circle is the Manicouagan impact feature.

enteen copper-nickel sulfide deposits in mafic and ultramafic rocks in the Grenville Province. They found that twelve occur along a single line, crudely parallel with the Grenville Front and 12 to 50 km southeast, as shown in Figure 1C. They suggested that this line might prove useful for prospecting. Burke and others (1977) suggested that it might be an extension of a Labrador Fold Belt suture, marked by fragments of oceanic crust. It now appears that the sulfide deposits are not all the same age and that most or all may substantially predate the Grenville orogeny. The two northernmost deposits lie within the area shown by Dimroth and others (1970) as an extension of the Labrador Fold Belt, and may be similar in age to formations in the Labrador Fold Belt near Knob Lake which gave Rb-Sr whole-rock isochron dates of 1816 ± 72 and 1860 m.y. (Fryer, 1972; adjusted using a decay constant of 1.42×10^{-11}/yr). Eight or nine of the deposits in the southwestern part of the line may be Archean and related to sulfide deposits at Chibougamau, Val d'Or, or Noranda-Rouyn because they lie well within a zone in the Grenville Province in which Rb-Sr whole-rock isochron dates exceed 2000 m.y., as shown by the dashed line in Figure 1C. Also, Sethuraman (1979) claimed that sulfide mineralization in the Echouani area (not one of the deposits used by Dorr and Laurin, 1971), 100 km east of Val d'Or, was in a zone of Archean volcanogenic sulfide mineralization that could be traced across the Grenville Front. Deformation attributed to the Grenville orogeny might have influenced the ease of recognition of some of these deposits by promoting diapirism that formed the large circular features that Dorr and Laurin (1971) described as the sites for many of them. It appears, however, that the line connects sulfide deposits of distinctly different ages. These deposits need not be associated with sutures of any age now that Naldrett and Macdonald (1980) have shown that nickel sulfide deposits can be found in mafic igneous rocks of intracontinental rifts.

Rondot (1978) proposed a suture, shown in Figure 1D, that was tied to geologic evidence for the existence of an ancient Atlantic-type continental margin in the Saint Maurice area of Quebec, bounded on the east by a slice of oceanic crust. According to Rondot, two nearby anorthosite bodies differ in that the one west of Saint Maurice is highly deformed, while that on the east is not. Rondot suggested that they had different deformation histories because they had been intruded either at different times or into separate continents. He used the latter explanation to extrapolate the suture northward, apparently keeping deformed anorthosites to the west of the line and undeformed ones to the east. He also used charnockitic rocks as a guide; he suggested that they formed about 1250 m.y. ago during subduction that he apparently believed was symmetrical on both sides of the closing ocean because he extended his suture through the center of the band of charnockitic rocks. However, he estimated that conditions at the peak of metamorphism in the charnockites were 5 to 9 kbar and 700 and to 800° C, for an average geothermal gradient of 30 to 45° C/km, much higher than for any known Phanerozoic subduction zone. He attributed only minor deformation and retrograde metamorphism to a Grenville-age continent-continent collision. At Manicouagan, Rondot tied the suture to ultramafic rocks that appear to lie within the extension of the Labrador Fold Belt shown by Dimroth and others (1970). From there to the northeast, he used the suture of Thomas and Tanner (1975); but he did not explain why he used only part of their line and why there are no charnockites along that portion.

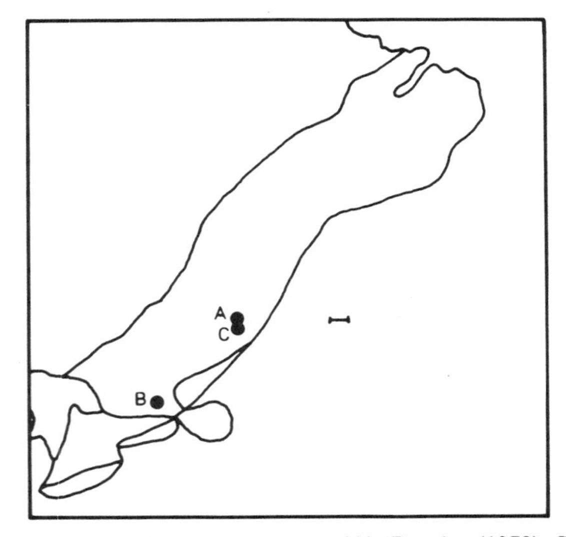

Figure 2. Proposed suture segments. (A): Rondot (1978), Saint-Maurice, Quebec. (B): Brown and others (1975), Bishops Corners, Ontario. (C): Stamatelopoulou-Seymour and MacLean (1977), Montauban-Les-Mines, Quebec.

Small Segments of Sutures

The work of Rondot (1978) in the Saint Maurice area, indicated by "A" in Figure 2, may support the hypothesis that a segment of suture exists there, even if his attempts to extrapolate it appear doubtful. One group of metasedimentary lithologies in that area resembles the sediments expected on an Atlantic-type continental margin. East of these Rondot described a narrow, north-south strip of mafic and ultramafic rocks that could be a remnant of oceanic lithosphere. He did not, however, present convincing evidence that this is the suture for the same continent-continent collision that has been suggested to explain the Grenville orogeny.

Brown and others (1975) suggested that mafic rocks near Bishops Corners, Ontario, indicated by "B" on Figure 2, might represent an island arc. Further studies in this area, including Moore (1977), Condie and Moore (1977), and Moore and Thompson (1980), led to the proposal of a series of tectonic events within the 1100 to 1250 m.y. time range suggested by Wynne Edwards (1972) for the Grenville orogeny. The Kaladar mafic complex, which consists of gabbro with ultramafic inclusions and mafic dikes, was interpreted by Moore and Thompson (1980) as oceanic crust, overlain conformably by an island arc complex consisting of a 4-km-thick sequence of tholeiitic basal flows and pillow lavas grading upward into a 3-km-thick sequence of calc-alkaline andesite with rhyolite and dacite. These volcanic rocks were correlated by the authors with the Tudor volcanics near Bancroft, where rhyolites near the top have been dated by the U-Pb concordia method on zircons as 1310 ± 15 m.y. old (Silver and Lumbers, 1966; revised to 1286 ± 15 m.y. by Davidson and others, 1979, to conform with new decay constants). Carbonates and clastic sediments of the Grenville Group are said to lie conformably on top of the Tudor volcanics, and similar metasedimentary rocks are found on top of the volcanic rocks in the Bishops Corners area (Moore and Thompson, 1980). Metamorphism affected the volcanic and sedimentary rocks before the intrusion of granodiorite and granitic plutons, some of which have been dated as 1250 ± 25 and 1125 ± 25 m.y. old, respectively, using the U-Pb concordia method on zircons (Silver and Lumbers, 1966; revised to 1226 and 1104 m.y. by Davidson and others, 1979). Moore and Thompson (1980) suggested that the early orogenic episode (1100 to 1250 m.y.) be called the Elzevirian Orogeny, after one of the granodiorite plutons. Following that event, the Flinton Group was deposited unconformably on the Grenville Group and arc volcanics, much of it as red beds in basins formed by block-faulting, suggesting extension and possible rifting of the crust. The rocks were then affected by a second episode of regional metamorphism and the Flinton Group metasediments were intruded by pegmatites that resemble those in the Haliburton Highlands that have been dated by the U-Pb zircon concordia method as 1050 m.y. old (Silver and Lumbers, 1966; revised to 1027 m.y. by Davidson and others, 1979). Deposition of the Flinton Group took place 1050 to 1080 m.y. ago (Moore and Thompson, 1980; 1020 to 1050 m.y. ago if revised dates are used). They suggested that the second regional metamorphic event, at approximately 1000 to 1050 m.y., be called the Ottawan Orogeny, as this is the dominant orogeny in the area.

A serious drawback for this study is that most of the isotopic dates were not obtained in the same area in which the relative ages were established, and correlations with the dated rocks heavily depend on lithologic similarities, rather than proven continuity. The Kaladar mafic complex presently lies between the Tudor volcanics and the proposed arc volcanics of the Bishops Corners area, so it could represent a margin sea between two island arcs or between an Andean arc (the Tudor volcanics on Archean crust) and an island arc. It is fairly clear that the Kaladar mafic complex is not the suture that formed at the time of the last major orogenic event (the Ottawan Orogeny of Moore and Thompson, 1980).

Another island arc was proposed by Stamatelpoulou-Seymour and MacLean (1977), in the Montauban-les-Mines area, indicated by "C" in Figure 2. These mafic metaigneous rocks are immediately southwest of the mafic and ultramafic rocks which Rondot (1978) suggested as a fragment of oceanic crust. Detailed mapping and careful application of isotopic dating will be required to determine the relationships between the proposed island arc and suture in this area and those near Bishops Corners, as well as the relationships of each of these areas to the major tectonic events of the Grenville orogenic belt.

The Llano uplift of central Texas is a relatively small area of Proterozoic outcrops that lies 1200 km from the nearest Grenville outcrops in the southern Blue Ridge and 2200 km from the Canadian Grenville Province. Zartman (1964) correlated these rocks with the Grenville Province on the basis of isotopic dates. Sengör and Butler (1977) indicated evidence for an initial rifting event in the Valley Spring Gneiss, a continental margin in the Packsaddle Formation, and possible pieces of obducted oceanic lithosphere in serpentinites of the Coal Creek body. In the southeastern part of the uplift, Garrison and others (1979) interpreted a complex of tholeiitic gabbro and basalt, intermediate volcanics, and shelf-edge sediments as an island arc. Those rocks were deformed and metamorphosed as granodiorite and basalt dikes were intruded. Rb-Sr whole-rock isochron dates indicate that arc formation and deformation took place 1100 to 1200 m.y. ago. Garrison and others (1979) also concluded that the narrow Coal Creek Serpentinite is within these arc rocks and was deformed and metamorphosed with them. According to Garrison (1980), the serpentinite was derived from harzburgite, a rock type commonly found at the base of obducted ophiolite complexes. He proposed that the serpentinite body is an ophiolitic fragment and an olistostrome in the volcaniclastic rocks of the arc flank. Later, possibly during uplift, large granitic plutons were intruded which give Rb-Sr whole-rock isochron dates from 1050 to 1070 m.y. (Garrison and others, 1979). The time of granite plutonism in the Llano area, 1050 to 1070 m.y., is nearly identical to the time of deposition of the Flinton Group in eastern Ontario. The Flinton Group was deposited between two episodes of deformation and before the most intense metamorphism in that area. In Phanerozoic orogenic belts, collisions show diachroneity along strike, so it is possible that the Llano is part of the Grenville belt and contains evidence for the same series of events; but it is also possible that the events in one area are completely unrelated to those in the other. In any case, if further work supports Sengör and Butler's (1977) and Garrison's (1980) models, then one would at least have a nearly contemporary example of plate tectonics to compare with features in areas more securely linked with Grenville events in Canada.

As the studies above suggest, there could be traces of several sutures inside the Grenville Province. The Grenville Front is apparently not a suture because rocks more than 1200 m.y. old can be traced as much as 300 km southeast of it, as shown by U-Pb concordia dates from zircons (Fig. 3A) and Rb-Sr whole-rock isochron dates (Fig. 3B). At least within this zone any candidate suture could mark the extension into the Grenville Province of an earlier Proterozoic suture, such as from the Labrador Fold Belt or the Southern Province, or of an Archean greenstone belt from the Superior Province. Beyond this zone of older rocks, the work of Moore and Thompson (1980) suggests that there could be more than one "Grenville" suture, one for each of the collision events that occurred during the time interval previously allowed for a single Grenville orogeny.

An intact ophiolite sequence within a continent can be taken as evidence for closure of an ocean, but a continuous strip of ophiolite should not be expected along the entire length of a suture. Even in the Himalaya, ophiolite is not found along some segments of the Indus Suture (Zhang and Yin, 1980). Cryptic sutures, lacking intact ophiolite, may be represented by ". . .no more than a sliver of serpentinite, a few flakes of fuchsite or merely a mylonite zone" (Burke and others, 1977). These sutures are to be expected in ter-

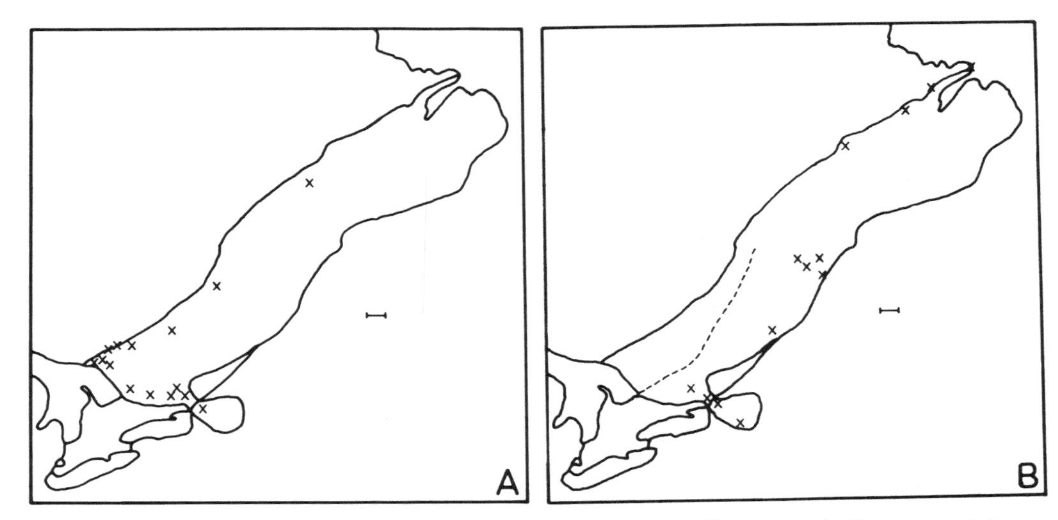

Figure 3. Radiometric dates older than 1200 m.y. in the Grenville orogen in Canada and the Adirondacks. (A): U-Pb concordia dates from Zircons. (B): Rb-Sr whole-rock isochron dates. Dashed line is the southeast limit of an area with many such dates.

ranes such as the Grenville orogenic belt that have been eroded to a deep level in the possible collision zone (Burke and Dewey, 1973a). The presence of ultramafic rocks of any kind in a ductile high strain zone should not be taken as proof of a suture, but it deserves closer examination. In the absence of dismembered ophiolite, geologic evidence from the surrounding area can narrow down the location of a suture zone. This evidence can include isotopic dates, and contrasts in lithologies, geologic history, or structural trends. Identification of the former edge of a continent using lithologies and structures typical of an Atlantic-type continental margin or an Andean or island arc may provide a strong indication of suturing. The location of an orogenic belt within a continent, with older continental rocks of different ages on either side in itself strongly suggests that a continent-continent collision took place. For the Grenville orogenic belt in North America, the "other side" of the belt has not been found attached to the belt.

KEWEENAW-GRENVILLE RELATIONSHIPS

Hypotheses

A genetic relationship between the Keweenaw belt and the Grenville orogenic belt, both shown in Figure 4, is suggested by the similarity in isotopic dates from the two areas. Comparisons with Phanerozoic intracontinental rifts and zones of continent-continent collision suggest four possible relationships, assuming that the Keweenaw is an intracontinental rift and the Grenville orogenic belt the result of a continent-continent collision:

1. None; the similarity in dates has no tectonic significance or is not as close as formerly believed (Burke and Dewey, 1973b);

2. The Keweenaw rift formed as an aulacogen, a failed arm of the same rift system that opened the ocean later closed in the Grenville collision;

3. The Keweenaw rift is an impactogen, a rift caused by the impact of the Grenville collision (Burke, 1980);

4. The Keweenaw rift formed as an aulacogen of a rift system that opened during the period commonly allowed for the Grenville orogeny, but between separate collision events that have not been well resolved, such as the two orogenies proposed by Moore and Thompson (1980) for southern Ontario.

Isotopic Dates

Isotopic dates are a key to narrowing the choice among these four possibilities. Because different types of dates provide information about different stages or events in the geologic history of a region, we consider three types: K-Ar dates from biotite concentrates and whole-rock samples, U-Pb concordia dates from zircons, and Rb-Sr whole-rock isochron dates. To avoid dates reset by Paleozoic events in the Appalachians, we consider only dates from the Adirondacks and westward, including the Canadian Grenville Province, the Keweenaw rift, and other rocks in the vicinity that may have been associated with rifting, such as mafic dikes, carbonatite complexes, and anorthosite massifs.

K-Ar Dates. K-Ar dates are quite abundant for the areas of interest, particularly whole-rock dates on fine-grained igneous rocks and biotite dates from coarser rocks of many types. These dates cannot be expected to provide much information about early events or stages, particularly in the Grenville Province, because the dates can indicate the time of intrusion only for igneous rocks that cooled quickly

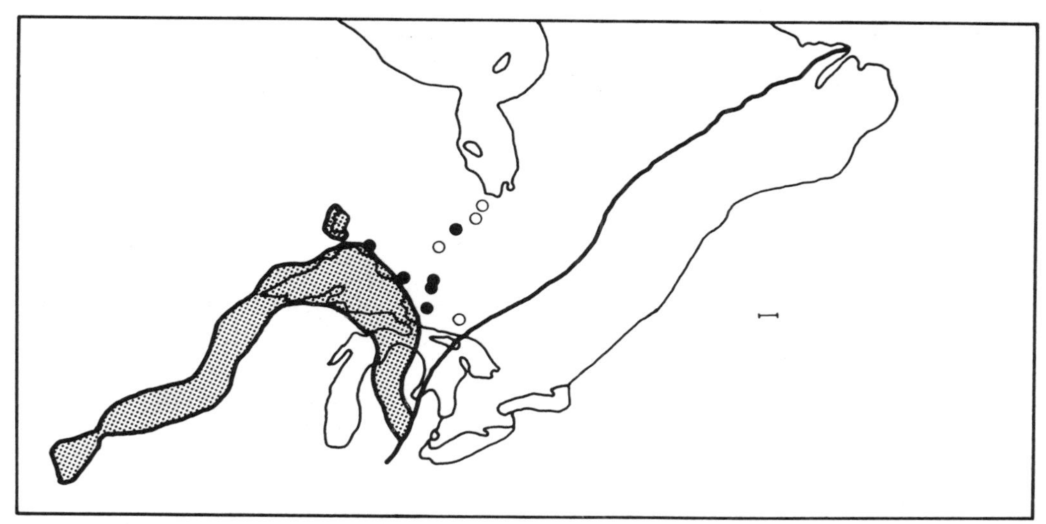

Figure 4. Grenville orogen (not decorated) and Keweenaw rift (stippled). Grenville Front in Canada is after Douglas (1972). Remainder of front and outlines of Keweenaw rift are after Halls (1978). Carbonatite complexes outside Grenville orogen are after Gittins and others (1967): Solid circles have K-Ar dates between 1020 and 1122 m.y.; open circles between 1566 and 1743 m.y. Michipicoten is an island at the eastern end of Lake Superior. The intrusions in a line from there to Hudsons Bay are called the Kapuskasing alkali intrusions.

and were never heated again. The argon diffusion closure temperature of biotite is approximately 300°C and even lower for feldspars (Hunziker, 1979), so biotite K-Ar dates in high-grade metamorphic rocks are set at a late stage of cooling. Whole-rock K-Ar dates, particularly from metadiabase, are probably dominated by feldspars because they will be the main source of potassium and radiogenic argon. Whole-rock dates, therefore, will indicate an even less distinct late stage of cooling in metamorphic areas. Because of the low closure temperatures of these minerals, dates from biotite and from feldspar-dominated rocks that originally did indicate the time of intrusion could be reset by rather weak heating later on.

K-Ar dates were early used to define the age of the Grenville orogeny (Stockwell, 1964), and 950 m.y. was often used as the time of the event. This date led Burke and Dewey (1973b) to suggest that the Keweenaw rift and Grenville orogenic belt might not be genetically related. They suggested that the Keweenaw rift was one arm of a plume-generated triad centered near Michipicoten, with other arms trending southeast through lower Michigan and northeast along the Kapuskasing zone of alkalic intrusions. According to this model, igneous activity in the rift began 1100 m.y. ago, and rifting never progressed as far as true, open ocean along any of the arms. If the time of the Grenville orogeny is taken as 950 m.y., then the orogeny occurred well after the beginning of rifting. However, if that date is interpreted as the average of postorogenic cooling dates, then relationships become possible. Examination of thermochron maps such as those of Harper (1967), based on biotite K-Ar dates, and Baer (1976), based on K-Ar dates from various micas, suggests that postorogenic cooling to the argon diffusion closure temperatures of micas may have been accomplished as early as 1100 m.y. ago along parts of the Grenville Front and proceeded gradually southeastward.

U-Pb Concordia Dates. The upper intercept on a U-Pb concordia curve of a line defined by isotopic ratios from zircons is generally agreed to give the date of original crystallization of igneous zircons. Most of the U-Pb concordia dates for the areas discussed have been published in abstracts or very short papers, giving this upper intercept date but little information about the sample sites and rock types or the geologic justification for combining certain samples into one line. Another problem is that two sets of uranium decay constants have been available in the last decade (Fleming and others, 1952; Jaffey and others, 1971). The latter set has now been adopted as part of IUGS standards (Steiger and Jäger, 1977), but it is not possible to adjust a concordia date precisely if only the upper intercept date has been provided. In cases where the adjustment has been made, for instance revisions by Davidson and others (1979) of dates from Silver and Lumbers (1966), the usual change for dates from the Grenville Province is a decrease of 20 to 30 m.y. In this paper U-Pb concordia dates are presented as published, and nearly all were calculated using the older set of decay constants.

As shown in Figure 5, only one specific U-Pb concordia date on zircons from Keweenaw rocks has been published, 1115 m.y. (Silver and Green, 1963), compiled from several Middle and Upper Keweenaw igneous rocks in Ontario, Minnesota, and Wisconsin. Silver and Green (1972)

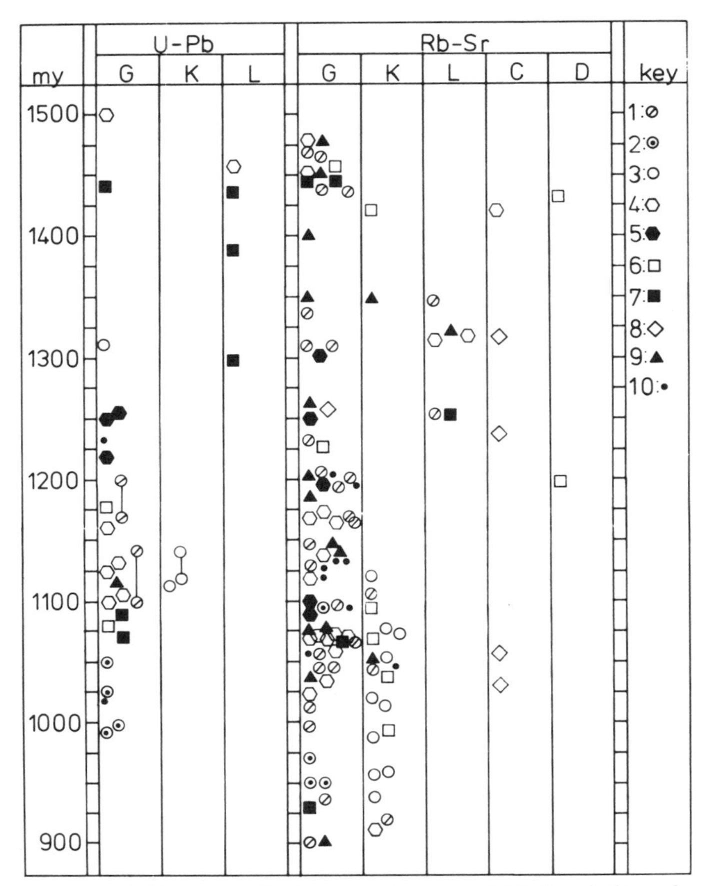

Figure 5. U-Pb concordia dates on zircons and Rb-Sr whole-rock isochron dates, 1500 to 900 m.y. Columns are: (G)-Grenville orogen, (K)-Keweenaw rift, (L)-Labrador, (C)-carbonatites and other alkaline complexes outside areas G and K, (D)-mafic dikes and sills outside areas G and K. Lithologies are: (1)-granite, (2)-granitic pegmatites, (3) rhyolite, felsite, (4)-monzonite, syenite, adamellite, mangerite, (5)-granodiorite, diorite, tonalite, dacite, trondhjemite, (6)-basalt, gabbro, diabase, (7)-anorthosite, (8)-carbonatite, nepheline syenite, (9)-metasediments, (10)-other, or not specified.

stated that additional U-Pb concordia dates, not published, indicate that most of the igneous activity took place 1140 to 1120 m.y. ago. In the Grenville Province and Adirondacks, U-Pb concordia dates range from 1460 to 990 m.y. The two oldest dates are from anorthositic complexes that are probably related to similar bodies in Labrador north of the Grenville Front. Dates from nepheline syenite, mafic volcanics, granodiorite, and granite in the Bancroft area of Ontario, from anorthosites in northern Labrador, and from dacitic volcanics(?) and alaskitic granites in the northwest Adirondacks are also older than dates from Keweenaw rocks. The dates from the Keweenaw igneous rocks coincide with dates from quartz monzonitic and syenitic rocks in southern Ontario and the Adirondacks, and are older than dates from granitic pegmatites in the same areas. Folding of Keweenawan rocks has been attributed to compression during the Grenville orogeny (Craddock, 1981), and suggests that deformation in and near the Grenville Province took place or continued after development of the Keweenaw rift. Keweenawan rocks have also been subjected to low-grade metamorphism that may be attributable to the Grenville orogeny (Jolly and Smith, 1972).

Dates from anorthosites and from nepheline syenite within the Grenville Province and Adirondacks, rocks that we interpret as possibly related to rifting, are at least 200 m.y. older than dates from Keweenawan igneous rocks; so it appears that Keweenawan rifting occurred long after rifting within the Grenville Province. The granodiorite, granite, and mafic volcanics of the Bancroft, Ontario, area are also older than the Keweenawan rocks, indicating that volcanic arc magmatism, or collision, or both, was underway in the Grenville Province before Keweenawan igneous activity began. In that case, the Keweenaw rift might be an impactogen, a rift extending into North America that was caused by the impact of the "other continent" presumed to have been involved in a Grenville continent-continent collision. Rifting should have begun during the early stages of the collision.

Rb-Sr Whole-rock Isochron Dates. Rb-Sr whole-rock isochron dates are more abundant for the areas of concern than U-Pb concordia dates, and all those used in this paper have been adjusted to conform with the current IUGS standard decay constant of 1.42×10^{-11}/yr. A disadvantage, by comparison with U-Pb concordia dates from zircons, is that Rb-Sr dates do not always date the same event or stage. In igneous rocks they tell the time of initial crystallization; in sedimentary rocks they are often interpreted as giving the time of diagenesis (but as Clauer, 1979, pointed out, only minerals that formed during diagenesis can be expected to date diagenesis); and in metasedimentary rocks these dates are often used for the time of the peak of metamorphism. Also, all of these dates can be disturbed or reset by a later metamorphic event, either to the time of the peak of that event, as shown by a study of Archean tonalitic plutons in the Grenville Province (Frith and Doig, 1975), or to some intermediate, apparently geologically meaningless date, as shown in southern Norway by Field and Råheim (1979).

A few igneous rock units from the areas of interest have been dated by both methods, as listed in Table 1. These dates match reasonably well, as expected if both provide the date of original crystallization for the igneous rocks and if the peak of metamorphism indicated by Rb-Sr dates from metasedimentary rocks was at the same time.

As shown in Figure 4, most of the Rb-Sr whole-rock isochron dates from the Keweenaw rift are in the range 1125 to 900 m.y., so the oldest are similar to U-Pb concordia dates from zircons, and the youngest are similar to the youngest U-Pb and Rb-Sr dates from the Grenville Province. Two dates from the Keweenaw rift are considerably

TABLE 1. COMPARISONS OF U-PB CONCORDIA DATES FROM ZIRCONS AND RB-SR WHOLE-ROCK ISOCHRON DATES IN THE GRENVILLE OROGEN AND KEWEENAW RIFT

Site, pluton or unit	Rock type	U-Pb (m.y.)	Rb-Sr (m.y.)
Duluth Gabbro, MN	Gabbro, granophyre		1118
Mellon Granite, WI	Granite		920
Endion Sill, MN	Diabase, intermediate rock, granophyre		1069
North Shore Volcanics, Ont.	Silicic volcanics		1120
Composite from above four	Rhyolitic, granitic	1115	
Blue Mountain, Ont.	Nepheline syenite	1300-1350	1258
Lake Muskoka, Ont.	Quartz monzonite	1440	1444

older: 1450 m.y. from mafic samples in the North Shore Volcanic Group, and 1349 m.y. from red beds of the Sibley Group, which underlies Keweenaw volcanics. The first date is suspect because the same samples combined with felsic volcanic rocks from the same group produced an isochron date of 1120 m.y. (Leeman, 1977). The second date could be the time of deposition or diagenesis of the red beds, as originally interpreted (Franklin and others, 1972), or might record some aspect of the source area. If further studies of basal Keweenawan rocks consistently produce such old dates, then perhaps the main mafic activity took place in a reactivated rift. Rifting events to the east and northeast as early as 1350 m.y. are indicated by dates from anorthosites and associated rocks in the Grenville Province; and in Labrador north of the Grenville Front, in rift-facies sediments and volcanic rocks of the Seal Lake Group, and possible rift-related alkaline intrusive rocks and mafic dikes elsewhere in the eastern Canadian Shield.

Further examination of Figure 5 shows that granitic rocks in the Grenville Province and Adirondacks give Rb-Sr whole-rock isochron dates covering a broad range. Field relationships suggest that some of these dates older than 1300 m.y. may be from much older granitic rocks in which the dates were reset by anorthosite intrusion. Others are from granitic bodies close to the Grenville Front which may be related to older igneous rocks in the Southern and Superior Provinces, possibly partially reset. Some of the younger dates might also be reset in rocks originally intruded much earlier, but the substantially continuous series of dates from 1250 to 900 m.y. suggests that igneous activity and metamorphism were continuous through that interval. If those dates represent a single orogenic event, then the Rb-Sr dates, like the U-Pb dates, allow the possibility that the Keweenaw rift is an impactogen, a split in North America caused by a Grenville collision. The older date from the Sibley Group allows the possibility that this impactogen might have reactivated an older rift, perhaps an aulacogen of a pre-Grenville rift system.

Another possibility is suggested by the sequence of events worked out by Moore and Thompson (1980). If more than one collision event took place in the 1100 to 1250 m.y. time range, with rifting between these episodes, then the Keweenan rift could be an aulacogen of that rift system. The date inferred by Moore and Thompson (1980) for rifting and deposition of the Flinton Group, 1050 to 1080 m.y., is 100 m.y. too young to perfectly match the few dates that suggest the time of onset of rifting in the Keweenaw rift. The times for both events, however, depend on a small number of isotopic dates and could change as more are obtained.

SOUTHERN PROVINCE-LABRADOR FOLD BELT RELATIONSHIPS

Hypotheses

The Southern Province and the Labrador Fold Belt resemble each other in several ways. They both contain linear belts in which similar types of sedimentary and volcanic rocks have been deposited and into which similar types of plutonic rocks have been intruded. Deformation and regional metamorphism took place in both areas after Archean time and before the Grenville orogenic event, and both intersect the Grenville Front at high angles. An actual connection and possible genetic relationships have been suggested by some features shown in Figures 7 and 9:

1. The Labrador Fold Belt can be traced into the Grenville Province and appears to change trend to the southwest;
2. There are three smaller areas of post-Archean, pre-Grenville sedimentary rocks immediately northwest of the Grenville Front between the two belts;
3. The Huronian Supergroup of the Southern Province extends northeast along the Grenville Front toward the smaller areas mentioned above.

One possible relationship is that the sedimentary rocks in both belts were deposited at the same time on a single, continuous, subsiding Atlantic-type continental margin, with the link concealed in the Grenville Province. Present margins of this type are not straight and consist of segments at varying angles to each other, determined at the time of rifting (Dewey and Burke, 1974); so it is conceivable that two segments could be nearly parallel, as are the Southern Province and the Labrador Fold Belt. The link inside the Grenville Province might be close to the Grenville Front, so as to include the three smaller areas of post-Archean sedimentary rocks. If the main continental margin was far to the southeast, then the three small areas might have been along one or more aulacogens extending far into the continent.

Another possibility is that both belts were subjected to deformation and metamorphism by the same tectonic event, associated with subduction or collision. In this case, dates for these effects should be in the same time interval, allowing for along-strike diachroneity.

A third possibility is that the two belts are similar because they were produced by similar series of tectonic events, but not at the same time nor in any physical continuity. Isotopic dates set at each stage of the Wilson Cycle would not have to match, and each belt would extend independently into the Grenville Province. The younger of the two might have once truncated or overprinted the older just as the Grenville orogeny affected them both.

Deposition

As was the case for the Canadian Grenville Province, the Southern Province is formally defined by isotopic dates (Stockwell, 1964), between 1500 and 1900 m.y. The area coincides with the extent of the Huronian Supergroup. Geologists working in the Southern Province observed early on that the Huronian rocks seemed to disappear to the southeast along what is now considered part of the Grenville Front. Quirke and Collins (1930) believed that they could identify several small areas of deformed and metamorphosed Huronian rocks within the region of granitic gneisses southeast of Killarney, and even made some correlations between rocks in these pockets and specific formations in the Southern Province. The field work shown in Quirke and Collins (1930) extended 10 to 15 km southeast of the Grenville Front, and they suggested a possible relationship between Huronian rocks and Grenville Group metasedimentary rocks in the Bancroft area, nearly 300 km from the front. They proposed that the Huronian and Grenville sediments were deposited at the same time, with the Grenville Group representing deeper-water facies. Isotopic dates indicate that the Huronian rocks were deposited unconformably on Archean continental basement after 2400 m.y. ago and before intrusion of mafic dikes and sills collectively known as the Nipissing diabase. Rb-Sr whole-rock isochron dates from Nipissing rocks at widely separated locations in the Southern Province are 2110 ± 78 m.y. (Van Schmus, 1965), 2110 ± 80 and 2117 ± 27 m.y. (Fairbairn and others, 1969), and are interpreted as times of intrusion. Dates of the same type are also available from the Abitibi mafic dikes (2102 ± 68 m.y., Gates and Hurley, 1973) and the Otto alkaline stock (2115 ± 80 m.y., Bell and Blenkinsop, 1976), intruding Archean rocks of the Superior Province nearby. These dates suggest a short, widespread rifting event in the region. As shown in Figure 6, a few

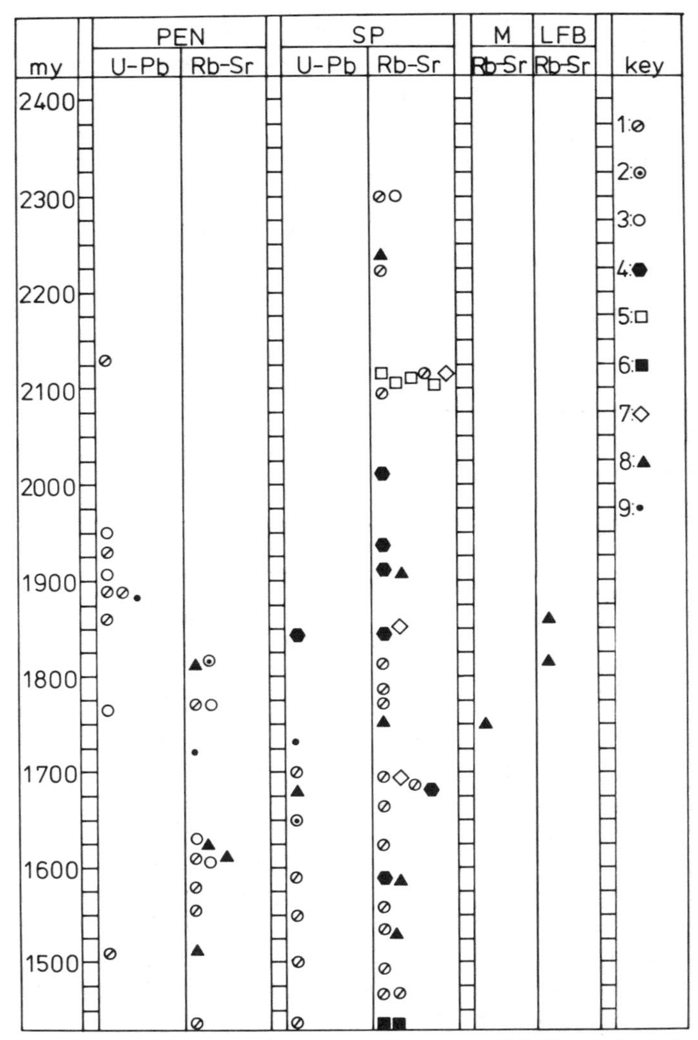

Figure 6. U-Pb concordia dates on zircons and Rb-Sr whole-rock isochron dates, 2400 to 1450 m.y. Columns are: (PEN)-Penokean area, (SP)-Southern Province and adjacent part of Grenville orogen, (M)-Mistassini Lake area, (LFB)-Labrador Fold Belt. Lithologies are: (1)-granite, quartz monzonite, granodiorite, quartz diroite, (2)-pegmatite, (3)-rhyolite, felsic volcanics, (4)-all rocks of the Sudbury Irruptive, (5)-mafic dikes and sills, diabase, gabbro, (6)-anorthosite, adamellite, other related rocks, (7)-alkali syenite, carbonatite, (8)-paragneisses, metasediments, (9)-not sepcified.

isochron dates between 2400 and 2100 m.y. are available from volcaniclastic and sedimentary rocks of the Huronian Supergroup, but they do not help set narrower limits on the time of deposition. As previously mentioned, a U-Pb zircon concordia date of 1310 m.y. (Silver and Lumbers, 1966) for the Tudor volcanics sets the earliest possible date for deposition of the Grenville Group.

In the Labrador Fold Belt, Dimroth (1972) concluded that the sediments of the Kaniapiskau Group were deposited after intrusion of some southeast-trending mafic dikes that cut Archean rocks west of the fold belt. Apparently, the only available date on those dikes is an average of K-Ar dates from four whole-rock samples, a biotite concentrate, and a hornblende concentrate, of 2145 m.y. (Fahrig and Wanless, 1963; no error estimate given). This date might have been reset by later metamorphism; but if it is the time of intrusion, then the sediments of the Labrador Fold Belt were deposited after the Huronian rocks although the difference could be accounted for by diachroneity along strike. Fryer (1972) obtained Rb-Sr whole-rock isochron dates of 1860 and 1816 ± 72 m.y. from slates near the top of the Labrador Fold Belt sequence, which he interpreted as dates of deposition or diagenesis. He suggested that deformation began soon after deposition of the younger of the two units dated. Clauer's (1979) analysis suggests that such dates probably do not date diagenesis, and in this case, may have been reset by metamorphism at a somewhat later stage.

Several correlations have been suggested for the post-Archean sedimentary rocks in the three smaller areas along the Grenville Front, based almost entirely on lithologic similarities. The patches of clastic rocks near Chibougamau have been correlated with the Gowganda Formation of the Southern Province because both appear to have been deposited in paraglacial alluvial fans and glacial lakes (Long, 1974), but there is a gap of 500 km between the two areas. The Gowganda Formation extends farthest to the northeast along the Grenville Front within the Southern Province.

The sedimentary rocks around Mistassini Lake contain major proportions of dolomite and iron formation, so McGlynn (1968a) suggested a correlation with carbonates and iron formation in the Labrador Fold Belt. Gastil and Knowles (1960) and Dimroth and others (1970) traced Labrador Fold Belt lithologies into the Grenville Province toward the southwest, parallel with the Grenville Front, as far as the Manicouagan impact structure and possibly no more than 100 km from Mistassini Lake, but did not show any direct connection.

Frarey and Roscoe (1970) correlated the basal clastic unit of the Mistassini Group with the neighboring Otish Mountain Group although outcrop is not continuous. Long (1974) suggested that the Mistassini Group is younger than the Otish Mountain Group because the latter contains no dolomite clasts, but it is not clear, that the source area included the area of deposition of the Mistassini Group. The Otish Mountain Group has also been correlated with the Lorrain Formation (S. M. Roscoe, in McGlynn, 1968b), directly above the Gowganda Formation in the Cobalt Group. Stringing together the correlations, the Mistassini Group could be correlated with the Lorrain Formation or some higher part of the Cobalt Group. This is at least consistent with the contention of Frarey and Roscoe (1970) that the atmosphere did not contain enough oxygen to form iron formation until the time of deposition of the Cobalt Group.

Of the three smaller post-Archean depositional areas, isotopic dates are available only from Mistassini Lake. Fryer (1972) obtained an Rb-Sr whole-rock isochron date of 1740 ± 54 m.y. from slates above and below the iron formation within the Temiscamie Formation, the uppermost unit of the Mistassini Group. This date is 70 to 90 m.y. younger than the dates he obtained from slates above and below the upper iron formation of the central Labra-

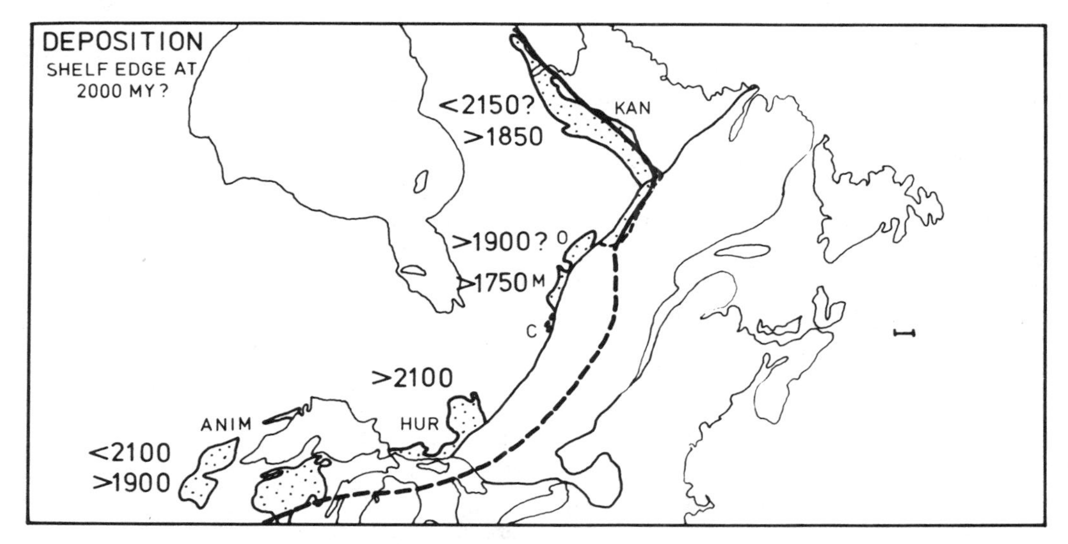

Figure 7. Hypothetical shelf edge at 2000 m.y., assuming that Animikie and related rocks (ANIM) in the Penokean area and Kaniapiskau (KAN) rocks in the Labrador Fold Belt were being deposited at this time. Huronian rocks (HUR) in the Southern Province were deposited earlier. Ages of deposition for the Otish (O), Mistassini Lake (M), and Chibougamau (C) areas are poorly constrained. ANIM area after van Schmus (1976), KAN area after Dimroth and others (1970), M and C areas after Hofmann (1978), other areas after Douglas (1972).

dor Fold Belt. Fryer interpreted his Temiscamie date as the time of deposition, but Fahrig and Chown (1973) interpreted it as the time of diagenesis or low-grade metamorphism. The work of Clauer (1979) suggests the latter may be true or that the date may have been reset by Grenville metamorphism. Two K-Ar biotite dates have been obtained in or very near mafic dikes that cut at least the lowermost formation of the Mistassini Group: 1934 ± 58 and 1959 ± 58 m.y. (Wanless and others, 1968). These dates are not quite old enough to convincingly link the Mistassini Group with the Huronian Supergroup, and they may have been reset by later metamorphism. In short, the available isotopic dates are not sufficient to decide whether the sediments in the three small areas can be correlated with the Huronian Supergroup or the Kaniapiskau Group.

West of the Southern Province, surrounding Lake Superior, there are some additional metasedimentary rocks that could be correlated with the Huronian Supergroup. According to Young (1981), the Chocolay Group, along the south shore of Lake Superior, was deposited before approximately 2000 m.y. ago. It was deformed and intruded by granite at 2000 m.y., before deposition of the Menominee Group. Cambray (1978), however, placed deposition of the Chocolay Group after 2000 m.y. and mentioned no major deformation before deposition of the Menominee sediments. In the Felch area of northern Michigan, Van Schmus (1976) and Larue (1981) suggested that some of the metasedimentary rocks (referred to as the Dickinson Group by Larue) were deposited before 2100 m.y. ago. In Michigan and Minnesota, the Animikie Group and related rocks were deposited after about 2100 m.y. and before about 1900 m.y. ago (Van Schmus, 1976).

In Figure 7 we have drawn a speculative continental shelf edge for 2000 m.y. ago. At that time deposition was taking place in the areas of the Animikie Group and Kaniapiskau Group, but deposition of the Huronian Supergroup was already over. The abundance of Nipissing dikes and sills in the Southern Province suggests that rifting at that time may have succeeded nearby, so the shelf edge may not have been far away from the preserved portions of the Southern Province. We have not attempted to place the three smaller post-Archean depositional areas on this continental margin because the isotopic dates are not sufficient to decide when they were deposited.

Deformation, Metamorphism, and Igneous Activity

In the Southern Province there is structural evidence that some deformation of Huronian rocks preceded intrusion of the Nipissing diabase (Van Schmus, 1976), particularly in the western part of the region. The possibility of an orogenic event of some type before 2100 m.y. is also supported by Rb-Sr whole-rock isochron dates from a few granitic bodies near the Grenville Front, including 2301 ± 147 m.y. near Timagami (Grant, 1964) and 2233 m.y. from the Murray granite (Gibbins and NcNutt, 1975) on the south edge of the Sudbury structure, although this granite has also been the source of younger dates.

TABLE 2. COMPARISONS OF U-PB CONCORDIA DATES FROM ZIRCONS AND RB-SR WHOLE-ROCK ISOCHRON DATES FROM GRANITES NEAR SUDBURY

Site or pluton	U-Pb (m.y.)	Rb-Sr (m.y.)
Near Bell Lake	1550	
Near Killarney	1590	1557, 1626
Near Chief Lake	1700	1664
Near French River		1689
General area		1537, 1713

Intrusion of Nipissing diabase dikes was the next major tectonic event in the area, at approximately 2100 m.y. Rifting in the vicinity may have succeeded in forming an aulacogen or Atlantic-type continental margin nearby. The next major event was apparently the development of the Sudbury Irruptive. Rb-Sr whole-rock isochron dates and one U-Pb concordia date on zircons from the norites and micropegmatites give dates ranging from 1840 to 2010 m.y. Because there are no U-Pb and Rb-Sr dates in this range for intermediate or acidic igneous rocks in the Southern Province or signs of regional metamorphism and deformation of Huronian rocks at that time, we tend to agree that the Sudbury Irruptive is the result of meteorite impact (Dietz, 1964).

There are numerous granitic intrusions in the Southern Province, particularly close to the Grenville Front, which give U-Pb and Rb-Sr dates between 1540 and 1720 m.y. As shown in Table 2, pairs of dates from plutons or groups of plutons match rather well, suggesting that all of the dates indicate the time of intrusion. The granitic bodies of this age appear to be most abundant in the area of greatest deformation and highest metamorphic grade, as shown in Figure 8. We suggest that a single tectonic event at this time, or early in the time range, produced both the metamorphic isograds and granitic intrusions. This may also be the post-Nipissing, post-Sudbury deformation event described by Brocoum and Dalziel (1974). U-Pb concordia and Rb-Sr isochron dates in the same range have also been obtained from granitic rocks up to 150 km into the Grenville Province.

In the Labrador Fold Belt no U-Pb concordia dates on zircons are available, nor are there any Rb-Sr whole-rock isochron dates on potentially synorogenic igneous rocks. It is, therefore, difficult to be certain of comparisons with dates for subduction or collision stages of the Wilson Cycle suggested for the Southern Province. K-Ar dates on biotite range from 1600 to 1850 m.y., so the 1816 and 1860 m.y.

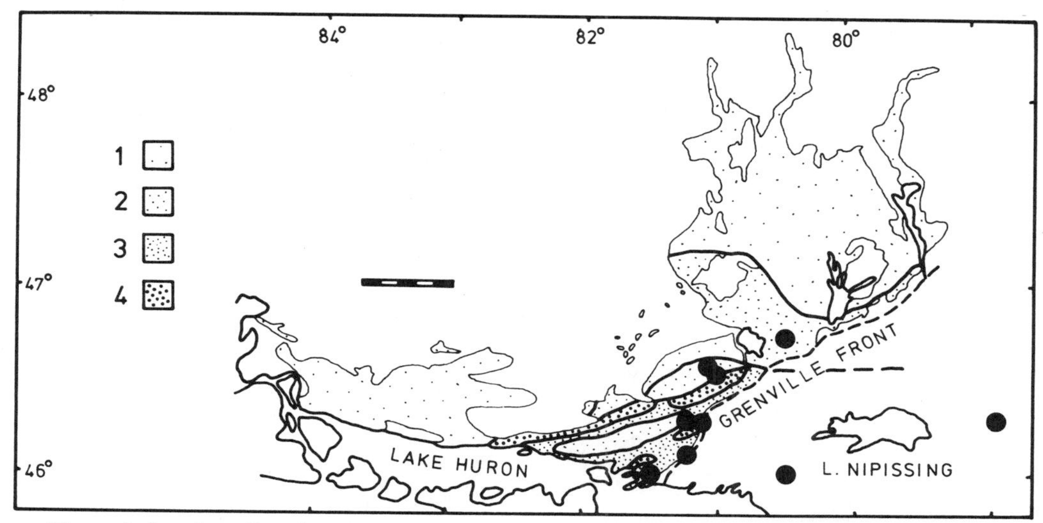

Figure 8. Southern Province metamorphism and granite intrusions. Metamorphic facies are: (1)-subgreenschist, (2)-low to middle greenschist, (3)-middle to upper greenschist, (4)-amphibolite (after Card and others, 1978). Black circles are granitic plutons with U-Pb concordia dates on zircons or Rb-Sr whole-rock isochron dates of 1550 to 1812 m.y. Dashed line extending east from Grenville Front near Sudbury is northern limit of dates of that range inside the Grenville orogen. Scale bar is 50 km.

Rb-Sr dates reported by Fryer (1972) from slates may indeed mark the peak of metamorphism rather than the time of deposition. If that is the case, then the single potential collision event in the Labrador Fold Belt occurred before the major post-Nipissing event in the Southern Province.

In the Chibougamau and Otish Mountain areas all deformation and metamorphism have been attributed to the Grenville orogeny (Long, 1974; Chown, 1979), based on structural evidence. If so, then neither the 1600 to 1700 m.y. event in the Southern Province, nor the 1850 event in the Labrador Fold Belt had much effect. In the Mistassini Lake area, Fryer (1972) remarked that two periods of deformation can be seen, with northeast-trending folds and faults related to the Grenville orogeny superimposed on gentle folds trending east and southeast. The single Rb-Sr whole-rock isochron date from this area, 1749 m.y. (Fryer, 1972), if it dates metamorphism rather than deposition, is at the high end of the range of dates from the granites in the Southern Province, and 70 to 110 m.y. younger than the dates from the Labrador Fold Belt. This is not sufficient evidence for making a correlation with deformation in either belt.

In the Lake Superior area there is some evidence for a deformational event at or before 2100 m.y., between deposition of the Chocolay and Menominee Groups along the south shore of Lake Superior (Young, 1981), and in the Felch Trough of northern Michigan (Van Schmus, 1976; Larue, 1981). The most conspicuous tectonic event in the middle Proterozoic in the area was the Penokean Orogeny, which affected Animikie sedimentary rocks and equivalents. This event occurred approximately 1850 to 1900 m.y. ago, as shown by U-Pb concordia dates on zircons from synorogenic granodioritic and granitic plutons in northern Wisconsin (Van Schmus, 1976). Later granites and rhyolites in central Wisconsin, 1750 to 1800 m.y. old, are probably also related to this event (Bickford and others, 1981). Other than dates from the Sudbury Irruptive there appear to be no signs of tectonic activity at this time in the Southern Province, so we infer that the Penokean Orogeny was not important there. The age range includes the time suggested for orogenic activity in the Labrador Fold Belt, but no physical connection between the two areas is immediately apparent.

In Table 3, note that some of the plutons from the Lake Superior area which were used to date the Penokean Orogeny give Rb-Sr whole-rock isochron dates that are as much as 200 m.y. younger. Van Schmus (1976) suggested that the U-Pb dates give the time of intrusion, but the Rb-Sr dates were reset. He associated this resetting with a

TABLE 3. COMPARISONS OF U-PB CONCORDIA DATES FROM ZIRCONS AND RB-SR WHOLE-ROCK ISOCHRON DATES IN THE "PENOKEAN" AREA

Site, pluton, or unit	Rock type	U-Pb (m.y.)	Rb-Sr (m.y.)
Hoskin Lake	Granite	1890	1772
Amberg	Granodiorite, quartz monzonite	1860	1579
Quinnesec Fm.	Volcanics	1905	≥1772
Central WI	Rhyolite, granite	1765	1606, 1553, 1630, 1608

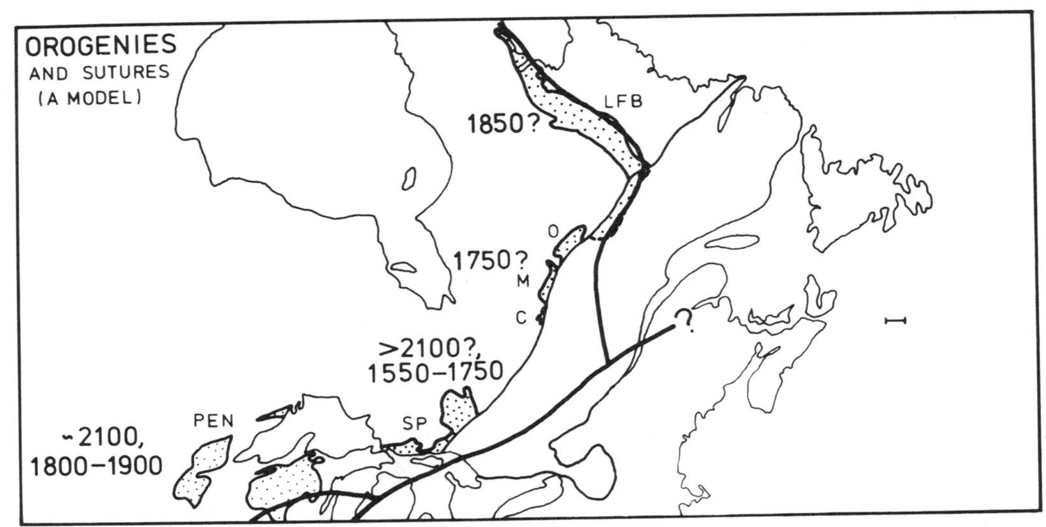

Figure 9. Hypothetical sutures for Proterozoic orogenies in eastern North America. Penokean collision (PEN), the oldest shown here, had no apparent effect on Huronian rocks in the Southern Province (SP). Next collision was in the Labrador Fold Belt (LFB). Last collision was in the Southern Province and extended south of the Penokean area. Otish, Mistassini Lake, and Chibougamau areas were apparently not disturbed until the Grenville orogeny.

time of mild retrograde metamorphism not accompanied by any major deformation or plutonism. Bickford and others (1981) and Dott (1981) tied dates in the 1600 to 1700 m.y. range to granites and rhyolites of that age in Iowa and northern Missouri and Kansas. Dott extended the correlation even to the Mazatzal belt in Arizona and New Mexico and suggested that a suture for this event must lie in Illinois and Iowa. We suggest an extension to the east to include the evidence for convergent tectonics in the Southern Province indicated by granitic plutons of this age range.

Younger dates, approximately 1500 m.y., are found in the Lake Superior area from "anorogenic" granitic plutons such as the Wolf River Batholith of Wisconsin (Van Schmus, 1976). As shown in Figure 6, similar dates have been obtained from some granitic and syenitic to monzonitic rocks in the Southern Province, and from anorthositic and syenitic rocks in the Grenville Province and in Labrador north of the Grenville Front. The anorthosites, at least, may be associated with some widespread tensional episode (Emslie, 1978).

To summarize, an orogenic event at or before 2100 m.y. ago, perhaps a continent-continent collision, affected the Southern Province and Lake Superior area, but the trend of the belt has not yet been determined. The Penokean Orogeny at 1850 to 1900 m.y. is the conspicuous deformation and metamorphic event in the Lake Superior area. In Figure 9 we have sketched a tentative suture for this event through the granitic and granodioritic intrusions in Wisconsin. Van Schmus (1981) has suggested that the Penokean event may have consisted of two or three stages and that these large plutons mark an island arc involved in the first collision.

Collision in the Labrador Fold Belt may also have taken place 1850 m.y. ago, based on the available dates, but the samples dated by Rb-Sr are not ideal for dating the peak of metamorphism and igneous activity. The suture for this event in Figure 9 follows the mafic and ultramafic rocks along the east side of the sedimentary and volcanic rocks of the belt. These mafic rocks have been traced by Gastil and Knowles (1960) and Dimroth and others (1970) into the Grenville Province, around a bend toward the southwest, as far as Manicouagan crater. Our extension of the line beyond that is very speculative but designed to be far enough from the three areas of post-Archean sedimentary rocks along the Grenville Front so as to have had little effect.

The next orogenic event, again possibly a continent-continent collision, judging from the occurrence of granite plutons occurred at approximately 1700 m.y., with major effects in the Southern Province. In Figure 9 we have drawn a hypothetical suture for this event which lies close to the granitic bodies and trends parallel with the higher metamorphic isograds of the Southern Province. To the west the suture truncates and then passes south of the Penokean suture, but close enough to the Lake Superior area to have caused retrograde metamorphism and resetting of Rb-Sr isochron dates. To the northeast the line was drawn so that it would stay close to the granitic plutons of this age within the Grenville Province. Beyond that area the extension is meant only to show that this orogenic belt would truncate the earlier belt extrapolated from the Labrador Fold Belt in the same manner that both were later truncated and overprinted by the Grenville event.

CONCLUSIONS

We have examined three regional problems involving Proterozoic rocks in eastern North America, using the assumption that the plate tectonic model developed for the Phanerozoic can be directly applied and emphasizing the role of the Wilson Cycle. We suggest that:

1. There may be several sutures within the Grenville orogenic belt, including some associated with pre-Grenville events. Proper identification will depend primarily on field evidence and isotopic dates. Geologists working in the region should not expect these sutures to conform with a simplified plate tectonic model, and could benefit from considering Phanerozoic sutures such as that of the Yarlung Dzangpo (Zhang and Yin, 1980).

2. The timing of Keweenaw rifting and the beginning of the Grenville orogeny, based on the small number of available U-Pb concordia dates on zircons and Rb-Sr whole-rock isochron dates, allow the possibility that the rift is a Grenville impactogen. It does not appear to be an aulacogen of the rift episode indicated by pre-Grenville dates from rift-related lithologies within the Grenville Province, but could have reactivated a rift formed at that time. It is also possible that the Keweenaw rift is an aulacogen of a rifting episode that occurred between subduction and collision events that have not yet been clearly resolved within the 1100 to 1250 m.y. time range until now used for a single Grenville orogeny.

3. The pre-Grenville Proterozoic history of eastern North America may be rather complex, with at least three orogenic events included in the southern part of the region. If the few isotopic dates now available are taken at face value, it is feasible that the main orogenic events in the Lake Superior area, Southern Province, and Labrador Fold Belt did *not* take place at the same time (the traditional Hudsonian Orogeny), and that the main event in the Southern Province may have caused the retrograde metamorphism seen in the Lake Superior area. Critical relationships between the Southern Province and Labrador Fold Belt have been obscured by Grenville-era deformation and regional metamorphism. They might, however, be discernable from additional U-Pb and Rb-Sr dates, and possibly Nd-Sm dates, from rocks selected for the purpose, such as any synorogenic plutonic rocks in the Labrador Fold Belt.

ACKNOWLEDGMENTS

We thank W.S.F. Kidd for critical reading of the manuscript and for very useful suggestions regarding the figures. We also thank three reviewers, all of whom made useful suggestions: Darrel Cowan, Ian Dalziel, and Alfred Kröner. The work of S. L. Anderson has been partially supported by NSF grant EAR 7911187 to G. W. Putnam.

REFERENCES CITED

Baer, A. J., 1976, The Grenville Province in Helikian times: a possible model of evolution, *in* Sutton, J., and others, co-chairmen, A discussion of global tectonics in Proterozoic times: Philosophical Transactions, Royal Society of London, v. 280, ser. A, p. 499–515.

——1981, Two orogenies in the Grenville Belt?: Nature, v. 290, p. 129–131.

Bell, K., and Blenkinsop, J., 1976, A Rb-Sr whole-rock isochron from the Otto Stock, Ontario: Canadian Journal of Earth Sciences, v. 13, p. 998–1002.

Bickford, M. E., and others, 1981, Origin of Middle Proterozoic granitic and rhyolitic rocks in the midcontinent region of North America: International Proterozoic Symposium, University of Wisconsin-Madison, Abstracts.

Bohlen, S., and Boettcher, A. L., 1980, The effect of magnesium on orthopyroxene-olivine-quartz stability: orthopyroxene geobarometry: EOS, v. 61, p. 393.

Bridgewater, D., 1965, Isotopic age determinations from S. Greenland and their geological setting: Meddelelser om Gronlands, v. 179, n. 4, 56 p.

Brocoum, S. J., and Dalziel, I.W.D., 1974, The Sudbury Basin, the Southern Province, the Grenville Front, and the Penokean Orogeny: Geological Society of America Bulletin, v. 85, p. 1571–1580.

Brook, M., Brewer, M. S., and Powell, D., 1976, Grenville age for rocks in the Moine of north-western Scotland: Nature, v. 260, p. 515.

Brown, P. E., Essene, E. J., and Kelly, W. C., 1978, Sphalerite geobarometry in the Balmat-Edwards district, New York: American Mineralogist, v. 63, p. 250–257.

Brown, R. L., Chappell, J. F., and Moore, J. M., Jr., 1975, An ensimatic island arc and ocean closure in the Grenville Province of southeastern Ontario, Canada: Geoscience Canada, v. 2, p. 141–143.

Burke, K., 1980, Intracontinental rifts and aulacogens, *in* Burchfiel, B. C., and others, co-chairmen, Continental tectonics, studies in geophysics: American Geophysical Union. p. 42–49.

Burke, K., and Dewey, J. F., 1973a, Orogeny in Africa, *in* Proceedings, Conference on African geology, December 1970, Ibadan, p. 583–608.

——1973b, Plume-generated triple junctions: key indicators in applying plate tectonics to old rocks: Journal of Geology, v. 81, p. 406–433.

Burke, K., Dewey, J. F., and Kidd, B. F., ed., 1976a, Dominance of horizontal movements, arc and microcontinental collisions during the later Permobile regime, *in* Windley, B. F., The early history of the Earth: New York, Wiley: p. 113–129.

——1976b, Precambrian paleomagnetic results compatible with contemporary operation of the Wilson cycle: Tectonophysics, v. 33, p. 287–299.

——1977, World distribution of sutures—the sites of former oceans: Tectonophysics, v. 40, p. 69–99.

Burwash, R. A., 1969, Comparative Precambrian geochronology of the North American, European, and Siberian shields: Canadian Journal of Earth Sciences, v. 6, p. 357–365.

Cambray, F. W., 1978, Plate tectonics as a model for the environment of deposition and deformation of the early Proterozoic (Precambrian X) of northern Michigan: Geological Society of America Abstracts with Programs, v. 10, p. 376.

Card, K. D., and others, 1978, Geology and mineral deposits of the Sudbury area, *in* Currie, A. L., and Mackasey, W. O., eds., Toronto '78, field trips guidebook: Geological Association of Canada, p. 260–279.

Chown, E. H., 1979, Structure and metamorphism of the Otish Mountain area of the Grenvillian foreland zone, Quebec: Summary: Geological Society of America Bulletin, Part I, v. 90, p. 13–15.

Clauer, N., 1979, A new approach to Rb-Sr dating of sedimentary rocks, *in* Jäger, E., and Hunziker, J. C., eds., Lectures in isotope geology: New York, Springer-Verlag, p. 30–51.

Condie, K. C., and Moore, J. M., Jr., 1977, Geochemistry of Proterozoic volcanic rocks from the Grenville Province, eastern Ontario, *in* Baragar, W.R.A., and others, eds., Volcanic regimes in Canada: Geological Association of Canada Special Paper 16, p. 149–168.

Craddock, C., 1981, Late Proterozoic tectonic evolution of the Lake Superior region: International Proterozoic Symposium, University of Wisconsin-Madison, Abstracts.

Davidson, A., and others, 1979, Regional synthesis of the Grenville Province of Ontario and western Quebec: Current Research, Geological Survey of Canada Paper 79-1B, p. 153–172.

Dewey, J. F., and Burke, K., 1973, Tibetan, Variscan, and Precambrian basement reactivation: products of continental collision: Journal of Geology, v. 81, p. 683–692.

——1974, Hot spots and continental breakup: some implications for collisional orogeny: Geology, v. 2, p. 57–60.

Dietz, R. S., 1964, Sudbury structure as an astrobleme: Journal of Geology, v. 72, p. 412–434.

Dimroth, E., 1972, The Labrador Geosyncline revisited: American Journal of Science, v. 272, p. 487–506.

Dimroth, E., and others, 1970, The filling of the circum-Ungava geosyncline, *in* Baer, A. J., ed., Basins and geosynclines of the Canadian shield: Geological Survey of Canada Paper 70–40, p. 45–142.

Dorr, A. L., and Laurin, A. F., 1971, Alignment of circular structures in mafic and ultramafic rocks: Transactions of the Canadian Institute of Mining, v.74, p. 206–209.

Dott, R. H., Jr., 1981, The Proterozoic red quartzite enigma in the north-central United States— resolved by plate collision?: International Proterozoic Symposium, University of Wisconsin-Madison, Abstracts.

Douglas, R.J.W., 1972, Tectonics (map, scale 1:15,000,000), *in* The National Atlas of Canada: Geological Survey of Canada.

——1980, Proposals for time classification of Precambrian rocks and events in Canada and adjacent areas of the Canadian Shield, Part 2: a provisional standard for correlating Precambrian rocks, Geological Survey of Canada Paper 80–24.

Emslie, R. F., 1978, Anorthosite massifs, rapakivi granites, and Late Proterozoic rifting of North America: Precambrian Research, v. 7, p. 61–98.

Fahrig, W. F., and Chown, E. H., 1973, The paleomagnetism of the Otish Gabbro from north of the Grenville Front, Quebec: Canadian Journal of Earth Sciences, v. 10, p. 1556–1564.

Fahrig, W. F., and Wanless, R. K., 1963, Age and significance of diabase dyke swarms in the Canadian shield: Nature, v. 200, p. 934–937.

Fairbairn, H. W., and others, 1969, Correlation of radiometric ages of Nipissing diabase and Huronian metasediments with Proterozoic events in Ontario: Canadian Journal of Earth Sciences, v. 6, p. 489–497.

Field, D., and Råheim, A., 1979, Rb-Sr total rock isotope studies on Precambrian charnockitic gneisses from south Norway: Evidence for isochron resetting during a low-grade metamorphic-deformational event: Earth and Planetary Science Letters, v. 45, p. 32–44.

Fleming, E. H., Jr., Ghiorso, A., and Cunningham, B. V., 1952, The specific alpha-activities and half-lives of ^{234}U, ^{235}U., and ^{238}U: Physics Review, v. 88, p. 642–652.

Franklin, J. M., Poulsen, K. H., and McIlwaine, W. H., 1972, Stratigraphy of the Sibley Group, a Helikian red bed sequence: Geological Society of America Abstracts with Programs, v. 4, p. 509.

Frarey, M. J., and Roscoe, S. M., 1970, The Huronian Supergroup north of Lake Huron, *in* Baer, A. J., ed., Basins and geosynclines of the Canadian Shield: Geological Survey of Canada Paper 70–40, p. 143–158.

Frith, R. A., and Doig, R., 1975, Pre-Kenoran tonalitic gneisses in the Grenville Province: Canadian Journal of Earth Sciences, v. 12, p. 844–849.

Fryer, B. J., 1972, Age determinations in the circum-Ungava Geosyncline and the evolution of Precambrian banded iron formations: Canadian Journal of Earth Sciences, v. 9, p. 652–663.

Garrison, J. R., Jr., 1980, The Coal Creek Serpentinite, Llano Uplift, Texas: a fragment of an incomplete Precambrian ophiolite: Geological Society of America Abstracts with Programs, v. 12, p. 431.

Garrison, J. R., Jr., Long, L. E., and Richmann, D. L., 1979, Rb-Sr and K-Ar geochronologic and isotopic studies, Llano Uplift, central Texas: Contributions to Mineralogy and Petrology, v. 69, p. 361–374.

Gastil, G., and Knowles, D. M., 1960, Geology of the Wabush Lake area, southwestern Labrador and eastern Quebec, Canada: Geological Society of America Bulletin, v. 71, p. 1243–1254.

Gates, T. M., and Hurley, I. M., 1973, Evaluation of Rb-Sr dating methods applied to the Matachewan, Abitibi, Mackenzie, and Sudbury dike swarms in Canada: Canadian Journal of Earth Sciences, v. 10, p. 900–919.

Gibbins, W. A., and McNutt, R. H., 1975, The age of the Sudbury nickel irruptive and the Murray granite: Canadian Journal of Earth Sciences, v. 12, p. 1970–1989.

Gittins, J., Macintyre, R. M., and York, D., 1967, The ages of carbonatite complexes in eastern Canada: Canadian Journal of Earth Sciences, v. 4, p. 651–655.

Grant, J. A., 1964, Rubidium-strontium isochron study of the Grenville Front near Lake Timagami, Ontario: Science, v. 146, p. 1049–1053.

Halls, H. C., 1978, The Late Precambrian geology of the central North American rift system, *in* Ramberg, I. B., and Neumann, E. R., eds., Tectonics and geophysics of continental rifts: Dordrecht, Holland, D. Reidel Publishing Co., NATO Advanced Study Institute, Series C., v. 37, p. 111–121.

Harper, C. T., 1967, On the interpretation of potassium-argon ages from Precambrian shields and Phanerozoic orogens: Earth and Planetary Science Letters, v. 3, p. 128–132.

Hofmann, H. J., 1978, New stromatolites from the Aphebian Mistassini Group, Quebec: Canadian Journal of Earth Sciences, v. 15, p. 571–585.

Hunziker, J. C., 1979, Potassium-argon dating, *in* Jäger, E., and Hunziker, J. C., eds., Lectures in isotope geology: New York, Springer-Verlag, p. 52–76.

Irving, E., Emslie, R. F., and Ueno, H., 1974, Upper Proterozoic paleomagnetic poles from Laurentia and the history of the Grenville Structural Province: Journal of Geophysical Research, v. 79, p. 5491–5502.

Irving, E., and McGlynn, J. C., 1976, Proterozoic magnetostratigraphy and the tectonic evolution of Laurentia, *in* Sutton, J., and others, eds., A discussion on global tectonics in Proterozoic times: Philosophical Transactions of the Royal Society of London, v. 280, ser. A., p. 433–468.

Jaffey, A. H., and others, 1971, Precision measurements of half-lives and specific activities of ^{235}U and ^{238}U: Physics Reviews, Part C, v. 4, p. 1889–1906.

Jolly, W. T., and Smith, R. E., 1972, Degradation and metamorphic differentiation of the Keweenawan tholeiitic lavas of northern Michigan, U.S.A.: Journal of Petrology, v. 13, p. 273–310.

Klein, C., 1979, Diagenetic and metamorphic reactions in iron-formations from the Labrador Trough: Geological Association of Canada—Mineralogical Association of Canada Program with Abstracts, v. 4,

p. 61.
Larue, D. K., 1981, Evolution of a purported Early Proterozoic passive margin, Lake Superior region: revelations from the collision zone in southcentral northern Michigan and adjacent Wisconsin: International Proterozoic Symposium, University of Wisconsin-Madison, Abstracts.
Leeman, W. P., 1977, Pb and Sr study of Keweenawan lavas and inferred 4 b.y.-old lithosphere beneath part of Minnesota: Geological Society of America Abstracts with Programs, v. 9, p. 1068.
Long, D.G.F., 1974, Glacial and paraglacial genesis of conglomeratic rocks of the Chibougamau Formation (Aphebian), Chibougamau, Quebec: Canadian Journal of Earth Sciences, v. 11, p. 1236–1252.
Max, M. D., 1979, Extent and disposition of Grenville tectonism in the Precambrian continental crust adjacent to the North Atlantic: Geology, v. 7, p. 76–78.
McGlynn, J. C., 1968a, Mistassini Subprovince, Superior Province, *in* Douglas, R.J.W., ed., Geology and economic minerals of Canada: Geological Survey of Canada Economic Geology Report 1, Part A, p. 59–60.
——1968b, Southern Province, *in* Douglas, R.J.W., ed., Geology and economic minerals of Canada: Geological Survey of Canada Economic Geology Report 1, Part A., p. 108–119.
McWilliams, M. O., and Dunlop, D. J., 1978, Grenville paleomagnetism and tectonics: Canadian Journal of Earth Sciences, v. 15, p. 687–695.
Miller, J. A., Matthews, D. H., and Roberts, D. G., 1973, Rocks of Grenville age from Rockall Bank: Nature Physical Science, v. 246, p. 61.
Moore, J. M., Jr., 1977, Orogenic volcanism in the Proterozoic of Canada, *in* Baragar, W.R.A., and others, eds., Volcanic regimes in Canada: Geological Association of Canada Special Paper 16, p. 127–148.
Moore, J. M., Jr., and Thompson, P. H., 1980, The Flinton Group: a Late Precambrian metasedimentary succession in the Grenville Province of eastern Ontario: Canadian Journal of Earth Sciences, v. 17, p. 1685–1707.
Naldrett, A. J., and Macdonald, A. J., 1980, Tectonic settings of Ni-Cu sulphide ores: their importance in genesis and exploration, *in* Strangway, D. W., ed., The continental crust and its mineral deposits: Geological Association of Canada Special Paper 20, p. 633–657.
Putman, G. W., and Sullivan, J. W., 1979, Granitic pegmatites as estimators of crustal pressures—a test in the eastern Adirondacks, New York: Geology, v. 7, p. 549–553.
Quirke, T. T., and Collins, W. H., 1930, Disappearance of the Huronian: Geological Survey of Canada Memoir 160, 112 p.
Rondot, J., 1978, Stratigraphie et métamorphisme de la région du Saint-Maurice: Metamorphism in the Canadian Shield, Geological Survey of Canada Paper 78–10, p. 329–352.
Sengör, A.M.C., and Butler, J. C., 1977, The Llano Uplift, central Texas: a Proterozoic example of continental collision?: Geological Society of America Abstracts with Programs, v. 9, p. 72–73.
Sethuraman, K., 1979, Discovery of an Archean volcanigenic environment in the Grenville structural province, Echouani area, Quebec: Geological Association of Canada—Mineralogical Association of Canada Program with Abstracts, v. 4, p. 78.
Silver, L. T., and Green, J. C., 1963, Zircon ages for Middle Keweenawan rocks of the Lake Superior region: EOS, v. 44, p. 107.
——1972, Time constants for Keweenawan igneous activity: Geological Society of America Abstracts with Programs, v. 4, p. 665–666.
Silver, L. T., and Lumbers, S. B., 1966, Geochronological studies in the Bancroft-Madoc area of the Grenville Province, Ontario, Canada: Geological Society of America Special Paper 87, p. 156.
Stamatelopoulou-Seymour, K., and MacLean, W. H., 1977, The geochemistry of possible metavolcanic rocks and their relationship to mineralization at Montauban-Les-Mines, Quebec: Canadian Journal of Earth Sciences, v. 14, p. 2440–2452.
Steiger, R. H., and Jäger, E., 1977, Subcommission on geochronology: convention on the use of decay constants in geo- and cosmochronology: Earth and Planetary Science Letters, v. 36, p. 359–362.
Stockwell, C. H., 1964, Fourth report on structural provinces, orogenies, and time-classification of rocks of the Canadian Precambrian shield, *in* Age determinations and geological studies: Geological Survey of Canada Paper 64–17, Part II, p. 1–21.
Tarney, J., Dalziel, I.W.D., and de Wit, M. J., 1976, Marginal basin 'Rocas Verdes' complex from S. Chile: a model for Archaean greenstone belt formation, *in* Windley, B. F., ed., The early history of the Earth: New York, Wiley, p. 131–146.
Thomas, M. D., and Tanner, J. G., 1975, Cryptic suture in the eastern Grenville Province: Nature, v. 256, p. 392–394.
Van Schmus, W. R., 1965, The geochronology of the Blind River-Bruce Mines area, Ontario, Canada: Journal of Geology, v. 73, p. 755–780.
——1976, Early and Middle Proterozoic history of the Great Lakes area, North America: Philosophical Transactions of the Royal Society of London, v. 280, ser. A, p. 605–628.
——1981, Possible interpretations of the Penokean Orogeny: International Proterozoic Symposium, University of Wisconsin-Madison, Abstracts.
Wanless, R. K., and others, 1968, Age determinations and geological studies, K-Ar isotopic ages, Report 8: Geological Survey of Canada Paper 67–2, Part A, 141 p.
Wilson, J. T., 1968, Static or mobile Earth: the current scientific revolution: American Philosophical Society Proceedings, v. 112, p. 309–320.
Wynne Edwards, H. R., 1972, The Grenville province, *in* Price, R. A., and Douglas, R.J.W., eds., Variations in tectonic style in Canada: Geological Association of Canada Special Paper 11, p. 262–334.
Young, G. M., 1980, The Grenville orogenic belt in the North Atlantic continents: Earth Science Reviews, v. 16, p. 277–288.
——1981, Tectono-sedimentary history of early Proterozoic rocks of the northern Great Lakes region: International Proterozoic Symposium, University of Wisconsin-Madison, Abstracts.
Zartman, R. E., 1964, A geochronologic study of the Lone Grove pluton from the Llano uplift, Texas: Journal of Petrology, v. 5, p. 359–408.
Zhang, R., and Yin, J. (chief compilers), 1980, A scientific guidebook to south Xizang (Tibet): Organizing Committee, Symposium on Qinhai-Xizang (Tibet) Plateau, Academia Sinica, Beijing, China, 104 p. and map.

MANUSCRIPT ACCEPTED BY THE SOCIETY APRIL 14, 1983

Printed in U.S.A.

Geological Society of America
Memoir 161
1983

Geochemical, isotopic, and paleomagnetic tests of early sial-sima patterns: The Precambrian crustal enigma revisited

A. Y. Glikson
*Australian Bureau of Mineral Resources, Geology and Geophysics
Canberra, ACT
Australia*

ABSTRACT

Geochemical parameters and isotopic indices of Precambrian silicic igneous rocks record largely ensialic crustal environments during 2.5 to 1.0 b.y. ago. Simatic crustal regimes have evidently coexisted (i.e., southwest and central United States, Fennoscandia, Venezuela) though their extent remains unclear. The significance of initial $Sr^{87}/^{86}$ ratios (Ri) and large-ion-lithophile (LIL) element data is considered: both tend to be higher in Proterozoic than in Archean silicic igneous suites, suggesting, respectively, predominance of ensialic and ensimatic anatectic processes. The ensialic nature of middle Proterozoic crustal reworking is supported by Sm/Nd study of composite North American samples yielding Archean model ages. Estimates of average crustal compositions are allowed by Precambrian sediments. K/Na ratios, rare earth elements (REE), and Ri values of Proterozoic sediments indicate derivation from differentiated sialic source terrains, including a high proportion of K-rich silicic igneous rocks. This contrasts with the mafic and Na-rich nature of Archean greenstone-tonalite terrains and derived sediments. The relative paucity of oceanic crustal signatures during 2.5 to 1.0 b.y. ago, calculations of minimum crustal growth rates, limits on the thickness and volume of the Proterozoic sial, and paleomagnetic apparent polar wander paths (APWP) render the evidence difficult to reconcile with plate tectonics processes and/or with present-day Earth surface dimensions. The observed coincidence of APWP for Laurentia, Greenland, Africa, and Australia during 2.3 to 1.6 b.y. ago implies a preexistence of equivalents of the Atlantic, Indian, and Pacific ocean basins in approximately their modern positions—a conclusion faced by major geological, geochemical, and isotopic objections. It may appear from the Proterozoic record that during 2.5 to 1.0 b.y. ago almost three fourths of the continental crust has already existed. If so, five alternative models are considered with regard to the nature of the other three-fourths of the crust: (1) global sial of continental thickness; (2) a thin global sial; (3) dispersed sial and sima plates; (4) a hemisphere-size simatic regime; (5) global sial on a smaller radius Earth. An apparent inability of models 1, 2, 3, and 4 to account for the unrecorded Proterozoic crust is indicated, which directs attention toward model 5. Objections to and constraints on radial expansion are considered. Rapid expansion rates in the order of 10 mm/year during the Mesozoic-Cenozoic are unlikely. However, slow expansion rates in the order of 0.5 to 1.0 mm/year during early and middle Precambrian times may be capable of accounting for the questions posed by the geochemical, isotopic, and

paleomagnetic data. This enigma remains open for further investigation, notably by paleomagnetic and isotopic studies of the worldwide system of ca. 2.4-b.y.-old basic dykes, which could provide a definitive time/place reference grid.

INTRODUCTION: THE PRECAMBRIAN CRUSTAL ENIGMA

Two independent lines of evidence give rise to a major paradox regarding the Precambrian Earth. The first is based on geochemical and isotopic tests of sial/sima crustal distribution during the Proterozoic (2.5 to 0.6 b.y. B.P.). The second is based on paleomagnetic apparent polar wander paths (APWP) for the early to middle Proterozoic. This paper considers the mutual compatibility of these criteria which, when combined, pose an enigma concerning early Earth's surface dimensions and radii.

During the Archean (3.9 to 2.5 b.y. B.P.), a dominance of ensimatic anatexis (two-stage mantle melting) is indicated by low large-ion-lithophile (LIL) element abundances, heavy rare earth elements (REE) depletion, and low initial Sr^{87}/Sr^{86} ratios (Ri) of silicic igneous rocks (Arth and Hanson, 1975; Moorbath, 1977; O'Nions and Pankhurst, 1978; Collerson and Bridgwater, 1979; Glikson, 1976a, 1979a; Pride and Muecke, 1980). By contrast, the bulk of early and middle Proterozoic (2.5 to 1.0 b.y. B.P.) silicic igneous suites is characterized by high LIL elements, Europium depletion, and low to high Ri values, suggesting prevalence of ensialic anatectic processes within largely contiguous ensialic regimes (Engel and Kelm, 1972; Rutland, 1976; Wynne-Edwards, 1976; Glikson, 1976b, 1979b, 1980a; Piper, 1976; McElhinny and McWilliams, 1977). Precambrian sediments show a temporal increase in LIL elements, total REE, light REE/heavy REE ratios, minimum Ri values of carbonates, and a secular decline in Na/K, Mg, Ni, Cr, and V, reflecting a change from tonalite-greenstone dominated provenance to K-rich granite dominated provenance terrains (MacPherson, 1958; Fahrig and Eade, 1968; Engel et al., 1974; Veizer and Compston, 1976; Naqvi, 1978; Taylor, 1979; Sheraton, 1980). Isotopic Pb/Pb data (Patterson and Tatsumoto, 1964; Slawson et al., 1963) Rb/Sr data (Armstrong, 1968), and Sm/Nd data (McCulloch and Wasserburg, 1978) indicate that the bulk of juvenile mantle-derived materials accreted into sial during, and largely toward the end of, the Archean.

During 2.5 to 1.0 b.y. ago well over 60% of the continental crust had already been in existence. Limits on the volume and distribution of sial during this era are provided by crustal thickness indicators based on metamorphic *P-T* indicators (Tarney and Windley, 1977; O'Hara, 1977; Newton, 1977), estimates of deformation (Shackleton, 1976), and paleomagnetic APWP data (Irving and Park, 1972; McElhinny and McWilliams, 1977). From these constraints, during most of the Precambrian at least 70 percent of the Earth surface must have been occupied by oceanic-type crust. It is therefore surprising that, unlike the pre-2.5-b.y. and post-1.0-b.y. eras, simatic relics (greenstones and ophiolites) and products of ensimatic anatexis (Na-rich volcanic and plutonic acid rocks) are remarkably scarce in early and middle Proterozoic terrains. Is it possible that simatic regimes which occupied the majority of the Earth surface during 1500×10^6 years have left little or no trace in the geological record? The concept that an inert, nonaccreted, and nonsubducted oceanic crust may have existed during most of the Proterozoic (Baer, 1980) is difficult to reconcile with high heat generations and thereby convection rates calculated for this era (Lambert, 1976), nor is it consistent with the intense tectonic and thermal activity in Proterozoic ensialic mobile belts (Glikson, 1980b). In any tectonic model, the formation, spreading, and destruction of simatic crust would have resulted in intersection of the basalt solidus, generation of silicic partial melts, and sialic accretion.

A closely akin problem arises from the coincidence of APWP of North America and Africa during 2.3 to 1.9 b.y. and of Greenland and Australia during 1.8 to 1.6 b.y. ago (Embleton and Schmidt, 1979; Schmidt and Embleton, 1981). These overlaps, if valid, imply present-day angular distances between shields in the early and middle Proterozoic, and thereby preexistence of antecedent analogues of the Pacific, Atlantic, and Indian ocean basins in their approximate modern positions. Such a conclusion, however, is difficult to reconcile with the cross-Atlantic match between Precambrian provincces (Hurley et al., 1976) and with the absence of signatures of subducted, obducted, or reworked sima as circum-Atlantic, circum-Pacific, and circum-Indian ocean Proterozoic belts. Furthermore, had sialic plates converged into Pangea in the late Proterozoic and subsequently returned to their early Proterozoic positions in post-Permian times, some kind of crust-mantle "memory" is implied (Schmidt and Embleton, 1981).

These questions are discussed in this paper with reference to geochemical and isotopic indices for Precambrian sial/sima distribution. Silicic plutonic and volcanic suites provide criteria for identification of crustal environments and nature of their source materials. By contrast, applications of basalt geochemistry to classification of tectonic regimes (Pearce and Cann, 1973; Pearce et al., 1977) are hindered by vertical and lateral mantle heterogeneities (Green, 1971; Jaques et al., 1978). Whereas individual geochemical or isotopic criteria may not provide unique indi-

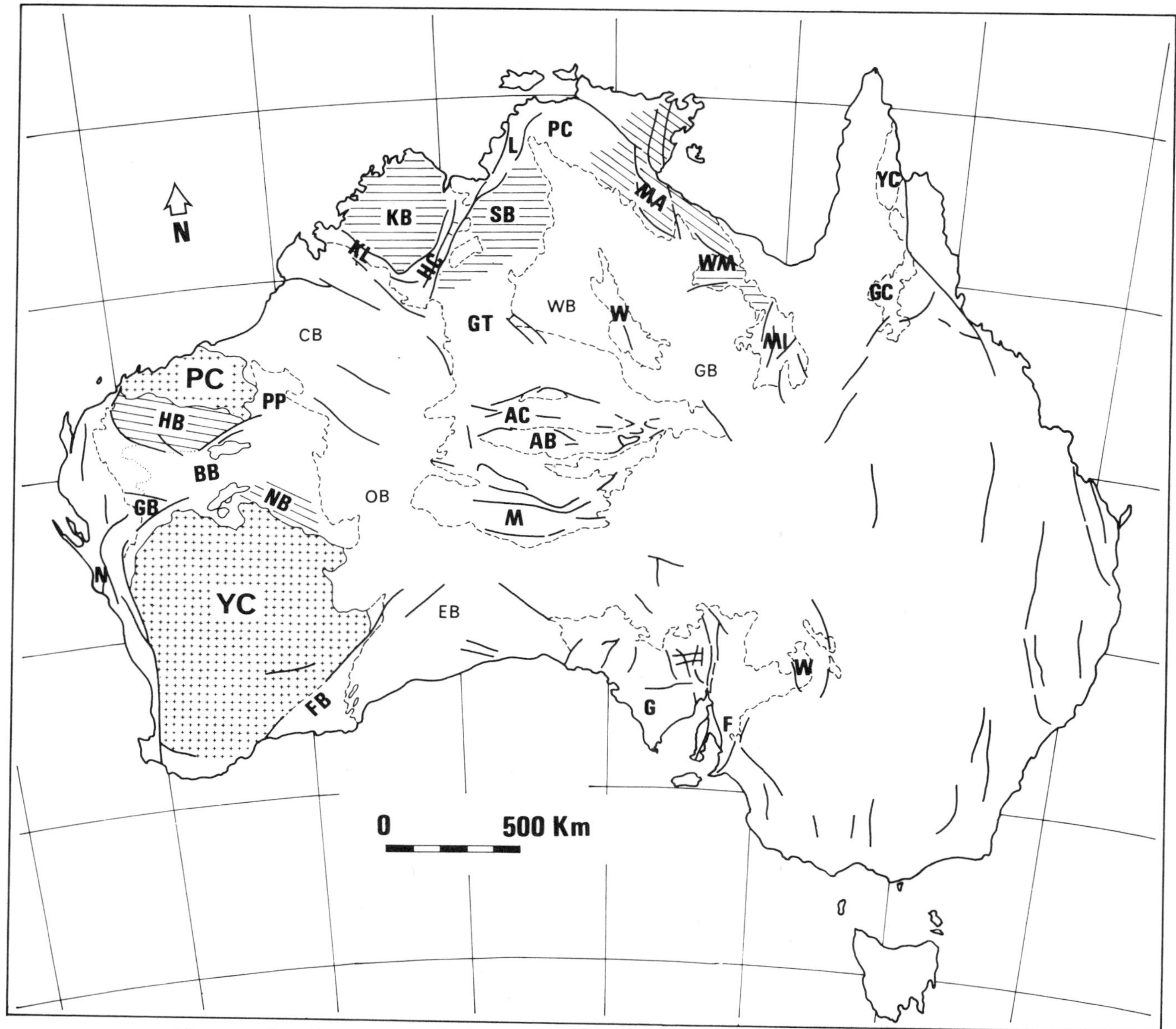

Figure 1. Locality map of principal Australian Precambrian units including units cited in Tables 1 and 2. PC, Pilbara Craton; YC, Yilgarn Craton; FB, Fraser Belt; NB, Nabberu Basin; N, Northampton Block; GB, Gascoyne Block; BB, Bangemall Basin; HB, Hamersley Basin; PP, Patterson Province; KB, Kimberley Block; KL, King Leopold Belt; HC, Halls Creek Belt; SB, Sturt Block; L, Litchfield Block; PC, Pine Creek Block; MA, McArthur Block; WM, Westmoreland Block; MI, Mount Isa Block; YC, Cape York Complex; GC, Georgetown Craton; GT, Granites-Tanami Block; AC, Arunta Complex; AB, Amadeus Basin; M, Musgrave Block; G, Gawler Craton; F, Flinders Block; W, Willyama Complex. Younger basins: CB, Canning Basin; OB, Officer Basin; EB, Eucla Basin; WB, Wiso Basin; GB, Georgina Basin.

cators of source composition, when combined these criteria furnish conclusive evidence on the nature of the parental crust and may be used as a guide to the early sial/sima distribution. When the geochemical-isotopic and paleomagnetic lines of evidence converge, definitive controls on the composition and the spatial and temporal distribution of the Precambrian crust are possible

GEOCHEMICAL AND ISOTOPIC CRITERIA FOR PRECAMBRIAN SIAL/SIMA DISTRIBUTION

A computer data file of silicic igneous and metamorphic rock analyses has been compiled. Australian data are from the Archean Yilgarn (28 analyses) and Pilbara (131) cratons, and the Proterozoic Cape Naturaliste (25), Fraser

TABLE 1. GEOCHEMICAL DATA FOR AUSTRALIAN PRECAMBRIAN SILICIC IGNEOUS ROCKS

Formation	Terrain	Number analyses	References
Archaean			
trondhjemite pebbles, Kurrawang	Yilgarn, W.A.	7	Glikson and Sheraton, 1972
granites, Kalgoorlie-Norseman	"	18	Oversby, 1975
porphyries, Kalgoorlie-Norseman	"	av. of 50	O'Beirne, 1968
granodiorite, Kambalda	"	1	"
adamellite, Mungari	"	1	"
Duffer Formation (dacite and rhyolite)	Pilbara, W.A.	64	Glikson and Hickman, 1981
Wyman Formation (rhyolites)	"	23	"
granites, east Pilbara	"	26	Oversby, 1976
Shaw & Mt Edgar batholith	"	av. value	Blockley, 1973
Mondana adamellite	"	1	Hickman and Lipple, 1975
Moolyella granite	"	1	"
Mt Edgar batholith	"	15	Glikson, 1979a
Proterozoic			
acid granulites & amphibolite-facies gneiss	Cape Naturaliste, W.A.	25	Lambert, 1967
acid granulites	Fraser Range, W.A.	4	"
acid to subacid granulites	Musgrave Range, W.A.	7	"
Argylla Formation (acid volcanics)	Mt Isa-Cloncurry, NW Qld	29	Rossiter and Ferguson, 1980
Leichhardt Metamorphics (acid volcanics)	"	13	"
Argylla Formation, dacites	"	av. of 6	Wilson, 1978
Argylla Formation, rhyolites	"	av. of 30	"
Leichhardt Metamorphics, dacites	"	av. of 2	"
Leichhardt Metamorphics, rhyolites	"	av. of 17	"
Cliffdale Volcanics	Westmoreland, NW Qld	30	Mitchell, 1976
Forsayth and Esmeralda granites	Georgetown, NE Qld	9	Sheraton and Labonne, 1978
various granites	Pine Creek, N.T.	19	Ferguson et al., 1980
Cullen granite	Pine Creek, N.T.	5 averages	Ewers and Scott, 1977
Winnecke Formation	Granites-Tanami, N.T.	5	Blake et al., 1977
The Granites Granite	"	3	"
Slaty Creek Granite	"	3	"
Lewis Granite	"	4	"
Pollock Hill Fm (volcanics)	"	6	"
Mt Webb Granite	"	6	"
dacite, rhyodacite, rhyolite	Gawler Block, S.A.	8	Giles, 1977
Chandabka caldera	"	30	Branch, 1978

Range (4), Musgrave Range (7), Mount Isa–Cloncurry (46), Westmoreland (30), Georgetown (9), Pine Creek–Alligator River (24), Granites-Tanami (35), and Gawler (38) Blocks (Fig. 1). A breakdown and references are in Table 1. In addition to the Australian data, Archean silicic igneous rocks from the Barberton-Swaziland craton (53), Greenland-Labrador (24), Scotland (8), Venezuela (37), and Minnesota (10) are included in frequency distribution plots. A computer program for storage and retrieval of Rb-Sr isochron age and initial Sr^{87}/Sr^{86} data as written, including subroutines for Ri versus age plots, calculation of crustal residence model time for assumed Rb/Sr ratios of precursor crust, plots of residence time versus age, and of mantle derivation time versus crustal residence time. A total number of 612 isochrons were stored, including data from Australia (187), Antarctica (43), Africa (115), Canada (168), United States (40), South America (12), Greenland-Labrador (50), and Fennoscandia (7). A breakdown is given in Table 2. While necessarily incomplete, these compilations are probably comprehensive enough to reveal possible geochemical and isotopic trends.

TABLE 2. AUSTRALIAN PRECAMBRIAN AND PALEOZOIC Rb/Sr ISOCHRON AGE DATA LOCATIONS AND SOURCES

Geological Unit	Province	Rb/Sr age interval (b.y.)	Number of isochrons	References
Australia				
granites, gneiss	Wheat Belt, Yilgarn, W.A.	2.6-3.0	26	Arriens, 1971
granite, gneiss	Eastern Goldfields, Yilgarn, W.A.	2.5-2.7	10	Compston and Turek, 1973; Bennet et al., 1975; Roddick et al., 1975; Cooper et al., 1978; Chapman et al., 1980.
granite	Murchison Goldfield, Yilgarn, W.A.	2.6	2	Muhling and DeLaeter, 1971
granite, gneiss	Pilbara, W.A.	2.2-3.1	13	DeLaeter and Trendall, 1970; DeLaeter and Blockley, 1972; DeLaeter et al., 1975; DeLaeter et al., 1977; Cooper et al., 1980
granite gneiss	Fraser Range, W.A.	1.2-2.6	8	Arriens and Lambert, 1968; Bunting et al., 1976
granite, volcanics, metamorphics	Kimberley, W.A.	1.5-2.1	8	Bennet et al., 1975
granulite, granite, gneiss	Musgrave Ranges S.A.	0.9-1.6	26	Arriens and Lambert, 1969; Gray, 1979
granite	Granites-Tanami, N.T.	1.5-1.8	7	Page et al., 1976
granite, volcanics	Tennant Creek, N.T.	1.4-1.8	5	Black, 1977
granite, migmatite	Arunta, N.T.	1.0-1.6	4	Marjoribanks and Black, 1974; Allen and Black, 1979
granite, gneiss	Pine Creek, N.T.	1.6-2.5	13	Page et al., 1980
Volcanics, granite	Mount Isa-Cloncurry, Qld	1.4-1.8	21	Page 1978
volcanics, granites	Georgetown, Qld	1.4-1.5	3	Richards et al., 1966
volcanics	Gawler Block, S.A.	1.8-2.6	8	Cooper et al., 1976; Fanning et al., 1980
gneiss, metamorphics	Willyama Complex, N.S.W.	1.5-1.7	5	Bennet et al., 1975
granites	Tasman geosyncline	0.4-0.5	24	Roddick and Compston, 1977; Compston and Chappel, 1979

Major Elements in Silicic Igneous Suites

An effective classification of silicic igneous rocks is obtained on the An-Ab-Or ternary (O'Connor, 1965) (Fig. 2). The Archean data plot extensively in the trondhjemite field, with significant extension into the granite sensu stricto field and only a few points in the more An-rich tonalite, granodiorite, and adamellite fields. By contrast, the Proterozoic data plot mainly in the granite sensu stricto and adamellite fields. A petrogenetic classification on the Qz-Ab-Or diagram (Fig. 3) shows that, whereas Archean magmas crystallized largely in the plagioclase fractionation field under moderately high pH_2O (up to ca. 7 kb), Proterozoic melts concentrated in the K-feldspar-plagioclase-quartz low-pH_2O eutectic zone. K-rich rhyolites of the Wyman Formation, Pilbara Block, plot near the Qz-Or join, representing likely metasomatic elvan-type porphyries (Glikson and Hickman, 1981). Frequency distribution diagrams for Archean and Proterozoic silicic igneous and metamorphic rocks from the Australian and other Precambrian shields (Fig. 4) indicate (1) a broad overlap of SiO_2 values, with maxima in the 67% to 73% range; (2) distinct K_2O peaks for Archean (1.0 to 1.5%) and Proterozoic (5.0 to 5.5%) data; (3) generally high MgO and CaO abun-

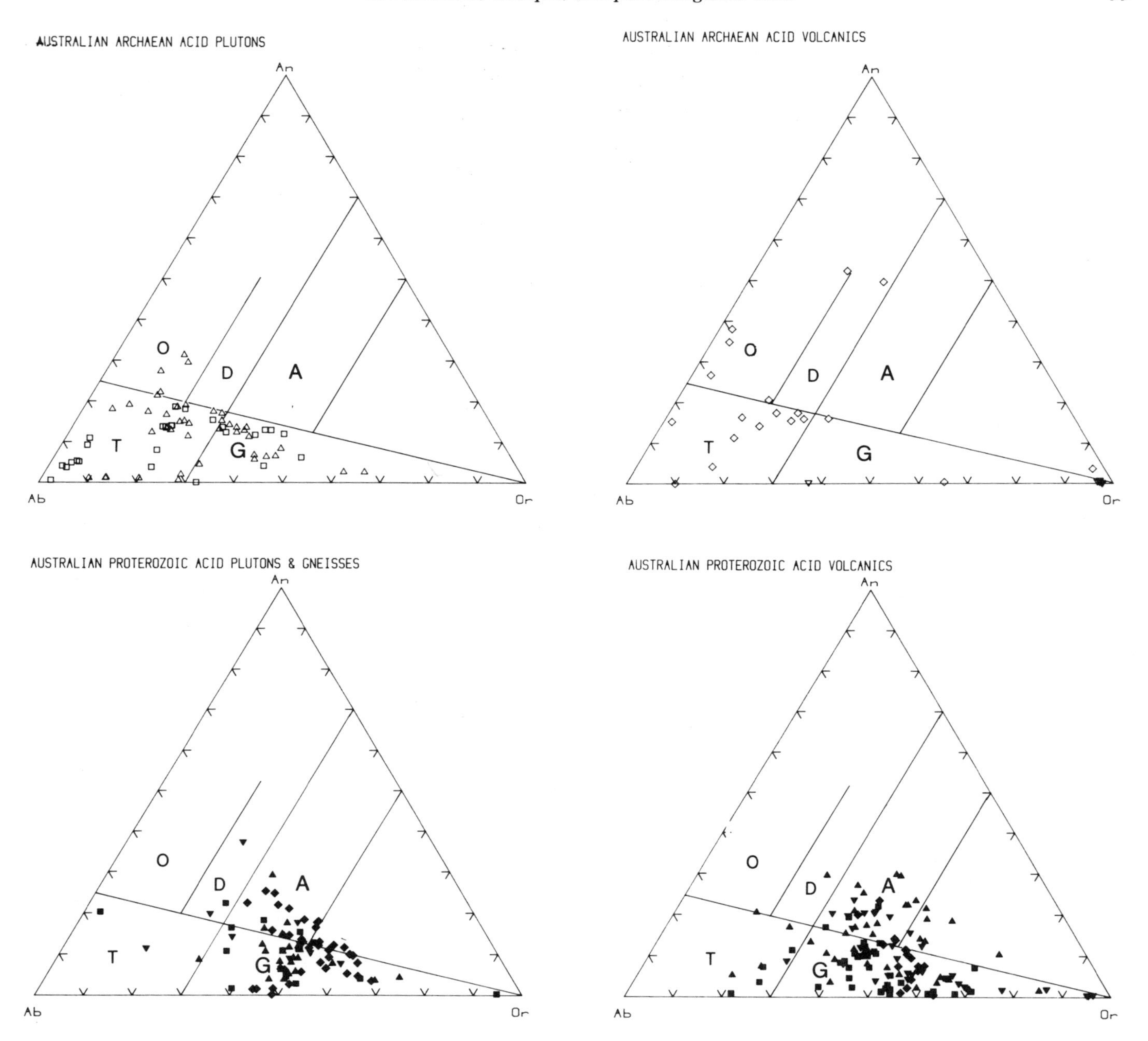

Figure 2. An-Ab-Or diagrams for Australian Archean and Proterozoic acid plutonic and volcanic rocks. Petrochemical classification according to O'Connor (1965): T, trondhjemites; O, tonalites; D, granodiorites; A, adamellites; G, granite (s.s.). Symbols: (A) Archean acid plutons: open upright triangles, Pilbara; open squares, Kalgoorlie-Norseman (Yilgarn). (B) Archean acid volcanics: open diamonds, Duffer Formation (Pilbara); open inverted triangles, Wyman Formation (Pilbara). (C) Proterozoic acid plutons and gneisses: solid diamonds, Musgrave, Fraser, and Cape Naturaliste gneiss and granulite; solid squares, The Granites-Tanami granites; solid upright triangles, Pine Creek Block granites; inverted triangles, Georgetown Block granites. (D) Proterozoic acid volcanics: solid squares, Gawler Block volcanics; solid diamonds, The Granites-Tanami volcanics; solid upright triangles, Leichhardt and Argylla Volcanics, NW Queensland; solid inverted triangles, Cliffdale Volcanics, Westmoreland. Data sources in Table 1.

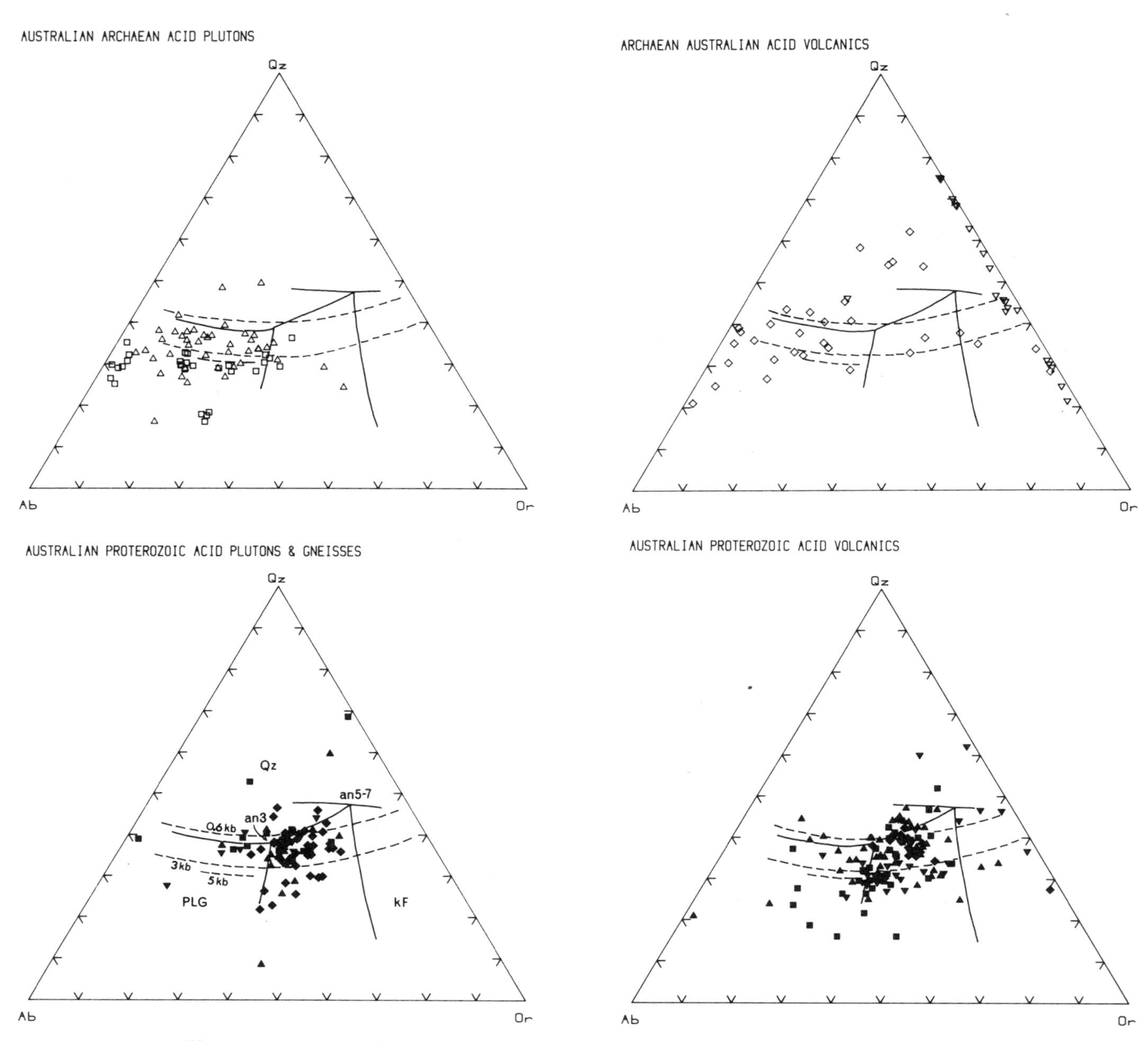

Figure 3. Qz-Ab-Or diagrams for Australian Archean and Proterozoic acid plutonic and volcanic rocks. Symbols as in Figure 2. Data sources in Table 1. Plg, plagioclase crystallization field; KF, K-feldspar crystallization field; Qz, quartz crystallization field; continuous lines, phase boundaries; discontinuous lines, cotectic variations with pressure.

dances in Archean as compared to Proterozoic suites. These differences reflect either relatively advanced magmatic fractionation of the Proterozoic magmas, or/and a derivation of the latter from more differentiated sources.

Large-Ion-Lithophile (LIL) Elements in Silicic Igneous Suites

Because of their very low crystal/liquid partition coefficients (K_d), the incompatible LIL elements, Rb, Ba, Zr, Nb, U, Th, Pb, and REE are progressively enriched upon magmatic fractionation, providing useful indicators of (1) source composition and (2) degrees of partial melting and fractional crystallization. Frequency distribution plots of Archean and Proterozoic Rb, Pb, Ba, Sr, U, Th, Zr, and Y abundances (Fig. 5) reveal the distinct geochemistry of silicic igneous suites of these eras. The Rb peak for the Proterozoic data (140 to 200 ppm) exceeds that for the Archean (60 to 80 ppm) by more than a factor of 2. Similar relations are observed for Pb (Archean peak—5 to 10 ppm;

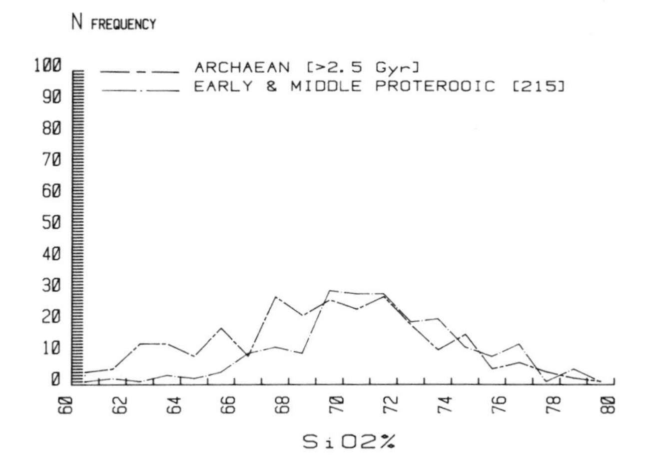

K2O FREQUENCY: PRECAMBRIAN ACID IGNEOUS ROCKS
N FREQUENCY
ARCHAEAN [>2.5 Gyr] [312]
EARLY & MIDDLE PROTEROZOIC [216]
K2O%

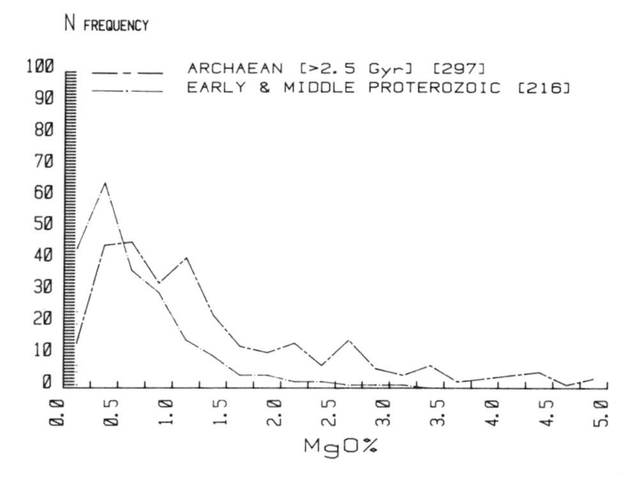

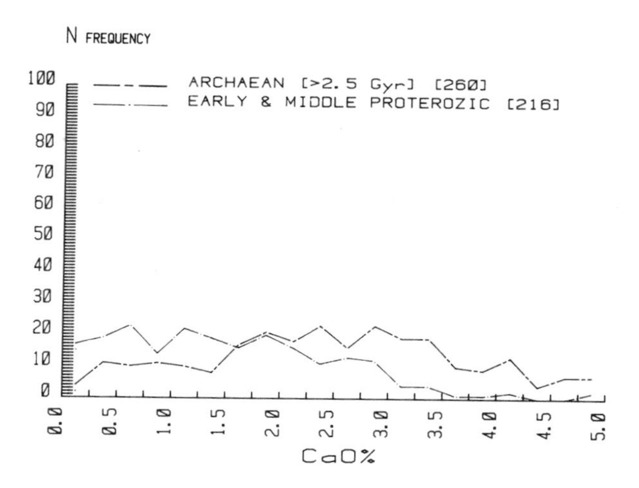

Figure 4. Frequency distribution of SiO_2, K_2O, MgO and CaO in Archean and Proterozoic acid igneous rocks. Numbers of samples in square brackets. Data sources for Australia are in Table 1. Other data are from Barberton-Swaziland (53), Greenland-Labrador (24), Scotland (8), and Minnesota (10).

Proterozoic peak—25 to 35 ppm), Ba (Archean peak—300 to 400 ppm; Proterozoic peak—800 to 1,2,00 ppm), U (Archean peak—1 to 2 ppm; wide scatter of Proterozoic values), Th (Archean peak—5 to 10 ppm; Proterozoic maxima—15 to 45 ppm). The differences with respect to Zr and Y are less pronounced: for Zr an Archean peak of 150 to 200 ppm compares with a Proterozoic peak of 200 to 250 ppm. For Y the Archean peak at 10 to 15 ppm contrasts with a flat wide-scatter of the Proterozoic data. Archean silicic suites tend to have high Sr levels relative to Proterozoic suites, in agreement with the higher CaO abundances of the former (Fig. 4). Whether the marked differences in alkali and LIL trace elements arise from source differences or from the degree of magmatic differentiation is considered later. The differences between Archean and Proterozoic silicic suites are also expressed on major/major, major/trace, and trace/trace, and trace/trace element ratio frequency plots (Fig. 6). The Archean rocks display a wide variation of Na_2O/K_2O ratios, Rb/Sr maximum below 0.2, K/Rb mode at 250 to 300, K/U mode at 5,000 to 7,500, K/Th mode at 1,000 to 2,000, and K/Ba mode at 10 to 25. The Proterozoic data define a sharp Na_2O/K_2O peak at 0.5 to 0.75, display a wide scatter of Rb/Sr ratios with a peak at 0.9 to 1.0, and show concentrations of K/Rb at 150 to 250, K/U at 2,500 to 5,000, and K/Th at 1,000 to 1,500. These relations express enrichment in the Proterozoic rocks of Rb, U, and Th relative to K, that is, a higher degree of fractionation related to the ionic radii sequence of these

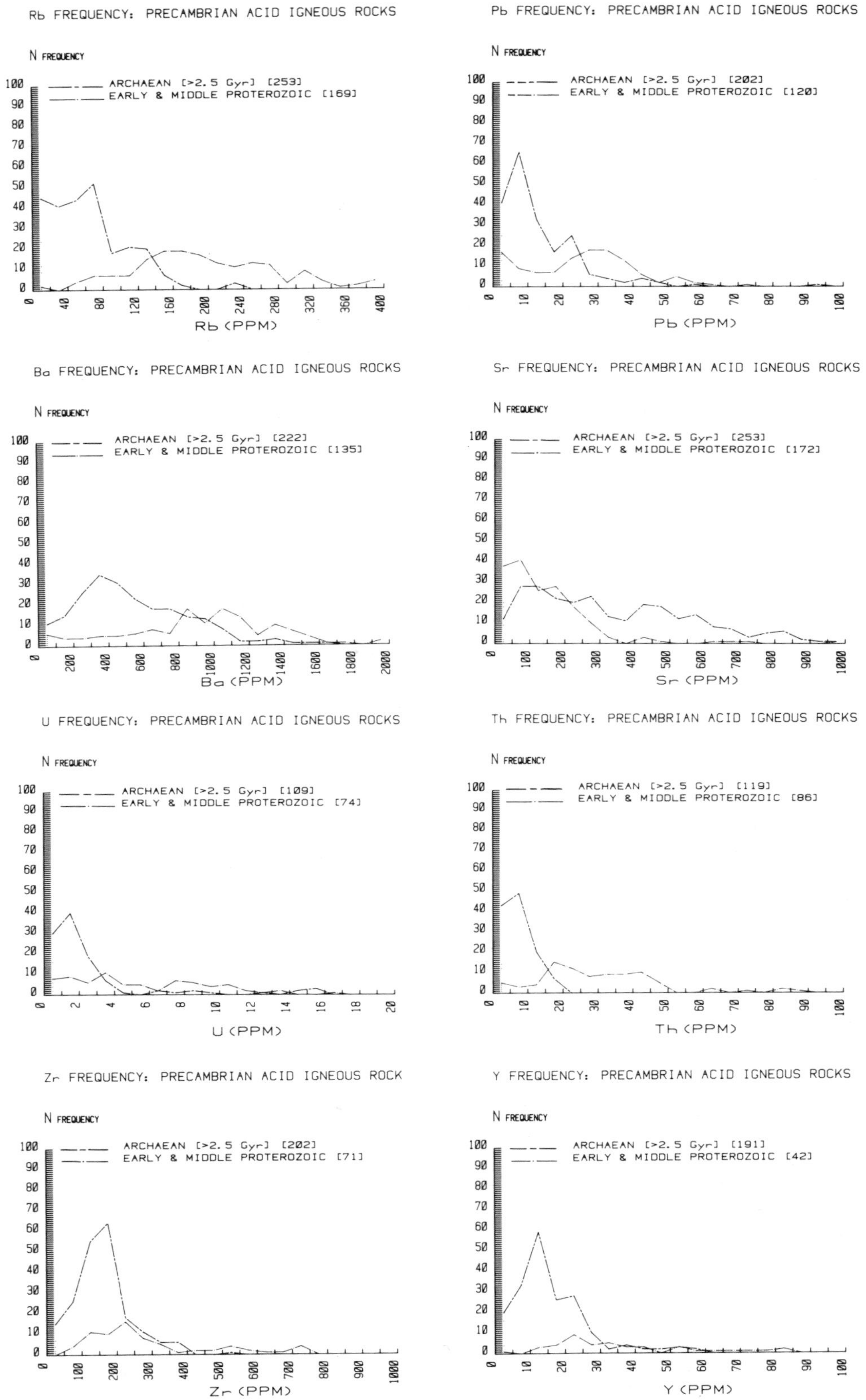

Rb FREQUENCY: PRECAMBRIAN ACID IGNEOUS ROCKS

N FREQUENCY

ARCHAEAN [>2.5 Gyr] [253]
EARLY & MIDDLE PROTEROZOIC [169]

Rb (PPM)

Pb FREQUENCY: PRECAMBRIAN ACID IGNEOUS ROCKS

N FREQUENCY

ARCHAEAN [>2.5 Gyr] [202]
EARLY & MIDDLE PROTEROZOIC [120]

Pb (PPM)

Ba FREQUENCY: PRECAMBRIAN ACID IGNEOUS ROCKS

N FREQUENCY

ARCHAEAN [>2.5 Gyr] [222]
EARLY & MIDDLE PROTEROZOIC [135]

Ba (PPM)

Sr FREQUENCY: PRECAMBRIAN ACID IGNEOUS ROCKS

N FREQUENCY

ARCHAEAN [>2.5 Gyr] [253]
EARLY & MIDDLE PROTEROZOIC [172]

Sr (PPM)

U FREQUENCY: PRECAMBRIAN ACID IGNEOUS ROCKS

N FREQUENCY

ARCHAEAN [>2.5 Gyr] [109]
EARLY & MIDDLE PROTEROZOIC [74]

U (PPM)

Th FREQUENCY: PRECAMBRIAN ACID IGNEOUS ROCKS

N FREQUENCY

ARCHAEAN [>2.5 Gyr] [119]
EARLY & MIDDLE PROTEROZOIC [86]

Th (PPM)

Zr FREQUENCY: PRECAMBRIAN ACID IGNEOUS ROCK

N FREQUENCY

ARCHAEAN [>2.5 Gyr] [202]
EARLY & MIDDLE PROTEROZOIC [71]

Zr (PPM)

Y FREQUENCY: PRECAMBRIAN ACID IGNEOUS ROCKS

N FREQUENCY

ARCHAEAN [>2.5 Gyr] [191]
EARLY & MIDDLE PROTEROZOIC [42]

Y (PPM)

Figure 5. Frequency distribution of Rb, Pb, Ba, Sr, U, Th, Zr, and Y in Archean and Proterozoic acid igneous rocks. Numbers of samples in square brackets. Data sources as in Figure 4.

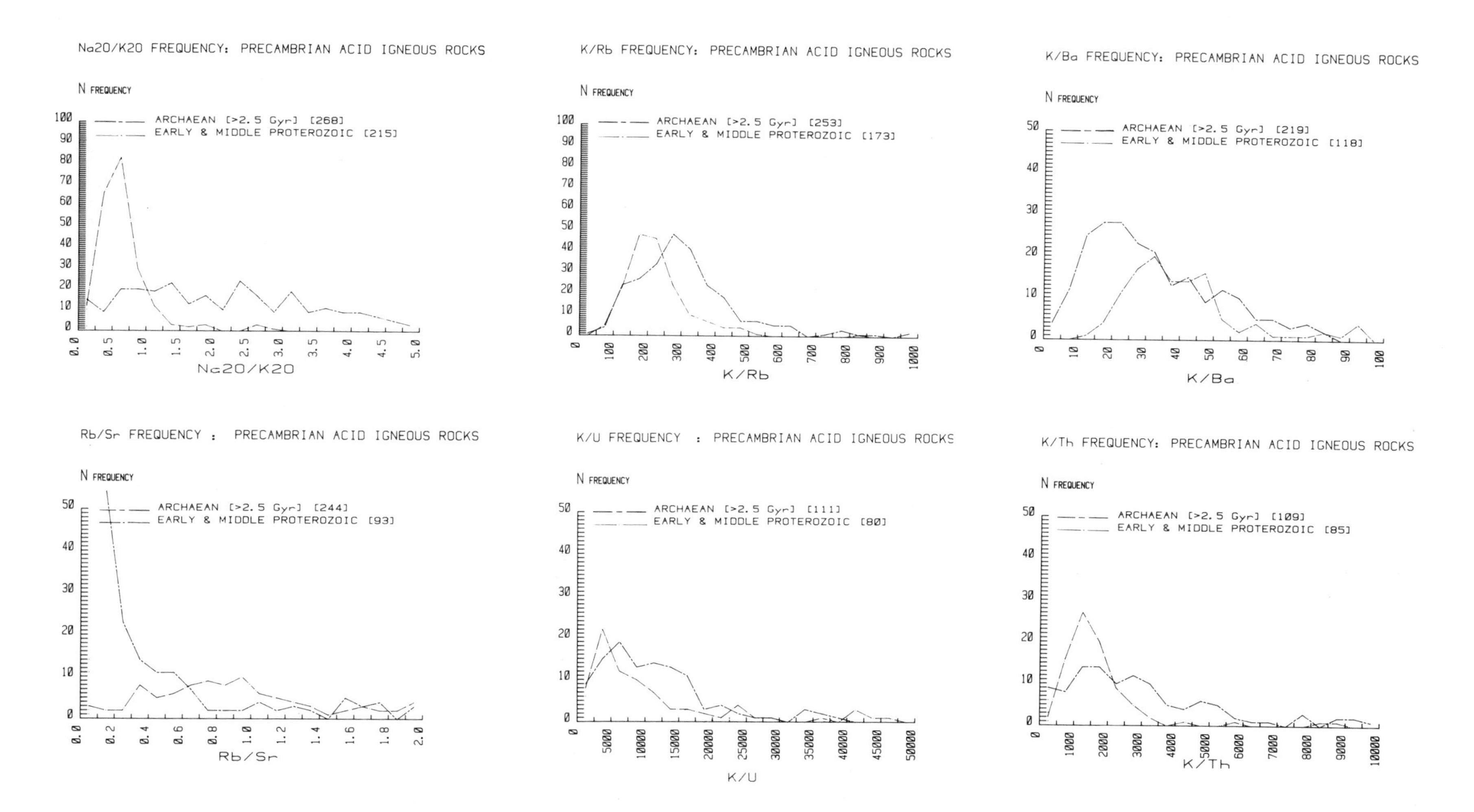

Figure 6. Frequency distribution of Na_2O/K_2O, Rb/Sr, K/Rb, K/U, K/Ba, and K/Th ratios in Archean and Proterozoic acid igneous rocks. Numbers of samples in square brackets. Data sources as in Figure 4.

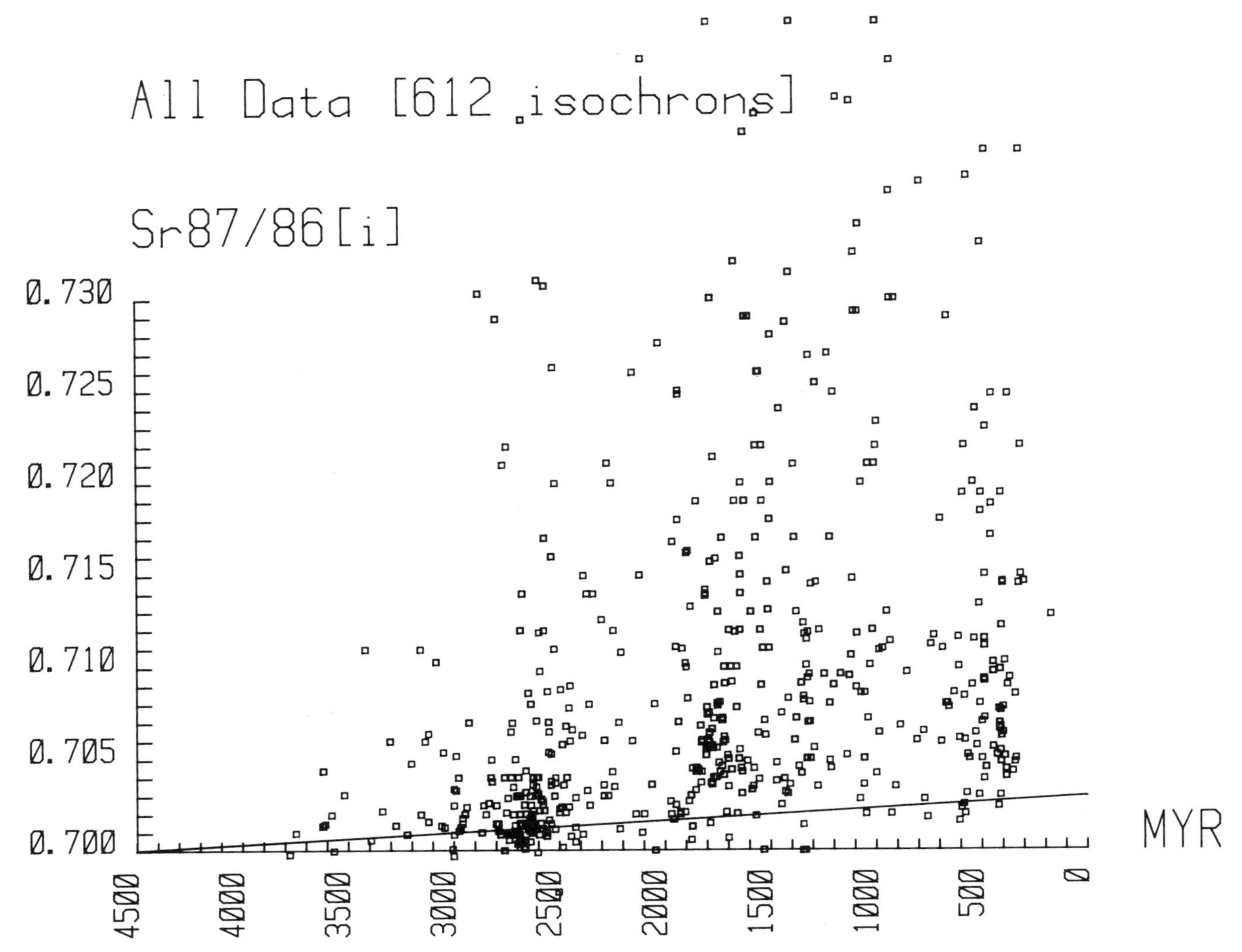

Figure 7. Initial Sr^{87}/Sr^{86} ratios (Ri) plotted against corresponding Rb-Sr isochron ages (612 isochrons). Data sources for Australia in Table 2. Data for other continents include Africa (105 isochrons), Antarctica (42 isochrons), Canada–United States (199 isochrons), Greenland-Labrador (59 isochrons); (data sources not listed for space reasons). The mantle growth line for Sr^{87}/Sr^{86} is based on Rb/Sr = 0.03.

elements (Taylor, 1966). By contrast, the Proterozoic K/Ba maximum (30 to 35) is higher than the Archean (15 to 25), suggesting preferential incorporation of Ba relative to K in residual plagioclase.

Initial Sr^{87}/Sr^{86} Ratios

The significance of primary Sr isotopic ratio (Ri) to the composition and crustal residence time of the source materials from which the measured rocks were derived (Hurley et al., 1962; Moorbath, 1976) depends on several assumptions: (1) single-stage mantle derivation of the source materials, (2) Rb/Sr ratio of the source materials, and (3) the secular mantle Sr^{87}/Sr^{86} growth based on an assumed mantle Rb/Sr ratio and on the Ri values of meteorites and mid-ocean-ridge basalts. Possibly the most uncertain assumption is the second, rendering the definition of maximal crustal residence time suspect. However, it is generally true that high-Ri materials reflect high Rb/Sr of their parental or source rocks, while low-Ri materials reflect either derivation from basic crust or/and from low Rb/Sr granulites or Na-rich silicic igneous precursors.

In Figure 7 Ri versus age plots are presented for 612 Rb-Sr isochrons from Australia, Antarctica, Canada, United States, South America, Greenland-Labrador, and Fennoscandia. Figure 8 portrays Ri frequency distribution plots for Archean, Proterozoic, and Paleozoic systems. Archean ages concentrate in the range 2.8 to 2.6 b.y., and Archean Ri values cluster about the mantle growth lines, mainly the 0.700 to 0.704 range. The Proterozoic data dis-

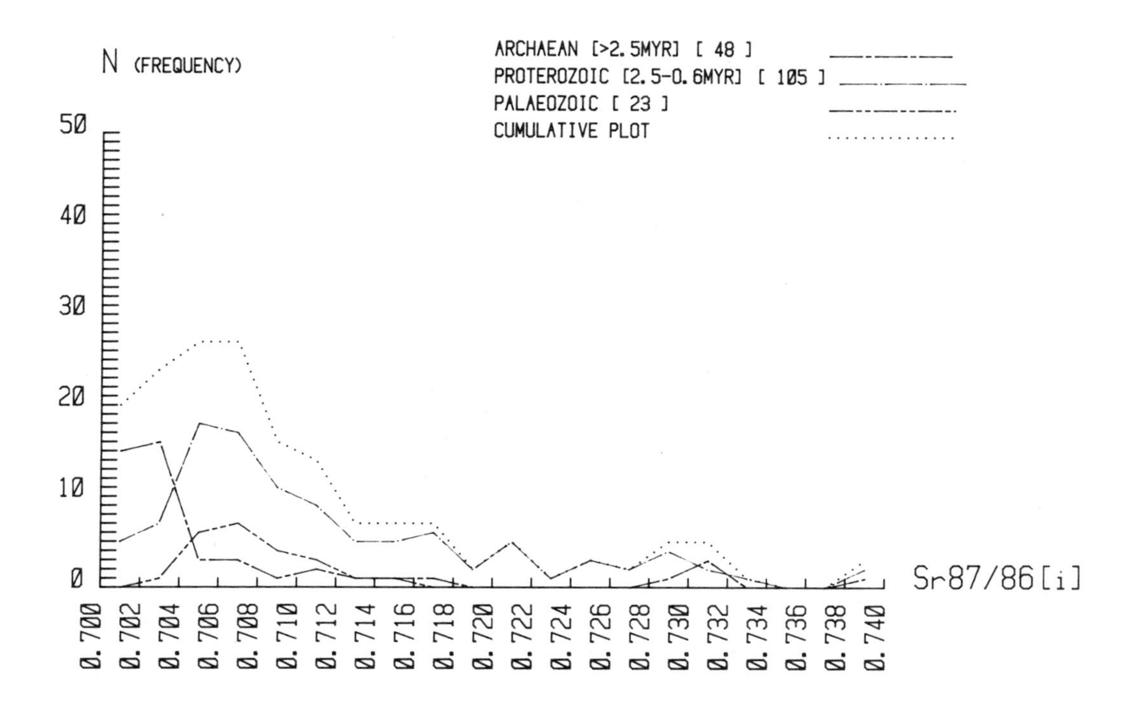

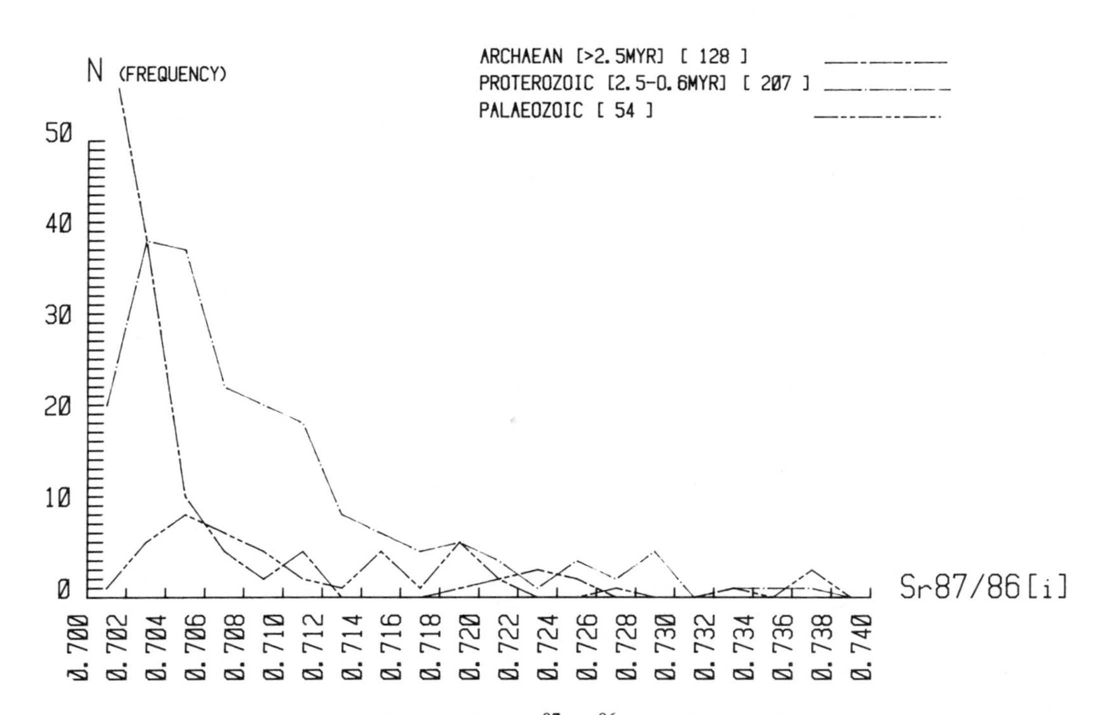

Figure 8. Frequency distribution of initial Sr^{87}/Sr^{86} ratios for acid igneous rocks from Australian and other terrains, showing breakdown into Archean, Proterozoic, and Paleozoic groups. Data sources as for Figure 7.

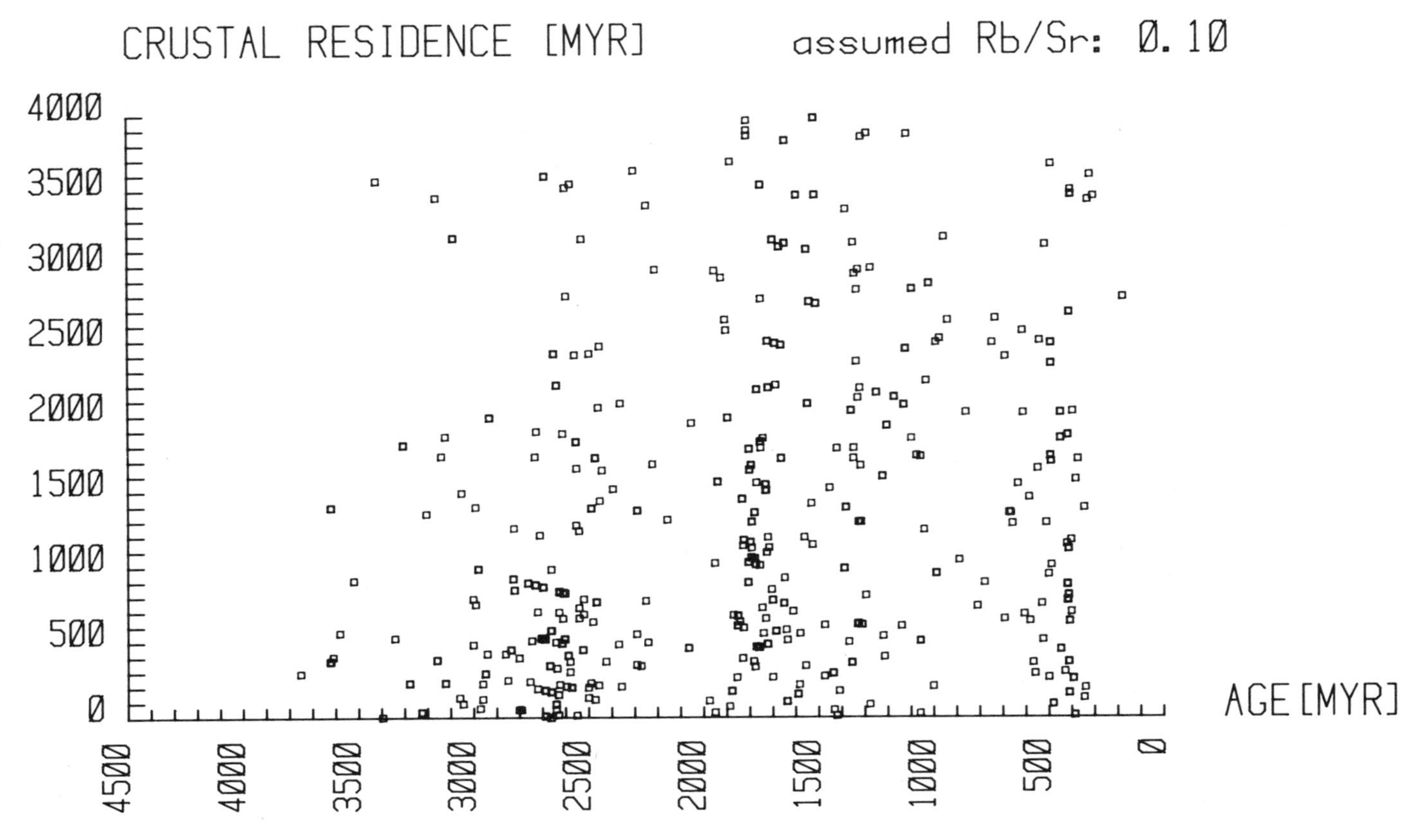

Figure 9. Plots of crustal residence time (CRT) versus age for 612 Rb-Sr isochrons from Australia and other continents. The CRT figures are single-stage mantle derivation model values calculated from the initial Sr^{87}/Sr^{86} ratio assuming Rb/Sr = 0.10 for parental crustal materials. Data sources as in Figure 7.

play a peak concentration between 1.8 and 1.6 b.y. and Ri values of 0.702 to 0.706, but many values fall in the 0.706 to 0.712 range, well above the mantle growth line. The Paleozoic data span a wide range, but their peak concentration (0.704 to 0.708) is slightly nearer to the mantle growth line than the Proterozoic data. These relations indicate the importance of differentiated high Rb/Sr sialic source materials in the Proterozoic, as compared to Archean and Paleozoic data. Single-stage model crustal residence times (CRT) calculated from the Ri data are plotted against ages in Figure 9, indicating CRT between 0 and 700 m.y. B.P. for Archean rocks and between 400 and 1700 m.y. B.P. for Proterozoic rocks, assuming Rb/Sr ratio of parental crust at 0.1 (a value typical of tonalites and granulites and also of many basic rocks). The Paleozoic data display a wide scatter. Plots of CRT against mantle derivation time (MDT) (MDT = age-CRT) (Fig. 10) indicate possible derivation of the bulk of the Proterozoic magmas and metamorphic rocks by partial melting and reworking of Archean crust, and of many Paleozoic rocks by reworking of Proterozoic materials. The gaps between the Archean, Proterozoic, and Paleozoic data zones reflect the age gaps between the 2.6 to 2.8, 1.6 to 1.8, and 0.4 to 0.5 AE peaks.

However, an alternative interpretation of the Proterozoic Ri data can be made in terms of the metamorphism of Rb-rich silicic igneous rocks, as suggested by Wyborn and Page (1983) in connection with the Mount Isa region, Northwestern Queensland. This requires that the Rb-rich precursors were derived from yet older silicic materials or, alternatively, indicates major alkalies influx prior to metamorphism. In this case, no involvement of Archean crust is implied. Metamorphism in itself cannot account for the high values of the Proterozoic rocks, unless preceded by major addition of alkalies. This point is supported by the generally low Ri values of metamorphosed Archean gneisses in several continents (Fig. 7).

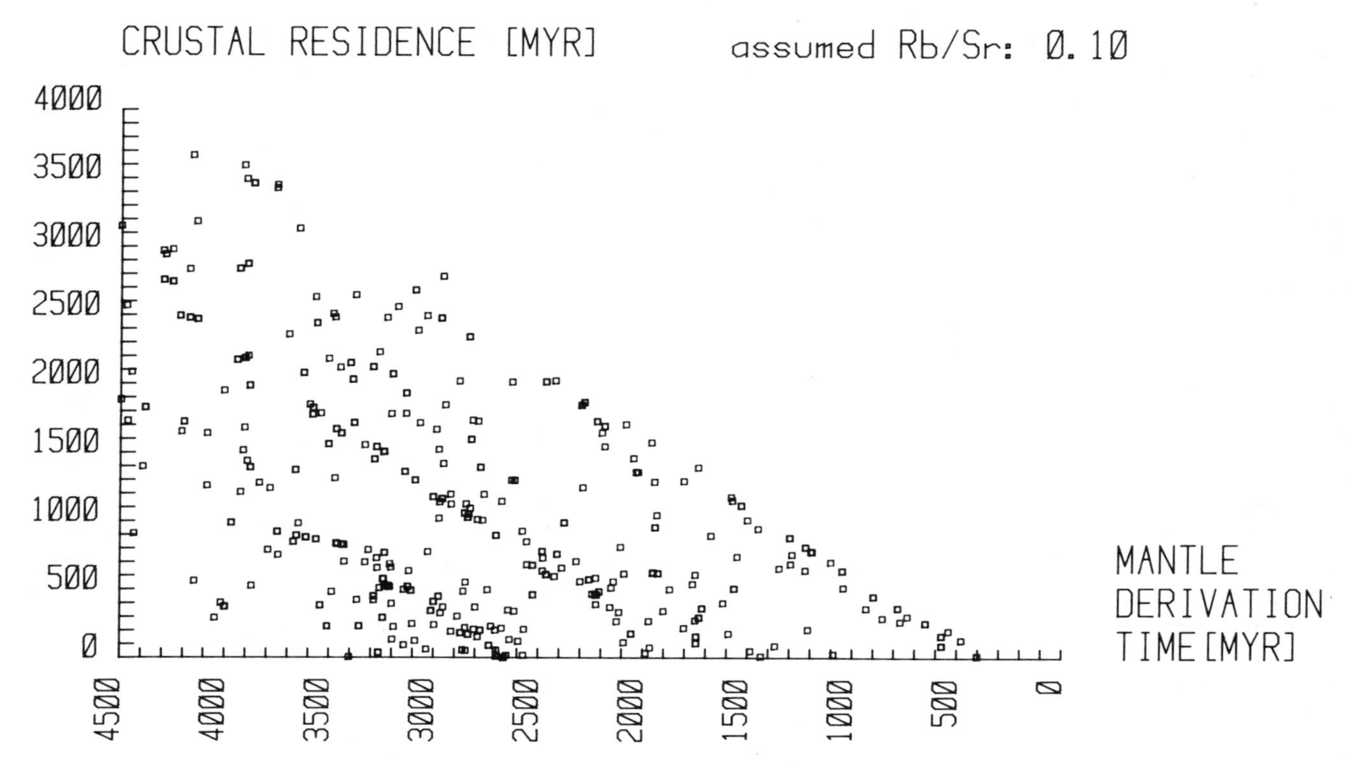

Figure 10. Plots of crustal residence time (CRT) versus mantle derivation time (MDT) for 612 Rb-Sr isochrons from Australia and other continents (MDT = age-CRT). The CRT figures are single-stage mantle derivation model values calculated from the initial Sr^{87}/Sr^{86} ratio assuming Rb/Sr = 0.10 for parental crustal materials. Data sources as in Figure 7.

Significance of Precambrian Silicic Igneous Suites

The major elements, trace elements, and Ri isotopic data converge to indicate derivation of the Archean Na-rich acid rocks largely from basic source materials, for the following reasons:

1. Generation of Na-dacite liquid by partial melting of olivine tholeiite is experimentally demonstrable (Green and Ringwood, 1968; Lambert and Wyllie, 1972) and is consistent with the low LIL abundances in these rocks. The depleted heavy REE patterns shown by Archean silicic igneous rocks (Arth and Hanson, 1975; Condie and Hunter, 1976; Glikson, 1976a; Collerson and Bridgwater, 1979) require equilibration of the melts with garnet and/or amphibole and thereby a basic source. The low Ri values are consistent with derivation from materials with mantle-type Rb/Sr ratios.

2. Derivation of dacitic melts by partial fusion of low Rb/Sr granulitic or tonalitic source rocks, although consistent with the low Ri values, would be likely to yield eutectic granitic-adamellitic LIL-high magmas, but such are comparatively rare in the Archean except as late high-level bodies.

3. It is possible that some Na-rich acid igneous rocks were generated by total anatexis of older tonalites and trondhjemites. However, observations in high-grade metamorphic terrains indicate that anatexis normally progresses through segregation of early eutectic melt fractions along foliation/banding structures, are reflected by banded gneisses and migmatites. The separation of plagioclase-mafic phase bearing paleosome fractions from the mobile K-feldspar-quartz–dominated neosome fractions involves strong chemical fractionation. Solid-state emplacement of Na-rich acid plutons is commonly suggested by their highly sheared margins; however, this is a late-stage postconsolidation phenomenon, as evident from widely preserved intrusive contacts with the Archean greenstones. It is unlikely that the Na-rich silicic magmas represent the residual crystal mush of earlier fractionation events, as this would imply abundance of complimentary high-level K-rich intrusions,

which are comparatively minor in the Archean. Thus, an origin by partial melting of largely basic source materials is the most favoured petrogenetic model.

By contrast to the simatic derivation of the bulk of Archean silicic igneous rocks, the bulk of the Proterozoic data are compatible with silicic source melting, that is, anatexis of granitic and/or sedimentary rocks. Many important exceptions to this dichotomy are known; for example, late Archean high-level K-rich granites and adamellites are common in places, and middle Proterozoic Na-rich plutons occur in several terrains, for example, Flin-Flon (Manitoba), Mexico-Colorado-Central United States (Penokean orogeny), Fennoscandia (Bell et al., 1975; Stauffer et al., 1975; Barker et al., 1976; Barker and Millard, 1979). In the southwestern United States very low Ri values were measured on 1.6 to 1.85-b.y.-old rocks (peak at 0.702 to 0.703) and on 1.4 to 1.5-b.y.-old rocks (peak at 0.704 to 0.705) (Condie and Budding, 1979). By contrast to the generally high Ri values of Australian Proterozoic rocks (most common range 0.704 to 0.712), Canadian Proterozoic Ri values are relatively low (peak at 0.705 to 0.706). However, Sm/Nd isotope studies of composite samples from the Churchill Province in Saskatchewan and Baffin Island have yielded model ages of T_{CHUR} = 2.68 and 2.74 b.y., respectively (CHUR = chondritic upper mantle reservoir) (McCulloch and Wasserburg, 1978). This indicates that the low-Ri 1.8 to 1.9-b.y. ages common in the Churchill Province reflect metamorphic resetting of older Archean crust—a conclusion that casts doubt on the significance of low Ri values in general. It is possible that extensive Proterozoic terrains concealed under younger basins, or which have not as yet been geochemically and isotopically investigated, are of two-stage mantle melting origin. The existence of such terrains would drastically modify the scale of the problem discussed in this paper. At the present state of knowledge, however, it appears that the bulk of the lower and middle Proterozoic rocks (2.5 to 1.0 b.y.) documented to date have arisen by ensialic anatexis.

Significance of Sedimentary Geochemical and Isotopic Data

Thanks to mixing effects of the hydrosphere, the geochemistry of sedimentary rocks—notably argillites, chert, and carbonates—yield more confident estimates of crustal source composition than the spatially restricted igneous units. MacPherson (1958) has shown a decrease in the Ni, Cr, and V abundances in Canadian slates from the Archean to the Proterozoic. This corresponds to the high K, Ti, U, and Th and low Na, Cr, Ni, Mg, and Ca of Canadian Proterozoic crustal averages compared to Archean averages (Fahrig and Eade, 1968). On the basis of a study of clastic sedimentary rocks worldwide, Engel et al. (1974) demonstrated a sharp increase in K_2O/Na_2O from about 0.5 to 0.8 prior to 2.6 b.y. B.P. to about 1.1 to 3.0 between 2.2 and 0.6 b.y. B.P., followed by a sharp decline to 0.7 to 1.2 from about 0.4 b.y. B.P. (Fig. 11). Sr isotopic data for sea water as deduced from the study of carbonates (Veizer and Compston, 1976) indicate a linear increase of Sr^{87}/Sr^{86} minimum ratios from 0.701 to 0.702 in the Archean, a marked rise to 0.705 between 2.5 and 2.1 b.y. B.P., then an increase to the 0.709 value of present-day sea water, with a negative perturbation from about 0.6 b.y. (Fig. 11). A study of metamorphosed pelitic rocks from the Indian Shield has shown high Al, Ti, Fe, Mg, Cr, and Ni, and low Si, K, Rb, and Sr for 3.2- 3.5-b.y.-old sediments (Naqvi, 1978). Sheraton (1980) reported high Mg and low K and Rb of pre-3.0-b.y. metapelites and high K, Rb, Pb, Ba, and Th of late Archean-Proterozoic metapelites from Antarctica. Taylor (1979) summed up the differences in the REE patterns of Archean and Proterozoic pelitic sediments: The Archean rocks have low total REE, low light/heavy REE ratios, and high Eu/Eu* (i.e., no Eu anomalies). The Proterozoic sediments have progressively higher total REE, somewhat higher light/heavy REE ratios, and lower Eu/Eu* (negative Eu anomalies) (Fig. 11). The above observations are explicable in terms of secular changes in the composition of Archean and Proterozoic source terrains of the sediments, namely, from greenstone-tonalite systems to K-granite-dominated systems, and are consistent with the geochemical and isotopic variations shown by the silicic plutonic and volcanic suites reviewed above.

Pb/Pb isotopic studies of detrital feldspars suggest that the bulk of the North American continental crust differentiated from the mantle during the 3.5 to 2.5-b.y. interval (Patterson and Tatsumoto, 1964)—a conclusion supported by Pb-Th-U and Rb-Sr isotopic systematics (Slawson et al., 1963; Armstrong, 1968). Evidently, at the present state of knowledge, many lines of evidence converge to indicate the Archean as an era dominated by sima-to-sial transformation and the early to middle Proterozoic as an era during which the bulk of continental crust was already in existence. The question discussed below follows: Had extensive simatic regimes existed during 2.5 to 1.0 b.y. ago, why is there such a meagre record of sima-to-sial transformation and continental accretion during this interval? Central to the consideration of this problem is a review of spatial distribution of the Proterozoic crust, as indicated by paleomagnetic data.

PALEOMAGNETIC EVIDENCE ON PROTEROZOIC SIAL/SIMA PATTERNS

Paleomagnetic studies of Proterozoic rocks in Australia (McElhinny and Embleton, 1976), Africa (McElhinny et al., 1968; Piper et al., 1973), and North America (Irving and Park, 1972; Irving and McGlynn, 1976) have shown that coincident apparent polar wander paths (APWP) are delin-

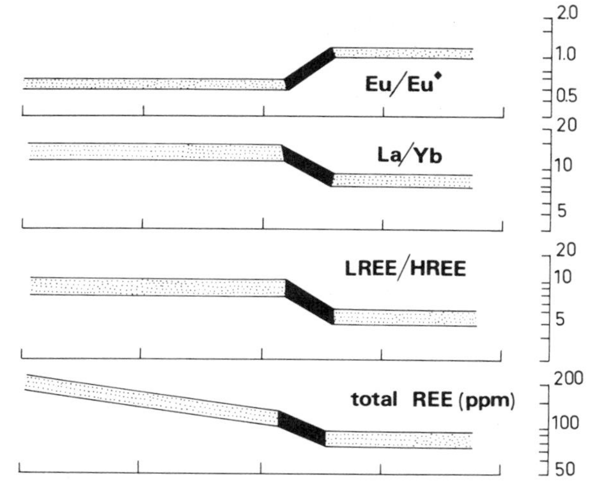

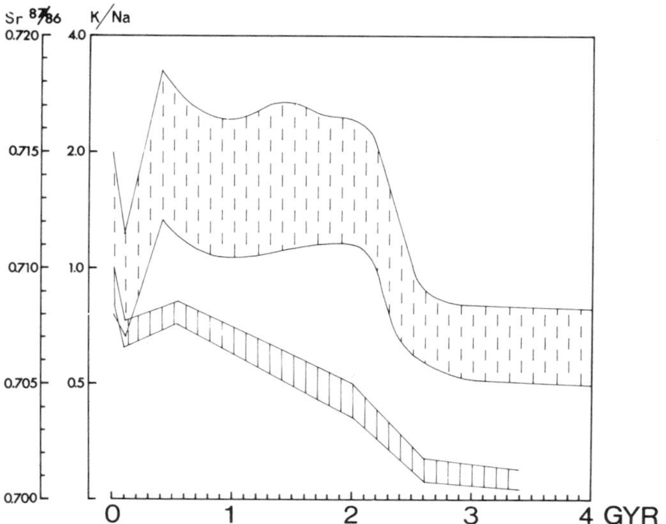

Figure 11. Distribution of Sr^{87}/Sr^{86} of carbonates (vertically lined) (Veizer and Compston, 1976), K/Na of detrital sediments (vertically dashed) (Engel et al., 1974), total rare earth element (REE), abundances, light REE/heavy REE ratios, La/Yb and Eu/Eu* (Eu* = assumed smooth curve distribution value) (Taylor, 1979) with time (Gyr: 10^9 years).

eated by cratons within each of these continents, that is, individual cratons have maintained essentially constant relative positions during time intervals indicated by the dated paleomagnetic poles (McElhinny and McWilliams, 1977). This conclusion has been criticized by Burke et al. (1976) who pointed out that each of the APWP is incomplete, which renders possible alternative interpolations of individual poles. However, insofar as all the data fit onto a single APWP, this curve inherently provides the most likely interpretation (McElhinny and McWilliams, 1977). Other criticism of the joint APWPs may be made on the basis of the commonly unknown primary (igneous) ages of the poles; however, this is not necessarily a prerequisite insofar as the ages represent major secondary events which effected the magnetic properties of the rocks as well. Thus, unless the observed overlaps are dismissed as accidental—a most unlikely proposition—their consistent occurrence in several shields must represent contiguous intercratonic intracontinental relations. This conclusion is in agreement with a wide range of geological, geochemical, and isotopic evidence indicating the ensialic nature of intercratonic mobile belts (Wynne-Edwards, 1976; Glikson, 1976b; Rutland, 1976; Kröner, 1976).

Piper (1976) attempted correlations between Proterozoic APWP on the single-continent Pangea model and suggested an integrity of the sialic crust between 2.6 and 1.0 b.y. ago, a conclusion criticized by Briden (1976) as premature. Embleton and Schmidt (1979) and Schmidt and Embleton (1981) arrived at the surprising observation that, when retained in their present-day geographic positions, the Precambrian shields of North America, Greenland, Africa, and Australia portray closely coincident APWP segments for early and middle Proterozoic time spans. Thus, the 2.3 to 1.9-b.y. North American and African APWP and the 1.8- to 1.6-b.y. North American, Greenland, and Australian APWP closely overlap. Because of limits on the extent of the Proterozoic sial, this requires existence of Proterozoic simatic crustal domains in positions broadly identical to the modern Atlantic, Indian, and Pacific ocean basins. As discussed below, such an interpretation is geologically unacceptable. Moreover, in view of the well-established paleogeographic and paleomagnetic contiguity of Gondwanaland and Laurentia during the Paleozoic, such a geotectonic regime would have been succeeded by late Proterozoic continental convergence and by post-Permian return to original geographic positions, implying some kind of crust-mantle "memory." Neither problem would arise on an Earth with a smaller radius, had radial growth proceeded parallel with Mesozoic-Cenozoic plate tectonics. However, paleoradii analysis using Ward's least pole scatter method (McElhinny et al., 1978; Schmidt and Clark, 1980) militates against significant changes of Earth radii during the past 400 m.y.. An apparent conflict, therefore, arises between the conclusions that arise from Proterozoic and post-Permian paleomagnetic data. This problem and those arising from the geochemical and isotopic evidence are at the centre of the discussion to follow.

Embleton and Schmidt's (1979) reconstruction has been criticized by Irving and McGlynn (1981) on the basis of doubts regarding the ages of some of the Laurentian poles. The joint APWPs have also been questioned by A. E. Baer (pers. commun., 1981). Further data are needed to ascertain this reconstruction.

NATURE OF THE PRECAMBRIAN EARTH

Inherent in the interpretation of the geochemical, iso-

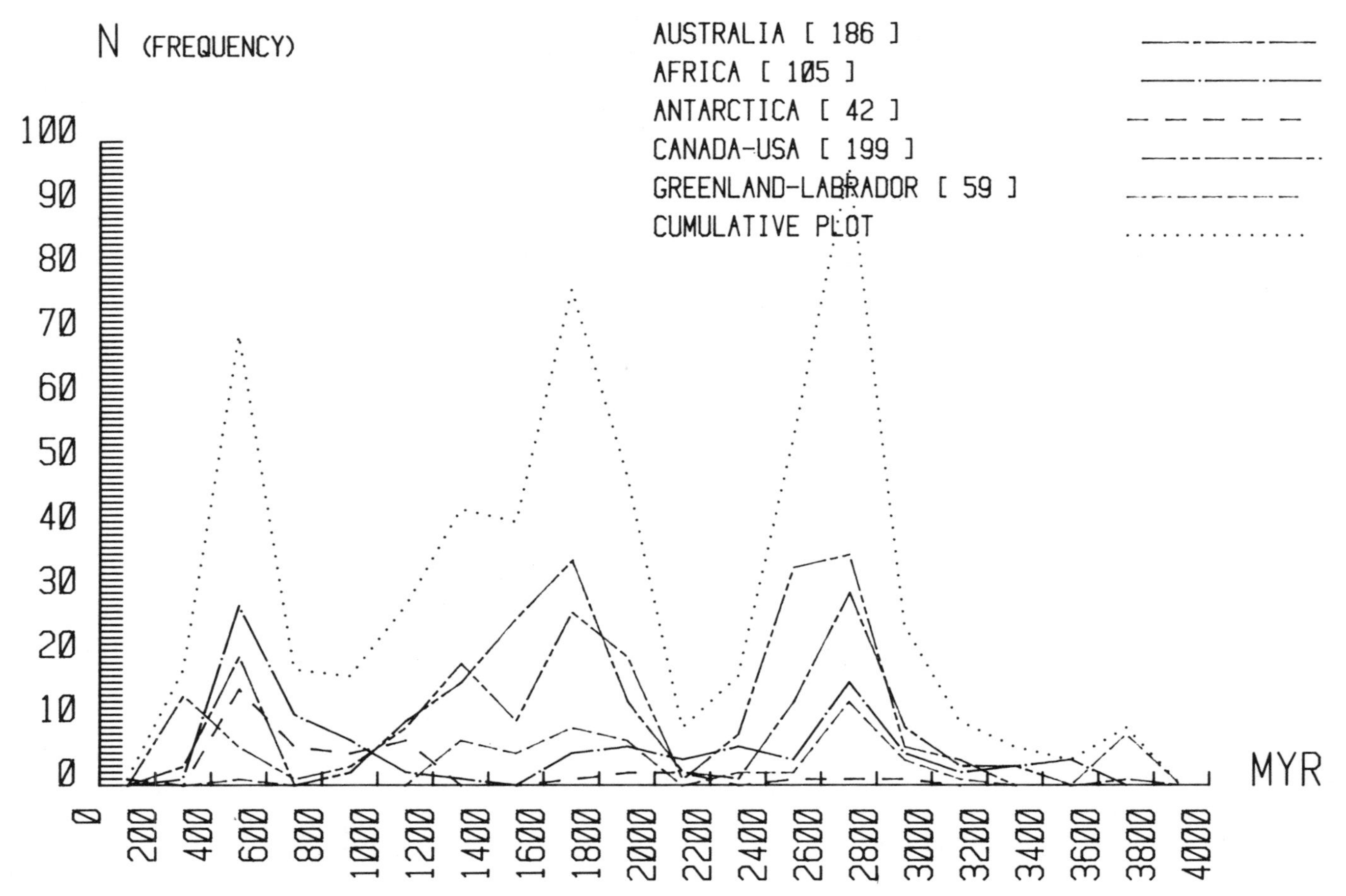

Figure 12. Rb-Sr isochron ages frequency distribution, including data from Australia, Africa, Antarctica, Canada–United States, and Greenland-Labrador. Numbers of samples in square brackets. Data sources as in Figure 7 and Table 2.

topic, and paleomagnetic evidence are major questions concerning the early history of the Earth, notably the significance of the major thermal peaks represented by isotopic age maxima at 2.8 to 2.6 b.y., 1.8 to 1.6 b.y., and 0.5 to 0.4 b.y. (Fig. 12). Alternative sial-sima distribution models for the 2.5 to 1.0 b.y. era discussed earlier (Glikson, 1979b; 1980a; 1980b; Baer, 1980) include the following possibilities: (1) a global sial crust of continental thickness, (2) a global thin sial crust, (3) a proterozoic supercontinent surrounded by contiguous sima, (4) dispersed continent/ocean (sial/sima) models, (5) a global sialic crust on a small-radius Earth.

Model (1) is unacceptable on account of the limits on the volume of sial from its present-day abundance. Model (2) is inconsistent with (a) thickness estimates of the Precambrian crust, indicating 30 to 80 km of crust from metamorphic mineral assemblages (Tarney and Windley, 1977; O'Hara, 1977; Newton, 1977), as also supported by stratigraphic and structural evidence; (b) paleomagnetic APWP constraints on lateral migration and agglomeration of the Precambrian sialic crust; and (c) structural limits on deformation within cratons and mobile belts (Shackleton, 1976). Both models (3) and (4) are difficult to reconcile with the scarcity of ophiolites, two-stage mantle melting products, and the range of geochemical and isotopic signatures as previously discussed in this paper. Paleomagnetic APWP evidence requires the integrity of relative craton positions within the major shields, and present-day angular distances between Laurentia, Greenland, Africa, and Australia, as previously discussed.

Given that the peak of new crust formation is defined at 2.8 to 2.6 b.y. B.P. (Figs. 8, 12) given an active convecting mantle, the question can be asked, Why was sima-to-sial transformation by two-stage mantle melting not completed at an earlier stage? If sima is continuously accreted and consumed, given high heat-generation rates (Lambert, 1976) and high sea-floor spreading rates, the Archean sima would have been transformed to sial in the early Archean. There is some isotopic evidence that Archean granite-forming events followed closely (within ca. 200 m.y.) in the wake of greenstone-forming events, reinforcing the above question. Since Archean crust occupies no more than 60% of present-day continental crust (Goodwin, 1974), by 2.5 b.y. ago no more than 20% of the Earth surface could have been covered by sial. Why is there so little evidence of the simatic crust, which post-2.5 b.y. must have occupied some 80% of the Earth surface, and why is there so little evidence for its transformation to sial?

In an attempt to resolve this question, Baer (1980) suggested that a stable, thick oceanic crust in a pre–plate tectonics crustal regime would not have been subducted, thereby leaving little trace in the geological record. This concept is in agreement with Green's (1975) suggestion that under high geothermal gradient the gabbro-eclogite transformation and consequently subduction would not have taken place in the early Precambrian. These views received much support from Kröner (1981), who suggested that a modified form of plate tectonics operated in pre-1.0-b.y. time, involving small relative movements of sialic cratons but no opening and closing of major ocean basins. However, these concepts give rise to the following considerations:

1. REE patterns of Archean Na-dacites, tonalites, and trondhjemites commonly reflect strong depletion in the heavy REE, which can be explained by fractionation of high-Kd phases such as garnet and/or amphibole, and thereby formation of garnet granulite or eclogite (Arth and Hanson, 1975; Condie and Hunter, 1976; Glikson, 1976a; 1979a; Collerson and Bridgwater, 1979; Jahn et al., 1981). This suggests that, at least in places, Archean geothermal gradients did permit the gabbro-eclogite transition.

2. Inherent in a view of Proterozoic oceanic crust as a stable entity would be the absence of mid–ocean ridge accretion and thus presumably of mantle convection. Ongoing simatic accretion without subduction would result in an insurmountable volume problem (see below). Since evidence for formation of sima and for sima-to-sial transformation is widespread in Archean, upper Proterozoic, and Paleozoic terrains, a 1,500-m.y. lull in this activity is difficult to understand. This is all the more so as the middle Proterozoic is a period of extensive ensialic tectonic, metamorphic, and anatectic activity within a mobile belts network culminating about 1.8 to 1.6 b.y. B.P. (Fig. 12) (Holmes, 1951; Cahen and Snelling, 1966; Clifford, 1968; Plumb and Derrick, 1975). Whatever factors underlie the development of ensialic mobile networks, it is inconceivable that they have been confined to the continental crust and underlying lithosphere and that they did not effect contemporaneous simatic regimes. Whether mobile belts systems were related to mantle convection (Dearnley, 1966; Clifford, 1968) or to deep lithospheric featuring, the oceanic crust would have been deformed, reworked, and partially melted. Little evidence of such processes is observed in the early and middle Proterozoic record.

Assuming a plate tectonic model, in a conservative estimate, a minimum of $500 \times 10^6 km^3$ of two-stage mantle melting products would have resulted by spreading and subduction along a 20,000-km-long ridge system, given a 5-km-thick oceanic crust, double spreading rate of 2 cm/year, and partial melting of subducted sima at 30% (Glikson, 1980a). Volumes greater by several factors would be expected in a thermally active convecting mantle-crust system, but no large enough geochemically compatible 2.5- to 1.0-b.y.-old terrains have to date been identified. If the constraints imposed by Embleton and Schmidt's (1979) APWP data are accepted, circum-Atlantic, circum-Indian, and circum-Pacific ocean belts would have constituted major loci of sima-to-sial transformation processes in early and middle Proterozoic times, but little or no evidence for such activity is recognized in these regions. This absence contrasts with the widespread retention of evidence for destruction of Paleozoic oceanic crust in the circum-Pacific belt, central Asia, and the Hercynian, Caledonian, and Appalachian orogenic belts (e.g., Harrington, 1974; Crook and Felton, 1975). Evidence for incipient rifting accompanied by basic volcanic activity and opening and cratonization of simatic gaps becomes progressively manifest from about 1.0 AE (Kröner, 1977; 1981). Prominent examples are the Gariep (Namibia), Liberia, Hoggar, and Keweenawan rifted volcanic systems and the Red Sea ophiolite-bearing diorite- and granodiorite-dominated belt–a major site of simatic divergence and subsequent cratonization. Other examples of this activity are simatic gaps associated with the Grenville Province (Brown et al., 1975) and extensive thrust faulting in central Australia. From about this time, divergent APWP patterns became increasingly common (McElhinny and Embleton, 1976), which, together with the geological and geochemical evidence, indicates a breakdown of previously contiguous continental crustal regions. The well-preserved record of these developments clearly indicates that when sial/sima dispersion occurs it leaves diagnostic signatures in the crustal record, which reinforces the questions raised by the scarcity of such signatures in 2.5- to 1.0-b.y.-old terrains.

The crustal volume problem is represented in Figure 13. Assuming that sial growth by two-stage mantle melting commenced about 4.0 b.y. ago, for a modern sima accretion rate of $3.2 km^2$/year the Earth would have been completely cratonized (covered by sial) at present (Fig. 13a). The observed volume of continental crust if only compatible with a low accretion rate of about $0.8 km^2$/year, contrary to that expected as a result of thermally active

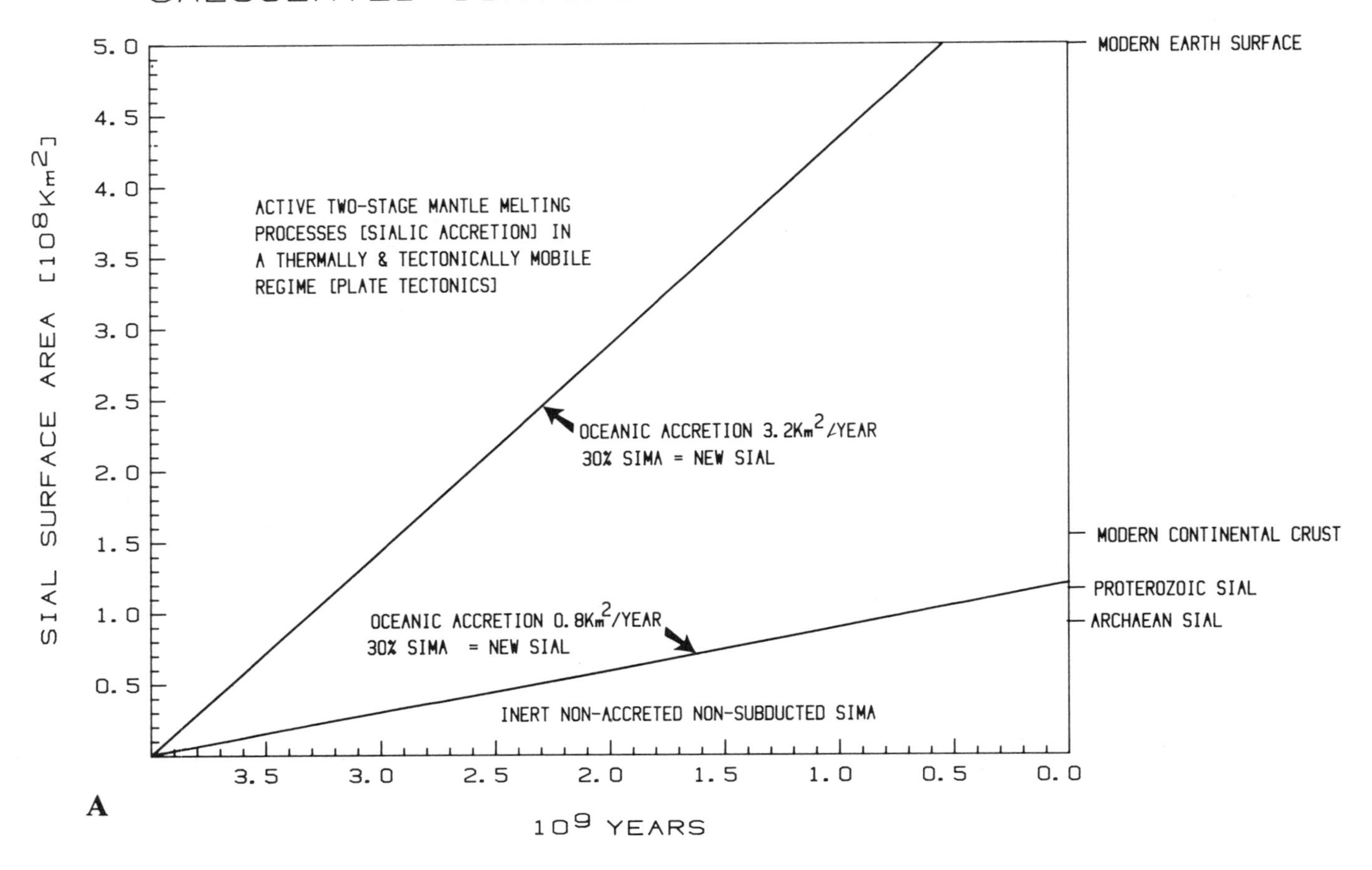

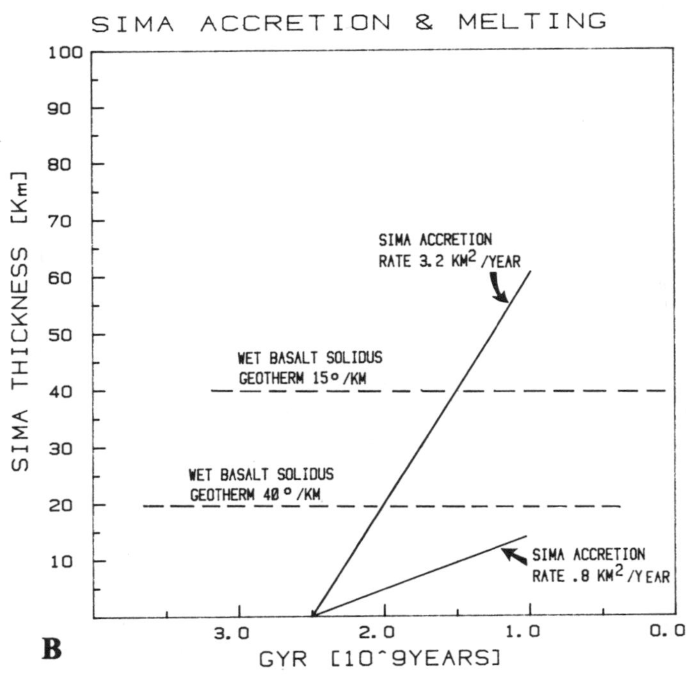

Figure 13. (a) Calculated continental crust (sial) growth curves assuming 0.8 km^2/year and 3.2 km^2/year accretion of sima and 30% partial melting of sima to produce sial. (b) Calculated growth in thickness of sima assuming 0.8 km^2/year and 3.2 km^2/year accretion rates, and showing intersection with the wet basalt solidus (beginning of melting) under geotherms of 15°c/km and 40°C/km.

convective Precambrian mantle-crust systems. If no subduction of sima is assumed, the thickening of accreted simatic crust would be expected to result in partial melting at its base within less than 1,000 m.y., assuming a modern accretion rate and geothermal gradient, and much earlier if higher parameters are assumed (Fig. 13b). It is thus difficult to interpret the modern sial/sima ratio, unless both accretion and subduction were significantly retarded in the Precambrian.

The apparent inability of the above sial/sima distribution models to account for the geochemical, isotopic, and paleomagnetic data has, inevitably, resulted in renewed attention toward model (5) above (Glikson, 1976b; 1979b; 1980a; Embleton and Schmidt, 1979; Schmidt and Embleton, 1981), namely, the expanding Earth hypothesis (Hilgenberg, 1933; Egyed, 1956; Jordan, 1966; Owen, 1976; Carey, 1976). On a global continental crust enveloping an

Earth the radius of which is 60% of the modern radius *the geochemical, isotopic, and paleomagnetic enigmas arising from the Precambrian record would not pertain,* rendering the model potentially attractive. However, objections to Earth expansion render such a resolution highly controversial. Some of the principal arguments that have been advanced for and against the expanding Earth hypothesis are listed below, starting with the arguments supporting the hypothesis:

1. A better fit of the continents in pre-Jurassic times has been obtained on a smaller globe (Carey, 1976; Owen, 1976).

2. The lack of pre-Jurassic ocean crust preserved in situ in the present-day ocean basins requires globally *simultaneous* destruction of older oceanic crust, which is surprising.

3. The growth in dimensions of the Atlantic and Indian ocean basins since the Jurassic require, on a constant-radius Earth, a corresponding decrease in the circum-Pacific Ocean perimeter. However, extensional relations between Antarctica and Australia, Antarctica and South America, and in west Pacific marginal sea argue against circum-Pacific contraction (Meservey, 1969).

4. The northward migration of the continents, recorded by paleomagnetic pole data in the order of 20° to 30° since the early Mesozoic, is difficult to reconcile with the opening and spreading of the Arctic Ocean basin (Carey, 1976).

5. A reconstruction of Pangea on a present-day-radius Earth requires the preexistence of an eastward-widening Tethyan ocean basin in the Paleozoic, for which there is little geological evidence (Crawford, 1981).

Arguments which militate against expansion include:

1. Paleomagnetic analysis of McElhinny et al (1978) and Schmidt and Clark (1980) based on the Ward least scatter pole method disallows significant radius changes during the past 400 m.y.

2. In view of the shallow-water nature of Precambrian sediments, a development of ocean basins since the early Mesozoic implies that the bulk of the hydrosphere has been outgassed from the mantle at relatively late stages of Earth evolution (Stewart, 1983).

3. Little or no expansion is observed on the Moon, Mars, and Mercury, whose cratered ca. 4.0-AE crust has been little deformed (McElhinny et al, 1978).

Recently, Stewart (1983) has discussed criteria for detecting possible Earth radius changes, including (1) the strength and viscosity of the lithosphere and its response to expansion, (2) implications of paleomagnetic data, (3) implications of ocean-floor spreading patterns and Euler rotation poles, (4) quantitative estimates of subduction rates, (5) estimates from global sea-level changes, (6) implications of paleogravity to the paleoradius, and (7) paleoradius from the Earth's moment of inertia. In view of the limits imposed by these methods, he concluded that over the past 100 m.y. changes in paleoradius were certainly less than 4 mm/year and probably less than 1 mm/year. For most of the Phanerozoic (100 to 570 m.y. B.P.) changes in paleoradius were less than 0.6 mm/year. For the Precambrian, estimates based on inversion of paleogravity data, assuming unchanged Earth mass and gravitational constant, were applied, indicating that by the Archean the radius was within 2,500 km of the present value (Fig. 14). Thus, radial growth at a slow rate of about 1 mm/year is not precluded on present evidence and is capable of accounting for the geochemical and paleomagnetic questions discussed above.

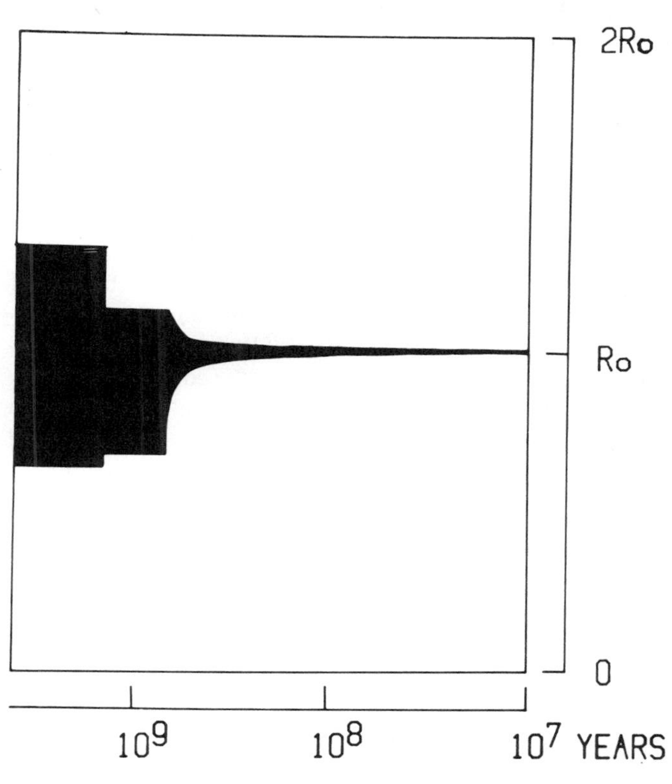

Figure 14. Geophysical limits on changes in the Earth radius (constrained within the black region) with age (from Stewart, 1983).

By far the most important objection to Earth growth is the lack of a suitable physical explanation. Theoretical support for expansion has originally been derived from Dirac's (1938) theory of secular decrease in the universal gravity (G) constant and from Hubble's observation of galactic recession and universal expansion. However, astronomical observations place limits on this process, indicating that G^*/G does not exceed 10^{-11}/year to 10^{-10}/year. In combination with mass accretion according to the steady-state universe theory, this rate would render permissible radial Earth growth of 0.2 to 0.3 mm/year (Wesson, 1980). Such an expansion rate would go a long way to explain the geological enigma discussed in this paper. However, continuous accretion in a steady-state model is nowadays not favoured in astrophysics, because the expected changes in the mass and luminosity of stars, such as the Sun, and the expected transformation of neutron stars to black holes are inconsistent with observations (Tryon, 1983). Effects of mass growth on the Earth-Moon system are also cited as an objection to expansion (Runcorn, 1981). By contrast, constant-mass expansion models are not ruled out. Had superdense matter formed at the core of the primordial Earth under high-pressure conditions resulting from a thick early atmosphere of hydrogen and hellium, subsequent disintegration of such matter could conceivably affect expansion (Tryon, 1983). It is another question whether such matter could have been metastably retained for some 3×10^9 years in the core, in order to account for radial growth in the upper Proterozoic and Phanerozoic.

The Precambrian crustal record may be explained by secular radial growth. Accepting the reality of convection and two-stage mantle melting processes, the Archean greenstone-tonalite cycles may reflect crustal extension, sima-accretion, and sima-consumption cycles. The 2.8- to 2.6-b.y. thermal peak may reflect global cratonization of sial on a smaller Earth. The 1.8- to 1.6-b.y. thermal peak may reflect a global tensional phase affecting development of and crustal reworking within ensialic mobile belt networks. From about 1.0 b.y. B.P., accelerated expansion could account for the progressive opening and subsequent cratonization of oceanic crustal gaps such as the Red Sea. Advanced stages of such processes would be represented by the more extensive Paleozoic oceanic regimes and the 0.5- to 0.4-b.y. thermal peak signifying cratonization. However, such a theory of crustal evolution, consistent as it is with a majority of geological, geochemical, isotopic, and paleomagnetic data, must await confirmation by (1) refined paleomagnetic tests and (2) physical theory. The first is now obtainable. The ca. 2.4-b.y. dyking phase recognized in almost every Precambrian shield provides a suitable spatial-temporal reference grid to test paleomagnetic inclination/distance paleoratios directly. Examples of such dykes are the Great Rhodesian Dyke and its satellites, the Jimberlana and Binneringie dyke system in southwestern Australia, the Black Ridge dyke and its satellites in the Pilbara (NW Western Australia), early Proterozoic dyke systems in Canada, and similar dykes in Antarctica, India, and other terrains. These dykes are commonly little deformed and unmetamorphosed, rendering them ideal for paleomagnetic work combined with accurate Sm/Nd isotopic dating. Once a large body of paleomagnetic measurements and isotopic data is available, inclination/distance ratios can be tested both within large shields (Laurentia, Africa) and/or on confident reconstructions (e.g., Africa–South America, Australia-Antarctica) with direct bearing on the paleoradius at 2.4 b.y. The consequences of such a test, whether it confirms or rejects the expanding Earth theory, would be far reaching.

ACKNOWLEDGMENTS

I thank A. E. Baer, Preston Cloud, H. J. Harrington, A. L. Jaques, K. A. Plumb, A. D. Stewart, and S. Sun for their constructive comments and criticism. This paper is published with the permission of the Director, Australian Bureau of Mineral Resources, Geology and Geophysics.

REFERENCES CITED

Allen, A. R., and Black, L. P., 1979, The Harry Creek deformed zone, a retrograde schist zone of the Arunta Block, central Australia: Journal of the Geological Society of Australia, v. 26, p. 17–28.

Armstrong, R. L., 1968, A model for the evolution of strontium and lead isotopes in a dynamic Earth: Reviews of geophysics, v. 6, no. 2, p. 175–199.

Arriens, P. A., 1971, The Archean geochronology of Australia: Geological Society of Australia Special Publication, v. 3, p. 11–24.

Arriens, P. A., and Lambert, I. B., 1969, On the age and strontium isotopic geochemistry of granulite-facies rocks from the Fraser Range, western Australia, and the Musgrave Ranges, Central Australia: Geological Society of Australia Special Publication no. 2, p. 377–388.

Arth, J. G., and Hanson, G. N., 1975, Geochemistry and origin of the early Precambrian crust of northeastern Minnesota: Geochimica et Cosmochimica Acta, v. 39, p. 325–362.

Baer, A. J., 1980, Comment *on* The missing Precambrian crust: Geology, v. 8, p. 114–117.

Barker, F., and Millard, H. T., 1979, Geochemistry of the type trondhjemite and three associated rocks, Norway, *in* Barker, F., ed., Trondhjemites, dacites and related rocks: Amsterdam, Elsevier, p. 517–528.

Barker, F., Arth, J. G., Peterman, Z. E., and Friedman, I., 1976, The 1.7–1.8-b.y.-old trondhjemites of southwestern Colorado and northern New Mexico: Geochemistry and depths of genesis: Geological Society of America Bulletin, v. 87, p. 189–198.

Bell, K., Blenkinsop, J., and Moore, J. M., 1975, Evidence for a Proterozoic greenstone belt from Snow Lake: Nature, 258, p. 689–701.

Bennett, R., Page, R. W., and Bladon, G. M., 1975, Catalogue of isotopic age determinations on Australian rocks, 1966–1970: Bureau of Mineral Resources Report no. 162.

Black, L. P., 1977, A Rb-Sr geochronological study in the Proterozoic Tennant Creek Block, central Australia: Bureau of Mineral Resources Journal of Australian Geology and Geophysics, v. 2, p. 111–122.

Blake, D. H., Hodgson, I. M., and Muhling, P. C., 1979, Geology of the Granites-Tanami region, Northern Territory and Western Australia: Bulletin of Bureau of Mineral Resources, Geology and Geophysics, no. 197.

Blockley, J. G., 1973, Geology of Western Australian tin deposits: Australian Institute of Mining and Metallurgy Symposium Proceedings, May 1973, p. 131–140.

Branch, C. D., 1978, Evolution of the middle Proterozoic Chandabooka caldera, Gawler Range acid volcano-plutonic Province, South Australia: Journal of the Geological Society of Australia, v. 25,

p. 199–218.

Briden, J. C., 1976, Application of palaeomagnetism to Proterozoic tectonics: Philosophical Transactions of the Royal Society of London, ser. A., v. 280, p. 405–416.

Brown, R. F., Chappell, J. F., Moore, J. M., and Thompson, P., 1975, An ensimatic island arc and ocean closure in the Grenville Province of southeastern Ontario: Geoscience Canada, v. 2, p. 141–144.

Bunting, J. A., DeLaeter, J. R., and Libby, W. G., 1976, Tectonic subdivision and geochronology of the northeastern part of the Albany-Fraser Province, Western Australia: Geological Survey of Western Australia 1975 Annual Report, p. 117–126.

Burke, K., Dewey, J. F., and Kidd, W.S.F., 1976, Precambrian palaeomagnetic results compatible with contemporary operation of the Wilson cycle: Tectonophysics, v. 33, p. 287–299.

Cahen, L., and Snelling, N. J., 1966, The geochronology of equatorial Africa: Amsterdam, North Holland Publishing Company.

Carey, S. W., 1976, The expanding Earth—an essay review: Earth Science Reviews, v. 11, p. 105–143.

Chapman, H. J., DeLaeter, J. R., Gorton, M. P., Anderson, L. F., Bickle, M. J., Binns, R. A., and Groves, D. I., 1980, Isotopic study of granitic rocks from the central Yilgarn Block, Western Australia [abs.]: 2nd International Archaean Symposium, Perth, 1980.

Clifford, T. N., 1968, African structure and convection: Transactions of the Leeds Geological Association, v. VII (5), p. 291–301.

Collerson, K. D., and Bridgwater, D., 1979, Metamorphic development of early Archean tonalitic and trondhjemitic gneisses, Saglek area, Labrador, *in* Barker, F., ed., Trondhjemites, dacites and related rocks: Amsterdam, Elsevier, p. 205–273.

Compston, W., and Chappell, B. W., 1979, Sr-isotope evolution of granitoid source rocks, *in* McElhinny, M. W., ed., The Earth, its origin, structure and evolution: London, Academic Press, p. 377–426.

Compston, W., and Turek, A., 1973, Radiometric age limits for the provenance and deposition of the Kurrawang Beds, Coolgardie Goldfield, Western Australia: Journal of the Geological Society of Australia, v. 29, pt. 2, p. 217–222.

Condie, K. C., and Budding, A. J., 1979, Geology and geochemistry of Precambrian rocks, central and south-central New Mexico: New Mexico Institute of Mining and Technology Memoir, 35, 58 p.

Condie, K. C., and Hunter, D. R., 1976, Trace element geochemistry of Archean granitic rocks from the Barberton region, South Africa: Earth and Planetary Science Letters, v. 29, p. 389–400.

Cooper, J. A., Fanning, C. M., Flook, M. M., and Oliver, R. L., 1976, Archean and Proterozoic metamorphic rocks of southern Ayre Peninsula, South Australia: Journal of the Geological Society of Australia, v. 23, p. 287–292.

Cooper, J. A., Nesbitt, R. W., Platt, J. P., and Mortimer, G. E., 1978, Crustal development in the Agnew region, Western Australia, as shown by Rb/Sr isotopic and geochemical studies: Precambrian Research, v. 7, p. 31–59.

Cooper, J. A., James, P. R., and Rutland, R.W.R., 1980, Rb/Sr dating of granitic intrusions in relation to the stratigraphic and deformational history of the Pilbara Block, Western Australia [abs.]: 2nd International Archean Symposium, Perth, 1980.

Crawford, A. R., 1981, Central Asia and Earth expansion [abs.]: Expanding Earth Symposium Abstracts, University of Sydney.

Crook, K.A.W., and Felton, E. A., 1975, Tasman geosyncline greenstones and ophiolites: Journal of the Geological Society of Australia, v. 22, p. 117–131.

Dearnley, R., 1966, Orogenic fold belts and a hypothesis of Earth evolution, *in* Aherns, L., Press, F., Runcorn, S. K., and Urey, H. C., eds., Physics and chemistry of the Earth: London, Pergamon Press, v. VII, p. 1–114.

DeLaeter, J. R., and Blockley, J. G., 1972, Granite ages within the Archean Pilbara block, Western Australia: Journal of the Geological Society of Australia, v. 19, p. 363–370.

DeLaeter, J. R., and Trendall, A. F., 1970, The age of the Copper Hills porphyry: Geological Survey of Western Australia, 1969 Annual Report, p. 54–58.

DeLaeter, J. R., Lewis, J. D., Blockley, J. G., 1975, Granite ages within the Shaw batholith, Pilbara region, Western Australia: Geological Survey of Western Australia, 1974 Annual Report, p. 73–79

DeLaeter, J. R., Hickman, A. H., Trendall, A. F., and Lewis, J. D., 1977, Geochronological data concerning the eastern extent of the Pilbara Block: Geological Survey of Western Australia, 1976 Annual Report, p. 56–61.

Dirac, P.A.M., 1938, A new basis for cosmology: Proceedings of the Royal Society of London, v. A 165, p. 199.

Egyed, L., 1956, The change in the Earth's dimensions determined from palaeogeographical data: Geofisica Purae Applicata, v. 33, p. 42–48.

Embleton, B.J.J., and Schmidt, P. W., 1979, Recognition of common Precambrian polar wandering reveals a conflict with plate tectonics: Nature, v. 282, p. 705–707.

Engel, A.E.J., and Kelm, D. L., 1972, Pre-Permian global tectonics: A tectonic test: Geological Society of America Bulletin, v. 83, p. 2325–2340.

Engel, A.E.J., Itson, Sonja P., Engel, C. G., Stickney, D. M., and Gray, E. J., 1974, Crustal evolution and global tectonics: A petrogenetic view: Geological Society of America Bulletin, v. 85, p. 843–858.

Ewers, G. R., and Scott, P. A., 1977, Geochemistry of the Cullen Granite, Northern Territory: Bureau of Mineral Resources Journal of Australian Geology and Geophysics, v. 2, p. 165–176.

Fahrig, W. F., and Eade, K. E., 1968, The chemical evolution of the Canadian Shield: Canadian Journal of Earth Sciences, v. 5, p. 1247–1252.

Fanning, C. M., Oliver, R. L., and Cooper, J. A., 1980, The Carnot gneisses, a metamorphosed Archean supracrustal sequence in southern Eyre Peninsula: Journal of the Geological Society of Australia, v. 27, p. 45.

Ferguson, J., Chappell, B. W., and Goleby, A. B., 1980, Granitoids in the Pine Creek geosynclines, *in* Ferguson, J., and Goleby, A. B., eds., Uranium in the Pine Creek Geosyncline: International Atomic Energy Agency, Vienna, p. 73–90.

Giles, C. W., 1977, Rock units in the Gawler Range Volcanics, Lake Everard area, South Australia: Quarterly Geological Notes, Geological Survey of Southern Australia, v. 61, p. 7–16.

Glikson, A. Y., 1976a, Trace element geochemistry and origin of early Precambrian acid igneous series, Barberton Mountain Land, Transvaal: Geochimica et Cosmochimica Acta, v. 40, p. 1261–1280.

——1976b, Archean to early Proterozoic shield elements: Relevance of plate tectonics: Geological Association of Canada Special Publication, no. 14, p. 489–516.

——1979a, Early Precambrian tonalite-trondhjemite sialic nuclei: Earth Science Reviews, v. 15, p. 1–73.

——, 1979b, The missing Precambrian crust: Geology, v. 7, p. 449–454.

——1980a, Precambrian sial-sima relations: Evidence of Earth expansion, *in* Green, D. H., ed., Creativity and orthodoxy in the frontiers of earth science: Amsterdam, Elsevier, p. 193–234.

——1980b, Reply to the missing Precambrian crust: Geology, v. 8, p. 114–117.

Glikson, A. Y., and Hickman, A. H., 1981, Geochemistry of Archean volcanic successions, eastern Pilbara Block, Western Australia: Bureau of Mineral Resources Australian Resources 81/36.

Glikson, A. Y., and Sheraton, J. W., 1972, Early Precambrian trondhjemitic suites in Western Australia and northwestern Scotland, and the geochemical evolution of shields: Earth and Planetary Science Letters, v. 17, p. 227–242.

Goodwin, A. M., 1974, Precambrian belts, plumes and shield development: American Journal of Science, v. 274, p. 987–1028.

Gray, C. M., 1979, Geochronology of granulite facies gneisses on the western Musgrave Block, central Australia: Journal of Geological Society of Australia, v. 25, p. 403–414.

Green, D. H., 1971, Composition of basaltic magmas as indicators of conditions of origin: Application to oceanic volcanism: Philosophical Transactions of the Royal Society of London, ser. A, v. 268, p. 707–725.

—— 1975, Genesis of Archean peridotitic magmas and constraints on Archean geothermal gradients and tectonics: Geology, v. 3, p. 15–18.

Green, T. H., and Ringwood, A. E., 1968, Genesis of the calc-alkaline igneous rock suite: Contributions to Mineralogy and Petrology, v. 18, p. 105–162.

Harrington, H. J., 1974, The Tasman geosyncline in Australia: Geological Society of Australia, Qld. Division, University of Queensland.

Hickman, A. H., and Lipple, S. L., 1975, Explanatory notes on the Marble Bar 1:250,000 geological sheet, western Australia: Geological Survey of Western Australia Record 1974/20.

Hilgenberg, O. C., 1933, Vom wachsenden Erdball: Berlin, 56 p. (cited in Carey, 1970a).

Holmes, A., 1951, The sequence of Precambrian orogenic belts in south and central Africa: 18th International Geological Congress, p. 254–269.

Hurley, P. M., Hughs, H., Faure, G., Fairbairn, H. W., and Pinson, W. H., 1962, Radiogenic strontium 87 model of continent formation: Journal of Geophysical Research, v. 67, p. 5315–5334.

Hurley, P. M., Fairbairn, H. W., and Gaudette, H. E., 1976, Progress report on early Archean rocks in Liberia, Sierra Leone and Guyana and their general stratigraphic setting, *in* Windley, B. F., ed., Early history of the Earth: London, Wiley & Sons, p. 511–524.

Irving, E., and McGlynn, J. C., 1976, Proterozoic magnetostratigraphy and tectonic evolution of Laurentia: Philosophical Transactions of the Royal Society of London, ser. A., v. 280, p. 433–468.

Irving, E., and Park, J. K., 1972, Hairpins and superintervals: Canadian Journal of Earth Sciences, v. 9, p. 1318–1324.

Jahn, B., Glikson, A. Y., Peucat, J. J., and Hickman, A. H., 1981, REE geochemistry and geochronology of Archean silicic volcanics and granitoids from the Pilbara Block, Western Australia: Geochimica et Cosmochimica Acta, v. 45, p. 1633–1652.

Jaques, A. L., Chappell, B. W., and Taylor, S. R., 1978, Geochemistry of LIL-element enriched tholeiites from the Marum ophiolite complex, northern Papua-New Guinea: Bureau of Mineral Resources Journal of Australian Geology and Geophysics, v. 3, p. 297–310.

Jordan, P., 1966, The expanding Earth (Trans. A. Beer, 1971: Pergamon, Oxford.

Kröner, A., 1976, Proterozoic crustal evolution in parts of southern Africa and evidence for extensive sialic crust since the end of the Archean: Philosophical Transactions of the Royal Society of London, ser. A, v. 280, p. 541–553.

—— 1977, Precambrian mobile belts of southern and eastern Africa—ancient sutures or sites of ensialic mobility? A case for crustal evolution towards plate tectonics: Tectonophysics, v. 40, p. 101–135.

—— 1981, Precambrian plate tectonics, *in* Kröner, A., ed., Precambrian plate tectonics: Amsterdam, Elsevier, p. 57–83.

Lambert, I. B., 1967, Investigations of high grade regional metamorphic and associated rocks [Ph.D. thesis]: Australian National University, Canberra.

Lambert, I. B., and Wyllie, P. J., 1972, Melting of gabbro (quartz eclogite) with excess water to 35 kilobars, with geological implications: Journal of Geology, v. 80, p. 693–708.

Lambert, R. St. J., 1976, Archean thermal regimes, crustal and upper mantle temperatures and a progressive evolutionary model for the Earth, *in* Windley, B. F., ed., Early history of the Earth: London, Wiley & Sons, p. 363–376.

MacPherson, H. G., 1958, A chemical and petrographic study of Precambrian sediments: Geochimica et Cosmochimica, Acta, v. 14, p. 73–92.

Marjoribanks, R. W., and Black, L. P., 1974, The geology and geochronology of the Arunta complex north of Ormiston Gorge, central Australia: Journal of the Geological Society of Australia, v. 21, p. 291–299.

McCulloch, M. T., and Wasserburg, G. J., 1978, Sm-Nd and Rb-Sr chronology of continental crust formation: Science, v. 200, p. 1003–1011.

McElhinny, M. W., and Embleton, B.J.J., 1976, Precambrian and Early Palaeozoic palaeomagnetism in Australia: Philosophical Transactions of the Royal Society of London, ser. A, v. 280, p. 417–431.

McElhinny, M. W., and McWilliams, M. O., 1977, Precambrian geodynamics: a palaeomagnetic view: Tectonophysics, v. 40, p. 137–159.

McElhinny, M. W., Briden, J. C., Jones, D. L., and Brock, A., 1968, Geological and geophysical implications of paleomagnetic results from Africa: Review of Geophysics, v. 6, p. 201–238.

McElhinny, M. W., Taylor, S. R., and Stevenson, D. J., 1978, Limits to the expansion of Earth, Moon, Mars, and Mercury and to changes in the gravitational constant: Nature, v. 271, p. 316–321.

Meservey, R., 1969, Topological inconsistency of continental drift on the present size Earth: Science, v. 166, p. 609–611.

Mitchell, J. E., 1976, Precambrian geology of the Westmoreland Region, Northern Australia, Part II—Cliffdale Volcanics: Bureau of Mineral Resources of Australia Record 1976/34.

Moorbath, S., 1976, Age and isotope constraints for the evolution of Archean crust, *in* Windley, B. F., ed., Early history of the Earth: London, Wiley & Sons, p. 351–362.

—— 1977, Ages, isotopes and the evolution of Precambrian continental crust: Chemical Geology, v. 20, p. 151–187.

Muhling, P. C., and DeLaeter, J. R., 1971, Ages of granitic rocks in the Poona-Dalgaranga area of the Yilgarn Block, Western Australia: Geological Society of Australia Special Publication no. 3, p. 25–32.

Naqvi, S. M., 1978, Geochemistry of Archean metasediments: Evidence for prominent anorthosite-norite-troctolite in the Archean basaltic primordial crust, *in* Windley, B. F., and Naqvi, S. M., eds., Archean geochemistry: Amsterdam, Elsevier, p. 340–360.

Newton, R. C., 1977, Experimental evidence for the operation of very high pressures in Archean granulite metamorphism [abs.]: Archean Geochemistry Symposium Abstracts, Hyderabad, p. 73–75.

O'Beirne, W. R., 1968, The acid porphyries and porphyroid rocks of the Kalgoorlie area [Ph.D. thesis]: University of Western Australia, Perth.

O'Connor, J. T., 1965, A classification of quartz-rich igneous rocks based on feldspar ratios: U.S. Geological Survey Professional Paper 525B.

O'Hara, M. J., 1977, Thermal history of excavation of Archean gneisses from the base of the continental crust: Journal of the Society of London, v. 134.

O'Nions, R. K., and Pankhurst, R. J., 1978, Early Archean rocks and geochemical evolution of the Earth's crust: Earth and Planetary Science Letters, v. 38, p. 211–236.

Oversby, V. M., 1975, Lead isotopic systematics and ages of Archean acid intrusives in the Kalgoorlie-Norseman area, Western Australia: Geochimica et Cosmochimica Acta, v. 39, p. 1107–1125.

—— 1976, Isotopic ages and geochemistry of Archean acid igneous rocks from the Pilbara, Western Australia: Geochimica et Cosmochimica Acta, v. 40, p. 817–829.

Owen, H. G., 1976, Continental displacement and expansion of the Earth during the Mesozoic and Cainozoic: Philosophical Transactions of the Royal Society of London, ser. A, v. 281, p. 223–291.

Page, R. W., 1978, Response of U-Pb zircon and Rb-Sr total rock and mineral systems to low-grade regional metamorphism in Proterozoic igneous rocks, Mount Isa, Qld, Australia: Journal of the Geological Society of Australia, v. 25, p. 141–164.

Page, R. W., Blake, D. H., and Mahon, M. W., 1976, Geochronology and related aspects of acid volcanics, associated granites and other Proterozoic rocks in the Granites-Tanami region, northwestern Australia: Bureau of Mineral Resources Journal of Australian Geology and Geophysics, v. 1, p. 1–13.

Page, R. W., Compston, W., and Needham, R. S., 1980, Geochronology and evolution of the late Archean basement and Proterozoic rocks in the Alligator Rivers uranium field, Northern Territory, Australia, *in* Ferguson, J., and Goleby, A. B., eds., Uranium in the Pine Creek Geosyncline: International Atomic Energy Agency, Vienna, p. 39–68.

Pearce, J. A., and Cann, J. R., 1973, Tectonic setting of basic volcanic rocks determined using trace element analyses: Earth and Planetary Science Letters, v. 19, p. 290–300.

Pearce, T. H., Gorman, B. E., and Birkett, T. C., 1977, The relationships between major element chemistry and tectonic environment of basic and intermediate volcanic rocks: Earth and Planetary Science Letters, v. 36, p. 121–132.

Patterson, C. C., and Tatsumoto, M., 1964, The significance of lead isotopes in detrital feldspar with respect to chemical differentiation within Earth's mantle: Geochimica et Cosmochimica Acta, v. 28, p. 1–22.

Piper, J.D.A., 1976, Palaeomagnetic evidence for a Proterozoic supercontinent: Philosophical Transactions of the Royal Society of London, ser. A, v. 280, p. 469–490.

Piper, J.D.A., Briden, J. C., and Lomax, K., 1973, Precambrian Africa and South America as a single continent: Nature, v. 245, p. 244–247.

Plumb, K. A., and Derrick, G. M., 1975. Geology of the Proterozoic rocks of the Kimberley to Mount Isa region, *in* Knight, C. L., ed., Economical Geological Australian Papua-New Guinea: Australian Institute of Mining and Metalurgy Monograph 5, p. 217–252.

Pride, C., and Muecke, G. K., 1980, Rare earth element geochemistry of the Scourian Complex, NW Scotland—evidence for the granite-granulite link: Contributions to Mineralogy and Petrology, v. 73, p. 403–412.

Richards, J. R., White, D. A., Webb, A. W., and Branch, C. D., 1966, Isotopic ages of acid igneous rocks in the Cairns Hinterlands, North Queensland, Australia: Bureau of Mineral Resourcejs Geology and Geophysics Bulletin, no. 88.

Roddick, J. C., and Compston, W., 1977, Strontium isotopic equilibration: A solution to the paradox: Earth and Planetary Science Letters, v. 34, p. 238–246.

Roddick, J. C., Compston, W., and Durney, D. W., 1975, The radiometric age of the Mount Keith granodiorite, a maximum age estimate for an Archean greenstone sequence in the Yilgarn block, Western Australia: Precambrian Research, v. 3, p. 55–78.

Rossiter, A. G., and Ferguson, J., 1980, A Proterozoic tectonic model for Northern Australia and its economic implications, *in* Ferguson, J., and Goleby, A. B., eds., Uranium in the Pine Creek Geosyncline: International Atomic Energy Agency, Vienna, p. 209–232.

Runcorn, S. K., 1981, Geophysical tests of the Earth expansion hypothesis [abs.]: Expanding Earth Symposium Abstracts, University of Sydney.

Rutland, R.W.R., 1976, Orogenic evolution of Australia: Earth-Science Reviews, v. 12, p. 161–196.

Schmidt, P. W., and Clark, D. A., 1980, The response of palaeomagnetic data to Earth expansion: Geophysical Journal of the Royal Astronomical Society, v. 61, p. 95–100.

Schmidt, P. W., and Embleton, B.J.J., 1981, A geotectonic paradox: Has the Earth expanded? Journal of Geophysics, v. 49, p. 20–25.

Shackleton, R. M., 1976, Shallow and deep level exposures of the Archean crust in India and Africa, *in* Windley, B. F., ed., Early history of the Earth: London, John Wiley & Sons, p. 317–322.

Sheraton, J. W., 1980, Geochemistry of Precambrian metapelites from East Antarctica and metamorphic variations: Bureau of Mineral Resources Journal of Australian Geology and Geophysics, v. 5, p. 279–288.

Sheraton, J. W., and Labonne, B., 1978, Petrology and geochemistry of acid igneous rocks of northeast Queensland: Australia Bureau of Mineral Resources Bulletin, no. 169.

Slawson, W. F., Kanasewich, E. R., Ostic, R. G., and Farquhar, R. M., 1963, Age of the North American crust: Nature, v. 200, p. 413–414.

Stauffer, M. R., Mukherjee, A. C., and Koo, J., 1975, The Amisk Group: An Aphebian(?) island arc deposit: Canadian Journal of Earth Sciences, v. 12, p. 2021–2035.

Stewart, A. D., 1983, Quantitative limits to the palaeoradius of the Earth, *in* Carey, S. W., ed., The expanding earth—A Symposium: University of Sydney, Australia, p. 305–320.

Tarney, J., and Windley, B. F., 1977, Chemistry, thermal gradients and evolution of the lower continental crust: Journal of Geological Society of London, v. 134, p. 153–172.

Taylor, S. R., 1966, The application of trace element data to problems in petrology, *in* Physics and chemistry of the Earth: New York, Pergamon, v. 6, p. 133–213.

——, 1979, Chemical composition and evolution of the continental crust: The rare earth element evidence, *in* McElhinny, M. W., ed., The Earth, its origin, structure and evolution: London, Academic Press, p. 353–376.

Tryon, E. P., 1983, Cosmology and the expanding Earth, *in* Carey, S. W., ed., The expanding earth—A Symposium, University of Sydney, Australia, p. 349–358.

Veizer, J., and Compston, W., 1976, Sr^{87}/Sr^{86} in Precambrian carbonates as an index of crustal evolution: Geochimica et Cosmochimica Acta, v. 40, p. 905–914.

Wesson, P. S., 1980, Does gravity change with time?: Physics Today, July 1980, p. 32–37.

Wilson, I. H., 1978, Volcanism on a Proterozoic continental margin in northwestern Queensland: Precambrian Research, v. 7, p. 205–235.

Wyborn, L.A.I., and Page, R. W., Chemical and isotopic constraints on the source regions of the Kalkadoon and Ewenbatholiths, Mt. Isa inlier, and their implications for early Proterozoic crustal evolution in Australia [abs.]: Sixth Australian Geological Convention, Canberra, p. 191.

Wynne-Edwards, H. R., 1976, Proterozoic ensialic orogenesis: The millipede model of ductile plate tectonics: American Journal of Science, v. 270, p. 927–953.

Manuscript Accepted by the Society April 14, 1983

Printed in U.S.A.

Geological Society of America
Memoir 161
1983

Geochemistry of Early Proterozoic sedimentary rocks and the Archean/Proterozoic boundary

S. R. Taylor
S. M. McLennan
Research School of Earth Sciences
Australian National University
Canberra 2601, Australia

ABSTRACT

The uniformity of rare-earth element (REE) patterns in clastic sedimentary rocks, due to the low solubility and short residence times of REE in the oceans, provides overall average upper crustal compositions for these elements. Effects of weathering, diagenesis, and metamorphism are minor. Local provenance is recorded in first-cycle sediments, but is rapidly erased with sediment maturity. The REE patterns in Archean sedimentary rocks indicate that the Archean crust was not highly evolved. It appears to have been dominated by basaltic and Na-rich granitic rocks (tonalites and trondhjemites). The REE patterns in Proterozoic and later sedimentary rocks indicate a major episodic break at the Archean/Proterozoic boundary. This is consistent with a change to a more differentiated upper crust, dominated by granodiorites, with negative Eu anomalies. These are inferred to result from intracrustal melting, during which Eu is retained in a plagioclase-rich lower crust. Detailed descriptions of the change in REE patterns at the Archean/Proterozoic boundary are given for the Huronian (Canada) and Pine Creek Geosyncline (Australia) successions. Evidence from these successions, the Hamersley basin (Australia), and the Pongola (South Africa) sequence indicates that the change in upper crustal composition was not isochronous, but extended over a period from about 3.2 to 2.5 Ga ago. Abundance tables are given for the Proterozoic continental crust, upper and lower crusts, and the Archean crust. A model for continental crust evolution suggests that the evolution of the present crust began in the Archean and that most of the volume of the crust was formed from the mantle between 3.2 and 2.5 Ga. This was followed closely by intracrustal melting which produced the Proterozoic upper crust.

1. RARE-EARTH ELEMENT PATTERNS AS INDEXES OF UPPER CRUSTAL COMPOSITION

Igneous rocks display a wide diversity of REE patterns, ranging from light rare-earth element (LREE) depleted patterns typical of Mid-Ocean Ridge Basalts (MORB) to extreme LREE-enriched patterns typical of many late-stage granites. In contrast, mature clastic sedimentary rocks display uniform patterns. For example, post-Archean shales from Australia, Europe, and North America all show a remarkable uniformity, with La_N/Yb_N typically about 9.5 ± 1.5 and $Eu/Eu^* = 0.65 \pm 0.05$ (Fig. 1). The uniform nature of these patterns is due to three basic causes: (1) The REE are transferred nearly quantitatively from source rocks into clastic sediments. (2) The solubility and residence time in sea water of the REE are low. (3) Mixing processes during sedimentation are thorough. Some comments on these points occur in the text, but a first-order conclusion is that the REE patterns in mature clastic sedimentary rocks represent an overall average of REE patterns in upper crustal rocks exposed to weathering. Accordingly, they provide a method of estimating upper crustal compositions.

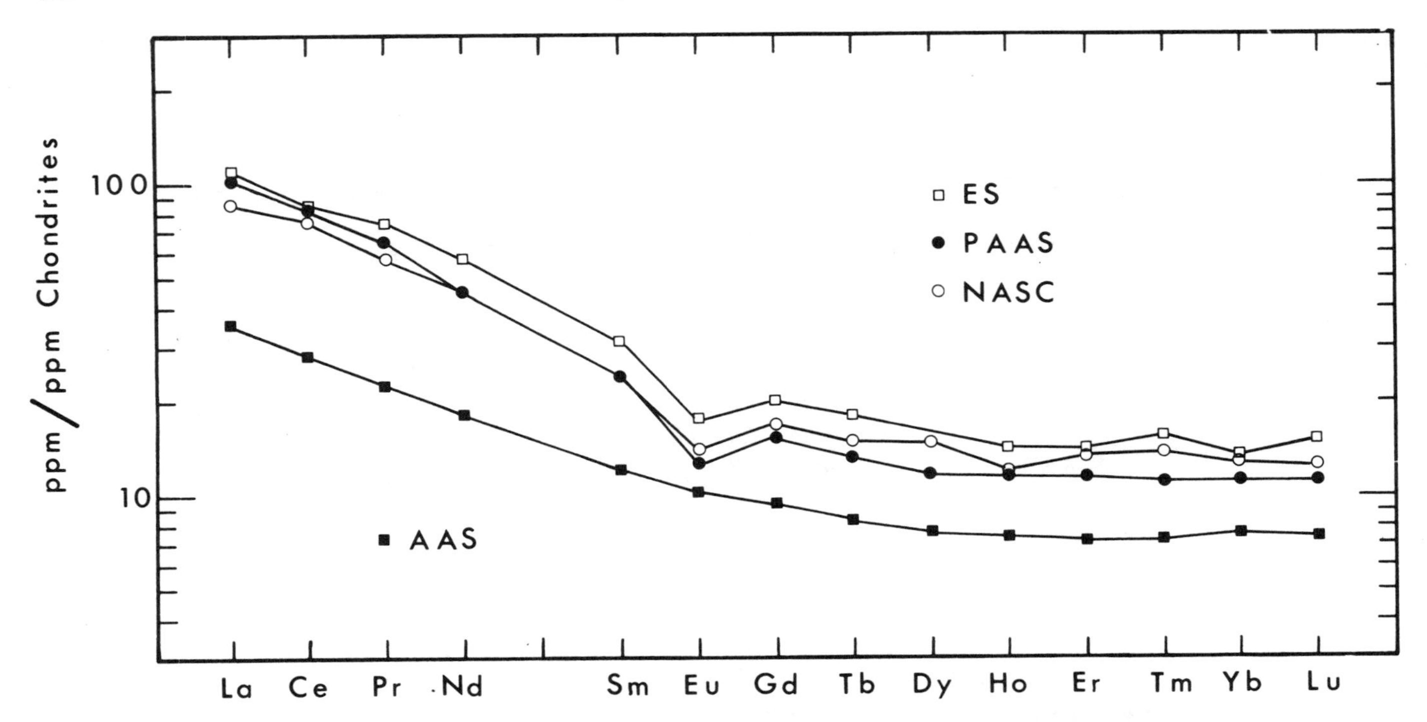

Figure 1. REE patterns normalized to chondrites, of various post-Archean shale composites and averages. Included are the European shale composite (ES), North American shale composite (NASC), and post-Archean averages Australian shale (PAAS). Also shown is an estimate of the average shale from the Archean-aged Yilgarn Block, Western Australia (AAS). Note the uniform nature of the post-Archean data with high ΣREE, La_N/Yb_N, and negative Eu-anomaly. Such patterns support the idea of a granodiorite composition for the upper continental crust. The Archean pattern, with lower ΣREE, La_N/Yb_N, and no Eu-anomaly, is similar to modern calc-alkaline andesites and suggests a more mafic exposed crust during the Archean (see text for discussion).

2. EFFECTS OF WEATHERING, DIAGENESIS, AND METAMORPHISM

It has been argued by many authors, and is the general theme of this paper, that REE in most clastic sedimentary rocks reflect the average REE pattern in the upper continental crust. Thus, a basic question is whether weathering, erosion, deposition, diagenesis, or metamorphism affect sedimentary REE patterns. It is clear that the overall effect of low-temperature processes such as weathering and diagenesis must be minor. REE abundances in natural waters are very low; for example, the total REE content of sea water is trivial, amounting to that present in the upper 0.2 mm of ocean-floor sediment (Haskin and Paster, 1979). The REE content in common chemical sediments such as carbonates and evaporates is also typically very low. Thus, from simple mass balance considerations, it is clear that the bulk of REE is transported into clastic sedimentary rocks.

Few studies are available on REE behaviour during weathering (see Ronov et al., 1967; Cullers et al., 1975; Nesbitt, 1979). It is generally agreed that there is an overall enrichment in total REE in weathering profiles, but the nature and magnitude are difficult to assess. Of more importance to sedimentary REE studies is the possibility of fractionation during weathering. There may be an increase in La_N/Yb_N in some weathering profiles (Ronov et al., 1967; Duddy, 1980), although Nesbitt (1979) recognized a profile with heavy rare-earth element (HREE) enrichment. Ronov et al. (1967) concluded the intensity of effects was related to the lithology being weathered. Thus, rocks with unstable mineralogy during weathering, such as ultramafic and mafic volcanics, show considerably more effect than rocks with relatively stable mineralogy, such as granites and granodiorites. The transport of REE into sedimentary basins is primarily a result of mechanical rather than chemical transport, and it is unlikely that redistribution of REE *within* weathering profiles would have a significant effect on REE patterns in well-mixed sedimentary rocks.

Chaudhuri and Cullers (1979) examined the effects of diagenesis on Pliocene-Miocene sediments from the Gulf of Louisiana. The REE patterns were generally similar to typical post-Archean sedimentary rocks, although enriched in ΣREE. Some variations in ΣREE and La_N/Yb_N (Eu/Eu* remained constant) were observed but not related to diagenetic processes. The authors concluded that the REE characteristics were mainly controlled by provenance consideration.

Mobility of REE has been noted during some types of metamorphism where very high fluid-rock ratios are encountered, such as in submarine weathering, spilitization, and other hydrothermal activity (Floyd, 1977; Hellman and Henderson, 1977; Humphris et al., 1978; Ludden and Thompson, 1978). The possibility of hydrothermal processes affecting sedimentary rocks is considerably less than for igneous rocks such as oceanic basalts, although notable exceptions occur (McLennan and Taylor, 1979). A number of studies dealing with regional metamorphism have considered rocks from greenschist to granulite facies and detected no or very little REE mobility (Green et al., 1969, 1972; Cullers et al., 1974; Muecke et al., 1979). Others have suggested mobility only in the very highest grades of metamorphism, such as granulite grade (Frey, 1969; Collerson and Fryer, 1978).

3. PROVENANCE

The effects of provenance on sedimentary REE patterns was recently evaluated by Bhatia and Taylor (in prep.). REE patterns in first-cycle sediments derived from a single lithology faithfully mirror their parental source rocks. Thus post-Archean sedimentary rocks derived from island-arc volcanics have "andesitic" REE patterns, with no Eu anomaly (e.g., Baldwin Formation; Nance and Taylor, 1977), while Archean sediments derived mainly from sodic-rich granites or felsic volcanics show steep LREE enriched patterns (Nance and Taylor, 1977; Jenner et al., 1981; unpublished data, this laboratory). Greywackes derived from island-arc volcanics, from granites, and from recycled sedimentary rocks all reflect the characteristics of their source material (Bhatia and Taylor, in prep.). Shales from the same sequence tend towards typical average post-Archean REE characteristics with increasing recycling.

Thus, in evaluating crustal abundances and evolution of the REE, it is necessary to choose material derived from recycled sedimentary rocks. Where first-cycle sediments are sampled, they should be derived from a fairly complex provenance (determined from sandstone and conglomerate petrography).

4. THE EUROPIUM ANOMALY

The ultimate cause of the distinct behaviour of europium is due to the differences in ionic radius between Eu^{3+} (r = 1.066A) and Eu^{2+} (r = 1.25A), (radii for 8-fold CN, Shannon, 1976). Under reducing conditions, Eu^{2+} enters different lattice sites to the other REE, closely mimicking the behaviour of Sr^{2+} (r = 1.26A), during crystal-liquid fractionation.

In post-Archean sedimentary rocks, a depletion in Eu, relative to the other REE, is commonly observed. Is this Eu depletion of surficial origin due to surface oxidation-reduction processes, or does it reflect an inherent property of upper crustal rocks? Under the present oxidizing conditions at the surface of the Earth, Eu is probably trivalent. The introduction of an oxidizing atmosphere at about 2.3 Ga ago does not appear to have a discernible effect on the behaviour of Eu. Thus, Archean sedimentary REE patterns have no anomaly (see section 5), while post-Archean sedimentary patterns show significant REE depletion. This is the reverse of that expected from the introduction of an oxidizing atmosphere. Accordingly, we conclude that the observed Eu depletion in post-Archean sedimentary rocks is not due to surficial processes but is inherited, and is an inherent property of the post-Archean upper crust.

Is the Eu depletion of crustal or mantle origin? The continental crust is ultimately derived from the mantle (Taylor, 1967), but no common igneous rocks derived from the mantle exhibit consistent or systematic Eu anomalies. Localized depletion or accumulation of plagioclase accounts for the exceptions. Calcium-rich plagioclase is not a stable phase at pressures exceeding 10 kbar (about 40-km depth). Accordingly, Eu enrichment or depletion in the Earth is a crustal or shallow mantle process. The Eu depletion observed in upper crustal rocks is thus likely to be intracrustal in origin (since plagioclase is the only common mineral that accommodates divalent Eu).

5. REE PATTERNS IN ARCHEAN SEDIMENTARY ROCKS

The REE patterns in Archean sedimentary rocks are somewhat less uniform than those typical of post-Archean times, and this provides some interesting information on the composition and nature of the Archean crust. An average pattern from the Yilgarn Block, Western Australia, is shown in Figure 1. This has an La_N/Yb_N ratio of 4.5 and has no Eu anomaly ($Eu/Eu^* \sim 1$). The total REE abundance is about 70. As noted earlier, some Archean sediments have steep LREE-enriched patterns indicating local derivation from acidic parent rocks; others have flat REE (e.g., Akilia and Malene supracrustal rocks) indicating a basaltic parent. Others (e.g., Yellowknife, Jenner et al., 1981), which sample a fairly wide area, have La_N/Yb_N ratios higher than average. These characteristics have been discussed at length in several papers (Jenner et al, 1981; Taylor and McLennan, 1981a, 1981b, 1981c). There appears to be no doubt that the Archean sedimentary rocks are providing a widespread sampling of the exposed Archean crust (Taylor and McLennan, 1981b) and that granitic terrains, as well as greenstone belts, are being adequately sampled and represented (Taylor and McLennan, 1981a, 1981b, 1981c). Accordingly, we are able to use the

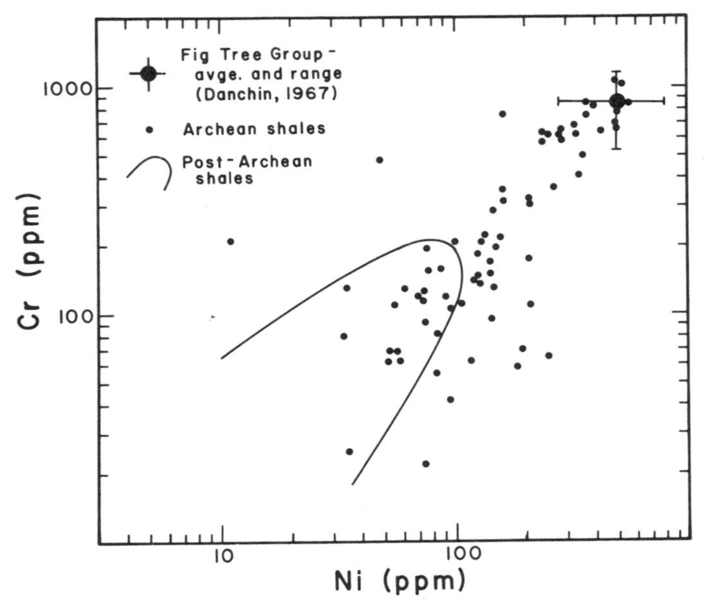

Figure 2. Plot of Cr versus Ni for Archean shales. A field encompassing most post-Archean shales (compiled from the literature) is also shown for comparison. The Archean data are taken from Bavinton and Taylor (1980) and unpublished results from this laboratory. Chromium and nickel abundances are highly scattered in Archean shales and overlap the post-Archean field. Many of the Archean data do show much higher Cr and Ni abundances, and the average Archean shale would have much higher Cr and Ni than the average post-Archean shale.

Archean sedimentary REE patterns as indicators of Archean upper crustal composition and environment.

The REE patterns in Archean sedimentary rocks resemble those of modern island-arc volcanic rocks, but they may also be derived from a bimodal basaltic-tonalitic (trondhjemitic) suite. This question has been extensively discussed (Taylor and McLennan, 1981a, 1981b, 1981c). Various observations favor the latter alternative. The changes in La/Yb ratios of the patterns and the occasional presence of end members favor the bimodal hypothesis rather than the island-arc model for the Archean crust. Taylor (1977) attempted to use Ni-Cr relationships to distinguish between the two models, since a basaltic (tholeiitic) component would contribute more Ni and Cr than an island-arc model (at least from modern analogues). More data (Fig. 2) have allowed some resolution of this problem (Taylor and McLennan, 1981). Archean sedimentary rocks appear to be inherently richer in Ni and Cr than do those of post-Archean time. It is, of course, more difficult to derive crustal averages from these two elements, with their complex behaviour during weathering, erosion, and sedimentation, than is the case for relatively insoluble elements such as the REE (and Th) (McLennan and Taylor, 1980a). Nevertheless, Ni and Cr data for the Archean rocks show an overall enrichment, consistent with the bimodal model.

Further caveats need to be borne in mind. For example, Archean sediments are more likely to be one-cycle greywackes, since the continental nuclei may be small and subject to rapid erosion.

Were the Archean continental nuclei separate or joined in a primitive Pangea? Two observations support the concept of small discrete nuclei, separated from one another. The first is that REE patterns in Archean sedimentary rocks show more provinciality than do those of post-Archean time. Thus, the Yellowknife sequence has higher La/Yb ratios than the West Australian rocks. If the Archean continental crust formed one coherent mass, more uniformity should be observed. A second observation is that the change from Archean to post-Archean patterns is not isochronous but occurs in differing regions over periods ranging from 3.0 to 2.3 Ga. If these regions were adjacent, sedimentary mixing processes would have eliminated these distinctions (see section 3).

The absence of a negative Eu anomaly in Archean sedimentary rocks provides further evidence about Archean crustal evolution. The production of K-rich granites, ignimbrites, and other rocks that result from intracrustal melting must have been at a minimum. These rocks typically have a significant, sometimes extreme, depletion in Eu. Such rocks, although present, must constitute less than 10% of the exposed Archean crust. Amounts in excess of 10% would be reflected by a discernible Eu depletion in the Archean sedimentary rock record.

A final conclusion from the REE evidence in Archean sedimentary rocks is that substantial amounts of the Archean crust must have been above sea level (cf. Hargraves, 1976).

6. REE PATTERNS IN PROTEROZOIC AND PHANEROZOIC SEDIMENTARY ROCKS

The preceding sections have dealt principally with the Archean record. This provides a background against which we now examine the REE record in Proterozoic sedimentary rocks. Phanerozoic data are included as well as Proterozoic, since the REE patterns in sedimentary rocks show no significant change between these eras. Three principal differences exist between REE patterns typical of Archean and of Proterozoic sedimentary rocks. The patterns are generally more uniform (see section 2, however), the La_N/Yb_N ratios are high, averaging 9.5 (± 1.5), and there is a pronounced and uniform depletion in Eu (Eu/Eu* = 0.65 ± 0.05). These characteristics have been noted and commented upon in several papers (e.g., Nance and Taylor, 1976; Taylor, 1979; Taylor and McLennan, 1981a, 1981b, 1981c; Jakes and Taylor, 1974). These data have been used to establish the upper crustal composition for post-Archean time (Taylor and McLennan, 1981a, 1981b, 1981c). The change from Archean to post-Archean patterns, although not isochronous (see section 6), is irreversible. Post-

Archean REE patterns swamp those derived from the Archean crust. Accordingly, the sedimentary REE data are consistent with a major increase in continental crustal area at that time.

7. THE ARCHEAN/PROTEROZOIC BOUNDARY

Thus far, the differences between Archean and post-Archean sedimentary rocks have been emphasized. We now address the cause of the change in REE patterns. The geochemistry of early Proterozoic sedimentary rocks has been examined in some detail in this laboratory and elsewhere (McLennan et al., 1979a; McLennan and Taylor, 1980b) for several years, and a reasonable model of REE evolution has emerged. In all places, the change in REE patterns in the upper crust (represented by the sedimentary data) appears to be related to widespread potassic magmatism (e.g., granites, granodiorites, rhyolites, ignimbrites) of intracrustal origin. The change in REE patterns in sedimentary rocks is recorded in Early Proterozoic successions, which record the unroofing and erosion of these Late Archean *upper* crustal additions. As emphasized below, the change in upper crustal composition was not isochronous on a world-wide scale but is represented by a rather protracted series of events lasting from about 3.2 to 2.5 Ga.

The Huronian

The Early Proterozoic Huronian succession, on the north shore of Lake Huron, Canada (Fig. 3), has received a great deal of attention since 1845, when Sir William Logan recognized the "great unconformity" between Archean basement and what is now termed "the Gowganda Formation." This sequence of mainly clastic sedimentary rocks reaches a maximum thickness of about 12 km and was deposited sometime between about 2.6 and 2.2 Ga ago (Van Schmus, 1965; Fairbairn et al., 1969; Gibbins and McNutt, 1975). The actual time of sedimentation was likely much less than this.

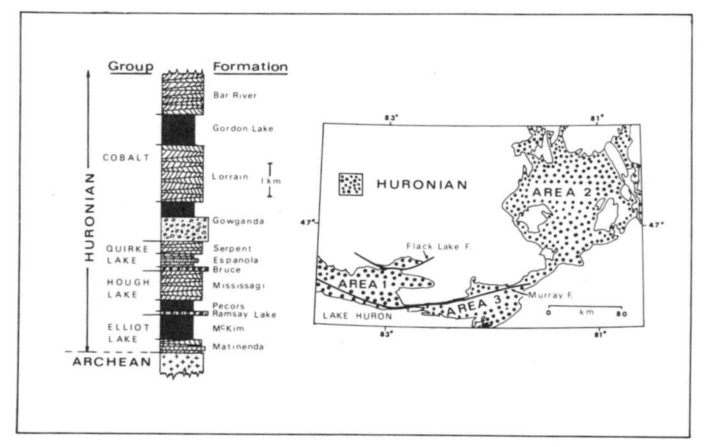

Figure 3. Location and generalized stratigraphy of the Early Proterozoic Huronian succession exposed on the north shore of Lake Huron, Canada.

The geochemistry of this sequence of sedimentary rocks has been examined, primarily by Grant Young and his coworkers (Young, 1969; 1973; McLennan et al., 1979a, 1979b). For the purposes of this discussion, the REE studies of McLennan et al. (1979a, 1979b) are most significant. Table 1 lists the average chemical composition of several selected fine-grained units in the Huronian succession. The Gowganda Formation (tillite and glacially derived mudstone) is not considered, since its unusual chemical composition is related to a glacial origin (Young, 1969; McLennan et al., 1979a). The Espanola Formation is the only Huronian formation characterized by abundant carbonate material (Young, 1973). The data in Table 1 (from McLennan et al., 1979b) are for the middle siltstone unit which contains the least amount of carbonate (generally $<15\%$) and therefore most comparable to other Huronian mudstone units.

Average REE patterns of the various formations are shown in Figure 4, and the gradual change in REE characteristics from the bottom to the top of the sequence is obvious. The REE patterns at the base (McKim and Pecors Formations) have Archean-style patterns. At the top (Gordon Lake Formation), REE patterns are identical to those of typical post-Archean sedimentary rocks. Although not displayed in the figure, the Espanola Formation data are in full agreement with such an evolutionary change.

The Ni and Cr data are also consistent with such an interpretation. The abundances of these elements in the lower formations (McKim and Pecors) are much higher (average Cr ~ 160 ppm; Ni ~ 80 ppm) than in the upper units (Table 1) and in post-Archean sedimentary rocks in general (Fig. 2).

Pine Creek Geosyncline

Early Proterozoic sedimentary rocks of the Pine Creek Geosyncline have recently been the subject of intensive study because of large uranium deposits in this area (Ferguson and Goleby, 1980). This sequence is about 14 km thick and was deposited between about 2.5 and 1.9 Ga ago, the most likely time of deposition being about 2.2 to 2.0 Ga (Page et al., 1980). Exposure is very poor so that the stratigraphy in any given area and general stratigraphic correlations are less well known than is the case for the Huronian succession (e.g., Needham et al., 1980).

McLennan and Taylor (1980b) examined REE characteristics of a selected suite of fine-grained sedimentary rocks and were able to divide the suite into two groups on the basis of REE geochemistry (Table 2, Fig. 5). Group I, from the lower part of the succession, has Archean-like REE patterns, although the La_N/Yb_N is higher than expected, probably due to a higher contribution of Na-rich

TABLE 1. AVERAGE CHEMICAL COMPOSITION OF HURONIAN FINE-GRAINED SEDIMENTARY ROCKS

	McKim Formation			Pecors Formation			Espanola Formation (siltstone member)			Serpent Formation			Gordon Lake Formation		
	$\bar{x}$	s.d.	n	$\bar{x}$	s.d.	n	$\bar{x}$	s.d.	n	$\bar{x}$	s.d.	n	$\bar{x}$	s.d.	n
SiO_2	59.60	2.98	8	61.06	3.95	13	52.95	7.36	4	72.30	-	2	69.03	8.52	7
TiO_2	0.77	0.07	8	0.76	0.12	13	0.45	0.05	4	0.46	-	2	0.39	0.09	7
Al_2O_3	20.42	1.71	8	18.58	2.83	13	12.42	1.01	4	12.66	-	2	15.37	4.43	7
FeO^T	6.14	1.19	8	6.42	1.21	13	4.13	0.56	4	3.49	-	2	3.24	1.25	7
MnO	0.06	0.01	8	0.06	0.02	13	0.13	0.06	4	0.02	-	2	0.02	0.01	7
MgO	2.20	0.36	8	2.73	0.32	13	5.46	1.70	4	1.41	-	2	1.61	0.62	7
CaO	0.72	0.39	8	0.68	0.30	13	7.56	2.65	4	0.95	-	2	0.25	0.28	7
Na_2O	1.33	0.44	8	1.59	0.58	13	1.44	0.63	4	1.75	-	2	1.30	1.07	7
K_2O	3.79	0.87	8	3.55	0.87	13	3.17	0.74	4	4.16	-	2	4.96	2.48	7
P_2O_5	0.08	0.02	8	0.10	0.03	13	0.09	0.02	4	0.09	-	2	0.12	0.18	7
L.O.I.	4.31	1.07	8	4.01	0.34	13	11.24	4.18	4	2.13	-	2	3.25	0.84	7
K_2O/Na_2O	3.2	1.2	8	2.6	1.4	13	3.0	2.4	4	3.7	-	2	23	34	7
Rb	147	43	8	139	34	13	142	29	4	-	-	-	201	92	7
Ba	830	199	8	838	298	13	1254	859	4	-	-	-	1037	533	7
Sr	160	82	8	146	88	13	83	24	4	-	-	-	25	15	7
Zr	152	39	8	186	25	13	129	46	4	-	-	-	284	96	7
Cr	161	50	8	163	46	13	103	43	4	-	-	-	56	24	7
Ni	75	12	8	81	18	13	43	6	4	-	-	-	14	7	7
Cu	65	27	8	71	36	13	24	22	4	-	-	-	46	96	7
Zn	91	26	8	90	35	13	42	16	4	-	-	-	23	13	7
Li	37	17	8	35	16	13	52	6	4	-	-	-	18	6	7
Ga	26	3	8	24	4	13	18	3	4	-	-	-	19	7	7
La	29	15	5	36	20	7	28	8	4	33	27	3	49	23	6
Ce	67	27	5	82	39	7	60	17	4	77	57	3	115	43	6
Nd	29	9	5	34	13	7	24	7	4	30	21	3	51	20	6
Sm	5.7	1.4	5	6.5	2.1	7	4.3	1.3	4	5.4	3.4	3	9.3	3.6	6
Eu	1.5	0.3	5	1.6	0.4	7	0.93	0.28	4	1.2	0.7	3	1.8	0.8	6
Gd	5.1	1.0	5	5.6	1.6	7	3.7	1.1	4	4.5	2.4	3	7.6	2.8	6
Dy	4.6	0.7	5	4.6	1.0	7	2.8	0.9	4	3.0	1.2	3	5.8	2.3	6
Er	2.7	0.5	5	2.8	0.6	7	1.5	0.4	4	1.9	0.8	3	3.9	1.6	6
Yb†	2.4	0.5	5	2.6	0.6	7	1.3	0.3	4	1.8	0.8	3	3.8	1.7	6
ΣREE	157	55	5	187	78	7	134	38	4	167	119	3	263	99	6
La_N/Yb_N	8.9	5.9	5	10.3	7.0	7	14.5	1.0	4	12.3	5.8	3	9.4	4.5	6
Eu/Eu^*	0.85	0.02	5	0.84	0.08	7	0.72	0.10	4	0.71	0.04	3	0.64	0.07	6
Y	27	4	8	27	5	13	16	8	4	-	-	-	52	15	7

Note: Data sources: McLennan (1977); McLennan et al. (1979a, 1979b).
- †Yb values estimated from chondrite-normalized diagrams.

granitic rocks in the source (McLennan and Taylor, 1980b). Group II, from the upper part of the sequence, has REE patterns indistinguishable from normal post-Archean sedimentary rocks. Thus, the trends in REE patterns for the Pine Creek Geosyncline are consistent with those from the Huronian succession.

Hamersley Basin

Early Proterozoic sedimentary rocks of the Mount Bruce Supergroup (up to >20 km thick) are well preserved in the Hamersley Basin of Western Australia (Trendall and Blockley, 1970; Trendall, 1976, 1979). Although noted for its large deposits of banded-iron formations, this sequence consists of mainly clastic sedimentary rocks and volcanics. The most reliable isotopic date on the sequence itself (W. Compston, pers. comm.) suggests U-Pb zircon age of 2.49 to 2.47 Ga for volcanics and tuffs from the Hamersley Group.

We have examined the geochemistry of fine-grained sedimentary rocks from throughout this sequence (unpublished data, this laboratory). The overall picture suggests that this sequence is *characterized* by post-Archean sedimentary REE patterns. Thus, these data are also consistent

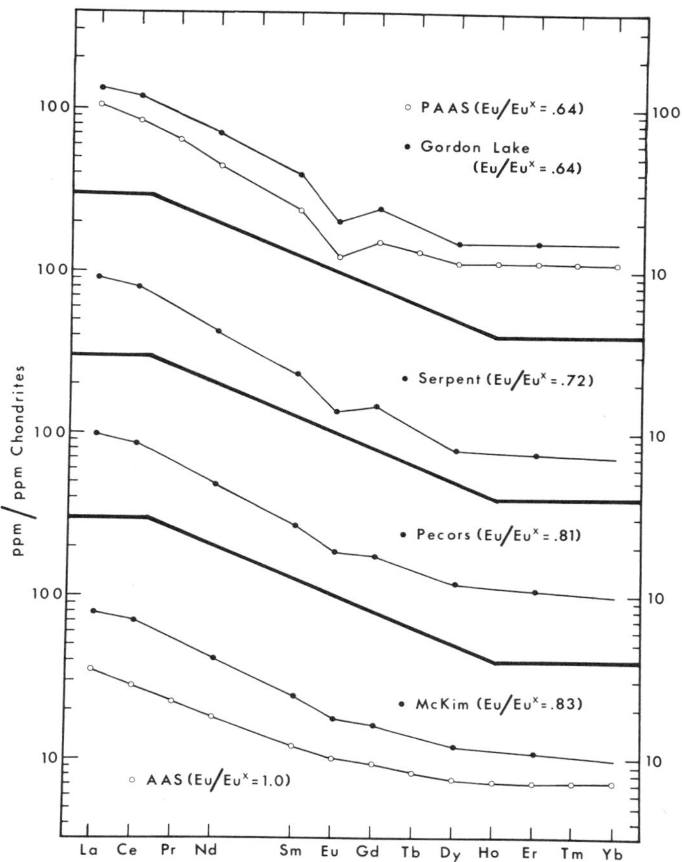

Figure 4. Average REE patterns of fine-grained sedimentary rocks from selected Early Proterozoic Huronian formations, presented in stratigraphic order (data from McLennan et al., 1979a). Also shown for comparison are AAS and PAAS. Lower Huronian units (McKim and Pecors Formations) are similar to AAS except for slightly higher ΣREE, La_N/Yb_N, and a slight negative Eu-anomaly. REE patterns from the top of the Huronian (Gordon Lake Formation) are indistinguishable from PAAS.

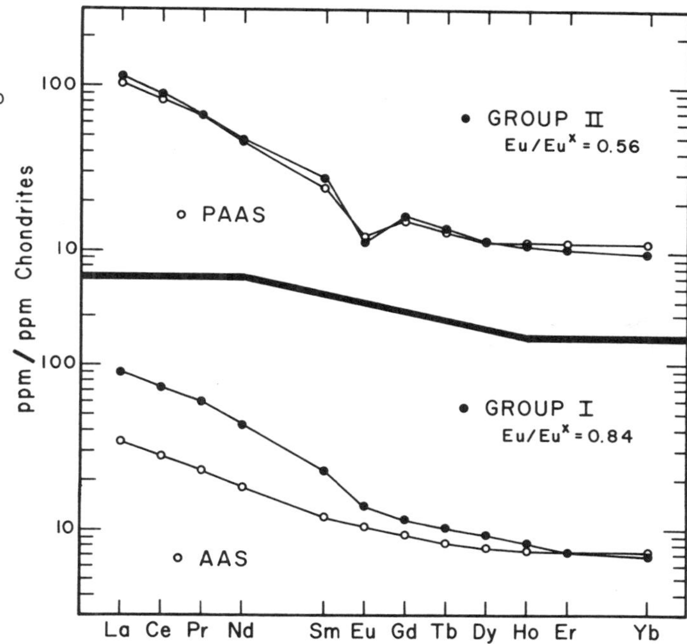

Figure 5. Average REE patterns of fine-grained sedimentary rocks from the Early Proterozoic Pine Creek Geosyncline sedimentary succession, Northern Territory, Australia. Group I represents the lower part of the succession and Group II represents the upper part. Also shown for comparison are AAS and PAAS. These data are consistent with the same pattern of sedimentary evolution seen for the Huronian succession.

with a major break in REE patterns at the Archean/Proterozoic boundary. In this case the gradual evolution in REE characteristics is not recorded.

Late Archean of South Africa

The widespread K-rich granitic magmatism, invoked for changing sedimentary REE patterns at the Archean/Proterozoic boundary, occurred much earlier (~3.2 to 3.0 Ga) in South Africa (Cloud, 1976; Young, 1978; Anhaeusser and Robb, 1980). Thus, a suitable test for the cause of changing REE characteristics is to examine late Archean sedimentary rocks from this area that were deposited after the widespread K-rich acidic igneous activity. We have examined sedimentary rocks from the ~3.0-Ga Pongola sequence (unpublished data, this laboratory). Although some diversity exists, post-Archean REE patterns appear common.

Non-Synchroneity of Archean/Proterozoic Boundary

Such data clearly demonstrate that the change in upper crustal composition was not isochronous on a worldwide scale but, instead, was a rather protracted event lasting from about 3.2 to 2.5 Ga. The fact that a significant change in upper crustal composition is recorded at different times in different regions reinforces the conclusion that Archean crustal blocks were discrete and widely separated, for otherwise a smearing out of the change in REE patterns would result. The data so far indicate that in a given region the change is fairly rapid. Rather small amounts of K-rich granitic or volcanic rocks (>10%) will impose a detectable Eu depletion in the sedimentary record. Thus, the provenance for the Pongola Supergroup must have been isolated from that of the Pine Creek Geosyncline.

The use of REE patterns to date this break must be accompanied by some caveats. Thus, first-cycle orogenic greywackes cannot be used, since they would record "Archean-style" patterns and indeed do (e.g., Devonian Baldwin formation, Nance and Taylor 1977, Recent deep-sea trench sediments: M. Perfit, pers. comm.).

8. PROTEROZOIC CRUSTAL COMPOSITION

The composition of the Proterozoic upper crust ap-

TABLE 2. AVERAGE CHEMICAL COMPOSITION OF PINE CREEK GEOSYNCLINE FINE-GRAINED SEDIMENTARY ROCKS

	Lower Pine Creek Geosyncline (Group I) (n = 4)		Upper Pine Creek Geosyncline (Group II) (n = 5)			(Group I)		(Group II)	
	$\bar{x}$	s.d.	$\bar{x}$	s.d.		$\bar{x}$	s.d.	$\bar{x}$	s.d.
SiO_2	57.98	2.58	75.58	6.75					
TiO_2	0.77	0.08	0.36	0.10					
Al_2O_3	20.22	1.23	11.95	4.20					
FeO_T	6.57	1.55	3.04	0.79					
MnO	0.04	0.03	0.03	0.01					
MgO	2.45	0.36	1.21	0.64					
CaO	0.12	0.10	0.29	0.40	Nb	15	3	13	7
Na_2O	0.44	0.33	0.91	1.16	Th	14	2	17	14
K_2O	4.89	0.97	3.74	1.50	U	4.1	1.4	4.3	3.8
P_2O_5	0.08	0.05	0.08	0.04	Zr	95	33	166	36
L.O.I.	5.14	1.42	1.24	1.44	Hf	3.6	2.2	5.6	0.8
K_2O/Na_2O	21	17	28	28	Sn	4.1	1.6	5.7	4.2
Cs	7.4	2.5	6.2	5.2	Mo	0.4	0.4	*	-
Rb	128	84	151	82	W	0.49	0.27	0.49	0.56
Ba	992	228	524	138	Th/U	3.6	0.9	4.3	1.0
Sr	53	32	59	47	Zr/Hf	28.6	6.6	29.7	4.3
Pb	42	57	13	10	Zr/Nb	6.1	1.5	16.7	9.1
La	34	6	42	19	La/Th	2.5	0.8	2.9	0.9
Ce	70	12	86	39	V	123	51	55	23
Pr	8.3	1.5	9.2	4.3	Sc	21	4	10	3
Nd	31	5.6	34	16	Ni	52	21	12	4
Sm	5.3	0.8	6.5	2.8	Co	25	9	8	2
Eu	1.2	0.2	0.99	0.28	Cu	15	19	16	23
Gd	3.5	0.7	5.1	2.4	Ga	25	2	15	6
Tb	0.59	0.09	0.81	0.40	V/Ni	2.6	1.0	4.7	1.8
Dy	3.5	0.8	4.5	2.0	Ni/Co	2.1	0.7	1.5	0.6
Ho	0.69	0.18	0.94	0.45	La/Sc	1.7	0.1	4.4	2.4
Er	1.8	0.4	2.6	1.4					
Yb	1.7	0.4	2.4	1.3	Bi	0.25	0.25	0.11	0.11
ΣREE	162.0	25.8	195.8	89.2					
Y	20	8	24	14					
La_N/Yb_N	14.5	4.0	12.3	2.6					
Eu/Eu^*	0.84	0.08	0.56	0.08					

Note: Data sources: Ferguson and Winer (1980); McLennan and Taylor (1980b).

pears to be essentially similar to that of "present-day" upper crust. REE patterns show no detectable change, except for a possible increase in total abundance, for about 2500 m.y. The increase in total REE, without change in slope, is most readily accounted for by sedimentary recycling (Veizer and Jansen, 1979). The upper crustal composition (Table 3) is close to that of granodiorite, among igneous rocks. It has been extensively evaluated in several recent papers (Taylor and McLennan, 1981a, 1981c; Taylor, 1979), and this discussion will not be repeated here.

In comparison with the Archean upper crust, it is enriched in large-ion-lithophile elements (e.g., K, Rb, Th, U, REE, except Eu, etc.) and depleted in ferromagnesian elements (notably Ni and Cr) (Fig. 2). These differences are consistent with an enrichment of the upper crust in "granitic" constituents in post-Archean time, in contrast to a much less fractionated upper crustal composition in Archean time. A corollary is that intracrustal melting was minor in the Archean.

Total Crustal Composition

The REE patterns in sedimentary rocks provide evidence only for the composition of the upper crust exposed to weathering, erosion, and sedimentation. The composition for the Archean upper crust may not be typical of the whole, even though intracrustal melting and the production of K-rich granites appear to have been minor. The crustal

TABLE 3. ELEMENTAL ABUNDANCES FOR C-1 CARBONACEOUS CHONDRITES (VOLATILE-FREE), THE PRIMITIVE-EARTH MANTLE, PRESENT EARTH CONTINENTAL CRUST, PRESENT UPPER AND LOWER CONTINENTAL CRUSTS, AND THE ARCHEAN UPPER CRUST

		C-1 Volatile free	Primitive Earth Mantle	Present Earth Crust	% in crust	Present Upper Crust	Present Lower Crust	Archean Upper Crust
Li	ppm	2.4	0.78	10	5.5	-	-	-
Be	ppm	0.072	0.10	1.5	6.6	-	-	-
B	ppm	2.4	3.3	-	-	-	-	-
Na	wt%	0.79	0.25	2.60	5.0	2.82	2.52	2.30
Mg	wt%	14.1	24.0	2.11	0.038	1.39	2.47	3.14
Al	wt%	1.29	1.75	9.5	2.3	8.47	10.0	8.25
Si	wt%	15.6	21.0	27.1	0.56	30.8	25.2	26.8
K	wt%	0.089	0.018	1.25	35.7	2.74	0.50	0.75
Ca	wt%	1.39	1.89	5.36	1.22	2.50	6.79	5.22
Sc	ppm	7.8	10.6	30	1.22	10	40	25
Ti	ppm	660	900	4800	2.3	3600	5400	5400
V	ppm	62	84	175	0.90	60	230	150
Cr	ppm	3500	3000	55	0.007	35	65	140
Mn	ppm	2700	1000	1100	0.47	600	1350	1300
Fe	wt%	27.2	6.2	5.83	0.41	3.50	7.00	7.38
Co	ppm	765	100	25	0.12	10	33	30
Ni	ppm	15100	2000	30	0.005	20	35	90
Cu	ppm	160	28	60	0.92	25	78	80
Zn	ppm	455	50	-	-	52	-	100
Ga	ppm	14	3	18	2.6	-	-	-
Rb	ppm	3.45	0.48	42	38	110	8	25
Sr	ppm	11.4	15.5	400	11.0	350	425	300
Y	ppm	2.1	2.9	22	3.4	22	22	15
Zr	ppm	5.7	7.8	100	5.5	240	30	100
Nb	ppm	0.45	0.60	11	7.9	25	4	5
Cs	ppm	0.29	<0.016	1.7	>45	3.7	0.7	-
Ba	ppm	3.6	4.9	350	30	700	175	240
La	ppm	0.367	0.50	19	15.4	30	14	12.6
Ce	ppm	0.957	1.30	38	12.6	64	25	26.8
Pr	ppm	0.137	0.19	4.3	9.8	7.1	2.9	3.1
Nd	ppm	0.711	0.967	16	7.1	26	11	13.0
Sm	ppm	0.231	0.314	3.7	5.1	4.5	3.3	2.78
Eu	ppm	0.087	0.12	1.1	4.0	0.88	1.2	0.90
Gd	ppm	0.306	0.42	3.6	3.7	3.8	3.5	2.85
Tb	ppm	0.058	0.079	0.64	3.5	0.64	0.64	0.48
Dy	ppm	0.381	0.52	3.7	3.0	3.5	3.8	2.93
Ho	ppm	0.085	0.12	0.82	2.9	0.80	0.83	0.63
Er	ppm	0.249	0.34	2.3	2.9	2.3	2.3	1.81
Tm	ppm	0.036	0.048	0.32	2.9	0.33	0.32	0.26
Yb	ppm	0.248	0.34	2.2	2.8	2.2	2.2	1.79
Lu	ppm	0.038	0.052	0.30	2.4	0.32	0.29	0.28
Hf	ppn	0.17	0.23	3.0	5.6	5.8	1.6	3
Tl	ppm	0.22	0.005	-	-	0.5	-	-
Pb	ppm	3.6	-	10	-	15	7.5	10
Bi	ppm	0.17	-	-	-	-	-	-
Th	ppm	0.051	0.070	4.8	30	10.5	1.95	2.9
U	ppm	0.014	0.018	1.25	30	2.5	0.63	0.75

Note: Data sources from Taylor and McLennan (1981c, Table 1).

thickness, however, appears to have been about 40 km, at least in the late Archean (3000 m.y. ago) (Newton, 1978; Tarney and Windley, 1977).

The Proterozoic upper crust cannot be representative of the 40-km-thick continental crust because of heat-flow and element balance arguments, which are well known (e.g., Taylor and McLennan, 1981a, 1981c; Taylor, 1967). The total crustal composition must be capable of generating the upper crust by intracrustal melting (unless one wishes to derive K-rich granites and granodiorites from the mantle, a view incompatible with much petrological and geochemical evidence). In addition, the composition must satisfy various geophysical constraints such as heat flow and density. The values in Table 3 for total crustal composition give a total crustal heat flow of 0.032 W/m^2 (0.76 HFU) for a 40-km-thick crust. For a total continental heat flow of 0.053 W/m^2 (1.2 HFU) (Lee, 1970), the average mantle-derived heat flux accordingly is 0.0183 W/m^2 (0.44 HFU) for a 40-km-thick crust, or 0.0263 W/m^2 (0.63 HFU) for a 30-km-thick crust. (M. Harrison, pers. comm.). A popular model for the *present-day* total crustal composition is that it is close to that of average island-arc volcanic rocks (Taylor, 1967). This view, which is supported by the uniformitarian observation of a viable present-day source, may be appropriate for Phanerozoic additions to the crust (see section 8) but may not be a useful model for the massive crustal additions occurring around the Archean/Proterozoic boundary. Much research is needed on the problems both of deriving a large fraction of the continental mass and of causing intracrustal melting to produce upper and lower crusts of distinct compositions between 3.2 and 2.5 Ga. Thus, the island-arc model may not be appropriate for the Proterozoic bulk crustal composition. However, the overall total crustal composition may not be very different from that deduced from the island-arc model, since the Archean crustal composition is not really different except for the higher content of Ni and Cr (Table 3). Accordingly, we use the composition established by the island-arc or "andesite" model, while recognizing its limitations.

Lower Crustal Compositions

The problems of making independent estimates of lower crustal compositions are serious. No large-scale averaging process, such as sedimentation, is available (except perhaps seismic velocity data). The material that is available (e.g., high-grade granulite terrains, or xenoliths) might well be atypical and provide a wide diversity of compositions. The models for total crustal compositions given here (Table 3) provide some predictions, in that *average* lower crustal material should contain positive Eu anomalies, complementary to the negative upper crustal values. Sm/Nd ratios should be near chondritic (0.325), and K/Rb ratios should be about 600.

9. A MODEL FOR CONTINENTAL CRUSTAL EVOLUTION

The continental crust of the Earth is ultimately derived from the mantle and, accordingly, provides some constraints on mantle composition. Table 3 provides several basic sets of data relevant to the problems of crustal composition. The first column provides estimates of the composition of carbonaceous chondrites, expressed on a volatile-free basis. The resemblance between these and solar abundances provides the justification for regarding them as close to the composition of the original solar nebula. The primitive terrestrial mantle (= present mantle plus crust) given in Table 3 shows that the Earth is depleted in volatile elements such as Rb and K, relative to the solar nebula.

The composition of the core is not included. It is considered that the core-forming siderophile elements were accreted directly as metal and are not relevant to the present discussion. The enrichment of the large-ion-lithophile elements in the continental crust is well displayed in column 4, which shows, for example, that nearly 36% of the potassium in the Earth has been concentrated in the continental crust.

There is no chemical or isotopic evidence for an early (before 4 Ga) crust on the Earth. Such a crust would have been destroyed by the pervasive meteoritic bombardment, which occurred throughout the solar system, from Mercury out to the satellites of Jupiter and Saturn. However, many theories for the formation of the Earth call for an early melting episode. Rapid early core formation, which apparently occurred, should have released enough energy to melt the silicate mantle. The evidence that at least half of the moon was melted lends credence to such early melting scenarios. Such melting, and subsequent crystallization, would be accompanied by removal of the incompatible elements to outer zones of the Earth. The evidence for such an event is lacking. This curious situation calls for investigation. Possibilities include very rapid recycling due to vigorous convection driven by combinations of higher heat flow (three times the present value), initial accretional energy, and temperature rise from core formation.

Figure 6 provides a schematic model for the growth and evolution of the continental crust, which is consistent with the previous discussion.

The earliest records of "continental" crust in Greenland (e.g., McGregor, 1973; Moorbath, 1975, 1977, 1978) are consistent with small nuclei. A reasonable model for the growth of the Archean crust is similar to that of Tarney et al. (1976). Basalts are derived from the mantle by partial melting. As piles of basalt accumulate, they sink back into the mantle, perhaps by a primitive form of sea-floor spreading. Formation of eclogite occurs at depth. Partial melting of this produces the tonalite-trondhjemite sodium-rich granites that contain typical LREE-enriched patterns.

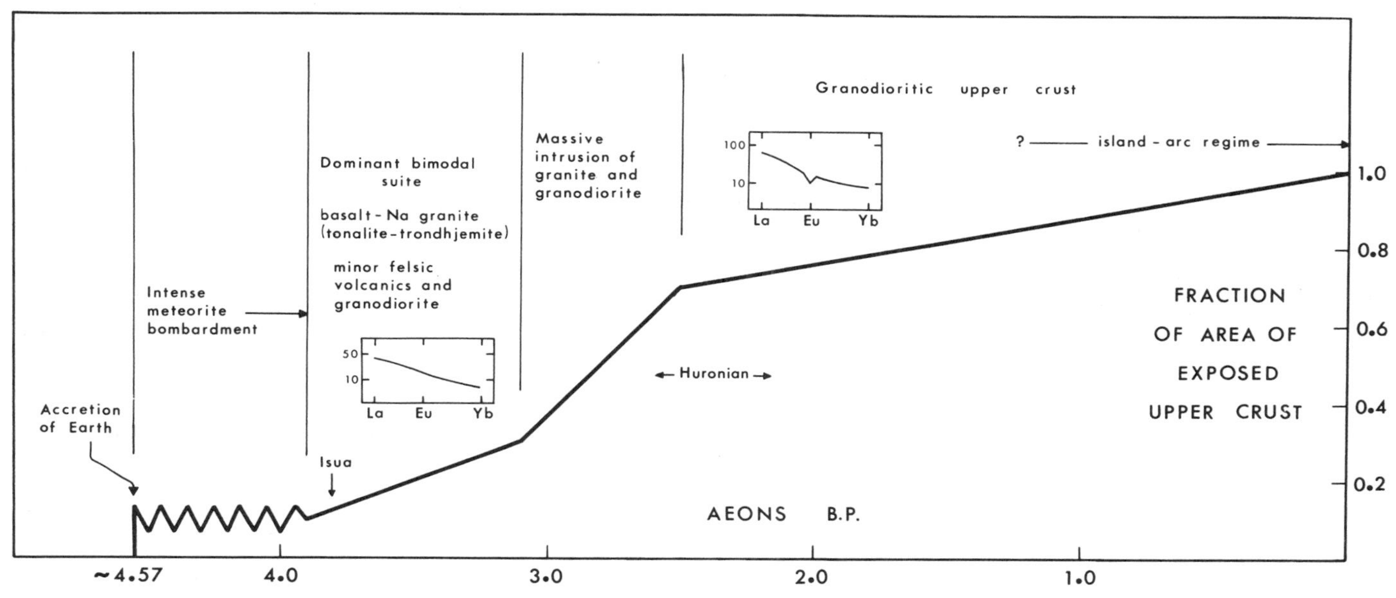

Figure 6. Schematic model of the evolution of the continental crust through geologic time. Average REE patterns of the upper crust (indicated by sedimentary rocks) are indicated. Also shown are some of the principal events of crustal evolution. The change in composition of the upper continental crust, probably associated with a major period of crustal growth, took place between about 3.2 and 2.5 b.y. B.P. This change is reflected sometime later in the Early Proterozoic sedimentary record (e.g., Huronian, Pine Creek Geosyncline).

Minor andesitic volcanism also occurs. The sedimentary rocks record an average of the bimodal tholeiitic-tonalitic suite, and local variations depend on the ratio of basic to acidic rocks present (e.g., Yellowknife). Intracrustal melting is minimal. The crust slowly increases in volume throughout the Archean.

Beginning at about 3200 m.y. ago, and occurring at different times in different regions, a major episodic change in the growth of the crust occurs. Two distinct but probably related events occur. The first is a massive increase in the volume of material added from the mantle to the crust. The second event is that intracrustal melting and the production of "granitic" (s.l.) magmas occur. These rise into the upper crust and form the presently observable upper crust dominated by granodioritic average compositions. During this intracrustal melting episode, Eu is retained in plagioclase in the lower crust, producing the characteristic Eu depletion, as recorded by the sedimentary sampling of the upper crust.

The large growth of continental material at the end of the Archean causes massive changes to sea-floor spreading regimes. The buoyant continental masses form barriers to the sea-floor spreading and basalt-sinking regime typical of Archean time. Modern-style linear subduction regimes are initiated, and calc-alkalic volcanism becomes the predominant method of producing evolved siliceous material from the mantle. It now provides the majority of new additions to the continents, although its contribution is probably less than 20% of the total continental mass.

Major unresolved problems are, (a) What was the type of igneous activity that led to the massive additions to the continents at the end of the Archean? (b) What was the source of the heat that produced the massive intracrustal melting, forming a granodioritic upper crust and a depleted lower crust at about the Archean/Proterozoic boundary?

REFERENCES CITED

Anhaeusser, C. R., and Robb, L. J., 1980, Magmatic cycles and the evolution of the Archaean granitic crust in the eastern Transvaal and Swaziland: Economic Geology Research Unit Information Circular No. 14, 11 p.

Bavinton, O. A., and Taylor, S. R., 1980, Rare earth geochemistry of Archean metasedimentary rocks from Kambalda, Western Australia: Geochimica et Cosmochimica Acta, v. 44, p. 639–648.

Chaudhuri, S., and Cullers, R. L., 1979, The distribution of rare-earth elements in deeply buried Gulf coast sediments: Chemical Geology, v. 24, p. 327–338.

Cloud, P., 1976, Major features of crustal evolution: Transactions of the Geological Society of South Africa, v. 79, Annexure 32 p.

Collerson, K. D., and Fryer, B. J., 1978, The role of fluids in the formation and subsequent development of early continental crust: Contributions to Mineralogy and Petrology, v. 67, p. 151–167.

Cullers, R. L., Yek, L.-T., Chaudhuri, S., and Guidotti, C. V., 1974, Rare earth elements in Silurian pelitic schists from N.W. Maine: Geochimica et Cosmochimica Acta, v. 38, p. 389–400.

Cullers, R. L., Chaudhuri, S., Arnold, B., Lee, M., and Wolf, C. W., 1975, Rare earth distributions in clay minerals and in the clay-sized fraction of Lower Permian Havensville and Eskridge shales of Kansas and Oklahoma: Geochimica et Cosmochimica Acta, v. 39, p. 1691–1703.

Danchin, R. V., 1967, Chromium and nickel in the Fig Tree Shale from South Africa: Science, v. 158, p. 261–262.

Duddy, J. R., 1980, Redistribution and fractionation of rare-earth and other elements in a weathering profile: Chemical Geology, v. 30, p. 363–381.

Fairbairn, H. W., Hurley, P. M., Card, K. D., and Knight, C. J., 1969, Correlation of radiometric ages of Nipissing diabase and Huronian metasediments with Proterozoic orogenic events in Ontario: Canadian Journal of Earth Sciences, v. 6, p. 489–497.

Ferguson, J., and Goleby, A. B. (editors), 1980, Uranium in the Pine Creek Geosyncline: Vienna, International Atomic Energy Agency, 760 p.

Ferguson, J., and Winer, P., 1980, Pine Creek Geosyncline: Statistical treatment of whole rock chemical data, *in* Ferguson, J., and Goleby, A. B., eds., Uranium in the Pine Creek Geosyncline: Vienna, International Atomic Energy Agency, p. 191–208.

Floyd, P. A., 1977, Rare earth element mobility and geochemical characterisation of spilitic rocks: Nature, v. 269, p. 134–137.

Frey, F. A., 1969, Rare earth abundances in a high-temperature peridotite intrusion: Geochimica et Cosmochimica Acta, v. 33, p. 1429–1447.

Gibbins, W. A., and McNutt, R. H., 1975, The age of the Sudbury Nickel Irruptive and the Murray Granite: Canadian Journal of Earth Science, v. 12, p. 1970–1989.

Green, T. H., Brunfelt, A. O., and Heier, K. S., 1969, Rare earth element distribution in anorthosites and associated high grade metamorphic rocks, Lofoten-Vesteraalen, North Norway: Earth and Planetary Science Letters, v. 17, p. 93–98.

——1972, Rare-earth element distribution and K/Rb ratios in granulites, mangerites and anorthosites, Lofoten-Vesteraalen, Norway: Geochimica et Cosmochimica Acta, v. 36, p. 241–257.

Hargraves, R. B., 1976, Precambrian geologic history: Science, v. 193, p. 363–371.

Haskin, L. A., and Paster, T. P., 1979, Geochemistry and mineralogy of the rare earths, *in* Handbook of physics and chemistry of the rare earths: North-Holland, v. 3, chap. 21, p. 1–80.

Hellman, P. L., and Henderson, P., 1977, Are rare earth elements mobile during spilitisation?: Nature, v. 267, p. 38–40.

Humphris, S. E., Morrison, M. A., and Thompson, R. N., 1978, Influence of rock crystallisation history upon subsequent lanthanide mobility during hydrothermal alteration of basalts: Chemical Geology, v. 23, p. 125–137.

Jakes, P., and Taylor, S. R., 1974, Excess Eu content in Precambrian rocks and continental evolution: Geochimica et Cosmochimica Acta, v. 38, p. 739–745.

Jenner, G. A., Fryer, B. J., and McLennan, S. M., 1981, Geochemistry of the Archaean Yellowknife Supergroup: Geochimica et Cosmochimica Acta, v. 45, p. 1111–1129.

Lee, W.H.K., 1970, On the global variations of terrestrial heat flow: Physics of the Earth and Planetary Interiors, v. 2, p. 332–341.

Ludden, J. N., and Thompson, G., 1978, Behaviour of rare earth elements during submarine weathering of tholeiitic basalt: Nature, v. 247, p. 147–149.

McGregor, V. R., 1973, The early Precambrian gneisses of the Godthaab district, West Greenland: Philosophical Transactions of the Royal Society of London, Series A, v. 273, p. 343–358.

McLennan, S. M., 1977, Geochemistry of some Huronian sedimentary rocks (north of Lake Huron) with emphasis on rare earth elements [M.Sc. thesis]: London, Canada, University of Western Ontario, 138 p.

McLennan, S. M., and Taylor, S. R., 1979, Rare earth element mobility associated with uranium mineralisation: Nature, v. 282, p. 247–250.

——1980a, Th and U in sedimentary rocks: Crustal evolution and sedimentary recycling: Nature, v. 285, p. 621–624.

——1980b, Rare earth elements in sedimentary rocks, granites and uranium deposits of the Pine Creek Geosyncline, *in* Ferguson, J., and Goleby, A. B., eds., Uranium in the Pine Creek Geosyncline: Vienna, International Atomic Energy Agency, p. 175–190.

McLennan, S. M., Fryer, B. J., and Young, G. M., 1979a, Rare earth elements in Huronian sedimentary rocks: Composition and evolution of the Post-Kenoran upper crust: Geochimica et Cosmochimica Acta, v. 43, p. 375–388.

——1979b, The geochemistry of the carbonate-rich Espanola Formation (Huronian) with emphasis on the rare earth elements: Canadian Journal of Earth Science, v. 16, p. 230–239.

Moorbath, S., 1975, The geological significance of Early Precambrian rocks: Proceedings of the Geological Association, v. 86, p. 259–279.

——1977, Ages, isotopes and evolution of the Precambrian continental crust: Chemical Geology, v. 20, p. 151–187.

——1978, Age and isotope evidence for the evolution of continental crust: Philosophical Transactions of the Royal Society of London, Series A, v. 288, p. 401–413.

Muecke, G. K., Pride, C., and Sarkar, P., 1979, Rare-earth element geochemistry of regional metamorphic rocks: Physics and Chemistry of the Earth, v. 11, p. 449–464.

Nance, W. B., and Taylor, S. R., 1976, Rare earth patterns and crustal evolution I. Australian post-Archaean sedimentary rocks: Geochimica et Cosmochimica Acta, v. 40, p. 1539–1551.

——1977, Rare earth elements and crustal evolution II. Archaean sedimentary rocks from Kalgoorlie, Australia: Geochimica et Cosmochimica Acta, v. 41, p. 225–231.

Needham, R. S., Crick, I. H., and Stuart-Smith, P. G., 1980, Regional geology of the Pine Creek Geosyncline, *in* Ferguson, J., and Goleby, A. B., eds., Uranium in the Pine Creek Geosyncline: Vienna, International Atomic Energy Agency, p. 1–22.

Nesbitt, H. W., 1979, Mobility and fractionation of rare earth elements during weathering of a granodiorite: Nature, v. 279, p. 206–210.

Newton, R. C., 1978, Experimental and thermodynamic evidence for the operation of high pressures in Archean metamorphisms, *in* Windley, B. F., and Naqvi, S. M., eds., Archean geochemistry: Amsterdam, Elsevier, p. 221–240.

Page, R. W., Compston, W., and Needham, R. S., 1980, Geochronology and evolution of the late-Archean basement and Proterozoic rocks in the Alligator Rivers uranium field, Northern Territory, Australia, *in* Ferguson, J., and Goleby, A. B., eds., Uranium in the Pine Creek Geosyncline: Vienna, International Atomic Energy Agency, p. 39–68.

Ronov, A. B., Balashov, Y. A., and Migdisov, A. A., 1967, Geochemistry of the rare earths in the sedimentary cycle: Geochemistry International, v. 4, p. 1–17.

Shannon, R. D., 1976, Revised effective ionic radii and systematic studies of interatomic distances in halides and chalcogenides: Acta Crystallographica, v. 32, p. 751–767.

Tarney, J., and Windley, B. F., 1977, Chemistry, thermal gradients and evolution of the lower continental crust: Journal of the Geological Society of London, v. 134, p. 153–172.

Tarney, J., Dalziel, I.W.D., and DeWit, M. J., 1976, Marginal basin 'Rocas Verdes' complex from S. Chile: A model for Archaean greenstone belt formation, *in* Windley, B. F., ed., The early history of the Earth: London, Wiley, p. 131–146.

Taylor, S. R., 1967, The origin and growth of continents: Tectonophysics, v. 4, p. 17–34.

——1977, Island arc models and the composition of the continental crust: American Geophysical Union, Maurice Ewing Series, v. 1, p. 325–335.

——1979, Chemical composition and evolution of the continental crust: The rare earth element evidence, *in* McElhinny, M. W., ed., The Earth: Its origin, structure and evolution: London, Academic Press,

p. 353–376.

Taylor, S. R., and McLennan, S. M., 1981a, The rare earth element evidence in Precambrian sedimentary rocks: Implications for crustal evolution, *in* Kröner, A., ed., Precambrian plate tectonics: Amsterdam, Elsevier, p. 527–548.

—— 1981b, Rare earth element evidence for the composition of the Archaean crust: Geological Society of Australia Special Publication, v. 7, p. 255–261.

—— 1981c, The composition and evolution of the continental crust: Rare earth element evidence from sedimentary rocks: Philosophical Transactions of the Royal Society of London, Series A, v. 301, p. 381–399.

Trendall, A. F., 1976, Geology of the Hamersley Basin: 25th International Geological Congress Excursion Guide #43A, 44 p.

—— 1979, A revision of the Mount Bruce Supergroup: Geological Survey of Western Australia Annual Report, 1978, p. 63–71.

Trendall, A. F., and Blockley, J. G., 1970, The iron formations of the Precambrian Hamersley Group, Western Australia with special reference to the associated crocidolite: Geological Survey of Western Australia Bulletin, v. 119, 366 p.

Van Schmus, W. R., 1965, The geochronology of the Blind River–Bruce Mines area; Ontario: Journal of Geology, v. 73, p. 755–780.

Veizer, J., and Jansen, S. L., 1979, Basement and sedimentary recycling and continental evolution: Journal of Geology, v. 87, p. 341–370.

Young, G. M., 1969, Geochemistry of early Proterozoic tillites and argillites of the Gowganda Formation, Ontario, Canada: Geochimica et Cosmochimica Acta, v. 33, p. 483–492.

—— 1973, Origin of carbonate-rich early Proterozoic Espanola Formation, Ontario, Canada: Geological Society of America Bulletin, v. 84, p. 135–160.

—— 1978, Some aspects of the evolution of the Archean crust: Geoscience Canada, v. 5, p. 140–149.

Manuscript Accepted by the Society April 14, 1983

Printed in U.S.A.

Geological Society of America
Memoir 161
1983

Proterozoic anorogenic granite plutonism of North America

J. Lawford Anderson
Department of Geological Sciences
University of Southern California
Los Angeles, California 90089

ABSTRACT

Anorogenic magnatic activity characterizes much of the late to mid-Proterozoic, from 1030 to 1770 m.y. ago, in a broad belt trending from the southwestern United States, northeastward through Labrador, across southern Greenland, and into the Baltic shield. The association of gabbroic to anorthositic rocks, a separate mangeritic series of primarily intermediate composition, and granite of definite rapakivi affinity comprise an anorogenic "trinity" of world-wide occurrence. With the exception of the 1.76 b.y. Montello batholith (Wisconsin), this episode in North America is restricted to the interval 1.0 to 1.5 b.y. and occurs in three distinct events. Over 70 percent of Proterozoic anorogenic magmatism occurs in a 1.41 to 1.49 b.y. old 600-1000 km wide belt trending from southern California to Labrador that volumetrically and age-wise is totally a North American phenomenon. Renewed anorogenic granite magmatism occurred form 1.34 to 1.41 and from 1.03 to 1.08 b.y. ago in lesser proportions. Although anorthositic and mangeritic rocks are abundant in some provinces (e.g., Labrador), rapakivi granite (in the broad usage of the term) represents by far the most abundant magma-type generated during this nonorogenic period.

The modal and mineral composition of these granitic rocks is distinctive and reflects the potassic and iron-enriched character of the magmas and the unique conditions under which crystallization occurred. Principal rock types include biotite ± hornblende granite to adamellite although numerous peraluminous, two-mica (biotite + celadonitic muscovite ± garnet) granites also occur. Crystallization of these epizonal granitic magmas occurred over the range of 640 to 790°C at low total pressures (most less than 2 kb) and at relatively dry conditions. A dramatic difference in crystallization conditions lies with the level of oxygen fugacity which ranges three orders of magnitude from low (ca. QFM) to high (above Ni-NiO), resulting in systematic differences in Fe-Ti oxide mineralogy and mafic silicate composition.

Compositionally, the granite magmas are subalkalic and marginally peraluminous (peralkaline varieties are rare to nonexistent). Although some hastingsite or riebeckite-bearing granites may have been derived from fractional crystallization of the mangeritic series, most are primary melts derived from fusion of lower crust material. The high potassium, Fe/Mg, Ba, and rare earth element (REE) composition of the granites is consistent with small degrees of fusion (10-30 percent) of calc-alkaline crust of quartz dioritic, tonalitic, and granodioritic material. Initial Sr isotopic ratios average 0.7051 ± .0025. The relatively low ratios are the result of short residence times (commonly 170 to 340 m.y.) with much of the crustal source being formed in a preceding orogenic event. An earlier melting episode need not have occurred for the source. The dry nature of the magmas is due to vapor under-

saturated melting of a metaigneous source with a total water budget less than 1 percent and tied up in relatively stable residual hydrous phases. The derivation of a marginally peraluminous melt from a metaluminous source is a consequence of variable amounts of residual hornblende ± clinopyroxene.

The generation of isolated crustal-derived magma under anorogenic conditions is considered to be the result of localized thermal doming in the mantle. The mantle-derived anorthositic and mangeritic magmas may have played an active role in generating the necessary heat of fusion at lower crustal levels. For North America, the 1.4 to 1.5 b.y. event does not have the consistent age progression of a track and is probably an incipient rift that failed to integrate into a world-wide plate system. At a more mature stage, the 1.0 to 1.1 b.y. Keweenawan episode and the midcontinent gravity high represents another unsuccessful rifting attempt of the Proterozoic North American craton. The isolated granite complexes of this age (Pikes Peak, Enchanted Rock, Red Bluff), as well as the earlier, localized 1.76 b.y. and 1.34 to 1.41 b.y. magmatic episodes, may be further representations of a thermal perturbation at mantle depths during this fragile period of crustal "stability."

INTRODUCTION

The late to mid-Proterozoic of North America, specifically the period from 1.03 to 1.49 b.y. ago, represents a unique stage of cratonic development characterized by abundant anorogenic magmatic activity (anorthosites, layered gabbros, charnockitic diorite to syenite suites, rapakivi granites, bimodal basalt-rhyolite suites, and tholeiitic dike and sill emplacement), the development of possible aulacogenic and epicratonic sedimentary basins, and obvious rift structures such as the midcontinent gravity high. The resultant igneous complexes were primarily emplaced, with few exceptions, outside or marginal to the Archean core of the craton and into relatively young continental crust that formed in a preceding orogenic episode (Fig. 1). Much of this older crust ranges in age from 1.7 to 1.9 b.y. but becomes progressively younger (1.6 to 1.2 b.y.) along the southern edge of the Precambrian craton. Although in part metasedimentary and mafic metavolcanic (greenstone belts), a major portion of the older crust consists of synorogenic calc-alkaline plutonic rocks of quartz diorite, tonalite, and granodiorite composition. The transition to anorogenic magmatism involved magmatic gaps ranging from 60 to 700 m.y. (most range 170 to 340 m.y.) and resulted in a distinct change in magma types that directly implies a major change in source material and tectonic setting.

This paper focuses on the petrogenetic evolution of the Proterozoic anorogenic granite magmas, which volumetrically represent the most profuse type of igneous activity associated with this period of relative crustal stability. Seventy-nine anorogenic granite complexes have been dated in North America (Table 1); yet far more examples may exist, particularly in the Grenville Province, where 1.1 b.y. regional overprinting may have obscured true ages (Emslie, 1980), in the midcontinent region, where they are buried by an extensive Phanerozoic cover, and in the southwestern United States where geochronologic control is presently limited. Recently termed A-type granites (Wones, 1979), many of these rocks are of the rapakivi suite. The latter refers to the original Finnish usage of the term rapakivi (Vorma, 1971). It refers to a kindred of primarily granitic rock types that may or may not have rapakivi texture but ubiquitously possess a number of mineralogical and compositional characteristics.

Although half of the noted complexes contain only granite or adamellite[1] (Fig. 2), their association with only slightly older mangeritic and gabbroic to anorthositic rock types is well known (Bridgewater and Windley, 1973; Emslie, 1978). This period of anorogenic magmatism in North America is only part of a major episode of igneous activity that extends northeastward across southern Greenland and into the Baltic shield. Kranck (1969) noted the common occurrence of anorthosite with rapakivi, but it is now recognized that the mangeritic igneous suite is a separate but important intermediate member of the association. Hence, the granites are part of a common anorogenic "trinity" that is suggestive of a cogenetic, but not necessarily comagmatic, relationship. Although this paper includes discussion of the other two rock suites, a complete overview of the association has been made by Emslie (1978). Morse (1982) has presented a detailed review specifically of the Proterozoic anorthosites.

DISTRIBUTION AND DESCRIPTION OF PROTEROZOIC ANOROGENIC GRANITES IN NORTH AMERICA

The only pre-1.5 b.y. known example of anorogenic

[1]The rock classification of Streckeisen (1976) is used throughout this paper with the single modification of dividing his granite field into one of granite (syenogranite) and adamellite (monzogranite). An orthopyroxene- (or fayalite + quartz) bearing intermediate series of jotunite (= diorite), mangerite (= tirilite, monzonite), syenite, and quartz syenite has charnockitic affinities and will be collectively termed mangeritic.

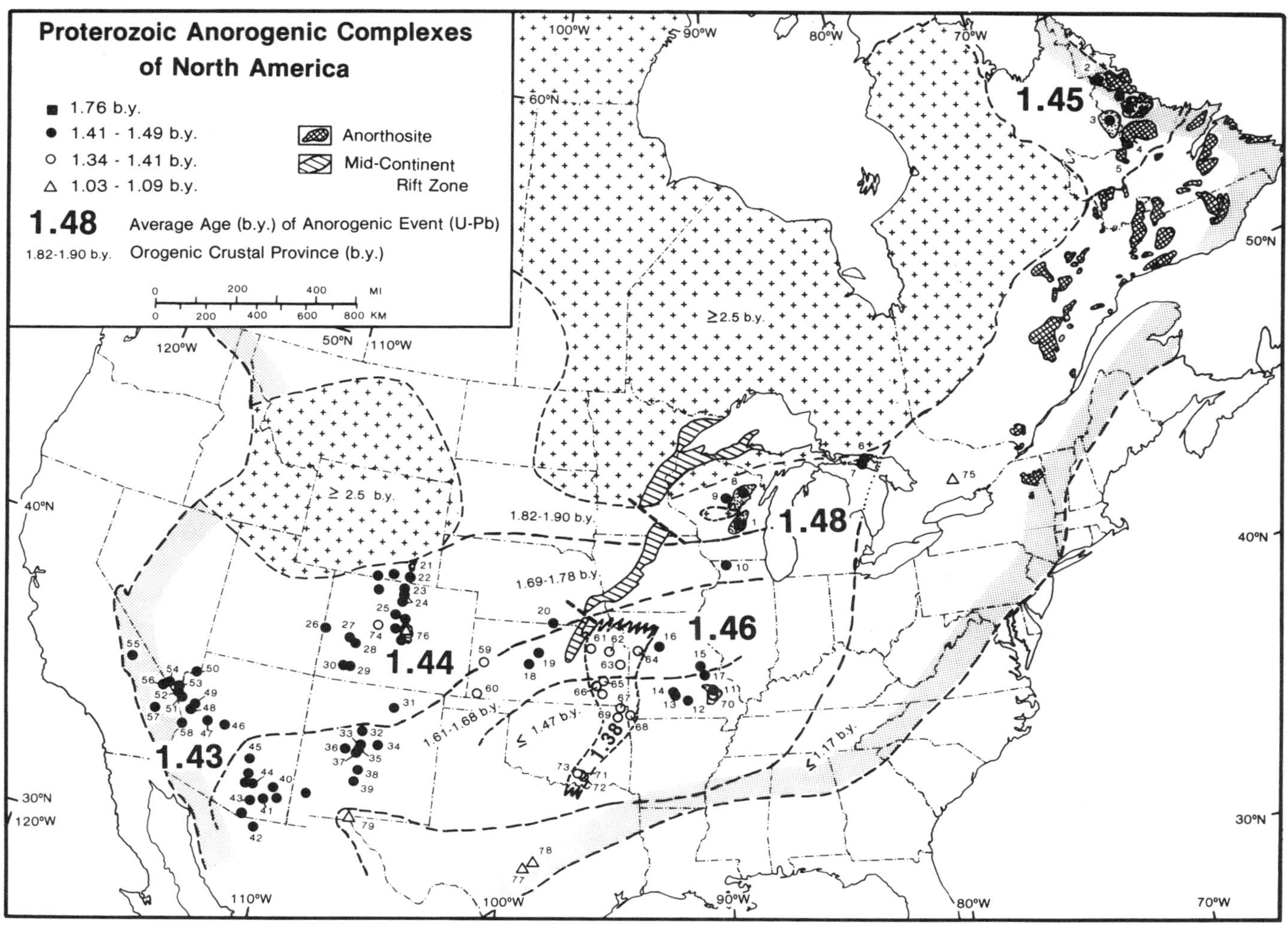

Figure 1. Distribution of Proterozoic anorogenic granite complexes of North America. Proterozoic orogenic provinces are from Silver (1968), Van Schmus and Bickford (1981), and Garrison (1981). Sources for dated anorogenic granites are given in Table 1 (numbered localities); the few undated localities (not numbered) are from Tweeto (1980) and Anderson and Silver (1977).

granite plutonism in the mid-Proterozoic of North America is the 1.76 b.y. Montello batholith of central Wisconsin (Anderson et al., 1980). Anorogenic complexes of this age are more common in the Greenland and Baltic shields and include the 1.74 to 1.76 b.y. old rapakivi granites of the Kap Farvel area, south Greenland (Gulson and Krogh, 1975), the 1.79 b.y. Revsund and Sorvik granites of central Sweden (Persson, 1978), and the 1.70 b.y. rapakivi massifs of Finland (Kouvo and Simonen, 1967, as referenced in Vorma, 1972). All other North America examples fall into three magmatic episodes, from 1.41 to 1.49 b.y., from 1.34 to 1.41 b.y., and from 1.03 to 1.08 b.y. Anorthosites and syenodiorite having an age of 1.2 b.y. occur in the San Gabriel Mountains and along the San Andreas fault of southwestern California; these rocks, however, form part of a terrane that is exotic to that area of North America (Silver, 1982).

The 1.4 to 1.5 b.y. Belt

The majority (over 70%) of anorogenic igneous activity is restricted to a 600 to 1000 km wide NE-SW belt trending from Labrador to southern California. All have ages in the range of 1.41 to 1.49 b.y. The full regional extent of this anorogenic event was not recognized until the mid-seventies (Van Schmus, et al., 1975a, b; Bickford and Mose, 1975) and was not specifically addressed in terms of conceptual tectonic models until the late seventies (Silver et al., 1977b; Emslie, 1978; Anderson and Cullers, 1978). Anorogenic complexes of this age are not common outside North America (the 1.45 b.y. Nordingra rapakivi granite of central Sweden (Kornfalt, 1976) is an exception). This belt seems to be a totally North American phenomenon and is separated by a 200 to 270 m.y. magmatic gap from similar complexes in south Greenland and Scandinavia.

TABLE 1. PROTEROZOIC ANOROGENIC GRANITES OF NORTH AMERICA AND NEARBY REGIONS: AGE AND ISOTOPIC DATA

No.[1]	Description	Age (b.y.)[2]	($^{87}Sr/^{86}Sr$)initial	Ref[3]
I.	Greenland and Baltic Shields			
	Kap Farvel Area, Greenland	1.740-1.755 (U/Pb)	-	1
	Revsund Plutonic Suite	1.785± .040 (Rb/Sr)	-	2
	Nordingra Granite Complex, Greenland			
	Rapakivi Granite	1.445± .020 (Rb/Sr)	0.725 ±.003	3
	Gabbro and Anorthosite	1.585± .030 (Rb/Sr)	0.7059±.0005	3
	Ragunda Rapakivi Massif, Sweden	1.320± .030 (Rb/Sr)	0.718 ±.006	3
	Wiborg Rapakivi Massif, Finland	1.70 (U/Pb)	-	4
II.	North America: Anorogenic Granites with an Age Greater than 1.5 b.y.			
1	Montello Batholith, Wisconsin	1.760± .005 (U/Pb)	0.7046±.0043[5]	5
III.	North America: Anorogenic Granites with an Age Between 1.41-1.49 b.y.			
2	Umiakovik Lake (Nain Complex), Labrador	1.45 ±0.30 (Rb/Sr)		6
	"Adamellite"		0.7075±.0037[5]	6
	Anorthosite		0.7045	6
3	Mistastin Lake Adamellite[4]	1.346± .015 (Rb/Sr)		7
	Adamellite		0.7082±.0003[5]	7
	Anorthosite		0.7036[5]	7
4	Harp Lake Complex, Labrador	1.44 (U/Pb)		8
5	Michigamau Complex, Labrador	1.46 (U/Pb)		8
6	Croker Island Complex, Ontario	1.475± .050 (Rb/Sr)	0.705	9
7	Manitoulin Island Biotite-Hornblende Adamellite, Ontario	1.467± .010 (U/Pb)	0.7078±.0010	10
8	Wolf River Batholith, Wisconsin	1.485± .015 (U/Pb)	0.7048±.0017	11
9	Wausau Syenite Complex, Wisconsin	1.456± .034 (Rb/Sr)	0.7022±.0017	11
10	Granite from Magnetic Anomaly (BHD)[6] Illinois	1.480± .020 (U/Pb)	0.7102±.0045	12
11	St. Francois Mountains Igneous Complex, Missouri	1.470± .020 (U/Pb)	0.7036-.7254[5]	13
12	Granophyric Biotite Granite (BDH), Shannon Co., Missouri	1.473± .026 (U/Pb)		14
13	Hornblende-Pyroxene diorite (BDH), LaClede Co., Missouri	1.465± .010 (U/Pb)		14
14	Gneissoid Granite (BDH), LaClede Co., Missouri	1.465± .007 (U/Pb)		14
15	Biotite Granite (BDH), Gasconade Co., Missouri	1.458± .010 (U/Pb)		14
16	Sheared Biotite Granite (BDH), Howard Co., Missouri	1.443± .012 (U/Pb)		14
17	Metarhyolite (BDH), Crawford Co., Missouri	1.455± .010 (U/Pb)		14
18	Sheared Granite (BDH), Rush Co., Kansas	1.530± .100 (U/Pb)		14
19	Biotite Granite (BDH), Russell Co., Kansas	1.450± .015 (U/Pb)		14
20	Red Willow Batholith (BDH), Nebraska	1.445± .015 (U/Pb)	0.7054±.0025	15
21	Laramie Anorthosite Complex, Wyoming	1.440± .015 (U/Pb)		16
	Syenite		0.7096	16
	Anorthosite		0.7024-.7045	16
22	Sherman Granite, Wyoming	1.380± .029 (Rb/Sr)	0.7036-.7065	17
23	Log Cabin Two-mica Granite, Colorado	1.390± .029 (Rb/Sr)	0.7031	17
24	Longs Peak Two-mica Granite, Colorado	1.419± .029 (Rb/Sr	0.7025	17
25	Silver Plume Two-mica Granite, Colorado	1.408± .050 (Rb/Sr)	0.7030	17
26	Two-mica Granite of Unaweep Canyon, Colorado	1.441± .056 (Rb/Sr)	0.701 ±.003[5]	18
26	Biotite Granodiorite of Unaweep Canyon, Colorado	1.440± .016 (U/Pb)	0.702 ±.001	18
27	Vernal Mesa Biotite-Hornblende Quartz Monzonite, Colorado	1.449± .039 (Rb/Sr)	0.7038±.0005	19
28	Curecanti Two-mica, Garnet Quartz Monzonite (Ademellite), Colo.[4]	1.390± .015 (Rb/Sr)	0.700 ±.003[5]	19
29	Eolus Biotite-Hornblende Quartz Monzonite, Colorado	1.440± .020 (U/Pb)	0.7043	20,21
30	Electra Lake Gabbro, Colorado	1.423± .050 (Rb/Sr)	0.7052	21
31	Rana Biotite Adamellite, New Mexico	1.442± .157 (Rb/Sr)	0.7113±.0071	22
32	Sandia Biotite Granite, New Mexico	1.437± .017 (U/Pb)	0.7027-.7060	23
33	Priest Biotite Adamellite, New Mexico[4]	1.569± .314 (Rb/Sr)	0.7029±.0064[5]	24
34	Pedernal Biotite Granite, New Mexico	1.471± .017 (Rb/Sr)	0.7027±.0005	25
35	Los Pinos Biotite Granite, New Mexico	1.480± .072 (Rb/Sr)	0.7078±.0205	26,24
36	Ladron Two-mica Adamellite, New Mexico[4]	1.319± .051 (Rb/Sr)	0.7101±.0037[5]	27

TABLE 1. Continued.

No.[1]	Description	Age (b.y.)[2]	($^{87}Sr/^{86}Sr$)initial	Ref[3]
37	Sepultura Biotite Granite, New Mexico[4]	1.350± .104 (Rb/Sr)	0.7488±.0333[5]	24
38	Oscura Two-mica Adamellite, New Mexico[4]	1.338± .026 (Rb/Sr)	0.7060±.0016[5]	27
39	Capitol Peak Two-mica Adamellite, New Mexico[4]	1.35 (Rb/Sr)		28
40	Stockton Pass Two-mica Granite, Arizona[4]	1.359± .039 (Rb/Sr)	0.7101±.0045[5]	29
41	Tungsten King Granite, Arizona	1.420± .010 (U/Pb)		30
42	Cananea Biotite Adamelite, Sonora, Mexico	1.440± .015 (U/Pb)		31
43	Continental Biotite-Hornblende Granodiorite, Arizona	1.42 (U/Pb)		30
44	Oracle Two-mica Granite, Arizona	1.44 (U/Pb)	0.7065	32,34
45	Ruin Two-mica Granite, Arizona	1.44 ± .02 (U/Pb)	0.7065	33,34
46	Dells Two-mica Granite, Arizona	1.42 ± .02 (U/Pb)		33
47	Lawler Peak Two-mica Granite, Arizona	1.411± .005 (U/Pb)		33
48	Holy Moses Biotite-Hornblende Granite, Arizona[4]	1.335± .023 (Rb/Sr)	0.7094[5]	35
49	Hualapi Biotite Granite, Arizona[4]	1.367± .069 (Rb/Sr)	0.7032	35
50	Gold Butte Biotite Granite, Nevada	1.450± .025 (U/Pb)		36
51	Davis Dam Biotite Granite, Nevada	1.450± .025 (U/Pb)		36
52	Biotite-Hornblende Granite, Newberry Mountains, Nevada	1.450± .025 (U/Pb)		36
53	Biotite-Hornblende Granite, Eldorado Mountains, Nevada	1.450± .025 (U/Pb)		36
54	Biotite Granite, McCulloch Mountains, Nevada	1.450± .025 (U/Pb)		36
55	Younger Two-mica Granite, World Beater Complex, California	1.411± .031 (Rb/Sr)	0.7390±.0180[5]	37
56	Mountain Pass Carbonatite - Syenite Complex, California[4]	1.436± .071 (Pb/Th)		37
57	Biotite Granite, Marble Mountains, California	1.43 (U/Pb)		38
58	Parker Dam Biotite-Hornblende Granite (Granite porphyry), Calif.[4]	1.326± .059 (Rb/Sr)	0.7043±.031[5]	39
III.	North America: Anorogenic Granites with an Age Between 1.34-1.41 b.y.			
59	Biotite-Hornblende Granite (BDH), Scott Co., Kansas	1.382± .002 (U/Pb)		14
60	Two-mica Granite (BDH), Stevens Co., Kansas	1.372± .020 (U/Pb)		14
61	Sheared Biotite Granite from Magnetic Anomaly (BDH), Riley Co., Kansas	1.382± .013 (U/Pb)		14
62	Biotite Granite from Magnetic Anomaly (BDH), Douglas Co., Kansas	1.339± .012 (U/Pb)		14
63	Biotite Granite from Magnetic Anomaly (BDH), Miami Co., Kansas	1.361± .006 (U/Pb)		14
64	Biotite-Hornblende Granite from Magnetic Anomaly (BDH), Jackson Co., Missouri	1.365± .101 (U/Pb)		14
65	Rose Dome Granite (Xenolith in Kimberlite), Woodson Co., Kansas	1.408± .021 (U/Pb)		14
66	Biotite Granite (BDH), Greenwood Co., Kansas	1.380± .033 (U/Pb)		14
67	Granophyric Microgranite Porphyry (BDH), Ottawa Co., Oklahoma	1.383± .008 (U/Pb)		14
68	Granophyric Granite (BDH), McDonald Co., Missouri	1.367± .003 (U/Pb)		14
69	Spavinaw Hornblende-Biotite Granite, Oklahoma	1.370± .020 (U/Pb)		14
70	Munger Granite Porphyry, Missouri	1.408± .012 (U/Pb)		13
71	Blue River Biotite Granite Gneiss, Oklahoma	1.396± .040 (U/Pb)		40
72	Tishomingo Biotite-Hornblende Granite, Oklahoma	1.374± .015 (U/Pb)		40
73	Troy Biotite Granite, Oklahoma	1.399± .095 (U/Pb)		40
74	St. Kevin Two-mica Granite, Colorado	1.394± .017 (U/Pb	0.7040	41
IV.	North America: Anorogenic Granites with an Age Between 1.03-1.08 b.y.			
75	Loon Lake Pluton, Ontario	1.065± .0013 (Rb/Sr)	0.7034	42
76	Pikes Peak Batholith, Colorado	1.030± .013 (Rb/Sr)		43
	Alkali Gabbro		0.7044	44
	Syenite-Quartz Syenite		0.7052-0.7063	44
	Fayalite-Biotite Granite and Biotite Granite		0.7067-0.7117	44
77	Enchanted Rock Batholith, Texas	1.048± .003 (Rb/Sr)	0.7048± .0007	45
78	Lone Grove Pluton, Texas	1.056± .001 (Rb/Sr)	0.7061± .0003	45
79	Red Bluff Complex, Franklin Mountains, Texas	1.025± .050 (Rb/Sr)		26

[1]Number refers to locality depicted on Figure 1.

[2]Age based on U/Pb - zircon (decay constants of Steiger and Jager, 1977), Rb/Sr whole rock ($\lambda = 1.42 \times 10^{-11}$ yr^{-1}), or Pb/Th - monazite

TABLE 1. Continued

No.[1]	Description	Age (b.y.)[2]	($^{87}Sr/^{86}Sr$ initial	Ref[3]

[3]References Cited: 1. Gulson and Krogh (1975); 2. Perrson (1978); 3. Kornfalt (1976); 4 Vorma, (1972); 5. Van Schmus (1980) and Van Schmus et al. (1975c); 6 Brand (1976); 7 Marchand and Crockett (1974); 8. Krogh and Davis (1973); 9. Van Schmus (1965); 10. Van Schmus et al. (1975a); 11. Van Schmus et al. (1975b); 12 Van Schmus et al. (1981); 13. Bickford and Mose (1975); 14. Bickford et al. (1981); 15. Van Schmus et al. (1982); 16. Subbarayudu et al. (1976); 17. Peterman and Hedge (1968); Peterman et al. (1968); Peterman et al. (1967); 18. Mose and Bickford (1969); Bickford and Cudzilo (1975); 19. Hansen and Peterman (1968); 20. Silver and Barker (1967); 21. Bickford et al. (1969); 22. Register and Brookins (1979); 23. Steiger and Wasserburg (1966); 24. Brookins et al. (1980); 25. Mukhopadhyay et al. (1975); 26. Muehlberger et al. (1966); 27. White (1978); 28. Condie and Budding (1979); 29. Swan, M.M. (1976); 30. Silver (1978); 31. Anderson and Silver (1977); 32. Shakel et al. (1977); 33. Silver et al. (1980); 34. Keith et al. (1980); 35. Kessler, E (1976); 36. Silver (1973) as referenced in Stewart and Carlson (1978); 37. Lanphere (1964); 38. Silver and McKinney (1962); 39. Davis et al. (1982); 40. Bickford and Lewis (1979); 41. Doe and Pearson (1969); 42. Dostal (1975);Heaman et al. (1982); 43. Hedge (1970); 44. Barker et al. (1976); 45. Garrison et al. (1979).

[4]Minimum or uncertain age; placement in this age-frame tentative.

[5]Initial ratio of $^{87}Sr/^{86}Sr$ uncertain due to possible disturbance of the Rb-Sr system.

[6]BDH = basement drill hole.

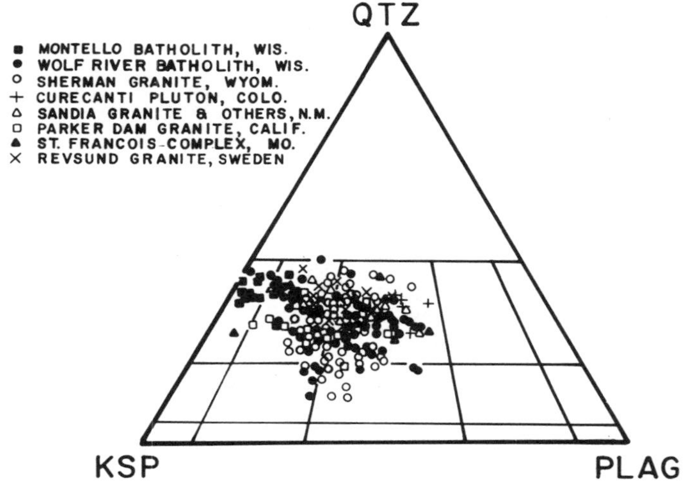

Figure 2. Modal composition of Proterozoic anorogenic granites. Data from Anderson et al. (1980), Anderson and Cullers (1978), Eggler (1978), Hansen (1964), Condie and Budding (1979), Davis et al. (1980), Bickford et al. (1981), and Persson (1978).

As can be noted in Figure 1 and Table 1, regional variations of age exist within the belt. Based on U-Pb (zircon), the older complexes tend to occur in the northern midcontinent with ages of about 1.48 ± .01 b.y. while younger dates occur to the northeast in Labrador (1.45 ± .01 b.y.), and to the southwest in the central midcontinent (1.46 ± .01 b.y.), the Front Range (1.44 ± .01 b.y.), and the southwestern United States (1.43 ± .02 b.y.). The entire anorogenic event occurred in the limited time span of 74 m.y. As depicted in Figure 1, the belt cuts across the southward-younging, orogenic age provinces of 1.82 to 1.90 b.y. (Penokean), 1.69 to 1.78 b.y., and 1.61 to 1.68 b.y. (Mazatzal). Only in the southern midcontinent (south Missouri, Kansas) is there an absence of older rocks indicating that in this region the belt may have cut across what was an inactive continental margin. Elsewhere, the belt is totally contained within the middle to early Proterozoic portion of the North American craton, being emplaced in orogenic rocks that formed 170 to 335 m.y. earlier.

Regional differences in rock types exist. The anorogenic granite intrusives of Labrador (Mistastin Lake, Umiakovik Lake), Wisconsin (Wolf River), Nebraska (Red Willow), and Wyoming (Sherman) occur in proximity to or contain older gabbro, anorthosite, and/or mangeritic rocks. Mantle-derived magmatic rocks are not obvious for the southwestern portion of the belt except for major NW- to NE-trending diabase dike swarms that have been noted for complexes in Colorado (bracketed in age between the Silver Plume and Sherman intrusives; Peterman et al., 1968, p. 2279) and in Missouri (Sylvester and Schultz, 1980). Although these granites are marginally metaluminous and contain biotite ± hornblende, the Labrador granites also contain pyroxene. Toward the southwest, anorogenic two-mica granites become abundant (see Table 1) such as the Silver Plume and other similar granites of Colorado, the Ladron adamellite of New Mexico, and the Oracle granite of Arizona. As described further below, differences also exist in the Fe-Ti oxide mineralogy. Although some of these granites are principally ilmenite-bearing (e.g., the Wolf River batholith), several are principally magnetite-bearing. In fact, many of the subsurface examples of this belt were recognized by their associated magnetic anomaly (Bickford et al., 1981; Van Schmus et al., 1981).

Alkalic rocks in this belt are rare; the only known examples are the Wausau syenite complex of Wisconsin and, possibly, the not well-dated Mountain Pass carbonatite-syenite complex of California.

Anorogenic Granites of 1.34 to 1.41 b.y. Age

Only recently recognized as a separate anorogenic event (Bickford and Lewis, 1979; Bickford et al, 1981), granites of the age range of 1.34 to 1.41 b.y. (U-Pb, zircon) form a distinct terrain from western Missouri and eastern Kansas to southern Oklahoma (Fig. 1, Table 1). Although most have been revealed by subsurface drilling, exposed examples include the Spavinaw and Tishomingo granites of

Oklahoma. Many of the granites have distinctive magnetic anomaly signatures. Only a few localities fall outside the terrain depicted in Figure 1, including the Munger granite porphyry (Bickford and Mose, 1975) of southwest Missouri and the St. Kevin granite (Doe and Pearson, 1969) of central Colorado. Although its age range has apparent continuity with the 1.4 to 1.5 b.y. event, the terrain cuts across the belt and began to form 35 m.y. after the earlier anorogenic activity had ceased. Moreover, the peak of igneous activity (1.38 b.y.) is separated by 80 m.y. from the mean age of 1.4 to 1.5 b.y. old rocks in that region. Rock types range from biotite-hornblende, biotite, and two-mica granite, many with epizonal characteristics.

Anorogenic Complexes of 1.0 to 1.1 b.y. Age

The overall volume of granites in this time frame is minor when compared with those having ages between 1.4 and 1.5 b.y. For North America, most anorogenic igneous terranes of this age are the anorthosite-quartz mangerite complexes of the Adirondacks and other portions of the Grenville Province which lack major granite intrusions. This may simply be due to a relatively deep level of exposure, particularly if the collision origin for the Grenville orogeny (Seyfert, 1980) is correct.

The most well-studied granitic complex of this age is the 1.03 b.y. Pikes Peak batholith of Colorado (Barker et al., 1975, 1976) which consists largely of biotite (± hornblende) granite with lesser amounts of older gabbro, quartz syenite, fayalite granite, and riebeckite granite. Border lithologies include not only representatives of the 1.4 to 1.5 b.y. belt but also gneisses as old as 1.71 b.y. (Peterman et al., 1968; Peterman and Hedge, 1968). Of essentially the same age and composition as the Pikes Peak, the 1.03 to 1.06 b.y. plutons of central and west Texas (Table 1) intrude a relatively young, "Grenvillian-"aged terrain that underwent regional metamorphism 1.13 to 1.17 b.y. ago (Garrison et al., 1979; Garrison, 1981).

One of the more striking Proterozoic tectonic features of North America is the midcontinent gravity high (Chase and Gilmer, 1973). Representing the surface exposures of this rift are the 1.09 to 1.12 b.y. plutonic and volcanic rocks of the Keweenawan Province of the Lake Superior region. Although mafic rocks predominate, the suite of volcanic rocks is bimodal and, based on the number of analyses (Green, 1972; Hubbard, 1975; Cullers and Anderson, unpublished data), rhyolite and rhyodacite, which are compositionally equivalent to anorogenic granites, constitute 17 to 18 percent.

MINERALOGY AND CONDITIONS OF CRYSTALLIZATION

The mineralogy of anorogenic granites is distinctive and reflects the potassic and iron-enriched composition of the magmas as well as the conditions of crystallization. This includes the modal predominance of alkali feldspar over plagioclase, the iron-rich character of the mafic silicates, and the near ubiquitous occurrence of fluorite as an accessory mineral phase. Consequently, the plutons are clearly separable from the older, synorogenic and calc-alkaline plutons of the older crust through which the magmas have invariably risen.

Feldspars

Plagioclase compositions commonly range from sodic andesine (An_{31-33}) to albite (An_{06-09}) reflecting the range of possible bulk composition. Zoning, both normal and oscillatory, is common. Coexisting alkali feldspar, usually perthitic, have integrated compositions which yield consistent tie line orientations (Anderson, 1980) with that of the coexisting plagioclase. Integrated alkali feldspar compositions range Or_{50-60} (coexisting with albite to sodic oligoclase) to Or_{70-80} (coexisting with calcic oligoclase and sodic andesine). Alkali granites low in anorthite component (e.g., biotite granite of the Montello batholith) commonly contain one feldspar, thus demonstrating the hypersolvus character of these magmas.

Classic rapakivi texture (mantling of plagioclase on alkali feldspar) occurs sporadically in the Proterozoic anorogenic granites of North America but is only fully developed in the wiborgite varieties (~90 percent of alkali feldspar being mantled). For North America, the wiborgite variety of rapakivi is uncommon. More common are the pyterlitic, even-grained, and porphyritic varieties which are also classic rapakivi rock types well described by Vorma (1971). Examples having well-developed rapakivi texture include the Mistastin Lake adamellite of Labrador (Emslie, 1980), the Waupaca adamellite and wiborgite porphyry of the Wolf River batholith of Wisconsin (Anderson, 1980), the Butler Hill granite of the St. Francois Mountains of Missouri (Lowell and Sides, 1973), the Red Bluff granite of the Franklin Mountains, Texas (McCutcheon, 1981), the Los Pinos granite of New Mexico (Brookins et al., 1980), and the granites of the Gold Butte region of Nevada (Volborth, 1962). As noted by Anderson (1980), plagioclase mantles usually have a composition that is identical to rims of adjacent zoned plagioclase crystals and, for most cases, can be assumed to be of magmatic origin involving a disequilibrium relationship between the feldspars and melt. Magma mixing (Hibbard, 1981) and peritectic reactions (Stewart and Roseboom, 1962; Abbott, 1978) are not considered to be appropriate mechanisms. In the author's opinion, models involving (1) local depletion and insufficient transfer of feldspar component adjacent to crystalzing crystals (Sederholm, 1928), or (2) shifting of the feldspar cotectic surface with devolatization or loss of confining pressure

(Stewart, 1959, p. 305) are most probable explanations. Both models are appropriate for high-level intrusions, such as rapakivi granite melts, which would be most susceptible to rapid changes in pressure and f_{H_2O}.

Olivine and Pyroxene

Olivine and pyroxene, while common in the mafic and mangeritic rocks, are usually absent in the biotite and/or hornblende-bearing granitic units of anorogenic complexes. As noted for the Nain complex (Smith, 1974), the Harp Lake complex (Emslie, 1980), the Wolf River batholith (Anderson, 1980), and the Pikes Peak batholith (Barker et al, 1975), both olivine and pyroxene become increasingly iron-rich in the more differentiated members of the mangeritic series. The olivine is essentially fayalite, but the amount of Mn_2SiO_4 can be significant.

Inverted pigeonite or hypersthene + ferroaugite + fayalite is a common assemblage in the less iron-enriched jotunites and mangerites, while in the more iron-enriched mangerites or quartz syenites fayalite + quartz + ferroaugite occur.

Amphiboles

Calciferous amphiboles from Phanerozoic anorogenic granites and the associated mangeritic to syenitic rocks commonly approach the end member hastingsite (MacLeod et al., 1971; Czamanske et al., 1977). However, analysed amphiboles (Fig. 3) from Proterozoic complexes of North America as well as the Wiborg massif of Finland (Simonen and Vorma, 1969) contain less tetrahedral aluminum (Al^{IV} = 1.18 to 1.70 atoms per 23 oxygens) and range from ferroedenitic to hastingsitic hornblende (Leake, 1978). Aside from this, these amphiboles usually remain iron-rich (Fe/Fe + Mg = 0.720-0.953), can contain up to 1 percent fluorine, and have a total Al_2O_3 ranging from 7.41 to 10.90 weight %. The only known exceptions are the possibly deuteric calcium amphiboles from a quartz syenite of the Pikes Peak batholith (Barker et al., 1975) which are notably low in Al_2O_3 (3.86-4.93 wt. %). Secondary grunerite is of common occurrence in quartz-poor varieties (SiO_2 less than 70 wt. %) of the granites and throughout the charnockitic series. This phase is also typically iron-rich (Fe/Fe + Mg = 0.799-0.971).

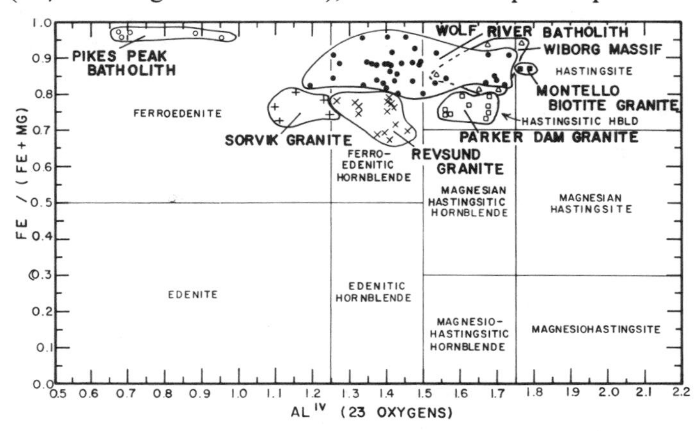

Figure 3. Composition of calciferous amphiboles from Proterozoic anorogenic granites in terms of Fe/Fe+Mg and Al^{IV} (23 oxygens). Data from Anderson et al. (1980), Anderson (1980), Anderson et al. (1979) and unpublished data, Perrson (1978), and Barker et al. (1975).

Biotite

The composition of biotite largely depends on rock composition and mineral assemblage. This is in part due to the absence of primary magnetite in many of these rocks (see below); as a result, the iron-rich character of the biotites (Fe/Fe + Mg = 0.80-0.99) corresponds to that of the whole rock for a given primary mineral assemblage. For anorogenic granites containing magnetite, the Fe/Fe + Mg of biotite is more variable reflecting a variation of the intensive parameters, particularly that of oxygen fugacity. This ratio for biotite coexisting with magnetite ranges 0.65 to 0.90 for the Wolf River batholith; 0.76 to 0.83 and 0.51 to 0.57 for the biotite and two-mica granites, respectively, of the Montello batholith; 0.57 to 0.70 for the Parker Dam granite of the Whipple Mountains of southern California (Davis et al., 1980; Anderson, unpublished data); and as low as 0.33 for granites of the Hualapai Mountains of Arizona (K. Kwok and J. L. Anderson, unpublished data). Biotite from anorogenic granites usually has variable amounts of aluminum in excess of the annite-phlogopite join (Fig. 4) involving the solution mechanism $Si + R^{2+} = Al^{IV} + Al^{VI}$. The range is in part due to bulk composition but also reflects the presence and composition of other minerals, such as plagioclase (Anderson, 1980). The latter is due to the anorthite component effectively concentrating the available Al at the expense of biotite.

One final observation concerning the composition of anorogenic biotite is its fluorine content which is commonly greater than 1.5 wt. % and is highest where it coexists with fluorite. As an example of the latter, biotite from the Hualapai granite, Arizona contains up to 3.1 wt. % F (K. Kwok and J. L. Anderson, unpublished data).

Muscovite

Muscovite occurs as a primary phase in the more peraluminous anorogenic granites. As shown by Anderson et al. (1980) for two-mica granites of the Montello batholith, the muscovite is usually far from ideal in composition. The amount of celadonite component can be high, ranging up to 29.3 percent, which accounts for the higher abundances of Si, Fe, Mg, Ti, and less Al relative to end-member muscovite. Most distinctive is the TiO_2 content (to 1.1 wt. %).

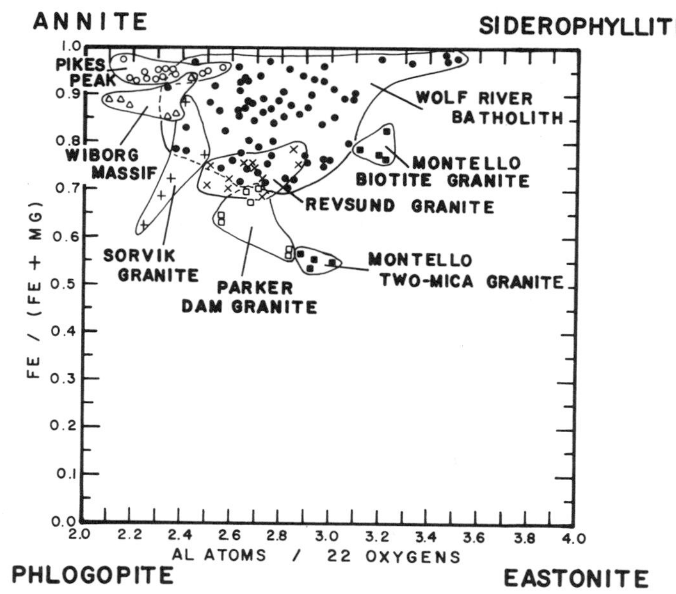

Figure 4. Composition of biotite from Proterozoic anorogenic granites in terms of Fe/Fe+Mg and Al^{Total} (22 oxygens). Sources of data are the same as for Figure 3.

Secondary muscovite (sericite) can also occur but can easily be discerned from plutonic muscovite by its much lower TiO_2 content (<0.33 wt. %).

Fe-Ti Oxides: Anorogenic Ilmenite- and Magnetite-Series

Ishihara (1977) has made the distinction between a magnetite-series and an ilmenite-series for granitic rocks. The magnetite-series, which Ishihara considered to be largely restricted to synorogenic metaluminous granitoids, contain magnetite (0.1-2 vol. %) ± ilmenite + high Mg/Fe biotite; the ilmenite-series, considered to be largely restricted to anorogenic granitoids, contain ilmenite (<0.1 vol. %) ± magnetite + low Mg/Fe biotite. These differences are attributed to differing levels of oxygen fugacity (high for magnetite-series, low for ilmenite-series) which is further addressed in the following section. The point to be made here is that Ishihara's proposal works well except it is now apparent that a previously unrecognized anorogenic magnetite-series exists among these Proterozoic granites of North America. It is unfortunate that many petrologic studies of anorogenic complexes have not fully characterized the oxide mineralogy. The two more well-known Proterozoic anorogenic granite batholiths of North America, the Pikes Peak and the Wolf River, are both of the ilmenite-series. Yet, many anorogenic granites contain an abundance of magnetite and very little or no ilmenite and thus constitute magnetite-series. From this author's own experience, this seems to be the case for most of the anorogenic granites of southern California and adjacent Arizona and is likely the case for many of the midcontinent examples which are represented by distinct, usually circular, magnetitic anomalies.

Intensive Variables

Estimates of temperature, pressure, and fugacity of H_2O, O_2, and other volatiles in anorogenic granites involve a number of different approaches. One of the more classic approaches has been comparison of normative rock composition with the experimental work in the system Qz-Or-Ab-An-H_2O. A compilation in the form of a grid for all existing minimum melt points over a range of pressure and Ab/An ratio has been utilized by Anderson and Cullers (1978) and is reproduced in Figure 5. In application, the composition of undifferentiated portions of plutons that have changed little since fusion can be utilized to estimate the depth of fusion. Likewise, extremely differentiated granites should depict a trend toward or cluster at an appropriate minimum for their level of emplacement. Such applications require a number of assumptions (Anderson and Cullers, 1978), and it is unlikely that a given granitic pluton, or portion thereof, should satisfy all of these criteria. Anorogenic granites, due to their intrinsic leucocratic composition, may be more appropriate for such an application except for their relatively dry and fluorine-rich nature. Fortunately, the displacement of minimum melt compositions for wet versus dry melting may be subparallel to the isobaric minimum melt curves (Luth, 1969). The shift of minima due to fluorine (Manning, 1981), which is toward the Ab corner, will most affect the differentiated granites and thus make emplacement depth estimates a minimum. Given these concerns, the fields for various Proterozoic anorogenic granites are consistent with magma generation (Fig. 5B) from a crustal source at an average of 7 to 10 kb (27 to 36 km). The spread of data along the isobars is likely due to variable source composition in terms of the normative plagioclase and/or H_2O content. Likewise, intrusion and subsequent differentiation (Fig. 5A) may have occurred at pressures less than 2 kb (<7.6 km), consistent with the clear epizonal nature of these plutons.

The range of mineralogy of anorogenic granites and associated rocks allows a number of alternatives for calculation of the intensive parameters based on compositions of coexisting feldspars, Fe-Ti oxides, biotite, pyroxenes, and fayalite among others. As discussed by Anderson (1980), such calculations may be complicated by incomplete phase equilibration during various stages of crystallization plus the possible effects of partial subsolidus reequilibration. Mineral equilibria in such igneous suites is possibly to be of a local nature (between adjacent phases) which warrants consideration in geothermometer-type applications.

Estimates of crystallization conditions for the mangeritic rocks of the Nain Province (Smith, 1974; DeWaard, 1976; Berg, 1977), the Adirondacks (Bohlen and Essene,

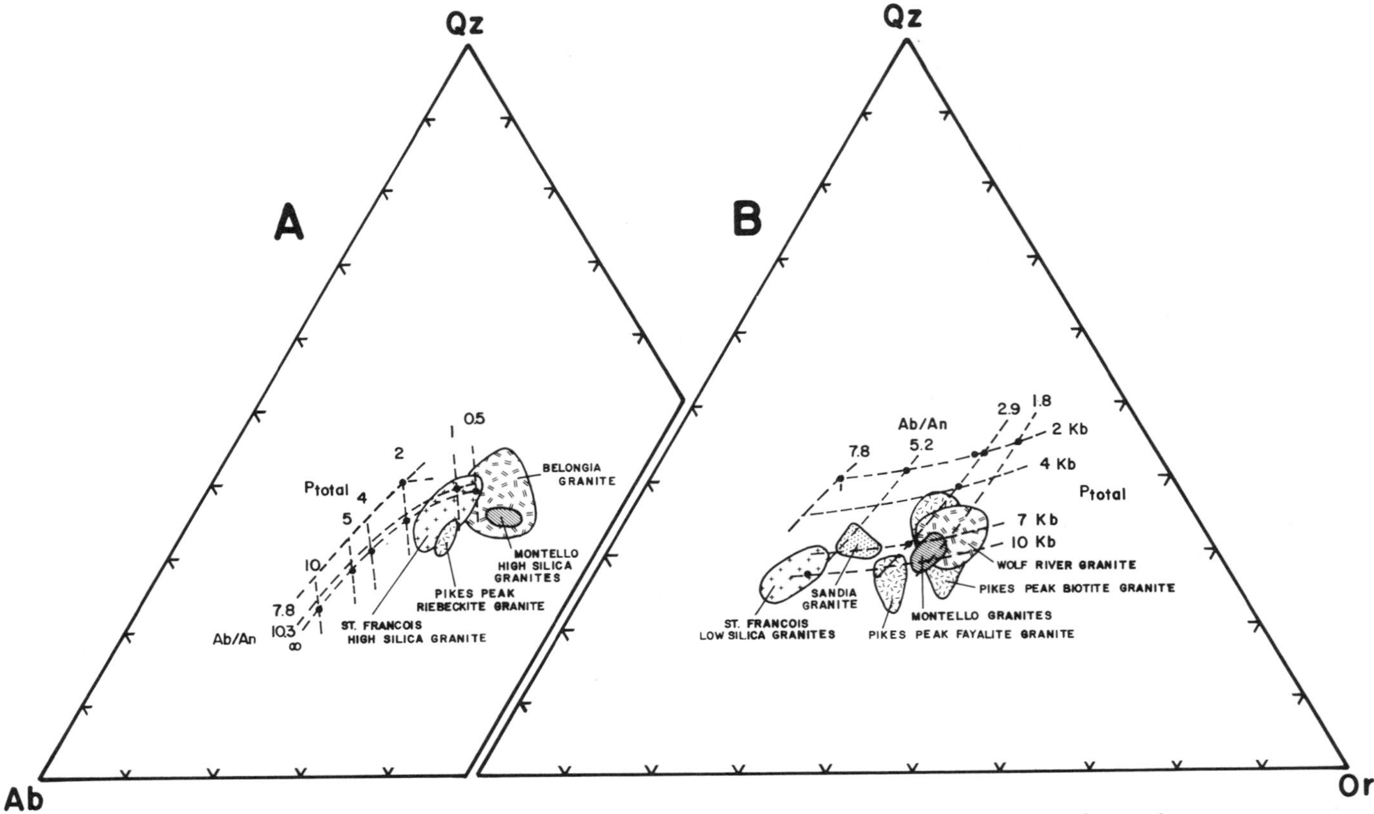

Figure 5. Normative quartz, albite, and orthoclase of Proterozoic anorogenic granites and comparison to experimental minimum melt compositions. Minimum melt experimental grid compiled from numerous sources (see Anderson and Cullers, 1978). Fields for anorogenic granites are based on data from Anderson and Cullers (1978), Barker et al. (1975), Anderson et al. (1980), Condie and Budding (1979), and Bickford et al. (1981).

1978), and the Wolf River batholith (Anderson, 1980) average at approximately 950 ± 100°C at very low levels of f_{H_2O} and on a T-f_{O_2} path that approximates well the quartz-fayalite-magnetite (QFM) buffer (Fig. 6). Pressure estimates include a maximum of 3.7 to 6.6 kb (14 to 24 km) for the Nain intrusives and 5.6 to 8.7 kb (21 to 32 km) for the Wolf River mangerites. The latter rock type occurs with anorthosite as blocks enclosed in younger rapakivi granite, and the above estimate corresponds well with their inferred depth of origin by partial melting.

Like the mangeritic rocks, some ilmenite-series granitic plutons, such as those of the Pikes Peak (Barker et al., 1975) and the Wolf River (Anderson, 1980) batholiths, seem to have crystallized at low oxygen fugacities (ca. QFM). This is depicted in Figure 6 and also has been found to be true for other anorogenic complexes, both Proterozoic (Stephenson and Hensel, 1978) and Phanerozoic (Czamanske et al., 1977; Wones, 1980). Yet, the numerous granites that comprise the anorogenic magnetite-series are notable exceptions to this generalization. This is also shown on Figure 6, for the Montello batholith (Anderson et al., 1980) and the Parker Dam granite where crystallization is inferred to have occurred at higher oxygen fugaci-

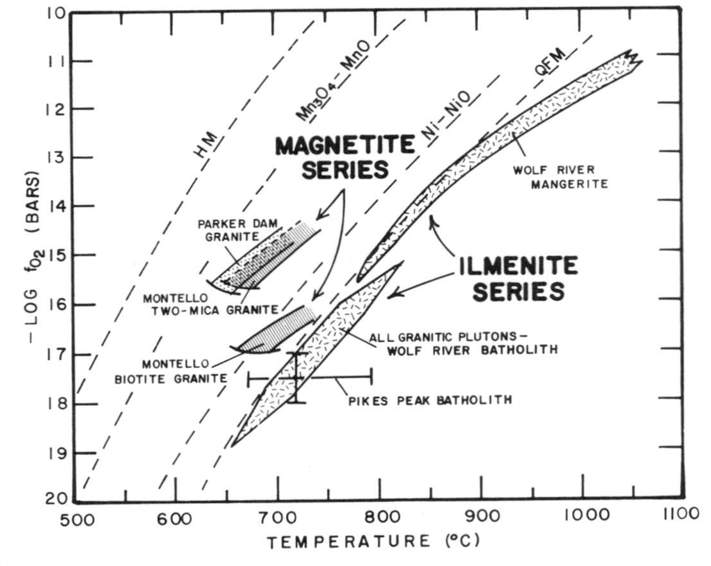

Figure 6. Estimated conditions of crystallization in terms of temperature and oxygen fugacity for Proterozoic anorogenic granites. Note that crystallization can occur under conditions of both high (magnetite-series) and low (ilmenite-series) oxygen fugacity. Sources of data are the same as for Figure 3.

ties, both above and below the Ni-NiO buffer. The higher fo_2 is reflected in a higher Mg/Fe of the biotite, a predominance of magnetite over ilmenite, and an earlier appearance of Fe-Ti oxides in the crystallization sequence. Crystallization temperatures are inferred to range from 640° to 790°, which at 0.5 to 2 kb is above the wet granite to adamellite solidus as expected for crystallization at conditions of $P_{H_2O} < P_{total}$.

Rapakivi granites have long been considered relatively dry, fluorine-rich magmas, largely due to the paucity of pegmatites and the common occurrence of fluorite, both as an accessory phase and as discrete crystals in miarolitic cavities (Sahama, 1948). Inferred low f_{H_2O} is also consistent with the late crystallization of the hydrous silicates, particularly biotite, which commonly follow quartz and the feldspars in the sequence of crystallization (Anderson, 1980). From the experimental studies of Maaloe and Wyllie (1975), this implies an H_2O content of less than 1.5 weight percent. Hence, the f_{H_2O}, although likely higher than that of the mangeritic rocks, was probably less than P_{total} for all but the final stages of crystallization.

GEOCHEMICAL CHARACTERISTICS AND MAGMA EVOLUTION

It has long been recognized that rapakivi granites and, in fact, all anorogenic granites, possess specific compositional characteristics that make them distinct from other granitic suites (Sederholm, 1928; Sahama, 1948; Savolahti, 1962). This includes high K_2O, K_2O/Na_2O, Fe/Mg, and F as well as low CaO, MgO, and Al_2O_3. It is now recognized that they are also enriched in many large ion lithophile elements (LILE) including Rb, Ba, Ga, Y, REE (except Eu), Zr, Th, Nb, and U.

To specifically address the compositional characteristics of this Proterozoic anorogenic event in North America, the author has compiled over 560 analyses from various complexes, the results of which are shown in Figures 7 through 10 and are summarized in Table 2.

Alkalinity

Both the K_2O (Table 2) and total alkalies (Fig. 7) of anorogenic granites are higher than that of calc-alkaline granitoids. However, these granites are rarely alkalic. Although the intermediate mangeritic rocks commonly fall in the alkalic field of Irvine and Baragar (1971), most anorogenic granites do not and should be termed subalkalic. Exceptions to this include some of the granites of the Wolf River batholith, the Pikes Peak batholith, and the Ragunda massif which trend into the alkalic field (Fig. 7).

Common reference to the alkaline nature of anorogenic complexes alludes to their low alkali-lime index (Peacock, 1939). Most complexes do not have the range of silica to allow use of this classification but the few that do indicate either alkali-calcic or alkalic indices (Fig. 8). Only the Wiborg massif, Finland, and the Parker Dam granite, California, have projected alkali-lime indices that fall into the calc-alkaline field (both 57.1).

Alumina-saturation

Shand (1927), in developing the principal of alumina-saturation, devised the now classic division of peralkaline ($K_2O + Na_2O > Al_2O_3$) metaluminous ($K_2O + Na_2O < Al_2O_3 < K_2O + Na_2O + CaO$), and peraluminous ($Al_2O_3 > K_2O + Na_2O + CaO$), all on a molecular basis. Figure 9 plots the molecular ratio $Al_2O_3/(CaO + Na_2O + K_2O)$ or A/CNK, as a function of SiO_2 (wt. %). The positive correlation of A/CNK and SiO_2 is apparent. In general, the mafic and intermediate rocks are metaluminous (A/CNK < 1), but the felsic rocks trend into the peraluminous (A/CNK > 1) field. Hence, most anorogenic granites straddle the metaluminous/peraluminous boundary and can appropriately be termed marginally peraluminous. The transition from metaluminous to marginally peraluminous is reflected in the mineralogical change from biotite-hornblende adamellite or granite to biotite granite. This can be the result of fractional crystallization of hornblende (also apatite, sphene). In addition, several anorogenic granites (Silver Plume, Oracle) are totally peraluminous and contain biotite or two micas ± garnet. These anorogenic two-mica granites are fundamentally different from S-type granitoids of orogenic belts (Chappell and White, 1974), for they still possess the modal and compositional attributes of anorogenic igneous rocks. This high value of alumina saturation may not be the result of differentiation but rather a direct reflection of the source material of the magma (discussed further below).

Iron-enrichment

The strong iron enrichment of anorogenic granites is depicted in Figure 10. The compositional contrast with the calc-alkaline character of their host terrains (Fig. 10c, h) represents a break to a fundamentally different type of magma.

A high Fe/Mg is also characteristic of the mangeritic suite, and even some of the associated gabbroic rocks are tholeiitic and thus iron-enriched. This apparent consanguinity within a given complex might imply that the anorogenic "trinity" constitutes a single comagmatic suite (Higgins, 1981), but the argument made here (see below) is that the uniformity is fortuitous and that more than one line of magma evolution is involved.

Some regional differences in iron-enrichment can be noted for these Proterozoic igneous complexes, specifically within the 1.4 to 1.5 b.y. magmatic belt. Many of these

TABLE 2. AVERAGE ANALYSES OF PROTEROZOIC ANOROGENIC GRANITES

Ref[1]	1	2	3	4	5	6	7	8	9	10
n[2]	(2)	(5)	(4)	(1)	(6)	(5)	(3)	(14)	(1)	(5)
SiO_2	73.60	71.71	64.90	72.9	68.22	73.30	75.73	75.41	65.64	68.62
TiO_2	.42	.35	.93	.21	.56	.31	.19	.19	1.20	.44
Al_2O_3	12.92	14.38	16.30	14.9	14.87	13.18	12.21	11.89	13.81	14.50
FeO[3]	3.39	1.97	5.04	1.45	4.36	2.67	2.06	1.70	6.07	2.98
MgO	.42	.33	1.20	.33	.45	.24	.13	.090	1.07	.93
MnO	.06	.03	.07	.01	.09	.05	.04	.03	.13	.08
CaO	.85	1.04	2.99	.66	1.94	1.09	.70	.53	2.85	1.79
Na_2O	3.19	3.91	3.06	2.95	3.59	3.13	2.92	3.27	3.61	4.03
K_2O	4.87	5.51	4.11	5.83	5.48	5.24	5.22	5.39	4.17	3.86
Total	99.72	99.23	98.60	99.24	99.56	99.21	99.20	98.50	98.55	97.23
K_2O+Na_2O	8.06	9.42	7.17	8.78	9.07	8.37	8.14	8.66	7.78	7.89
FeO/FeO+MgO	.890	.857	.808	.815	.909	.918	.940	.950	.850	.762
A/CNK[4]	1.071	1.007	1.093	1.205	.968	1.030	1.041	.976	.883	1.031
Rb	155	149	116	nd	109	179	211	184	95.2	119
Ba	1050	713	1650	nd	1627	854	538	441	1615	940
Sr	95	134	320	nd	145	88.6	39.7	27.7	206	198

Ref[1]	11	12	13	14	15	16	17	18	19	20
n[2]	(44)	(1)	(19)	(9)	-	(4)	(17)	(5)	(7)	(1)
SiO_2	75.77	66.44	72.59	70.4	67.38	75.32	73.61	74.29	72.30	69.2
TiO_2	.17	.82	.28	.29	.66	.05	.16	.26	.32	.76
Al_2O_3	12.36	14.27	13.36	14.0	15.25	13.74	13.91	12.30	13.83	13.70
FeO[3]	1.22	4.26	2.50	3.3	3.90	.82	1.43	2.62	2.41	4.33
MgO	.15	1.64	.14	.10	.96	.16	.22	.12	.50	1.00
MnO	.04	nd	.07	.09	.04	.07	.03	.04	.05	nd
CaO	.49	1.91	1.18	1.2	2.02	.66	.83	.80	1.50	2.75
Na_2O	3.44	3.79	3.31	4.2	2.80	3.67	3.30	3.37	3.34	3.29
K_2O	4.80	4.85	5.60	5.3	5.53	4.83	5.31	5.19	5.01	3.99
Total	98.44	97.98	99.03	98.88	98.35	99.32	98.80	98.99	99.26	99.02
K_2O+Na_2O	8.24	8.64	8.91	9.5	8.33	8.50	8.61	8.56	8.35	7.28
FeO/FeO+MgO	.891	.722	.947	.971	.802	.837	.867	.956	.828	.812
A/CNK[4]	1.052	.954	.979	.944	1.052	1.102	1.097	.975	1.014	.930
Rb	224	nd	nd	nd	254	251	nd	nd	nd	192
Ba	389	nd	nd	nd	1300	nd	nd	nd	nd	840
Sr	56	nd	nd	nd	233	47.9	nd	nd	nd	241

TABLE 2. Continued.

Ref[1]	21	22	23	24	25	26	27	28	29	30
n[2]	(1)	(1)	(1)	(11)	(1)	(5)	(1)	(11)	(15)	(37)
SiO_2	76.6	73.9	71.02	71.54	75.33	67.32	73.40	67.00	74.84	71.79
TiO_2	.07	.23	.43	.35	.22	.73	.20	.90	.22	.52
Al_2O_3	12.6	14.5	13.65	13.93	12.77	14.54	13.60	13.94	12.90	12.95
FeO[3]	1.01	1.26	2.51	3.51	1.35	4.30	2.19	5.15	1.74	3.66
MgO	.11	.37	1.11	.84	.42	1.04	.49	1.00	.22	.28
MnO	nd	nd	.07	.09	.07	.11	.03	.08	.03	.05
CaO	.67	.78	1.80	1.82	1.07	2.98	.40	2.44	.67	1.59
Na_2O	4.20	3.21	2.92	3.18	3.09	3.24	2.21	2.73	3.30	2.83
K_2O	4.14	5.09	4.62	3.44	4.31	3.78	5.94	5.28	5.29	5.48
Total	99.40	99.34	98.13	98.70	98.63	98.04	98.46	98.52	99.20	99.15
K_2O+Na_2O	8.34	8.30	7.54	6.52	7.40	7.02	8.25	8.01	8.59	8.31
FeO/FeO+MgO	.902	.773	.693	.807	.763	.805	.817	.837	.888	.929
A/CNK[4]	.999	1.188	1.044	1.136	1.092	.980	1.260	.952	1.043	.961
Rb	177	272	275	160	339	nd	nd	230	243	nd
Ba	190	687	455	1135	280	nd	nd	1111	183	nd
Sr	10	187	136	209	103	nd	nd	188	34	nd

[1]1. Snegamook Lake biotite granite, Hart Lake complex, Labrador (Emslie, 1980); 2. Loon Lake biotite granite (Dostal, 1975); 3. Manitoulin Island prophyritic quartz monzonite (adamellite), Ontario (Van Schmus, et al., 1975a); 4. Crocker Island quartz monzonite (adamellite), Ontario (Van Schmus, et al., 1975a; Card, 1965); 5, 6, 7. Wolf River biotite-hornblende granite (low-silica phase), Wolf River biotite granite, and Belongia biotite granite, respectively, of the Wolf River batholith. Wisconsin (Anderson and Cullers, 1978); 8. Biotite granite of the Montello batholith, Wisconsin (Anderson, et al., 1980); 9. Biotite-hornblende quartz monzonite of the Red Willow batholith, Nebraska (J. L. Anderson, unpublished data); 10, 11. Silvermine biotite-hornblende granite (adamellite) and Butler Hill biotite granite, respectively, of the St. Francois Mountains, Missouri (Bickford, et al., 1981a); 12. Spavinaw hornblende-biotite, granophyric granite, Oklahoma (Bickford and Lewis, 1979; Bickford, et al., 1981b); 13, 14. Biotite granite and biotite-fayalite granite, respectively, of the Pikes Peak batholith, Colorado (Barker, et al., 1975); 15. Silver Plume two-mica granite, Silver Plume, Colorado - U.S.G.S. rock standard GSP-1 (Flannigan, 1973); 16. Curecanti two-mica, garnet quartz monzonite (adamellite), Colorado (Hansen, 1964; Hansen and Peterman, 1969); 17. Two-mica granite of the Log Cabin batholith, Colorado (Eggler, 1968); 18 Trail Creek biotite-hornblende granite, a phase of the Sherman granite, Wyoming (Eggler, 1968); 19. Biotite granite of the Enchanted Rock batholith, Llano uplift, Texas (Hutchinson, 1956); 20. Sandia biotite granite (north phase), New Mexico (Condie and Budding, 1979); 21. Pedernal biotite granite, New Mexico (Condie and Budding, 1979); 22. Oscura two-mica adamellite, New Mexico (Condie and Budding, 1979); 23. Ruin two-mica granite, Arizona (Silver, et al., 1980); 24. Oracle two-mica granite, Arizona (S. Keith, personal communication, 1980); 25. Lawler Peak two-mica granite, Arizona (Silver, et al., 1980); 26. Continental biotite-hornblende granodiorite, Arizona (S. Keith, personal communication, 1980); 27. Younger two-mica granite of the World Beater complex, California (Lanphere, et al., 1964); 28. Parker Dam biotite-hornblende granite (granite porphyry), California (Davis, et al., 1980); 29. Ragunda biotite granite, Sweden (Kornfalt, 1976); 30. Average of numerous Finish rapakivi granites (Sahama, 1948).

[2]Number of analyses averaged; oxides as wt. %; Rb, Ba, and Sr as ppm.

[3]All Fe as FeO.

[4]A/CNK = molecular ratio $Al_2O_3/(CaO + Na_2O + K_2O)$; peraluminous = >1, metaluminous = <1.

nd = no data.

anorogenic granites have a FeO/(FeO + MgO) ratio greater than 0.90 (e.g., those of the Nain, Harp Lake, Wolf River, Sherman batholiths). Yet the granites of the southwest United States are less iron-rich such as the Parker Dam granite (California), the Hualapai granite (Arizona), the Continental granodiorite (Arizona), and the Sandia granite (New Mexico), which have values for this ratio between 0.78 to 0.86 (Fig. 10h). The markedly peraluminous Oracle, Lawler Peak, and Ruin (central Arizona) and Oscura, Capital Peak, and Ladron (central New Mexico) plutons are not iron-enriched and have ratios as low as 0.69 to 0.82 (Fig. 10g). This range of iron-enrichment probably reflects variations in the source and conditions of magma generation; plutons in this portion of the belt are hosted in crust that is, in part, eugeosynclinal and of the youngest age (1.61 to 1.70 b.y., Silver et al., 1977a) relative to the rest of the craton transected by this profound magmatic arc.

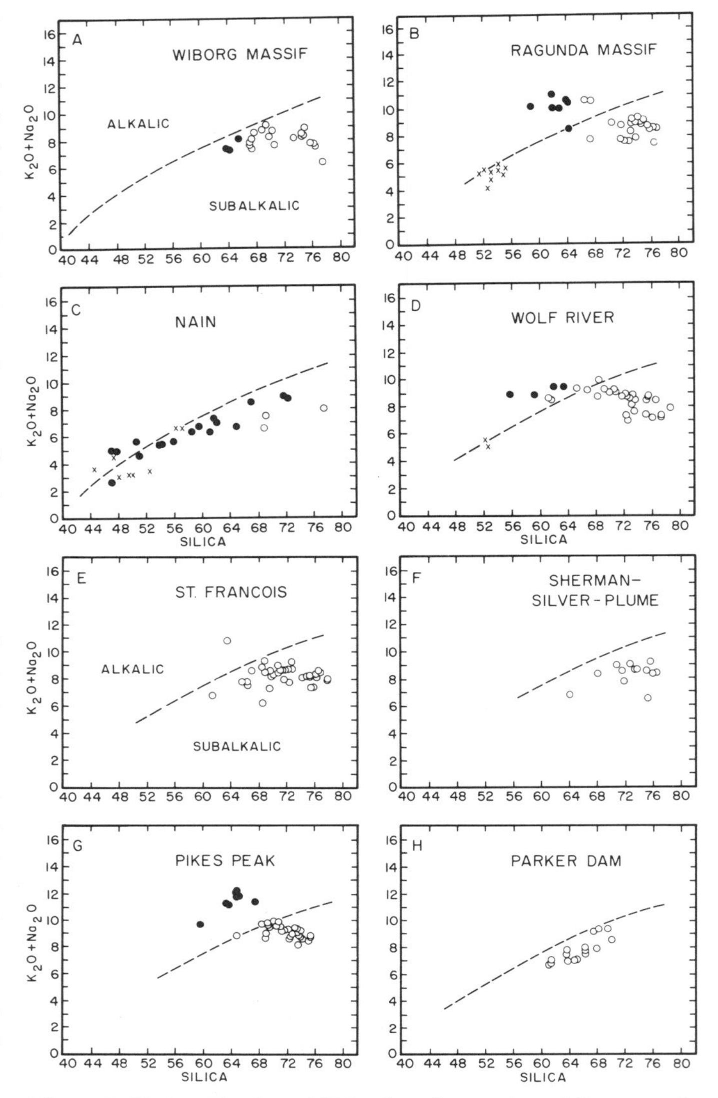

Figure 7. K_2O + Na_2O and SiO_2 data from selected Proterozoic anorogenic complexes: a. Wiborg (Fin.), b. Ragunda (Swed.), c. Nain (Lab.), d. Wolf River (Wis.), e. St. Francois (Mo.), f. Sherman and Silver Plume (Colo.-Wyom.), g. Pikes Peak (Colo.), h. Parker Dam (Calif.). Alkalic/subalkalic boundary from Irvine and Baragar (1971). Symbols: • granite, o charnockitic suite, + gabbro and anorthosite. All data are in weight percent. Sources of data are De Waard and Wheeler (1971), Kisvarsany (1972), and as noted in Table 2.

Trace Element and Sr Isotope Geochemistry

The abundance of the minor and trace elements in the Proterozoic anorogenic granites of North America displays a wide range, in part due to the differentiation processes active within the respective magma chambers.

The most commonly analyzed trace elements are Ba, Rb, and Sr. For the less silicic granites (SiO_2 = 68 to 74 percent), the Ba contents are high, ranging from 600 to 1600 ppm. Likewise, Rb ranges 90 to 250 ppm and Sr, 80 to 240 ppm. With increasing silica (SiO_2 = 75 to 78 percent), Ba and Sr commonly drop while Rb increases. The more differentiated granites have Ba ranging from 30 to 500 ppm, Rb ranging from 200 to 500 ppm, and Sr ranging from 5 to 100 ppm. These elemental variations have obvious implications for the nature of differentiation (i.e., minerals involved in fractional crystallization).

The rare earth element (REE) abundances follow Ba in being high. From the data of Barker et al. (1976), Anderson and Cullers (1978), Anderson et al. (1980), Condie and Budding (1979), and Cullers et al. (1981), it is apparent that the light rare earth elements (LREE) are enriched (100 to 500 times chondrite) relative to the heavy rare earth elements (HREE; range 20 to 60 times chondrite). A moderately negative Eu anomaly is common. Indeed, the rare earth abundances for the granites of the Pikes Peak, Wolf River, Red Willow, Montello, and St. Francois overlap (Fig. 11) yet also have sequentially lower total REE. Like the St. Francois, some of the anorogenic two-mica granites (Montello batholith, Silver Plume granite) also seem to have lower REE ranging from 90 to 300 times chondrite for LREE and from 15 to 25 times chondrite for HREE. Cullers et al. (1981) have suggested that the lower total REE of the St. Francois granites is due to a higher degree of fusion (~30 percent) during their generation relative to that for other anorogenic granites. Changes with differentiation include an increased negative Eu anomaly, yet changes for the other REE, however, vary; this aspect is discussed in the following section.

Initial Sr isotopic data are summarized in Table 1. The average initial ratio of $^{87}Sr/^{86}Sr$ (excluding data from the disturbed isochrons) is 0.7051 ± .0025. Lower ratios are commonly attained for the mangeritic and anorthositic rocks which range from 0.702 to 0.706. Of interest is the increase of initial ratios for the rocks of the Pikes Peak batholith (Barker et al., 1976) which increase from a low

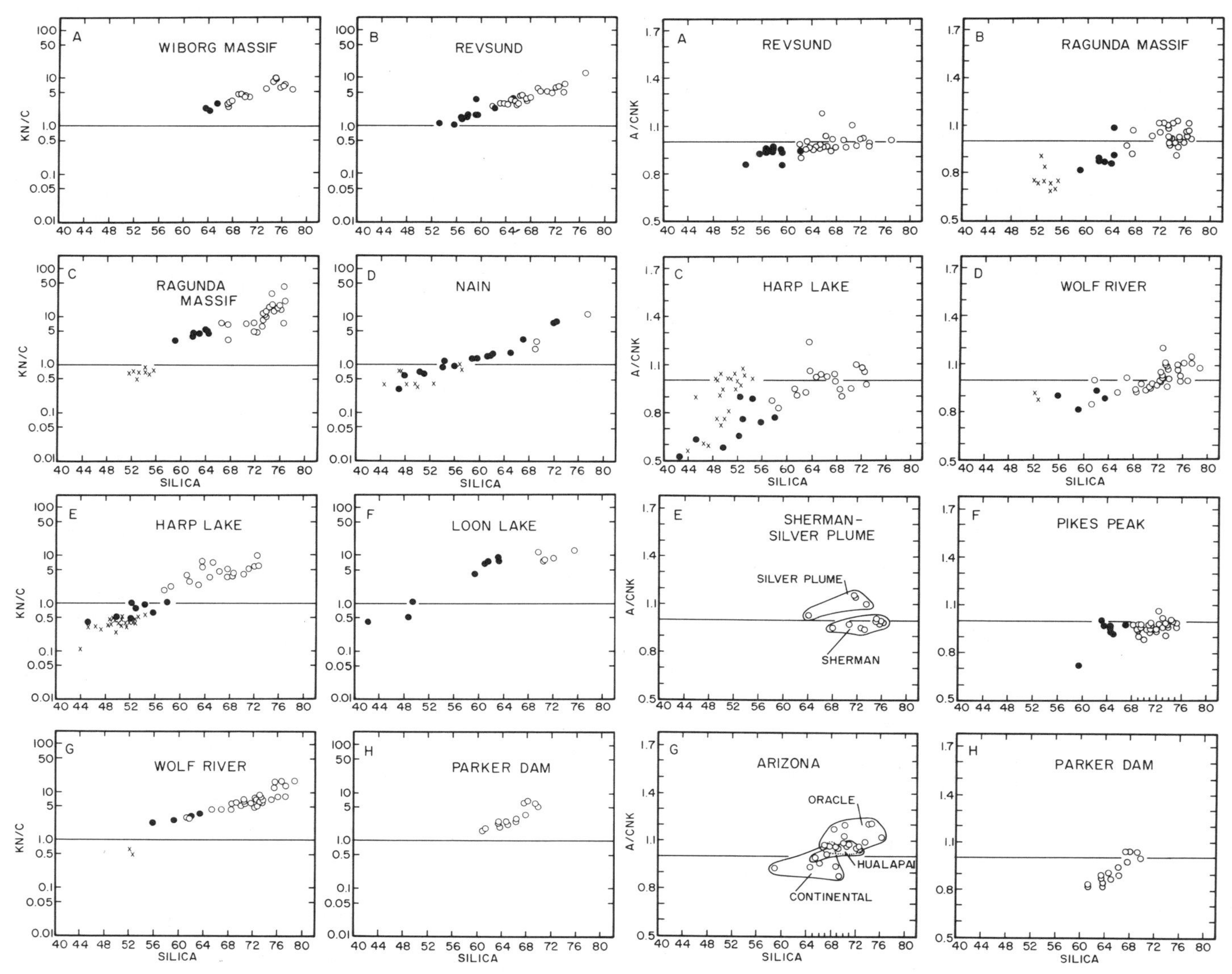

Figure 8. $(K_2O + Na_2O)/CaO$ (KN/C) and SiO_2 data from selected Proterozoic anorogenic complexes: a. Wiborg (Fin.), b. Revsund-Sorvik (Swed.), c. Ragunda (Swed.), d. Nain (Lab.), e. Harp Lake (Lab.), f. Loon Lake (Ont.), g. Wolf River (Wis.), h. Parker Dam (Calif.). Peacock index = SiO_2 where $(K_2O + NaO)/CaO$ equals unity. All data are in weight percent and symbols are as in Figure 7. Sources of data are as noted in Figure 7 and Table 2.

Figure 9. $Al_2O_3/(CaO + Na_2O + K_2O)$ and SiO_2 data from selected Proterozoic anorogenic complexes: a. Revsund (Swed.), b. Ragunda (Swed.), c. Harp Lake (Lab.), d. Wolf River (Wis.), e. Sherman and Silver Plume (Colo.-Wyom.), f. Pikes Peak (Colo.), g. Oracle, Continental, and Hualapai (Ariz.), h. Parker Dam (Calif.). $Al_2O_3/(CaO + Na_2O + K_2O)$, or A/CNK, value greater than one for peraluminous compositions, less than one for metaluminous compositions (molecular basis). Symbols as in Figure 7. Sources of data are H. Stensrud (personal communication, 1980), Perrson (1978), and as noted in Table 2.

ratio of 0.7044 for gabbro to 0.7052-.7063 for syenite and quartz syenite to 0.7067-.7117 for fayalite granite and biotite granite.

Constraints on Magma Evolution

A central question is whether or not the rapakivi granites represent derivative melts from a mafic, mantle-derived magma, or a parent melt derived directly from fusion of crustal material. Higgins (1981) has argued for a mantle origin on the basis that the composition of anorogenic granites is too uniform to be derived from the lower crust which must in itself be heterogeneous. Barker et al. (1975) have alternatively proposed that there is a different source for each member of the anorogenic "trinity": gabbro and anorthosite from a mantle source; mangerite and syenite from a quartz-poor, granulitic lower crust source; potassic granite from a granodioritic to granitic crust with some mixing with the syenitic liquids. Emslie (1980) and Fountain et al. (1981) also argued a mantle derivation for the

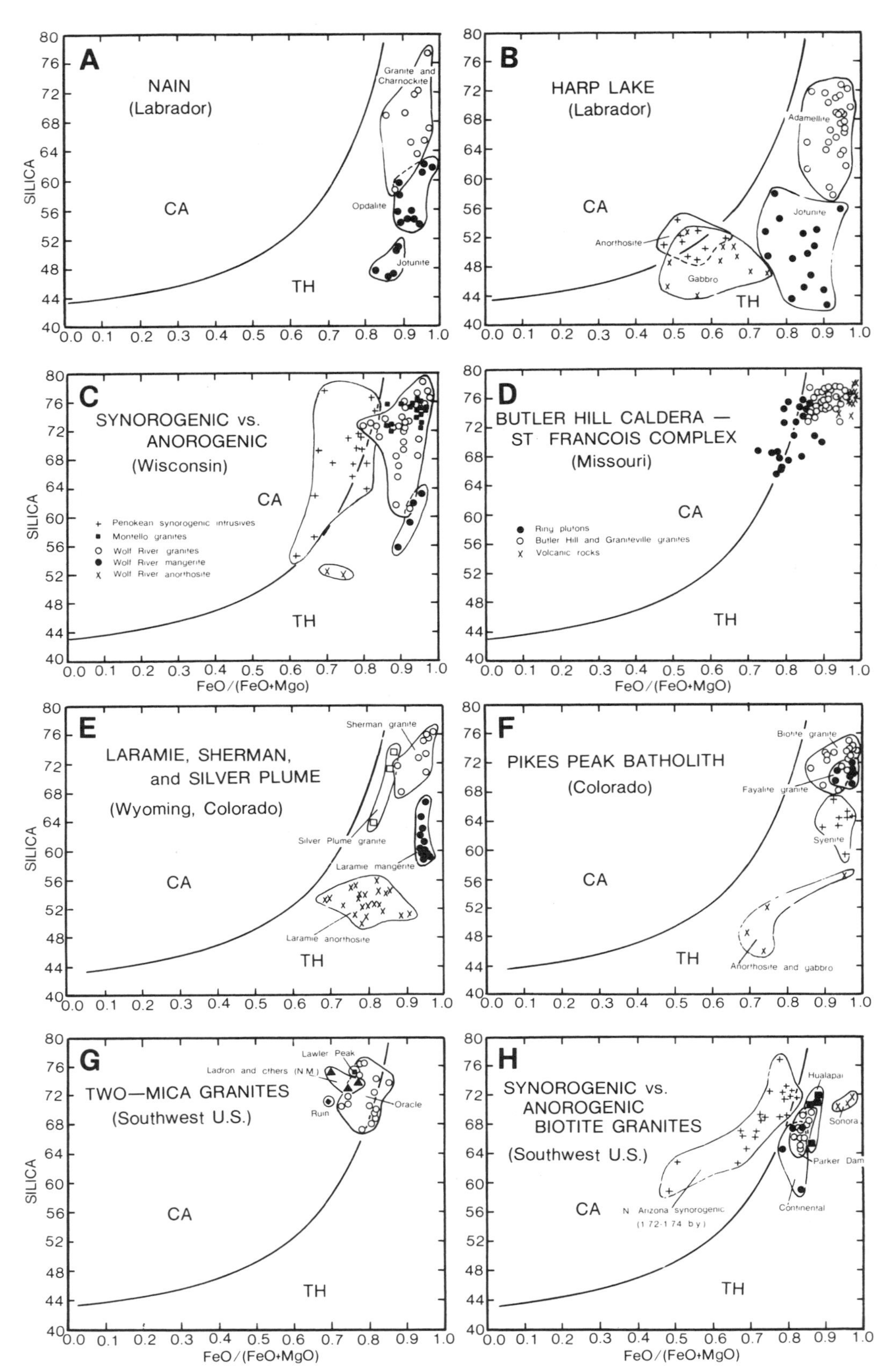

Figure 10. FeO/(FeO + MgO) and SiO_2 data from selected Proterozoic anorogenic complexes: a. Nain (Lab.), b. Harp Lake, (Lab.), c. Wolf River and Montello batholiths relative to older synorogenic (1.82 to 1.84 b.y.) granitoids (Wis.), d. St. Francois (Mo.), e. Laramie, Sherman, and Silver Plume (Wyom.-Colo.), f. Pikes Peak (Colo.), g. Two-mica granites-southwest U.S. (New Mex., Ariz.), h. Parker Dam (Calif.), Hualapai (Ariz.), Continental (Ariz.), and Caborca (Sonora) relative to older synorogenic (1.72 to 1.74 b.y.) granitoids. All Fe as FeO (wt. %). Sources of data include Koehnken (1976), Babcock et al. (1979), Volborth (1962), Stensrud (personal communication 1980) and as noted in Table 2.

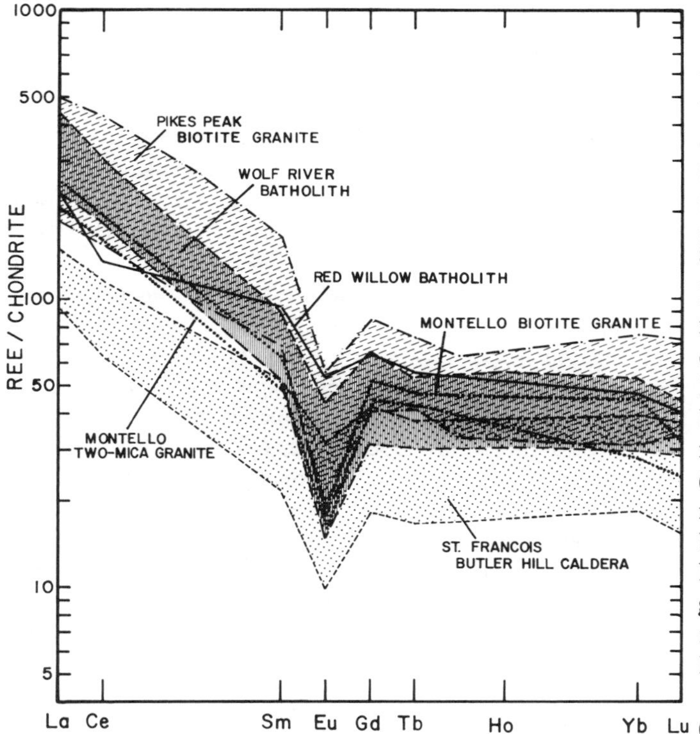

Figure 11. Rare earth element (REE) abundances of Proterozoic anorogenic granites: Biotite granite (main phase) of the Pikes Peak batholith (Barker et al., 1976), undifferentiated granite plutons of the Wolf River batholith (Anderson and Cullers, 1978), biotite and two-mica granites of the Montello batholith (Anderson et al., 1980), Red Willow batholith of Nebraska (Van Schmus et al., in prep), St. Francois complex (Cullers et al., 1981).

mafic rocks with anorthosite being formed by plagioclase accumulation from high-Al gabbroic magma. Similar to the model of Barker et al. (1975), Fountain et al (1981) further suggest, on the basis of REE data and increasing initial Sr isotope ratios, that the mangeritic liquids were produced by fusion of a quartz-poor lower crust, in this case eclogitic. They also suggest that the range of composition is due to assimilation of locally derived partial melt from adjacent gneisses. Anderson and Cullers (1978), Anderson et al. (1980), and Cullers et al. (1981) have argued that the elemental and isotopic composition of granites from the Wolf River batholith, Montello batholith, and the St. Francois complex, respectively, are compatible with small degrees of fusion (10 to 30 percent) of a quartz dioritic to granodioritic crustal source. The predicted source composition matches well the synorogenic, calc-alkaline metaigneous rocks that comprise much of the host Proterozoic terrains for these batholiths.

It seems certain that the anorogenic trinity represents a complex, yet cogenetic system. The genetic relationship, however, does not seem to be one of a comagmatic lineage but rather successive melting events originating in the mantle and passing upwards into the crust. As for the granitic magmas, the involvement of a significant crustal component in their source seems mandatory. An exception may be the small volumes of riebeckite or hornblende granite which, for the Pikes Peak batholith (Barker et al., 1975); and the Ragunda massif (Kornfalt, 1976), form a sodic and iron-enriched series that is separate from the more voluminous potassic granites and on trend with the associated syenitic or mangeritic rocks (Fig. 12). Although the initial $^{87}Sr/^{86}Sr$ ratio of most anorogenic granites is relatively low, this need not be a reflection of a mantle origin and, in fact, is that expected from the combination of short residence time and the low radiogenic nature of the mid-Proterozoic crust that host all of these anorogenic batholiths. Only the more radiogenic, metasedimentary rocks, such as the Idaho Springs Formation of Colorado (Peterman et al., 1968), would yield granitic magmas with ratios too high. Further isotopic confirmation has recently been provided by the Nd-Sm studies of DePaolo (1981) and Nelson and DePaolo (1982) who conclude that the anorogenic granites from the midcontinent, Wyoming, and Colorado are derived from heterogeneous Proterozoic crust having a model age of 1.8 b.y.

According to Loiselle and Wones (1979), Chappell (1979), and Collins et al. (1982), a crustal source for anorogenic granites should have been previously melted, which is

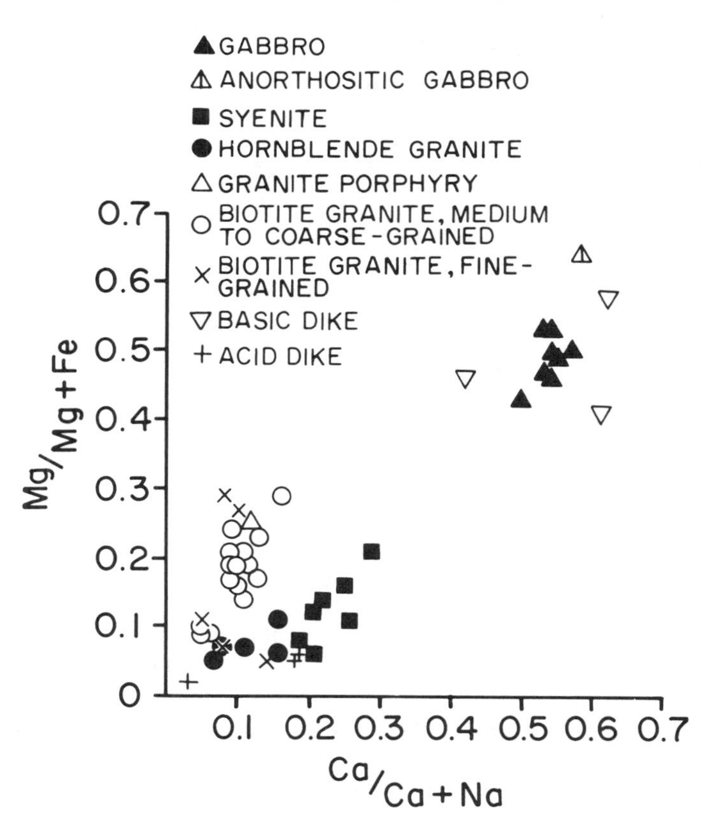

Figure 12. Atomic ratios for Mg/Mg + Fe versus Ca/Ca + Na for the two suites of the Ragunda Rapakivi massif (Sweden). From Kornfalt (1976).

to account for the dry nature of the magmas. This residual source, depleted in silica and many incompatible elements, is more appropriate for the generation of quartz-poor, mangeritic liquids (Dostal, 1975; Barker et al., 1975). For these granites, an alternative is a tonalitic to granodioritic metaigneous source. The latter has a total water budget of less than 1 percent which will largely be retained upon melting by the relatively stable hydrous phases. The amount of resultant vapor-undersaturated fusion is not expected to be large due to the large ΔT (~200°C) between that of the solidus and the disappearance of the less refractory phases including quartz, alkali feldspar, and biotite. Hence, the derived liquid will not be displaced far from a minimum melt composition and can be expected to be uniformly potassic, iron-enriched, with high total REE despite moderate variations in source composition. This conclusion is in direct contrast to that of Higgins (1981). The marginally peraluminous composition of anorogenic granites could be derived from partial melting of a calc-alkaline, metaluminous source (I-type of Chappell and White, 1974) if hornblende, clinopyroxene, and/or apatite constitute part of the residuum, which is in keeping with the rare earth models of Anderson and Cullers (1978), Anderson et al. (1980), and Cullers et al. (1981). In addition, a few granites may require some component of metasedimentary material in their source, such as proposed for plutons of the Taum Sauk Caldera, St. Francois Mountains (Cullers et al., 1981); a metasedimentary contribution, coupled with a greater amount of H_2O and melting, may aid in accounting for the composition of the more strongly peraluminous anorogenic granites (e.g., Silver Plume, Ladron, Oracle) which seem to have lower K/Na and Fe/Mg ratios and lower total REE.

Hence, anorogenic granites are likely primary magmas and are not part of a comagmatic series with anorthosite and mangerite. Differentiation within these plutons is possible, the result being a residual leucocratic derivative also of granite composition. Numerous anorogenic plutons seem to lack significant internal differentiation. Where differentiation has been identified, the changes in the trace element chemistry are striking. Although trends within the Redskin granite of the Pikes Peak batholith (Ludington, 1981) have been related to thermogravitational diffusion, most quantified differentiation models for these anorogenic granites (Anderson and Cullers, 1978; Anderson et al., 1980; Cullers et al., 1981) account for the observed changes by fractional crystallization. The changes in major elements, including possible increases or decreases in alumina saturation, and Rb, Sr, Ba, and Eu/Eu* seem to be principally controlled by the removal of alkali feldspar, plagioclase, biotite, and muscovite or hornblende. The other REE, however, which have been noted to be both enriched or depleted during fractionation, are strongly influenced by the role of the various accessory minerals, specifically allanite, zircon, sphene, and apatite.

CONCLUSIONS AND TECTONIC SIGNIFICANCE

The Proterozoic anorogenic granites of North America represent an unusual stage of cratonic development involving widely scattered batholithic intrusions. As part of an anorogenic "trinity" with anorthosite and mangeritic magmatism, the granites possess numerous compositional traits that set them apart from the older orogenic terrains they commonly intrude. Although small volumes of granite may be the result of fractionation from the mangeritic series, most of the large granite batholiths formed from fusion of the lower crust. The source material, formed during preceding Proterozoic orogenic episodes, contains large amounts of calc-alkaline, synorogenic granitoids (I-type). As a consequence of the low water content of the metaigneous source, the amount of fusion was small (20 ± 10 percent), thus accounting for the potassic, iron-rich, minimum melt composition that so well characterizes most anorogenic batholiths. Most of the granites are marginally peraluminous, a possible consequence of a clinopyroxene or hornblende-bearing residue resulting from the fusion. The low initial Sr isotopic ratios are the result of short residence times and/or the nonradiogenic character of the crustal source. A few of the anorogenic granites are markedly peraluminous, particularly in the western and southwestern United States. These rocks may contain both biotite and muscovite; some have high initial Sr ratios and are not as potassic or iron-rich. They may reflect a metasedimentary component in the source, slightly higher degrees of partial melting, and a changing character of the lower crust in these regions. These anorogenic granite magmas, due to their dry nature, were able to intrude into the upper levels of the crust (P_{total} <2 kb) with the shallower plutons yielding volcanic activity (e.g., St. Francois and Montello batholiths). Crystallization of the granites occurred at the temperature range of 640 to 790°C and over a wide range of oxygen fugacity which is reflected in their Fe-Ti oxide mineralogy, mineral chemistry, and crystallization sequence.

The generation of these isolated batholithic complexes must involve a tectonic setting quite different from that responsible for the older orogenic terrain into which they have intruded. It is well recognized that the latter involve igneous suites quite akin to those forming in margin-related settings today. Bickford et al (1981) and Van Schmus and Bickford (1981) have attempted to relate the 1.41 to 1.49 b.y. and the 1.34 to 1.41 b.y. anorogenic events to the preceding orogenic episodes by having them form in response to heating and partial melting within a tectonically thickened crust. The evidence for tectonic thickening is not apparent; however, Van Schmus and Bickford are attracted to this model by a supposed absence of mantle-derived igneous activity and the lack of older crust in the southern midcontinent region. There are several problems with this model: (1) significant anorogenic magmatism in North

America did not occur until all three of the preceding orogenic crustal provinces (Fig. 1) had formed; (2) the 1.41 to 1.49 anorogenic belt is not contained within one crustal province but rather cuts across all three provinces; (3) the anorogenic granite plutonism represents a clear break in tectonic style, composition, and age from the preceding orogenic igneous activity—the transition of which involved minimum magmatic gaps ranging from 170 m.y. (southeast Arizona to the central midcontinent) to 250 m.y. (southern California to Colorado) and 335 m.y. (Lake Superior region to Labrador); and (4) coeval mafic rocks, in the form of anorthosite, gabbro, or diabase dike swarms, do in fact occur from Labrador to Wyoming and Colorado. In view of the existing petrologic evidence that the mafic plutonic rocks crystallize at depths greater than that of the granites, their apparent absence in the southwestern United States may simply be an artifact of the depth of erosion.

Hence, the Proterozoic anorogenic igneous activity of North America cannot be related tectonically to the preceding orogenic episodes. Mantle-derived magmas were apparently involved and, in fact, provide the best mechanism for generation of the crustal fusion. The most appropriate tectonic regime must be one that allows some form of mantle diapirism. Both Anderson and Cullers (1978) and Emslie (1978) have noted the similarity of the anorogenic granites to the kinds of rocks found in extensional settings.

The 1.4 to 1.5 b.y. event does not seem to have the consistent age progression of a track and is probably an incipient rift that was aborted at an early prerift stage due to a failure to integrate into a world-wide plate system. Its overall dimensions are not unlike the presently developing east Africa rift system. This event may relate to the proposed rifting of western North America 1.4 to 1.5 b.y. ago (Burchfiel and Davis, 1975; Burke and Dewey, 1973), the main evidence of which are numerous epicratonic and aulacogenic(?) sedimentary troughs (Belt Group and equivalent strata) that were initiated at this time. At a more advanced stage, the 1.0 to 1.1 b.y. rocks defining the midcontinent gravity high must certainly represent an incipient rift that failed. The isolated granite complexes of this age (Pikes Peak, Enchanted Rock, Red Bluff) as well as the earlier 1.76 b.y. and 1.34 to 1.40 b.y. anorogenic events may be further representations of thermal perturbations at mantle depths during this fragile period of crustal "stability."

ACKNOWLEDGMENTS

The author wishes to thank Gordon Medaris for the invitation to participate in the symposium out of which this paper was produced. This paper represents the culmination of research spread over the past ten years; at various stages, this work has been supported by the Wisconsin Alumni Foundation (U. of Wisconsin), the Rudolf C. Foss Endowment for Mineralogical Research (U. of Southern California), and NSF grants EAR77-09695 and EAR-8120880. Critical reviews by Fred Barker, Pat Bickford, E. R. Brooks, Bob Cullers, and Warren Thomas and discussions with Ed DeWitt and Paul Sims greatly improved the final draft of this manuscript. Stan Keith and Harold Stensrud generously provided unpublished compositional data for anorogenic granites of Arizona. Lastly, the efforts of Sharon Wallace, who skillfully typed all versions of this manuscript, are sincerely appreciated.

REFERENCES CITED

Abbott, R. N., Jr., 1978, Peritectic reactions in the system An-Ab-Or-Qz-H_2O: Canadian Mineralogist, v. 16, p. 245–256.

Anderson, J. L., 1980, Mineral equilibria and crystallization conditions in the late Precambrian Wolf River rapakivi massif, Wisconsin: American Journal of Science, v. 280, p. 289–332.

Anderson, J. L., and Cullers, R. L., 1978, Geochemistry and evolution of the Wolf River batholith, a late Precambrian rapkivi massif in North Wisconsin, USA: Precambrian Research, v. 7, p. 287–324.

Anderson, J. L., Cullers, R. L., and Van Schmus, W. R., 1980, Anorogenic metaluminous and peraluminous granite plutonism in the mid Proterozoic of Wisconsin, U.S.A.: Contributions to Mineralogy and Petrology, v. 74, p. 311–328.

Anderson, J. L., Davis, G. A., and Frost, E. G., 1979, Field Guide to regional Miocene detachment faulting and early Tertiary(?) mylonitic terrains in the Colorado River trough, southeastern California and western Arizona: *in* Geologic Excursions in the Southern California Area (P. L. Abbott, ed.), San Diego State University, p. 109–133.

Anderson, T. H., and Silver, L. T., 1977, U-Pb isotope ages of granitic plutons near Cananea, Sonora: Economic Geology, v. 72, p. 827–836.

Babcock, R. S., Brown, E. H., Clarke, M. D., and Livingston, D. E., 1979, Geology of the older Precambrian rocks of the Grand Canyon Part II. The Zoraster Plutonic Complex and related rocks: Precambrian Research, v. 8, p. 243–275.

Barker, F., Hedge, C. E., Millard, H. T., O'Neil, J. R., 1976, Pikes Peak batholith: Geochemistry of some minor elements and isotopes and implications for magma genesis: *in* Epis, R. C., and Weimer, R. J., eds., Professional Contributions of the Colorado School of Mines, no. 8, p. 44–53.

Barker, F., Wones, D. R., Sharp, W. N., and Desborough, G. A., 1975, The Pikes Peak batholith, Colorado Front Range, and a model for the origin of the gabbro-anorthosite-syenite-potassic granite suite: Precambrian Research, v. 2, p. 97–160.

Berg, J. H., 1977, Regional geobarometry in the contact aureoles of the anorthositic Nain Complex, Labrador: Journal of Petrology, v. 18, p. 399–430.

Bickford, M. E., and Cudzilo, T. F., 1975, U-Pb age of zircon from Vernal Mesa-type quartz monzonite, Unaweep Canyon, west-central Colorado: Geological Society of America Bulletin 86, p. 1432–1434.

Bickford, M. E., Harrower, K. L., Hoppe, W. J., Nelson, B. K., Nusbaum, R. L., and Thomas, J. J., 1981, Rb-Sr and U-Pb geochronology and distribution of rock types in the Precambrian basement of Missouri and Kansas: Geological Society of America Bulletin, Part I, v. 92, p. 323–341.

Bickford, M. E., and Lewis, R. D., 1979, U-Pb geochronology of exposed basement rocks in Oklahoma: Geological Society of America Bulletin 90, p. 540–544.

Bickford, M. E., and Mose, D. G., 1975, Geochronology of Precambrian rocks in the St. Francis Mountains, southeastern Missouri: Geologi-

cal Society of America Special Paper 165, p. 48.
Bickford, M. E., Sides, J. R., and Cullers, R. L., 1981, Chemical evolution of magmas in the igneous terrane of the St. Francois Mountains, Mo., Part I: Field, petrographic, and major element data, Journal of Geophysical Research, v. 86, p. 10365–10386.
Bickford, M. E., Van Schmus, W. R., and Zietz, I., 1981, Interpretation of Proterozoic basement in the midcontinent: Geological Society of America Abstracts with Programs, v. 13, no. 7, p. 410.
Bickford, M. E., Wetherill, G. W., Barker, F., and Lee-Huh, C. N., 1969, Precambrian Rb-Sr chronology in the Needle Mountains, southwestern Colorado: Journal of Geophysical Research, v. 74, p. 1660–1676.
Bohlen, S. R., and Essene, E. J., 1978, Igneous pyroxenes from metamorphosed anorthosite massifs: Contributions to Mineralogy and Petrology, v. 65, p. 433–442.
Brand, S. R., 1976, Geochemical and petrological relations of anorthositic and charnockitic rocks in the Nain Complex, Labrador: Geological Society of America Abstracts with Programs, v. 8, p. 789.
Bridgwater, D., and Windley, B. F., 1973, Anorthosites, post-orogenic granites, acid volcanic rocks and crustal development in the North Atlantic Shield during the mid-Proterozoic: Geological Society of South Africa Special Publication 3, p. 307–317.
Brookins, D. G., Bolton, W. R., Condie, K. C., 1980, Rb-Sr isochron ages of four Precambrian igneous rock units from south central New Mexico: Isochron/west, v. 29, p. 31–37.
Burchfiel, B. C., and Davis, G. A., 1975, Nature and controls of Cordilleran orogenesis, western United States: Extensions of an earlier synthesis, American Journal of Science, v. 275A, p. 363–396.
Burke, K., and Dewey, J. F., 1973, Plume-generated triple junctions: Key indicators in applying plate tectonics to old rocks: Journal of Geology, v. 81, p. 406–433.
Card, K. D., 1965, The Croker Island complex, Ontario Department of Mines, GC 14, p. 11.
Chappell, B. W., 1979, Granites as images of their source rocks: Geological Society of America Abstracts with Programs, v. 11, p. 400.
Chappell, B. W., and White, A.J.R., 1974, Two contrasting granite types: Pacific Geology, v. 8, p. 173–174.
Chase, C. G., and Gilmer, T. H., 1973, Precambrian plate tectonics—the midcontinent gravity high: Earth Planetary Science Letters, v. 21, p. 70–78.
Collins, W. J., Beams, S. D., White, A.J.R., and Chappell, B. W., 1982, Nature and origin of A-type granites with particular reference to southeastern Australia: Contributions to Mineralogy and Petrology, v. 80, p. 189–200.
Condie, K. C., and Budding, A. J., 1979, Geology and geochemistry of Precambrian rocks, central and south-central New Mexico: New Mexico Bureau of Mines and Mineral Resources, Memoir 35, p. 59.
Cullers, R. L., Koch, R., and Bickford, M. E., 1981, Chemical evolution of magmas in the igneous terrane of the St. Francois Mountains, Mo., Part II, trace element evidence: Journal of Geophysical Research, v. 86, p. 10388–10401.
Czamanske, G. K., Wones, D. R., and Eichelberger, J. C., 1977, Mineralogy and petrology of the intrusive complex of the Pliney Range, New Hampshire: American Journal of Science, v. 277, p. 1073–1123.
Davis, G. A., Anderson, J. L., Frost, E. G., and Shackelford, T. J., 1980, Mylonitization and detachment faulting in the Whipple-Buckskin-Rawhide Mountains terrane, southeastern California and western Arizona *in* Davis, G. H., Coney, P. J., Crittenden, M., eds., Metamorphic Core Complexes, Geological Society of America Memoir 153, p. 79–129.
Davis, G. A., Anderson, J. L., Martin, D. L., Krummenacher, D., Frost, E. G., and Armstrong, R. L., 1982, Geologic and geochronologic relations in the lower plate of the Whipple detachment fault, Whipple Mountains, southeastern, California: A progress report: *in* Mesozoic-Cenozoic Tectonic Evolution of the Colorado River region, Arizona, California and Nevada (E. Frost, D. Martin, T. Cameron, eds.), p. 409–432.
DePaolo, D. J., 1981, Neodymium isotopes in the Colorado Front Range and crust-mantle evolution in the Proterozoic: Nature, v. 21, p. 193–196.
De Waard, D., 1976, Anorthosite-adamellite-troctolite layering in the Barth Island structure of the Nain Complex, Labrador: Lithos, v. 9, p. 293–308.
De Waard, D., and Wheeler, E. P., 1971, Chemical and petrologic trends in anorthositic and associated rocks of the Nain Massif, Labrador: Lithos, v. 4, p. 367–380.
Doe, B. R., and Pearson, R. C., 1969, U-Th-Pb chronology of zircons from the St. Kevin granite, Northern Sawatch Range, Colorado: Geological Society of America Bulletin 80, p. 2495–2502.
Dostal, J., 1975, Geochemistry and petrology of the Loon Lake Pluton, Ontario: Canadian Journal of Earth Science, v. 13, p. 1331–1345.
Eggler, D. H., 1968, Virginia Dale Precambrian Ring Dike Complex, Colorado-Wyoming: Geological Society of America Bulletin, v. 79, p. 1545–1564.
Emslie, R. F., 1978, Anorthosite massifs, rapakivi granites, and late Proterozoic rifting of North America: Precambrian Research, v. 7, p. 61–98.
——1980, Geology and petrology of the Harp Lake Complex, central Labrador: an example of Elsonian magmatism, Geological Survey Canadian Memoir 293, 136 p.
Flanagan, F. J., 1973, 1972 values for international geochemical reference samples: Geochimica et Cosmochimica Acta, v. 37, p. 1189–1200.
Fountain, J. C., Hodge, D. S., and Hills, F. A., 1981, Geochemistry and petrogenesis of the Laramie anorthosite complex, Wyoming: Lithos, v. 14, p. 113–132.
Garrison, J. R., 1981, Coal Creek serpentinite, Llano uplift, Texas: A fragment of an incomplete Precambrian ophiolite: Geology, v. 9, p. 225–230.
Garrison, J. R., Long, L. E., and Richmond, D. L., 1979, Rb-Sr and K-Ar geochronologic and isotopic studies, Llano uplift, Central Texas: Contributions to Mineralogy and Petrology, v. 69, p. 361–374.
Green, J. C., 1972, Field trip guide book for Precambrian North Shore volcanic group northeastern Minnesota: Minnesota Geological Survey, University of Minnesota, St. Paul, 36 p.
Gulson, B. L., and Krogh, T. E., 1975, Evidence of multiple intrusion, possible resetting of U-Pb ages, and new crystallization of zircons in the post-tectonic intrusions ("Rapakivi granites") and gneisses from south Greenland: Geochimica Cosmochimica Acta, v. 39, p. 65–82.
Hansen, W. R., 1964, Curecanti pluton, an unusual intrusive body in the Black Canyon of the Gunnison, Colorado: U.S. Geological Survey Bulletin 1181-D, p. D1-D15.
Hansen, W. R., and Peterman, Z. E., 1968, Basement rock geochronology of the Black Canyon of the Gunnison, Colorado, in Geological Survey Research 1968: U.S. Geological Survey Professional Paper 660-C, p. C80–C90.
Heaman, L. M., Shieh, Y., McNutt, R. H., and Shaw, D. M., 1982, Isotopic and trace element study of the Loon Lake pluton, Grenville Province, Ontario: Canadian Journal of Earth Sciences, v. 19, p. 1045–1054.
Hedge, C. E., 1970, Whole Rock Rb-Sr age of the Pikes Peak Batholith, Colorado: U.S. Geological Survey Professional Paper 700–B, p. 86–89.
Hedge, C. E., Peterman, Z. E., and Braddock, W. A., 1967, Age of major Precambrian regional metamorphism in the northern Front Range, Colorado: Geological Society of America Bulletin, 78, p. 551–557.
Hedge, C. E., Peterman, Z. E., Case, J. E., and Obradovich, J. D., 1968, Precambrian geochronology of the northwestern Uncompahgre Plateau: in Geological Survey research 1968, U.S. Geological Survey Professional Paper 600–C, p. C91–C96.

Hibbard, M. J., 1981, A magma-mixing origin of mantled feldspars: Geological Society of America Abstracts with Programs, v. 13, no. 3, p. 61.

Higgins, M. D., 1981, Origin of acidic anorogenic rocks, crust or mantle?' EOS, v. 62, no. 17, p. 437.

Hills, F. A., and Armstrong, R. L., 1974, Geochronology of Precambrian rocks in the Laramie Range and implications for the tectonic framework of Precambrian southern Wyoming: Precambrian Research, 1, p. 213–225.

Hubbard, H. A., 1975, Lower Keweenawan volcanic rocks of Michigan and Wisconsin: U.S. Geological Survey Journal of Research 3, p. 529–541.

Hutchinson, R. M., 1956, Structure and petrology of Enchanted Rock batholith, Llano and Gillespie Counties, Texas: Geological Society of America Bulletin, v. 67, p. 763–806.

Irvine, T. N., and Baragar, W.R.A., 1971, A guide to the chemical composition of the common volcanic rocks: Canadian Journal of Earth Sciences, v. 8, p. 523–548.

Ishihara, S., 1977, The magnetite-series and ilmenite-series granitic rocks: Mining Geology, v. 27, p. 293–305.

Keith, S. B., Reynolds, S. J., Damon, P. E., Shafiqullah, M., Livingston, D. E., and Pushkar, P. D., 1980, Evidence for multiple intrusion and deformation within the Santa Catalina-Rincon-Tortolita crystalline complex, southeastern Arizona: Geological Society of America Memoir 153, p. 217–267.

Kessler, E. J., 1976, Rb-Sr geochronology and trace element geochemistry of Precambrian rocks in the northern Hualapai Mountains, Mojave County, Arizona [M.S. Thesis]: Tucson, University of Arizona, 73 p.

Kisvarsanyi, E. B., 1972, Petrochemistry of a Precambrian igneous province, St. Francis Mountains, Missouri: Missouri Geological Survey Water Resource Report Investigation 51, 103 p.

Koehnken, P. J., 1976, Petrology of anorthosites from two localities in northwestern Sonora, Mexico [M.S. thesis]: Los Angeles, University of Southern California, 97 p.

Kornfalt, Karl-Axel, 1976, Petrology of the Ragunda rapakivi massif, central Sweden: Sveriges Geologiska Unders Okning C-725, p. 1–111.

Kranck, E. H., 1968, Anorthosites and rapakivi, magmas from the lower crust: *in* Y. W. Isachsen, ed., Origin of Anorthosite and related rocks, N. Y. State Museum of Science Service Memoir, v. 18, p. 93–98.

Krogh, T. E., and Davis, G. L., 1973, The significance of inherited zircons on the age and origin of igneous rocks—an investigation of the Labrador adamellites: Carnegie Institution Washington Yearbook, v. 72, p. 610–613.

Lanphere, M. A., 1964, Geochronologic studies in the eastern Mojave Desert, California: Journal of Geology, v. 72, p. 381–399.

Lanphere, M. A., Wasserburg, G.J.F., Albee, A. L., and Tilton, G. R., 1964, Redistribution of strontium and rubidium isotopes during metamorphism, World Beater Complex, Panamint Range, California: *in* Craig, H., Miller, S. L., Wasserburg, G. J., (eds.), Isotopic and Cosmic Chemistry, North Holland Pub. Co., p. 269–320.

Leake, B. E., 1978, Nomenclature of amphiboles: Canadian Miineralogist, v. 16, p. 501–520.

Loiselle, M. C., and Wones, D. R., 1979, Characteristics and origin of anorogenic granites: Geological Society of America Abstracts with Programs, v. 11, no. 7, p. 468.

Lowell, G. R., and Sides, J. R., 1973, The occurrence and origin of rapakivi granite in the St. Francois Mountains Batholith of southeast Missouri: Geological Society of America Abstracts with Programs, v. 5, no. 4, p. 332–333.

Ludington, S., 1981, The Redskin Granite: Evidence for thermogravitational diffusion in a Precambrian Granite Batholith: Journal of Geophysical Research, v. 86, p. 10423–10430.

Luth, W. C., 1969, The systems $NaAlSi_3O_8$-SiO_2 and $KAlSi_3O_8$-SiO_2 to 20 kb and the relationship between H_2O content, P_{H_2O} and P_{total} in granitic magmas: American Journal of Science, v. 267A, p. 325–341.

Maaloe, S., and Wyllie, P. J., 1975, Water content of a granite magma deduced from the sequence of crystallization determined experimentally with water-saturated conditions: Contributions to Mineralogy and Petrology, v. 52, p. 175–191.

MacLeod, W. N., Turner, D. C., and Wright, E. P., 1971, The geology of the Jos Plateau: General geology: Geological Survey of Nigeria Bulletin 32, v. 1, 110 p.

Manning, D.A.C., 1981, The effect of fluorine on liquidus phase relationships in the system Qz-Ab-Or with excess water at 1 kb: Contributions to Mineralogy and Petrology, v. 76, p. 206–215.

Marchand, M., and Crocket, J. H., 1974, The Mistastin Lake pluton and meteorite crater, northern Labrador: Geological Association of Canada, Program Abstracts, p. 58–59.

McCutcheon, T. J., 1981, The petrology of the late Precambrian granites in the northern Franklin Mountains: Geological Society of America Abstracts with Programs, v. 13, p. 242.

Miyashiro, A., 1974, Volcanic rock series in island arcs and active continental margins: American Journal of Science, v. 274, p. 321–355.

Morse, S. A., 1982, A partisan review of Proterozoic anorthosites: American Mineralogist, v. 67, p. 1087–1100.

Mose, D. G., and Bickford, M. E., 1969, Precambrian geochronology in the Unaweep Canyon, West-Central Colorado: Journal of Geophysical Research, v. 74, p. 1677–1687.

Muehlberger, W. R., Hedge, C. E., Denison, R. E., and Marvin, R. F., 1966, Geochronology of the midcontinent region, United States. Part 3, Southern area: Journal of Geophysical Research, 72, p. 5409–5426.

Mukhopadhyay, B., Brookins, D. G., and Bolivar, S. L., 1975, Rb-Sr whole rock study of the Precambrian rocks of the Pedernal Hills, New Mexico: Earth and Planetary Science Letters, v. 27, p. 283–286.

Nelson, B. K., and DePaolo, D. J., 1982, Crust formation age of the North American Midcontinent: Geological Society of America Abstracts with Programs, v. 14, no. 7, p. 575.

Peacock, M. A., 1931, Classification of igneous rocks: Journal of Geology, v. 39, p. 54–67.

Persson, L., 1978, The Revsund-Sorvik granites in the western parts of the province of Angermanland central Sweden: Sveriges Geologiska Undersokning, Series C, no. 741, 59 p.

Peterman, Z. E., Doe, B. R., and Bartel, A., 1967, Data on the rock GSP-1 (granodiorite) and the isotope-dilution method of analysis for Rb and Sr, in Geological Survey Research 1967: U.S. Geological Survey Professional Paper 575–B, p. B181–B186.

Peterman, Z. E., and Hedge, C. E., 1968, Chronology of Precambrian events in the Front Range, Colorado: Canadian Journal of Earth Sciences, v. 5, p. 749–756.

Peterman, Z. E., Hedge, C. E., and Braddock, W. A., 1968, Age of Precambrian events in the northeastern Front Range, Colorado: Journal of Geophysical Research, v. 73, no. 6, p. 2277–2296.

Registrar, M. E., and Brookins, D. G., 1979, Geochronologic and rare-earth study of the Embudo Granite and related rocks: New Mexico Geological Society Guidebook, 30th Field Conf., Santa Fe Country, p. 155–158.

Robertson, J. K., and Wyllie, P. J., 1971, Rock-water system, with special reference to the water-deficient region, American Journal of Science, v. 271, p. 252–277.

Sahama, T.L.G., 1948, On the chemistry of the east Fennoscandian rapakivi granites: Finland Comm. Geology Bulletin, v. 136, p. 15–65.

Savolahti, A., 1962, The rapakivi problem and the rules of idiomorphism in minerals: Bulletin Comm. Geology Finlande, v. 204, p. 33–111.

Sederholm, J. J., 1928, On orbicular granites: Bulletin Comm. Geology Finlande, v. 83, 105 p.

Seyfert, C. K., 1980, Paleomagnetic evidence in support of a middle Proterozoic (Helikian) collision between North America and Gondwanaland as a cause of the metamorphism and deformation in the Adirondacks: Geological Society of America Bulletin, Part I, v. 91, p. 118–120.

Shakel, D. W., Silver, L. T., and Damon, P. E., 1977, Observations on the history of the gneissic core complex, Santa Catalina Mountains, southern Arizona: Geological Society of America Abstracts with Programs, v. 9, p. 1169–1170.

Shand, S. J., 1927, The eruptive rocks: New York, John Wiley & Sons, 488 p.

Silver, L. T., 1968, Precambrian batholiths of Arizona: Geological Society of America Special Paper, v. 121, p. 558–559.

—— 1978, Precambrian formations and Precambrian history in Cochise County, southeastern Arizona: *in* Callendar, J. F., Wilt, J. C., and Clemons, R. E., Land of Cochise, New Mexico Geological Society, 29th Field Conference Guidebook, p. 157–163.

—— 1982, Evolution of crystalline rock terrains of the Transverse Ranges, southern California: Geological Society of America Abstracts with Programs, v. 14, no. 4, p. 234.

Silver, L. T., Anderson, C. A., Crittenden, M., and Robertson, J. M., 1977a, Chronostratigraphic elements of the Precambrian rocks of the southwestern and far western United States: Geological Society of America Abstracts with Programs, v. 9, no. 7, p. 1176.

Silver, L. T., and Barker, F., 1967, Geochronology of Precambrian rocks of the Needle Mountains, Southwestern Colorado: Pt. I., U-Pb zircon results [abs.]: Geological Society of America, Abstract for 1967, Special Paper 115, p. 204–205.

Silver, L. T., Bickford, M. E., Van Schmus, W. R., Anderson, J. L., Anderson, T. H., and Medaris, L. G., Jr., 1977b, The 1.4-1.5 b.y. transcontinental anorogenic plutonic perforation of North America: Geological Society of America Abstracts with Programs, v. 9, no. 7, p. 1176–1177.

Silver, L. T., and McKinney, C. R., 1962, U-Pb isotope age studies of a Precambrian granite, Marble Mountains, San Bernardino County, California: Geological Society of America Special Paper, v. 73, p. 65.

Silver, L. T., Williams, I. S., and Woodhead, J. A., 1981, Uranium in granites from the southwestern United States: Actinide parent-daughter system, sites, and mobilization: U.S. Department of Energy Open File Report GJBX–45, 315 p.

Simonen, A., and Vorma, A., 1969, Amphibole and biotite from rapakivi: Bulletin Comm. Geology, Finlande, v. 238, 28 p.

Smith, D., 1974, Pyroxene-olivine-quartz assemblages in rocks associated with the Nain Anorthosite massif, Labrador: Journal of Petrology, v. 15, p. 58–78.

Steiger, R. H., and Jager, E., 1977, Subcommission on Geochronology: Convention on the use of decay constants in geo- and cosmochronology: Earth Planetary Science Letter 36, p. 359–362.

Steiger, R. H., and Wasserburg, G. J., 1966, Systematics in the Pb^{208}-Th^{232}, $Pb^{201}U^{235}$, and $Pb^{206}U^{238}$ systems: Journal of Geophysical Research, v. 71, p. 6065–6068.

Stephenson, N.C.N., and Hensel, H. D., 1978, A Precambrian fayalite granite from the south coast of western Australia: Lithos, v. 11, p. 209–218.

Stewart, D. B., 1959, Rapakivi granite from eastern Penobscot Bay, Main: International Geology Congress, 20th, Mexico Proc., v. 11A, p. 283–320.

Stewart, D. B., and Roseboom, E. H., 1962, Lower temperature terminations of the three phase region plagioclase-alkali feldspar-liquid: Journal of Petrology, v. 3, p. 280–315.

Stewart, J. H., and Carlson, J. E., 1978, Geologic Map of Nevada, scale 1:500,000.

Streckeisen, A., 1976, To each plutonic rock its proper name: Earth Science Review, v. 12, p. 1–33.

Subbarayudu, G. V., Hills, A. F., and Zartman, R. E., 1975, Age and Sr isotopic evidence for the origin of the Laramie anorthosite and syenite complex, Laramie range, Wyoming: Geological Society of America Abstracts with Programs, v. 7, no. 7, p. 1287.

Swan, M. M., 1976, The Stockton Pass Fault: An element of the Texas Lineament [M.S. Thesis]: Tucson, University of Arizona, 119 p.

Sylvester, P. J., and Schultz, K. J., 1980, Geology and petrology of late Precambrian mafic rocks from the St. Francois Mountains, Missouri: EOS, American Geophysical Union Transactions, v. 61, no. 48, p. 1193.

Taggert, J. E., and Brookins, D. G., 1975, Rb-Sr Whole determinations for the Sandia Granite and Cibola Gneiss, New Mexico: Isochron/West, v. 12, p. 5–8.

Tweeto, O., 1979, Geologic Map of Colorado, scale 1:500,000.

Van Schmus, W. R., 1965, The chronology of the Blind River-Bruce Mines area, Ontario, Canada: Journal of Geology, v. 73, p. 755–780.

—— 1980, Chronology of igneous rocks associated with the Penokean Orogeny in Wisconsin: Geological Society of America Special Paper 182, p. 152–168.

Van Schmus, W. R., and Bickford, M. E., 1981, Proterozoic chronology and evolution of the midcontinent region, North America: *in* Precambrian Plate Tectonics, Kroner, A., ed., New York, Elsevier, Sci. Pub. Co., p. 261–296.

Van Schmus, W. R., Card, K. D., and Harrower, K. L., 1975a, Geology and ages of buried Precambrian basement rocks, Manitoulin Island, Ontario: Canadian Journal of Earth Sciences, v. 12, p. 1175–1189.

Van Schmus, W. R., Harrower, K. L., Anderson, J. L., and Cullers, R. L., 1982, Age and composition of a rapakivi pluton from the subsurface of Nebraska and Kansas (in preparation).

Van Schmus, W. R., Hoppe, W. J., and Montgomery, C. W., 1981, Age and geologic significance of Precambrian basement samples from northern Illinois and eastern Iowa: Geological Society of America Abstracts with Programs, v. 13, no. 7, p. 572.

Van Schmus, W. R., Medaris, L. G., and Banks, P. O., 1975b, Chronology of Precambrian rocks in Wisconsin, I: The Wolf River batholith, a rapakivi massif approximately 1500 m.y. old: Geological Society of America Bulletin, v. 86, p. 907–914.

Van Schmus, W. R., Thurman, E. M., and Peterman, Z. E., 1975c, Geology and chronology of Precambrian rocks in Wisconsin, II: Rb-Sr data for the older rocks in eastern and central Wisconsin: Geological Society of America Bulletin, v. 86, p. 1255–1265.

Volborth, A., 1962, Rapakivi-type granites in the Precambrian complex of Gold Butte, Clark Co., Nevada: Geological Society of America Bulletin, v. 73, p. 813–832.

Vorma, A., 1971, Alkali feldspars of the Wiborg rapakivi massif in southeastern Finland: Bulletin Comm. Geology Finlande, v. 246, p. 1–72.

—— 1972, On the contact aureole of the Wiborg rapakivi granite massif in southeastern Finland: Geological Survey of Finland Bulletin, v. 255, p. 1–28.

White, D. L., 1978, Rb-Sr isochron ages of some Precambrian plutons in south-central New Mexico: Isochron/West, v. 21, p. 8–14.

Whitney, J. A., and Stormer, J. C., Jr., 1976, Geothermometry and geobarometry in epizonal granitic intrusions: a comparison of iron-titanium oxides and coexisting feldspars: American Mineralogist, v. 61, p. 751–761.

Wobus, R. A., and Hedge, C. E., 1980, Rb-Sr isochron age of Precambrian plutons of the San Pedro Mountains, North-central New Mexico: Isochron/West, v. 27, p. 19–25.

Wones, D. R., 1979, Intensive parameters during crystallization of granitic plutons: Geological Society of America Abstracts with Programs, v. 11, p. 543.

—— 1980, Contributions of crystallography, mineralogy, and petrology to the geology of the Lucerne pluton, Hancock County, Maine: American Mineralogist, v. 65, p. 411–437.

Manuscript Accepted by the Society April 14, 1983

Printed in U.S.A

Geological Society of America
Memoir 161
1983

Metamorphism and thermal gradients in the Proterozoic continental crust

R. St J. Lambert
Department of Geology
University of Alberta
Edmonton, Alberta T6G 2E3
Canada

ABSTRACT

There is no simple relationship between a PT point derived for a metamorphic complex from mineral assemblage and composition data and the equilibrium geotherm which may be calculated for the crust. Transient or complex geotherms of various slopes may be generated by magmatic intrusion, rapid burial, rapid uplift or tectonic thickening, or almost any combination of these processes. Proterozoic metamorphic complexes yield PT conditions ranging from about 6 kb, 600° in the Wakeham Bay area to 3-5 kb, 750° in the Bear Province and 10 kb, 980° in the Musgrave Ranges. The lowest apparent geotherms lie in linear metamorphic belts, the highest in domal regions in the NW Canadian shield, while intermediate values occur in most granulite terrains. These can be related to equilibrium surface heat flows in the range 80 to 120 mW/m^2, with mantle heat flow of about 50 mW/m^2 for reasonable crustal compositions. The higher values can be simulated by intruding sloping sill-like bodies of basic magma into the crust at depths around 20 km; the complex heat transfer equations have not yet been solved for such situations, however, and calculations are inexact. Tectonic crustal thickening and erosion can produce similar effects; but in the absence of the former, the latter can most easily be caused by continental underplating by basic magma. Gradients are generally higher than in Phanerozoic orogenic belts, and no blueschist facies rocks have yet been substantiated in pre U. Proterozoic complexes.

INTRODUCTION: THE GENERAL PROBLEM

"There are so many imponderables in the thermal properties and histories of old metamorphic terrains that it might well be held to be unprofitable to try and describe their causes."

The authors of this singularly apposite statement were actually writing about L. Paleozoic events, not Proterozoic (Richardson and Powell, 1976, p. 265). When considering the other geological extreme, the Archean, I found that metamorphism of that age was nowhere of high-pressure type, but that all other facies series were possible (Lambert, 1976). I also concluded that "we have a long way to go before we can assert that Archean metamorphic gradients were of any particular type." In the following, it will be seen that metamorphism in the Proterozoic was also not of high P/T gradient type. With far more evidence available, however, I can assert that metamorphism did occur under a specific range of conditions corresponding to equilibrium surface heat flows of 80-120 mW/m^2, probably caused in part by igneous activity.

In my earlier review (of the Archean), I found a paucity of accurate descriptions and an inadequacy in the laboratory data base. I also observed, though not specifically noted, that in most Archean complexes there is only a limited range of rock compositions, making for difficulty in reconciling observations with a detailed petrogenetic grid. These restrictions are less apparent in Proterozoic complexes, particularly since publication of Paper 78-10 of the Geological Survey of Canada. However, I have come across the following difficulties in interpreting Proterozoic events:

(i) It is often not clear whether the complex is truly Proterozoic or Archean;

(ii) Systematic errors in ages and weaknesses in their interpretation do not permit resolution of igneous and metamorphic events, as is often the case in the Phanerozoic;

(iii) Almost all Proterozoic metamorphic complexes for which good descriptions are available are exposed in two dimensions only; and

(iv) The rock types involved are often polymetamorphic gneisses of uncertain primary origin and history.

Turning next to the actual process of metamorphism and the interpretation of mineral assemblages in the light of experimental studies, there have been a number of welcome developments. In particular, the repeated application of laboratory data on systems involving MgO-Al_2O_3-SiO_2 -H_2O and other oxides has led to a much better appreciation of the problems involved. The alumino-silicate triple point has been discussed endlessly: the compromise proposal of Greenwood (1976) of 550° C and 5 kb (500 MPa) may lead to a better definition of conditions. Detailed discussions of the applicability of the experimentally determined triple points have led to the conclusion that sometimes one, sometimes another, fits best in specific areas. This conclusion leads to the suspicion, well-founded in thermodynamics ("Plague of the small ΔG's" of Fyfe, Turner, and Verhoogen, 1958, p. 22) that metastable persistence or even initial crystallization out of theoretical stability fields may be a serious problem in solid-solid systems, even when chemical zoning and textural niceties have been accurately interpreted. I feel that the role of supposedly minor solid-solution or order-disorder effects in displacing reactions or in kinetics has not yet been fully evaluated, specifically Fe, Cr, and Ti in alumino-silicates (see Greenwood, 1976, p. 218); Ca, Mn, and Cr in garnets; and Mn and $(OH)^-$ in cordierite. As these minerals are among the principal geobarometers, pressure determinations are suspect—which is true for a number of other reasons in any case (controversial experimental results and simplifications in distribution-coefficient calculations being common problems).

There remain, even supposing that appropriate mineral assemblages are available and have been properly analysed, the many and varied problems associated with the relationship of estimated PT and the actual thermal history of the complex. Richardson (1970) pointed out that one region could possess a wide range of geotherms and thence of facies series. Later it was realized that thermal inertia could be a cause of problems of interpretation, and considerable attention was given to the role of different kinds of energy sources in regional metamorphism. Richardson and Powell (1976) found that it was possible for the Dalradian L. Paleozoic metamorphism to have developed simply as a result of burial and radioactive heating plus normal equilibration to the mantle and lower crust heat flux: the steady state geotherm was a reasonable approximation. However, a transient, nonequilibrium thermal model was described in which active erosion results in the upwards displacement of the geotherm, even leading to a possible rise in temperature in a given part of the complex with time as the pressure falls. That would lead to overprinting of earlier high P/T assemblages by high T/P assemblages, and minerals may form which require higher temperature conditions than a steady-state model would predict. This problem was discussed further by England and Richardson (1977) in conjunction with the thermal effects of tectonic thickening. The combination could produce an apparent or "metamorphic" geotherm, concave towards the temperature axis. Bickle and others (1975) also discuss the effect of erosion following overthrusting, the latter having created an initial thermal perturbation because of thermal inertia (Oxburgh and Turcotte, 1974). An interesting result of the study of Bickle and others (Fig. 8d, 1975) is that uplift of 0.5 mm/a for 30 Ma will increase a 25° C/km thermal gradient by 10°/km, equivalent to an increase in surface heat flow (q_o) of 20 mW/m^2. This conclusion, though highly qualified by the simplifications and assumptions in the model, will be seen to be relevant to the discussion below.

Finally, the role of igneous intrusions as perturbers of geotherms, which has been recognized for some time, has been considered theoretically by Jaeger (1964), England and Richardson (1977), and Wells (1979). Above the level of a single intrusion, the geotherm may be expected to be convex towards the temperature axis (the same as the standard case), and relaxation may be expected to follow a roughly isobaric path in the early stages of cooling. This will result in the preservation of the high thermal gradient prograde assemblages, modified by isobaric retrograde assemblages. In the case of successive intrusions of sills, underplating will produce the same, in general, above the sill complex as the single intrusion case; whereas a sequence of high-level sills ("overplating") will cause the development of a long-lasting negative thermal gradient beneath the sill complex, in which region temperatures will only reach equilibrium values towards the end of the cycle of events. The igneous intrusion case contains wide-ranging possibilities in thermal histories: metamorphic PT sequences which may relate to igneous intrusion were shown by Turner (1968, Fig. 8.4), Dewey and Pankhurst (1970), and Harte (1975, sequence E of Fig. 26).

By the time that the effects of erosion, tectonic thickening, and igneous intrusion are all included, the resultant geothermal gradient history will obviously be difficult to calculate and also to unravel in an actual example. In general, it will be concluded (in the following) that we do not see true equilibrium Proterozoic crustal geotherms preserved in metamorphic complexes. What we can learn about the thermal situation is that a Proterozoic continental crust relates more to crustal tectonic processes than to remoter parameters, such as mantle heat flow, continental crustal thickness, or average surface heat flow.

THE OVERALL THERMAL STRUCTURE PROBLEM

The process of cratonization (West, 1980) may well have taken several hundred million years to accomplish (500 Ma according to Vitorello and Pollack, 1980). During this time erosion must have occurred and there would have been every possibility of igneous events, both of which are capable of causing metamorphism and either lowering or resetting mineral ages through their radiogenic daughter product blocking temperatures. Without going into detail, it is clear that most Archean shields were essentially much as they are now in gross structure by 2.6 Ga; but in some areas, such as the Churchill Province, widespread retention of argon in minerals only began at 2.3 Ga, while true closure over large regions was not effected until 1.9 to 1.6 Ga. While in some areas there is clear evidence of major crust-forming events at the latter date, in other areas, all we have is reset metamorphic rock. Because simple cooling of a crustal block will not produce such an effect so long after initial cratonization, other processes must have been operative.

At the close of the Archean, global heat flow must have been higher than today's 80 mW/m^2, but how much higher is controversial. Davies (1980) mentioned a range of two to five times as great as at present, whereas Schubert and others (1980, Fig. 3) gave a curve showing a factor of about 2.5. McKenzie and Weiss (1980) showed graphs for various distributions of heat sources with average surface heat flow twice as great at the close of the Archean, but I argued for a lower value, about 1.6 times as great (Lambert, 1980). Further, it is not clear what fraction escaped through the oceans. With this range in estimates, it is very difficult to make a brief, yet reasoned case for any particular surface heat flow for an early Proterozoic continent or for any particular mantle heat flow (q_m). Assuming a mean mantle heat flow of 30 mW/m^2 today, the increased radiogenic heating 2.6 Ga ago would raise this to near 60 mW/m^2 assuming an approach to equilibrium (Lambert, 1976; McKenzie and Weiss, 1980). This reasonable assumption may be considered in conjunction with some simple crustal models to calculate some equilibrium geotherms.

For comparative purposes, my 1980 maximum thickness Archean continental crust (Table III, Lambert, op. cit.) may be considered, as at 1800 Ma. After removal of the top 5 km of sediment and granite, the crust contains:

	Thickness	Heat Production[1]
Metasediments and felsic gneisses	8 km	2.24 $\mu W/m^3$
Amphibolite and gneiss	10 km	1.18 $\mu W/m^3$
Pyroxene granulite	22 km	0.22 $\mu W/m^3$

[1]Giving 34 mW/m^2 surface heat flow

Assuming reasonable conductivities, this crust has an equilibrium geotherm reaching 1310° C at 40 km if q_m = 70 mW/m^2, an upper limit before dry melting begins. So q_m = 60 mW/m^2 beneath the stable continent would appear to be an effective maximum; and, bearing in mind that the craton should have begun to stabilize 2600 Ma ago, the mantle flux would probably have been much lower than 60 mW/m^2 at 1800 Ma. So in Figures 1 and 2 values of geotherms for q_o = 104, 84, and 64 mW/m^2 are shown, being the maximum possible (though not likely), the preferred, and the lowest possible values, respectively.

Alternatively, we must consider shield areas with a thinner amphibolite facies lower crust, founded on a thick greenstone succession, enriched in K and U becaus of seawater interaction and containing some differentiates. A possible shield would contain:

	Thickness	Heat production[1]
Metasediments	6 km	2.24 $\mu W/m^3$
Tonalite and granodiorite gneiss	12 km	1.18 $\mu W/m^3$
Amphibolite	12 km	0.81 $\mu W/m^3$[2]

[1]Giving 38 mW/m^2 at surface
[2]K = 0.9%; U = 0.7 ppm; Th = 3.0 ppm

The maximum temperatures in this crust are restricted by hydrous melting or by metamorphism to the granulite facies with accompanying degranitization. Mantle heat flows of 70, 50, and 30 mW/m^2 give temperatures at 30 km of 1080° C, 830° C, and 580° C, respectively. As the highest of these temperatures is well within the melting of granulite facies rocks depending on P_{H_2O}, it is above an upper bound; the lower heat flow q_m of 50 is again preferred and q_m = 30 the reasonable minimum as before. The three equilibrium geotherms for a 30 km crust with q_o of 108, 88, and 68 mW/m^2 are also shown on Figure 1 and 2.

METAMORPHISM IN THE CANADIAN SHIELD

The wealth of information contained in Geological

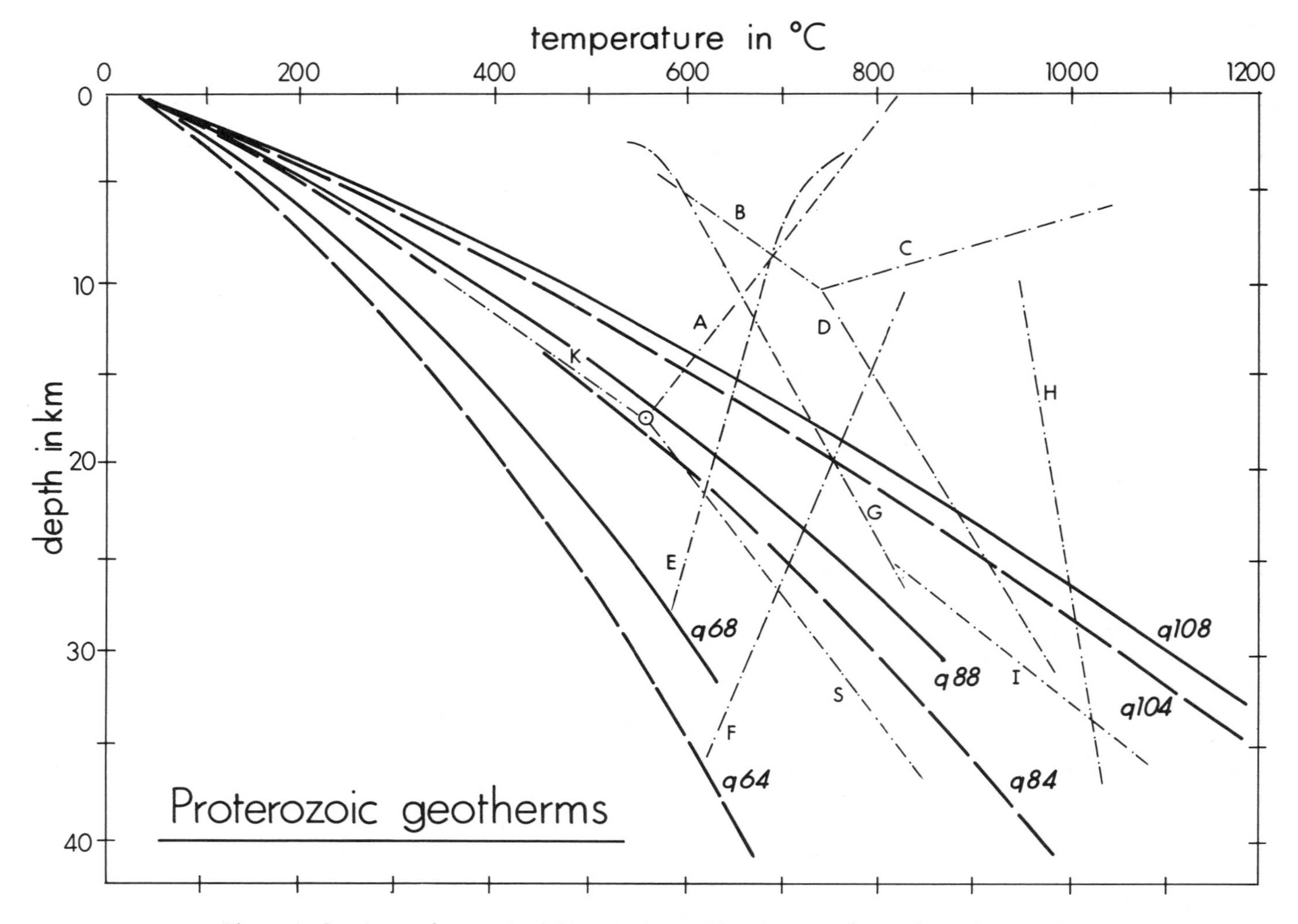

Figure 1. Geotherms for standard 30 and 40 km thick Proterozoic continental crust with various surface heat flows q in mW/m^2. Light lines indicate some principal metamorphic reactions: AKS, the aluminosilicates as recommended by Greenwood (1976); BC, upper stability limits of Fe-cordierite; D, upper limit of biotite, sillimanite, and quartz; E, minimum melting of granite; F, beginning of melting of basalt; G, upper limit of muscovite and quartz; H, incongruent melting of hornblende; I, low-pressure to intermediate-pressure granulite boundary. Curves shown are for $P_{H_2O} = P_{total}$. The hatched lines indicate the lower limit of anatexis (horizontal shading) and the lower limit of the granulite facies as commonly defined. Note that these reactions, commonly used to define PT conditions, mostly lie in the high T/P region.

Survey of Canada Paper 78-10 provides us with more up-to-date knowledge of this shield than we have for all the rest of the Proterozoic. There is a fairly clear division in Canada between metamorphism affecting curvilinear belts and wider areas of pre-existing shield. The simplest example of the former is the Labrador Trough and its correlated extensions (Dimroth and Dressler, 1978; Schimann, 1978). The latter includes much of the Churchill Province, although within this widely overprinted area local structural units may have resembled at one time a modern linear eugeosynclinal or miogeoclinal system (Lewry and others, 1978; Fraser, 1978; Nielsen and others, 1981). Some other areas cannot be so easily classified: parts of the Bear Province (Frith, 1978; Nielsen, 1978); the Minnesota-Wisconsin shield (Morey, 1978); and the majority of the Grenville Province (Bourne, 1978).

On reviewing these and earlier accounts of the Canadian shield, the predominant conclusion to be drawn is the truly regional character of events. We do not seem to find many examples of regions which are sharply demarked and which contain an integrated tectonic and metamorphic history that does not cross the borders of the system. We do not, in fact, have many cases of mobile belts which abut sharply against distinctly older cratons. Metamorphic and

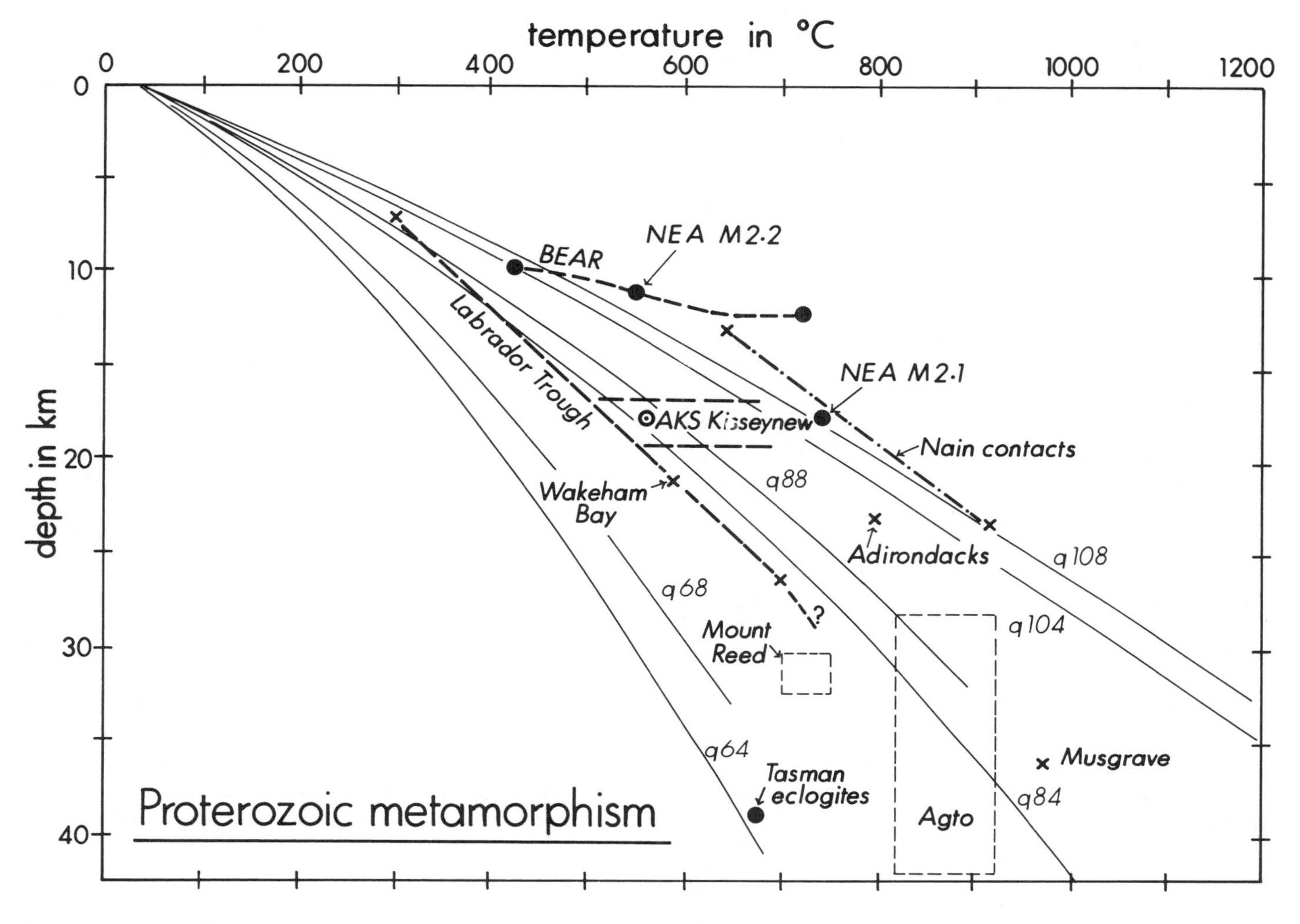

Figure 2. Geotherms as in Figure 1, with some suggested PT conditions for metamorphism in Proterozoic complexes. NEA = northeastern Alberta.

thermal (age-province) boundaries are not sharp in Proterozoic terrains.

Turning to actual examples, metamorphism in the most sharply defined systems has, not surprisingly, a character similar to that of Phanerozoic mobile belts. The Labrador Trough and the Cape Smith-Wakeham Bay belt contain metamorphic assemblages which are of Barrovian type (Dimroth and Dressler, 1978; Klein, 1978; Schimann, 1978; Fig. 2 of this paper). The metamorphism spread beyond the region of L. Proterozoic sediments into the adjacent basements (Dimroth and Dressler, 1978; Westra, 1978). Dimroth and Dressler concluded that large-scale burial metamorphism under a pile of nappes produced metamorphism along a geotherm which was the normal crustal geotherm. It approximates the calculated 1800-Ma geotherms for 30-40 km thick crusts with q_o = 84 to 88 mW/m^2 (Fig. 2). While it is interesting to note that Schimann's PT point agrees with and lies on Dimroth and Dressler's curve of estimated PT conditions, it is not entirely clear as yet whether we are seeing an isochronous Proterozoic geotherm exhumed in the Labrador Trough, or one of the more complex apparent metamorphic gradients discussed in the Introduction.

These records of comparatively high-pressure facies series in the Hudsonian events, while not the oldest examples (Thompson, 1978; Dymek, 1981), indicate the operation of processes which must resemble those of the Phanerozoic to some extent. Kyanite is also recorded north of the Fox River fold-belt, Manitoba, occurring with staurolite and sillimanite (Weber and Scoates, 1978).

Contrasting with the above, the situation in much of the Churchill Province is extraordinarily complicated and, in many areas, very poorly defined because of the extensive late thermal overprinting. Good descriptions are becoming available for northern Saskatchewan, northeastern Alberta, and the southern Northwest Territories. In these areas, granulite or retrogressed granulite is surrounded by amphibolite facies gneisses, with the bounding isograds forming ellipses or irregular looped areas (Lewry and others, 1978, Fig. 2; Fraser, 1978; Godfrey and Langenberg, 1978). The dimensions of the granulite areas are vast—individually in hundreds of kilometres in diameter—and together they form, in outcrop, about 10 percent of the surface of the pre-M. Proterozoic. Such studies as there are of the amphibolite facies gneisses, which occupy about 80 percent of the pre-Middle Proterozoic surface, suggest that they are underlain at no great depth by granulites, as the amphibolite facies gneisses seem to be in comparatively low-pressure facies series. This implies that the great bulk of the crust in these areas consists of granulites, possibly plus intrusives. In the shield in New Quebec, bordered by Hudson Bay, the Labrador Trough, and the Churchill Province, granulites and retrogressed granulites occupy 50 percent of the surface (from Fig. 1, Herd, 1978) while amphibolite facies rocks occupy most of the remainder. Studies of metamorphic conditions in these and similar areas include those of Klein (1978), Nielsen (1978), Nielsen and others (1981), Bailes and McRitchie (1978), Jackson and Morgan (1978), Bourne (1978), Whitney (1978), and Emslie (1981). The relevant petrogenetic grid for the upper amphibolite and granulite facies is very poorly defined compared with the 500-600° C range: geobarometry is necessarily based on broad generalizations, and accurate geothermometry is entirely reliant on estimates of P_{H_2O}. In those rare cases where carbonates or calc-cilicates occur, an independent estimate of P_{H_2O} may be available, assisting considerably in the endless debate relating to the stability of cordierite, garnet, hypersthene, and hornblende. PT estimates for granulite or near-granulite facies conditions have been provided by Klein (1978), Nielsen (1978), Nielsen and others (1981), Bailes and McRitchie (1978), Whitney (1978), Emslie (1981), and Pattison (1981). Of these, those of Nielsen and Pattison, working in a terrain dominated by cordierite over garnet and in which kyanite is absent, stand out as requiring far higher geotherms than any other. In Neilsen's area, there is no evidence that the isograds are controlled by exposed plutons. Further, in each area, granulite facies rocks must be close to the surface in most of the amphibolite facies areas. The cause of these high gradients is discussed below.

Attempts to categorize PT in the granulite terrains have produced results indicating equilibration at moderate thermal gradients (Fig. 2). The upper temperature limit of the Kisseynew Gneiss metamorphism, as exposed, is estimated at 750° C at between 16 and 19 km depth. This limit is close to that suggested by Nielsen and others for the first Proterozoic metamorphism in northeastern Alberta. The latter based their estimate on the breakdown of cordierite to give garnet, sillimanite, and quartz; Mg-Fe exchange between cordierite and garnet, and biotite and garnet; and also the breakdown of biotite. In the Kisseynew gneisses, the highest temperatures are marked by the reaction of biotite and sillimanite to produce garnet, cordierite, and melt. Pressure conditions were not so accurately estimated. In the Adirondacks, Whitney (1978, Fig. 2) found that application of current geothermometers and geobarometers to silica under- and oversaturated gneisses gave slightly different results. In discussing these results, he introduced the notion that the garnet "isograd" in the Adirondacks is actually a kinetically-controlled boundary developed during near-isobaric retrogressive cooling from much higher temperatures.

Thus, the conditions in the Adirondacks and Kisseynew could well have approached the Nain contact levels, as shown on Figure 2. These estimates, from Berg (1977), were based on cordierite, garnet, and hypersthene equilibria; especially on exchange reactions between cordierite and garnet; and also from the reaction hypersthene = olivine + quartz. Note that on Figure 2, the line drawn for Nain contacts represents the range of conditions estimated for a wide area and does not represent a geotherm. Further, the evidence for pressures above 21 km equivalent is slight. The observations of Berg are of considerable interest in considering the Kisseynew, northeastern Alberta, and Adirondack situations: one possible cause of the observed PT in these cases is clearly subjacent plutonic intrusion. However, the estimates of Berg are being revised, and the pressures mentioned above may be too high by about 2 kb (Morse, personal communication, 1981). If this revision is correct, the Nain contacts would appear to represent the highest T/P conditions recorded anywhere on a regional scale and are not very relevant to standard crustal geotherm problems.

Equally recently, Newton and Perkins (1981) have recalibrated the geobarometers which involve anorthite in granulites and have concluded that nine major regions, some Proterozoic but mostly Archean, underwent metamorphism which passed through PT points in the range 6.9 to 9.2 kb and temperatures of 750-950° C. The Adirondacks equilibrated at 8 kb, a slightly higher pressure than that given by Whitney and recorded on Figure 2. Perhaps though, Newton and Perkin's geobarometer is recording a reequilibration to lower PT conditions, as the feldspar geothermometer does. At these elevated temperatures, well above the blocking temperatures for diffusion of Sr in minerals, intercrystal diffusion of Fe and Mg is a distinct possibility while the other cations in six coordination sites may also be diffusing. If these continuous reactions occur in equilibrium, it is possible that textures will not be disturbed.

We may place the Agto metadolerites (Glassley and Søprenson, 1980) in the same general bracket as the other granulites. These dykes were intruded under conditions which permitted the development of amphibolite facies assemblages where P_{H_2O} was high, or garnet-granulite conditions where it was low, occurring during a single prograde event. The PT conditions were estimated from activity calculations, particularly those involving the edenite and tschermakite molecules. If the interpretation is correct, the Agto dykes record a moderate Proterozoic thermal gradient. This point will be considered further after discussion of Australian examples.

AUSTRALIAN EXAMPLES OF HIGH-GRADE METAMORPHISM

Two well-described areas in Australia yield useful information about lower crustal conditions in the Proterozoic. The Willyama Complex at Broken Hill underwent its main granulite facies metamorphism 1605 ± 40 Ma ago (the Olarian orogeny; Binns, 1964; Pidgeon, 1967; Glen and others, 1977). The isotopic data show that Pb and Sr isotopic equilibrium was reached; the tectonic study of Glen and others concludes that a L. Proterozoic sedimentary sequence containing basic sills underwent orogeny at that time. The region contains kyanite-staurolite schists, believed, but not proven, to be part of the same complex; the main sequence contains upper amphibolite transitional to pyroxene-granulite rocks. A second sillimanite isograd gives rise to cordierite-garnet assemblages, followed by an orthopyroxene isograd in basic assemblages. Although earlier researchers did not identify partial melting products, Phillips (1980) considered it to be important, in keeping with the high temperatures suggested by the occurrence of wollastonite in calc-silicates. In the absence of new detailed mineralogical studies, only general conclusions can be formed; however, the assemblages mentioned imply metamorphism under moderate gradient, volatile-poor conditions, perhaps near the gradient implied for Agto and Musgrave (Fig. 2).

The Musgrave area contains isolated but large inliers of 1200-Ma granulites, notable for their siliceous nature (98 percent granodiorite composition with average K_2O = 4.5 percent, 3 analyses) and interesting mineralogy (Moore and Goode, 1978). Using the reaction fo orthopyroxene and plagioclase as a geobarometer, the stability of hornblende and the assemblage mesoperthite-sillimanite as geothermometers, it was concluded that equilibrium was reached at 950-1000° C and 10-11 Kb (1-1.1 GPa). The area is notable for the mafic-ultramafic intrusions of the Giles Complex which are syntectonic and crystallized under the same PT conditions.

LATE PROTEROZOIC COMPLEXES

After the close of Grenville-age events, there seems to have been a general absence of tectonomagmatic activity on a global scale until 750 Ma ago, when small-scale events are recorded, becoming more frequent towards the Cambrian. In late Precambrian and Cambrian time, Avalonian, Cadomian, Bretonic, Assyntian, and Pan-African events have been variously recognized. My impression of these is that they are directly relatable to modern plate-tectonic regimes. In one instance in W. Tasmania, the oldest proven eclogites have been recorded (Råheim, 1976), assemblages including talc-garnet-kyanite-quartz and omphacite (Jd_{30})-garnet ($Ca_{23}Mg_{38}Fe_{39}$) eclogites. Råheim estimated conditions of 11 ± 1 Kb (1.1 GPa) and 670° ± 20° C, far cooler for that depth than any of the examples of Figure 2. The earliest recorded glaucophane-lawsonite facies rocks also formed in the same general period of time, in Anglesey (Barber and Max, 1979; Beckinsale and Thorpe, 1979). Whether earlier eclogite and blueschist facies rocks either developed or could have been preserved is very uncertain (England and Richardson, 1977, p. 206–207).

Lastly among natural examples, the early metamorphism in the Moinian of Scotland, dated at 750 or 1000 Ma, is an example of a Barrovian sequence overprinted by a second Barrovian sequence 250 Ma later. This region conveniently illustrates, in one small area, the problems which may well be uncovered from more detailed studies in older complexes. As in other Barrovian sequences, contemporaneous igneous rocks are scarce and partial melting is only on a small-scale at the present surface, unless the Northeast Highlands of Scotland prove to be of the same metamorphic age. Unravelling of the complexity was attempted by Lambert, Winchester, and Holland (1979), based on work on the thin calc-silicates in the metasediments (Winchester, 1972, 1974a and b). Other studies of the calc-silicates (Soper and Brown, 1971; and Tanner, 1976) add to the complexity of the record. Using petrography and whole-rock chemistry, Winchester was able to construct (P, T) - X diagrams and to map isogradic surfaces contoured in small compositional intervals on a spacing of one hundred metres or so. It was found that the Precambrian-age metamorphic sequence was inverted, as Soper and Brown had suggested on general structural grounds (1971, p. 323). The cause of this regional inversion may lie in extensive overthrusting of hot rock from the east during the 500-400-Ma events.

PROTEROZOIC METAMORPHISM AND IGNEOUS ACTIVITY

The complexity of metamorphism and the uncertainty which now surrounds the relation of estimated P, T from mineral assemblages to actual geotherms make discussion of Proterozoic geothermal gradients in metamorphosed zones almost academic. Some generalities seem to have meaning, however. Based on the discussion above and on Figure 1 and 2, I conclude that the lowest observed PT for a Proterozoic metamorphic complex lies near a standard crustal geotherm with q_o = 80 mW/m^2. As the crust would contribute about 30 mW/m^2, the remaining 50, being q_m, corresponds to today's mantle heat flux backdated on a thermal equilibrium assumption to 1800 Ma ago. This conclusion is probably oversimplified, but I would observe that the low thermal gradient complexes are generally devoid of contemporaneous igneous intrusions and partial melting phenomena, especially when compared with the upper amphibolite-granulite facies terrains of the Churchill Province.

The question, therefore, arises of how the high geothermal gradient complexes arose, or at least, how high-temperature mineral assemblages arose in them. Transitory enhancement of the geotherm by erosion is a possible, but not necessary, explanation of one Phanerozoic example, which was applied to rocks rising from 24 km. It may, therefore, be a possible explanation of the Proterozoic examples.

Alternatively, many of the latter are closely related to contemporaneous plutonic intrusions or partial melting; that is, to transient geotherms caused by convection of heat. Accordingly, some of Carslaw and Jaeger's 1971 equations and results from Jaeger (1964) have been applied to the Proterozoic situation. No complete solution seems to be available to the problem, which is to establish the maximum transient geotherm that will develop in an internally heated complex with some heating from below, and is intruded by a sill-like body at its liquidus. The latter two points are the first simplifications. Although Jaeger (1964) showed that latent heat of crystallization can be approximately allowed for by an arithmetic adjustment to the temperature of the intrusion, no quantification of the whole problem, allowing for varying thickness of the solidified part of the magma with time or for the effect of internal heating in the metamorphic complex, is available. As a further simplification, it can be shown that the maximum rise in temperature $\Delta T = T_m - T_g$ (T_m = metamorphic temperature, T_g = geotherm) will not vary much at a distance d froma sill of thickness 2d where cooling times are long or d is small (from Jaeger, 1964, Fig. 2a). Suitable values of t and d for this assumption to be valid are as used below. A further simplification is to neglect variations in internal (radiogenic) heating in the metamorphic complex, certainly valid for $t<10$ Ma as in these calculations. Finally, it is assumed that the sill cools at a uniform rate, which will not be correct; but again, at a distance >d from the intrusion, the effect of an early rapid cooling will not be significant, the time term always being of importance. Thus, maximum ΔT's were calculated for various hypothetical situations using the error function equation (Carslaw and Jaeger, 1971, p. 114) for cooling of a plane slab heated from below. Typical results are shown on Table 1 and Figure 3; the sill was intruded with its upper surface at 20 km depth in each case.

The effect of varying the cooling rate of the sill, holding all other variables constant, is shown in Table 1(a). The

TABLE 1. INCREASES IN TEMPERATURE AT GIVEN DISTANCES ABOVE A HORIZONTAL SILL

(a) ΔT(°C) at given heights above a 3 km basalt sill (T=1200° C) after given solidification and cooling times.

Cooling time		Height above top of sill (20 km depth)				
(Ma)	Km	7	8	9	10	11
1		207° C	164	127	98	75
2		229	199	167	144	123
3		220	197	172	154	133
4		216	195	176	161	144

(b) ΔT(°C) for given cooling times, at 6 km above the top of various basalt sills (T=1200° C).

Cooling time		Thickness of sills			
(Ma)	Km	1	2	3	4
1		86° C	172	258	344
2		88	177	265	354
3		83	164	250	334
4		79	157	236	314

cooling rate is not itself an independent variable, but the presently available equations do not govern this complex case. It will be seen from Table 1, however, that the effect of varying thickness is comparatively small in the region just over 4d from the sill, covering a factor of four in the cooling rate. These are the kinds of rates for such sills which we may estimate from Jaeger's work (1964, Fig. 2a).

Alternatively, we may consider the effect of varying the thickness of the sill and the cooling rate on the temperature at a fixed height above the sill (Table 1(b)). As the quantity of energy released from the sill rises with thickness, so in these simplified calculations does the increase in temperature rise proportionally. Of more importance is the approximate independence of ΔT with overall cooling time (vertical columns in Table 1(b)). Consequently, we may proceed to apply these simplified calculations to a natural case and draw some preliminary conclusions.

Some other results are shown on Figure 3; the sill was intruded with its upper surface at 20 km in each case. As seen in Figure 3a, comparatively thin tonalite sills, cooling quickly, do not produce high enough ΔT's to cause the Bear Province metamorphism of Nielsen (1978). Only one example of heating by a basaltic sill is shown, as all ΔT patterns for such sills are too steep on Figure 3 to come close to the Bear Province ΔT curves. The thicker sills, cooling more slowly, shown on Figure 3b give more realistic ΔT values, even approaching the right ΔT gradient in the thicker cases. However, no combination of time and thickness produces the right gradient, so horizontal sills may be ruled out: sloping or domal sills would give better approximations.

Perusal of the effect of varying all possible parameters suggests that either:

(a) The PT pattern of the Bear metamorphism could be caused by an igneous body that closely approached the present surface; or

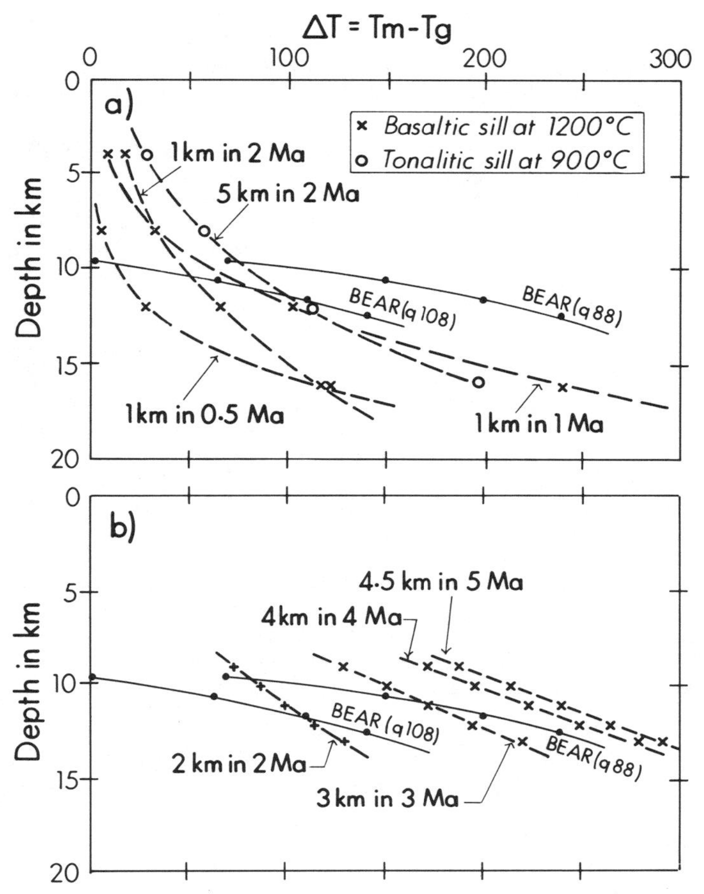

Figure 3. The estimated temperature excess above the calculated geotherms for the Bear Province metamorphism (BEAR (q88); BEAR (q108)) compared with some calculated transient temperatures caused by sills emplaced at 20 km depth, of varying thickness, cooling in specified periods of time; (a) some unlikely situations, and (b) some closer approaches to the required increase in temperature. The lowest ΔT curve is for a sill intruded horizontally at 16 km depth. Note that no single horizontal sill can cause the required ΔT; the slope, or the magnitude of ΔT, will always differ from that required. Time of cooling is not an independent variable, but as it cannot be evaluated easily (see text), calculations were carried out for a range of estimates of which a sample is shown.

(b) The pattern could be caused by an inclined or dome-shaped igneous body at an original depth of about 20 km.

If (a) is correct, however, the local geology suggests that there should have been extensive melting just below the present surface, the effect of which has not been observed.

The difficulty with the preceding discussion lies not only in the simplifications involved but also with the fact that suitable erosion might produce a similar transient geotherm, as discussed in the introductory section. The estimate mentioned there, of an increase of q_o of 20 mW/m^2 is of the right magnitude to produce all suggested Proterozoic PT points by departure from the standard equilibrium geotherm, except for the Bear Province case.

Nevertheless, erosion must have a cause and one suitable cause is thickening of the crust by intrusions at depth. So one concludes that the prime candidate for the cause of the majority of Proterozoic metamorphic complexes considered here is magmatic heat. In particular, the basement complexes, as distinct from linear metamorphic belts, could well have been metamorphosed up to granulite facies conditions by addition of basic magma to the lower level of the crust, which itself could crystallize directly to granulites. Such events would raise previous high-pressure complexes to the surface and would provide the thermal energy to reset argon clocks over wide regions.

To conclude, some internally consistent generalizations emerge:

(a) The few examples of linear metamorphic belts were metamorphosed to levels not exceeding the normal geotherm;

(b) This geotherm may be calculated for a normal thickness continental crust and an equilibrium mantle heat flux of 50 mW/m^2, as being equivalent to a continental surface heat flux of around 85 mW/m^2 giving temperatures of 810 to 860° C at 30 km;

(c) The large regions of amphibolite and granulite facies gneisses, which are not directly relatable to linear metamorphic belts in our present state of knowledge, were produced by the addition of magmatic heat from below to give a normal transient maximum geotherm with q_o = 110 mW/m^2;

(d) This process can reasonably be called underplating; it is one which appears to be widespread in the M. Proterozoic; and

(e) So far as the evidence is available, high P/T gradients did not exist in the L. and M. Proterozoic continental crust.

Finally, the role of internal radioactive heating in this problem has been deliberately neglected. The association of the high T/P gradients of the Bear and northern Churchill provinces with widespread major uranium mineralization might indicate that the role of radioactivity should be investigated further in this regard.

ACKNOWLEDGMENTS

The research recorded in this paper was carried out while holding NSERC Grant A-7489, which is gratefully acknowledged. Criticisms by Drs. C. Klein, T. P. Loomis, and R. C. Newton materially improved the text; their comments are much appreciated.

REFERENCES CITED

Bailes, A. H., and McRitchie, W. D., 1978, The transition from low to high grade metamorphism in the Kisseynew sedimentary gneiss belt, Manitoba: Geological Survey of Canada, Paper 78–10, p. 155–177.

Barber, A. J., and Max, M. D., 1979, A new look at the Mona Complex (Anglesey, North Wales): Journal of the Geological Society, v. 136, p. 407–424.

Beckinsale, R. D., and Thorpe, R. S., 1979, Rubidium-strontium whole-rock isochron evidence for the age of metamorphism and magmatism in the Mona Complex of Anglesey: Journal of the Geological Society, v. 136, p. 433–439.

Berg, J. H., 1977, Regional geobarometry in the contact aureoles of the anorthositic Nain complex, Laborador: Journal of Petrology, v. 18, p. 399–430.

Bickle, M. J., Hawkesworth, C. J., England, P. C., and Athey, D. R., 1975, A preliminary model for regional metamorphism in the Eastern Alps: Earth and Planetary Science Letters, v. 26, p. 13–28.

Binns, R. A., 1964, Zones of progressive regional metamorphism in the Willyama complex, Broken Hill District: Journal of the Geological Society of Australia, v. 11, p. 283–329.

Bourne, J. H., 1978, Metamorphism in the eastern and southwestern portions of the Grenville Province: Geological Survey of Canada Paper 78–10, p. 315–328.

Carslaw, H. S., and Jaeger, J. C., 1971, The conduction of heat in solids, 2nd Ed.: Oxford, 510 p.

Davies, G. F., 1980, Thermal histories of convective earth models and constraints on radiogenic heat production in the Earth: Journal of Geophysical Research, v. 85, p. 2517–2530.

Dewey, J. F., and Pankhurst, R. J., 1970, The evolution of the Scottish Caledonides in relation to their isotopic age pattern: Transactions of the Royal Society of Edinburgh, v. 68, p. 361–389.

Dimroth, E., and Dressler, B., 1978, Metamorphism of the Labrador Trough: Geological Survey of Canada Paper 78–10, p. 215–236.

Dymek, R. F., 1981, Supracrustal rocks, polymetamorphism, and evolution of the SW Greenland Archean gneiss complex: Transactions of the American Geophysical Union, v. 62, p. 420.

Emslie, R. F., 1981, Exceptionally high grade metapelitic gneisses in the Red Wine Mountains, southern Labrador: Geological Association of Canada Abstracts, v. 6, p. A–17.

England, P. C., and Richardson, S. W., 1977, The influence of erosion upon the mineral facies of rocks from different metamorphic environments: Journal of the Geological Society, v. 134, p. 201–213.

Fraser, J. A., 1978, Metamorphism in the Churchill Province, District of Mackenzie: Geological Survey of Canada Paper 78–10, p. 195–202.

Frith, R. A., 1978, Tectonics and metamorphism along the southern boundary between the Bear and Slave structural provinces: Geological Survey of Canada Paper 78–10, p. 103–113.

Fyfe, W. S., Turner, F. J., and Verhoogen, J., 1958, Metamorphic reactions and metamorphic facies: Geological Society of America, Memoir 73, p. 259.

Glassley, W. E., and Sørenson, K., 1980, Constant P_s-T amphibolite to granulite facies transition in Agto (West Greenland) metadolerites: implications and applications: Journal of Petrology, v. 21, p. 69–105.

Glen, R. A., Laing, W. P., Parker, A. J., and Rutland, R.W.R., 1977, Tectonic relationships between the Proterozoic Gawler and Willyama orogenic domains, Australia: Journal of the Geological Society of Australia, v. 24, p. 124–150.

Godfrey, J. D., and Langenberg, C. W., 1978, Metamorphism in the Canadian shield of northeastern Alberta: Geological Survey of Canada Paper 78–10, p. 129–138.

Greenwood, H. J., 1976, Metamorphism at moderate temperatures and pressures: in The Evolution of the Crystalline Rocks, Bailey, D. K., and MacDonald, R., eds., Academic Press, London, p. 187–259.

Harte, B., 1975, Determination of a pelite petrogenetic grid for the eastern Scottish Dalradian: Yearbook Carnegie Institution of Washington, v. 74, p. 438–446.

Herd, R. K., 1978, Notes on metamorphism in New Quebec: Geological Survey of Canada Paper 78–10, p. 79–83.

Jackson, G. D., and Morgan, W. C. , 1978, Precambrian metamorphism on Baffin and Bylot Islands: Geological Survey of Canada Paper 78–10, p. 249–267.

Jaeger, J. C., 1964, Thermal effects of intrusions: Reviews of Geophysics, v. 2, p. 443–466.

Klein, C., 1978, Regional metamorphism of Proterozoic iron-formation, Labrador Trough, Canada: American Mineralogist, v. 63, p. 898–912.

Lambert, R. St J., 1976, Archaean thermal regimes, crustal and upper mantle temperatures, and a progressive evolutionary model for the Earth: in The Early History of the Earth, Windley, B. F., ed., New York, John Wiley & Sons, p. 363–373.

—— 1980, The thermal history of the Earth in the Archaean: Precambrian Research, v. 11, p. 199–213.

Lambert, R. St J., Winchester, J. A., and Holland, J. G., 1979, Time, space and intensity relationships of the Precambrian and lower Paleozoic metamorphisms of the Scottish Highlands: in The Caledonides of the British Isles—Reviewed, Harris, A. L., Holland, C. H., and Leake, B. E., eds., Edinburgh, Scottish Academic Press, p. 363–367.

Lewry, J. F., Sibbalt, T.I.I., and Rees, C. J., 1978, Metamorphic patterns and their relations to tectonism and plutonism in the Churchill Province in Northern Saskatchewan: Geological Survey of Canada Paper 78–10, p. 139–154.

McKenzie, D. P., and Weiss, N., 1980, The thermal history of the Earth: in The Continental Crust and its Mineral Deposits, Strangway, D. W., ed., Geological Association of Canada Special Paper 20, p. 575–590.

Moore, A. C., and Goode, A.D.T., 1978, Petrography and Origin of granulite-facies rocks in the Western Musgrave block, Central Australia: Journal of the Geological Society of Australia, v. 25, p. 341–358.

Morey, G. B., 1978, Metamorphism in the Lake Superior region, U.S.A. and its relation to crustal evolution: Geological Survey of Canada Paper 78–10, p. 283–313.

Nielsen, P. A., 1978, Metamorphism of the Arseno Lake area, Northwest Territories: Geological Survey of Canada Paper 78–10, p. 115–122.

Nielsen, P. A., Langenberg, C. W., Baadsgaard, H., and Godfrey, J. D., 1981, Precambrian crustal conditions and evolution, northeastern Alberta, Canada: Precambrian Research, v. 16, p. 171–193.

Newton, R. C., and Perkins, D. III, 1981, Ancient granulite terrains—"eight kbar metamorphism": Transactions of the American Geophysical Union, v. 62, p. 420.

Oxburgh, E. R., and Turcotte, D. L., 1974, Thermal gradients and regional metamorphism in overthrust terrains with special reference to the Eastern Alps: Schweizerische Mineralogische und Petrographische Mitteilungen, v. 54, p. 641–662.

Pattison, D.R.M., 1981, Geothermobarometry applied to garnet-bearing granitoid plutons of the Hepburn and Wentzel batholiths, Wopmay orogen, N.W.T.: Geological Association of Canada Abstracts, v. 6, p. A–46.

Phillips, G. N., 1980, Water activity changes across an amphibolite-granulite facies transition, Broken Hill, Australia: Contributions to Mineralogy and Petrology, v. 75, p. 377–386.

Pidgeon, R. T., 1967, A rubidium-strontium geochronological study of the Willyama Complex, Broken Hill, Australia: Journal of Petrology, v. 8, p. 283–324.

Råheim, A., 1976, Collingwood River area: Journal of the Geological Society of Australia, v. 23, p. 313–327.

Richardson, S. W., 1970, The relation between a petrogenetic grid, facies series and the geothermal gradient in metamorphism: Fortschritte der Mineralogie, v. 47, p. 65–76.

Richardson, S. W., and Powell, R., 1976, Thermal causes of Dalradian metamorphism in the Central Highlands of Scotland: Scottish Jour-

nal of Geology, v. 12, p. 237–268.
Schimann, K., 1978, On regional metamorphism in the Wakeham Bay area, New Quebec: Geological Survey of Canada Paper 78–10, p. 245–248.
Schubert, G., Stevenson, D., and Cassen, P., 1980, Whole planet cooling and the radiogenic heat source contents of the Earth and Moon: Journal of Geophysical Research, v. 85, p. 2531–2538.
Soper, N. J., and Brown, P. E., 1971, Relationship between metamorphism and migmatization in the northern part of the Moine nappe: Scottish Journal of Geology, v. 7, p. 305–325.
Tanner, P.W.G., 1976, Progressive regional metamorphism of thin calcareous bands from Moinian rocks of Northwest Scotland: Journal of Petrology, v. 17, p. 100–134.
Thompson, P. H., 1978, Archean regional metamorphism in the Slave Structural Province—A new perspective on some old rocks: Geological Survey of Canada Paper 78–10, p. 85–102.
Turner, F. J., 1968, Metamorphic petrology: McGraw-Hill, N.Y. 403 p.
Vitorello, I., and Pollack, H. N., 1980, On the variation of continental heat flow with age and the thermal evolution of continents: Journal of Geophysical Research, v. 85, p. 983–995.
Weber, W., and Scoates, R.J.F., 1978, Archean and Proterozoic metamorphism in the north-western Superior Province and along the Churchill-Superior boundary, Manitoba: Geological Survey of Canada Paper 78–10, p. 5–16.
Wells, P.R.A., 1979, Chemical and thermal evolution of Archean sialic crust, southern West Greenland: Journal of Petrology, v. 20, p. 187–226.
West, G. F., 1980, Formation of continental crust: in The Continental Crust and its Mineral Deposits, Strangway, D. W., ed., Geological Association of Canada Special Paper 20, p. 117–148.
Westra, L., 1978, Metamorphism in the Cape Smith-Wakeham Bay area north of 61°N, New Quebec: Geological Survey of Canada Paper 78–10, p. 237–244.
Whitney, P. R., 1978, The significance of garnet "isograds" in granulite facies rocks of the Adirondacks: Geological Survey of Canada Paper 78–10, p. 357–366.
Winchester, J. A., 1972, The petrology of Moinian calc-silicate gneisses from Fannich Forest, and their significance as indicators of metamorphic grade: Journal of Petrology, v. 13, p. 405–424.
—— 1974a, The control of the whole-rock content of CaO and Al_2O_3 on the occurrence of the aluminosilicate polymorphs in amphibolite-facies pelites: Geological Magazine, v. 111, p. 205–211.
—— 1974b, The three-dimensional pattern of polyphase metamorphism in the Moinian assemblage of northern Ross-shire, Scotland: Journal of Geology, v. 82, p. 637–649.

MANUSCRIPT ACCEPTED BY THE SOCIETY APRIL 14, 1983

Printed in U.S.A.

Geological Society of America
Memoir 161
1983

The origin of Proterozoic and late Archean charnockites—evidence from field relations and experimental petrology

R. C. Newton
E. C. Hansen
Department of the Geophysical Sciences
The University of Chicago
Chicago, Illinois 60637

ABSTRACT

The period of earth history which includes Proterozoic and late Archean time (roughly 1.0-2.7 billion years ago) was punctuated by metamorphism at high temperature (700°-900°C) and high pressures (8 ± 2 kbar for many terrains) in a thick continental crust. Most of the known charnockites (quartzofeldspathic orthopyroxene-bearing granulites) were formed in this period. Archean charnockites were most commonly produced by metamorphism of amphibole-bearing "gray" gneisses whose precursors probably were, in many cases, calc-alkaline plutonic suites. Charnockites showing relic igneous textures are more characteristic of the later Proterozoic than of earlier time. Many large Proterozoic charnockite bodies had plutonic precursors of an anorogenic, alkalic-calcic suite that included massif anorthosites and rapakivi granites.

The definitive characteristics of most Archean and Proterozoic charnockites have resulted from granulite-facies metamorphism in the presence of CO_2-rich, H_2O-poor fluids. Chemical analyses, experimental petrology, fluid inclusion studies, and field relations in the Archean amphibolite-facies to granulite-facies transition region of southern India show that charnockitic metamorphism of gray gneiss may be either virtually isochemical or profoundly metasomatic. K-metasomatism and anatexis commonly attended charnockitic metamorphism, as H_2O-rich fluids were driven upwards ahead of a wave of hot CO_2. Dehydration and depletion of incompatible elements, especially Rb and U, followed migmatite formation. It is not yet clear whether the observed depletions can be entirely accounted for by leaching by a vapor phase or whether escape of anatectic melt is required to produce the most intense depletions.

The Proterozoic Adirondack and Grenville charnockite bodies are the result of a high-pressure metamorphic overprint on plutonic rocks originally emplaced at relatively shallow levels. The quartzofeldspathic igneous rocks were not consanguinous with associated anorthosites but may have been derived by melting of the deep crust during passage of gabbroic anorthosite magmas. Some orthopyroxene in very Fe-rich charnockites may be a primary magmatic phase, but the amount of uniquely magmatic charnockite is probably small.

The relationship of granulite metamorphism to periods of crustal accretion is

not clear at the present time. A source of heat and CO_2 is necessary for the metamorphism, and this may require major magmatic additions to the crust. Alternatively, liberation of CO_2, as well as high pressures, may have resulted from continental collision as a 15 to 30 km-thick continental segment overrode carbonate-bearing shelf sediments and evaporites of another. Opening and closing of a proto-ocean could explain the anorogenic magmatism of the Grenville province followed by granulite metamorphism. Similarities between Proterozoic and Archean granulite terrains suggest that such plate tectonic processes operated at least back to the late Archean.

ANCIENT HIGH-GRADE TERRAINS

The large tracts of granulite-facies rocks are in Precambrian shield terrains, with few exceptions. Some of the best known Proterozoic examples are the Grenville province of southeastern Canada; the Rogaland, Bamble, and Varberg areas of southern Norway and southwestern Sweden; and the Broken Hill district of New South Wales, Australia. Extensive late Archean granulites include the tracts in southern India and Sri Lanka, the Limpopo Belt of Zimbabwe and Botswana, and Enderby Land, Antarctica. All of these terrains contain metamorphic rocks of diverse protoliths, including demonstrable sediments, volcanics, and plutonic rocks.

The outstanding chemical and mineralogic characteristics which distinguish Precambrian granulite terrains from lower-grade areas are several. Foremost is *dryness,* reflected in the characteristic occurrence of pyroxenes, rather than or in addition to amphiboles and micas in a variety of lithologies. Also prominent is *depletion* in some, but not all high-grade rocks of certain minor elements, such as Rb, U, Th, and the heavy rare earth elements, relative to lower-grade rocks of otherwise similar compositions (Heier, 1973). Detailed petrographic studies of granulites have revealed the characteristic *CO_2-rich primary fluid inclusions* in minerals from both Proterozoic and Archean granulites (Touret, 1970), contrasting with the dominantly aqueous fluid inclusions of lower-grade crustal rocks. Quantitative mineralogical geothermometry and geobarometry have demonstrated the *high temperatures* which accompanied granulite crystallization, and, in many terrains, *high pressures* corresponding to considerable depth in the crust.

Attempts to distinguish Proterozoic and Archean granulites on chemical criteria have not yielded definite results (Heier, 1976). Structural and petrologic features of the mobile belt terrains are not absolutely age-discriminatory; each terrain is somewhat different from all others. Some Proterozoic granulite belts are dominated by clearly intrusive charnockites (pyroxene-bearing quartzofeldspathic rocks) associated with intermediate-plagioclase anorthosite massifs. Examples are the Adirondacks, the western Grenville of Quebec, and the Rogaland terrain of southwestern Norway. Other Proterozoic granulite areas, such as Broken Hill, Australia, and the Inari Complex of northern Finland, lack the anorthosite outcrops but are dominated by layered rocks of surficial origin (supracrustals). Massif anorthosites are not found in Archean granulite areas; rocks of obviously supracrustal origin, however, are abundant in some Archean terrains and may constitute "massifs" of layered rock, as in the Central Highlands of Sri Lanka (Cooray, 1969). All granulite terrains, including those of the Proterozoic anorthosite-charnockite plutonic association, however, contain abundant rocks of supracrustal origin, such as marbles, quartzites, K-rich pelites, and paraamphibolites.

THE 'CHARNOCKITE PROBLEM'

The most voluminous components of many high-grade terrains are orthopyroxene-bearing intermediate-to-felsic gneisses, or charnockites. The problem of the origin of these rocks, the "charnockite problem" (Pichamuthu, 1953), is still debated. Some of the controversy stems from divergent field observations. Many Proterozoic charnockites have indubitably igneous precursors, such as the massive Stark Complex of the Adirondacks, which sometimes shows relict igneous textures in spite of heavy metamorphic overprint (Brock, 1980). This probably applies to most Grenville charnockites associated with massif anorthosites (Martignole and Schrijver, 1977). However, metasedimentary charnockites are also recognized in the Adirondacks (DeWaard, 1969); and the great charnockitic highlands of south India and Sri Lanka feature charnockites interlayered with indubitably metasedimentary rocks, such as calc-silicates, graphitic gneisses, and quartzites (Cooray, 1962). Some charnockites of direct magmatic (nonmetamorphic) origin may occur in association with some low-pressure anorthosite massifs, such as the Nain, Labrador Complex (Morse, 1982).

Several processes leading to charnockites have been postulated and are debated intensively. The major hypotheses are listed below. They may be classified as primary igneous and metamorphic overprint hypotheses.

Freezing of relatively dry magmas at depth. The simplest hypothesis to explain orthopyroxene-bearing quartzofeldspathic granulites is freezing of relatively dry granitic to intermediate magma and slow cooling and recrystallization under deep-seated conditions (Holland and Lambert,

1975). Whether the magmas were generated by melting in a deep subduction zone or in the upper mantle, or by remelting of the crust, a certain amount of water is likely to have been present.

The conditions of H_2O undersaturation, Fe/Mg ratio, and SiO_2 content which would allow primary crystallization of orthopyroxene from granitic and intermediate magmas have not been yet defined experimentally. In comagmatic suites where orthopyroxene is thought to be of direct magmatic origin, as in the Nain, Labrador Complex, orthopyroxene occurs only in the more mafic and iron-rich compositions (Wheeler, 1960), and the complex was emplaced under upper crustal low-pressure conditions (Berg, 1977; Morse, 1982). The possibility that large charnockite bodies formed in a deep-seated environment by magmatic processes is still open to question. The experimental granite melting relations of Clemens and Wall (1981) show a restricted P-T field of orthopyroxene primary crystallization at low pressures, closing out at 7 kbar; it is not certain that any experimental study at higher pressure has yielded orthopyroxene. Analyses of orthopyroxene in experimental studies of melting in intermediate compositions have yielded pyroxenes of 3 or more wt. % CaO (e.g., Green, 1969), which may mean that they were Ca-poor clinopyroxene during the experimental conditions.

The idea that charnockites simply "froze that way" from primitive magmas has also been criticized from the point of view that no mantle source capable of yielding the voluminous intermediate and acid rocks of some terrains could be high enough in K/Rb to give the very high values of this ratio found in some charnockites (Rollinson and Windley, 1980). Various secondary depletion processes have been advocated. These processes must have operated on the charnockite precursors within, at most, a few hundred million years after emplacement in the crust in some cases (O'Nions and Pankhurst, 1978) in order to give the low observed Sr isotope ratios.

Differentiation-depletion in primitive or secondary magmas. A variant of the above hypothesis is that voluminous intermediate (tonalitic) magmas underwent fractional crystallization wth retention of H_2O and the incompatible elements in residual magmas (Holland and Lambert, 1975). Drury (1980) suggested that the interface between amphibolitic gneisses and granulite gneisses on Barra, Outer Hebrides might represent the boundary between frozen residual liquids and cumulates, respectively, from an original primitive magma body or bodies. Hubbard and Whitley (1979) and Petersen (1980) advocated a similar mechanism to explain charnockite-to-granite gradients of southwest Sweden and southwest Norway, respectively. Hubbard and Whitley thought that the Varberg plutons were derived from melting of massive graywacke beds. These authors used quantitative modelling of rare earth element partitioning between liquids and solids in support of the hypothesis. A positive europium anomaly in the granulite-facies rocks and a negative europium anomaly in some of the amphibolite-facies gneisses are in accord with this kind of differentiation.

Partial melting of the crust. The idea that charnockites, and granulites in general, are restites of anatexis (Fyfe, 1973) draws support from the experimental finding that granitic liquids can form from hydrous melting of intermediate quartzofeldspathic rocks at crustal pressures (Winkler and von Platen, 1961; Brown and Fyfe, 1970). H_2O and incompatible elements partition strongly into such liquids, and could be removed from the deeper crust by rise of granite bodies. Quantitative modelling of major element distributions in the New Quebec, Canada granulites (Nesbitt, 1980) and of minor elements in the Scourian granulites (Pride and Muecke, 1980) finds some support for charnockites as restites of about 20 percent partial melting of intermediate gneisses. Other granulites of various types have been explained chemically as restites after removal of granitic melts (Schmid, 1978; McCarthy, 1976). Several authors, making detailed element partitioning calculations, state that their charnockites in various areas are not satisfactorily explained by this mechanism (Wells, 1979; Field et al., 1980; Rollinson and Windley, 1980; Weaver, 1980).

Metamorphic overprint. The case for metamorphic origin of most charnockites was forceably put forward by P. G. Cooray (1969), who drew on his experience in the late Archean charnockitic terrains of Sri Lanka and southern India. His major emphasis was that granulite-grade metamorphism, operating on quartzofeldspathic rocks of various parentage, leads to an entity called charnockite.

Although high-grade metamorphism of charnockite precursors must have been under conditions of low P_{H_2O}, minor element and isotopic studies have shown emphatically that simple dry metamorphism is not sufficient; some pervasive fluid agency must be invoked to cause coarse recrystallization of many occurrences and the incompatible element depletion. Discovery of the primary CO_2-rich fluid inclusions of granulites (Touret, 1970) and charnockites (Madsen, 1977) has focussed attention on the possible role of carbonic fluids in granulite metamorphism (Collerson and Fryer, 1978; Newton et al., 1980). Abundant CO_2 necessary for granulite conversion of whole terrains which had a previous upper crustal history, as the supracrustals of the Adirondacks and the south Indian terrains, may have had sources in continental shelf carbonates or in carbonated mantle peridotite. Outgassing of a carbonated mantle (Sheraton et al., 1973; Drury, 1973; Tarney and Windley, 1977) during crustal accretion could have dried out and depleted extensive portions of the crust. However, recent geochronology suggests that granulite metamorphism occurred in some cases up to a few hundred million years after accretion, as in the late Archean Scourian granulite terrain of northwestern Scotland (Hamilton et al., 1979) and the Proterozoic Grenville province of Canada (Emslie, 1978). Although various authors have found evidence that high-pressure CO_2 can transport and deplete various minor elements, including the rare earths (Collerson and Fryer, 1978; Hynes, 1980), the hypothesis has not been modelled quantitatively. Most authors of REE analyses of high-grade rocks believe that the patterns result mostly from igneous history (e.g., Weaver, 1980).

EVIDENCE BEARING ON THE CHARNOCKITE PROBLEM

Field relations. Areas in which granulites are separated by transition zones from lower-grade terrains have been recognized for some time, as at Broken Hill, Australia (Binns, 1964) and the northwestern Adirondacks (Buddington, 1963). Isograds of progressive metamorphism have been mapped within these transition zones, the most important index mineral being orthopyroxene. The appearance of orthopyroxene may be composition-dependent—there is evidence that it appears in basic rocks at lower grade than in intermediate or acid rocks (Buddington, 1963; Field and Clough, 1976). The Adirondack isograds cut across plutons and show no evident relation to them. The Proterozoic Bamble and Rogaland granulite terrains contain more or less distinct and simple isograds (Touret, 1971), as do the early Proterozoic Broken Hill terrain (Binns, 1964) and the late Archean Pikwitonei Belt of Manitoba (Hubregtse, 1980). Hubregtse's map shows the orthopyroxene isograd nearly coinciding with the limit of well-defined greenstone troughs, although individual greenstone belts can be traced as attenuated and deformed high-grade relics into the Pikwitonei Belt. Similar field relations occur across the border zone of the Archean-Proterozoic Limpopo mobile belt (Mason, 1973). The late Archean progressive metamorphic tract of south India contains granitoids and greenstones of the greenschist facies in central Karnataka which grade into the granulite-grade "massifs" in southern Karnataka and northern Tamil Nadu (Pichamuthu, 1965). Other areas in which well-defined amphibolite-grade to granulite-grade transitions have been described are the early Proterozoic Finnish Lappland Complex (Hörmann et al., 1980) and the late Archean Buksefjorden, southwestern Greenland region (Wells, 1979).

Although several authors have mapped approximate orthopyroxene isograds and have noted the patchy appearance of charnockite in amphibolitic gneisses as granulite regions are approached (e.g., Hubbard, 1978; Wells, 1979; Wilson, 1978, p. 243), the critical interface between granulite and amphibolite terrains has not yet been described in much detail. Pichamuthu (1960) first noted the incipient development of charnockite in a quarry near Kabbal, Karnataka in the transition region between amphibolite-facies Peninsular Gneiss on the north, and the granulite-facies massifs on the south. There, small patches and stringers of dark charnockite cut across pre-existing foliation of migmatitic gneiss and are clearly later than the gneiss (Figs. 1, 2). The characteristic dark color of fresh charnockite is due to retrogressive chloritization of orthopyroxene (Howie, 1967). Petrographically, the charnockite at Kabbal is a coarsely recrystallized plagioclase-K-feldspar-quartz-orthopyroxene rock containing primary biotite but not primary amphibole (Pichamuthu, 1961; Ramiengar et al., 1978; Janardhan et al., 1979). The charnockitization process has been described by several workers as "metasomatic" and "rheomorphic," without being more specific. The latter designation refers to the highly migmatitic character of the Kabbal gneiss and the close association of acid injections with charnockite (Friend, 1981). Similar patchy development of charnockite in foliation-cutting veins in gneiss was noted by the present authors in the Stark Complex, near South Colton, New York. Brock (1980) described patchy metamorphism of the Stark Complex, in which all gradations from coarse granite, often rapakivi, to orthopyroxene-bearing granoblastic "green rock" were noted, and charnockitic veins cutting amphibolites were described at Cone Peak, central California coast, by Compton (1960).

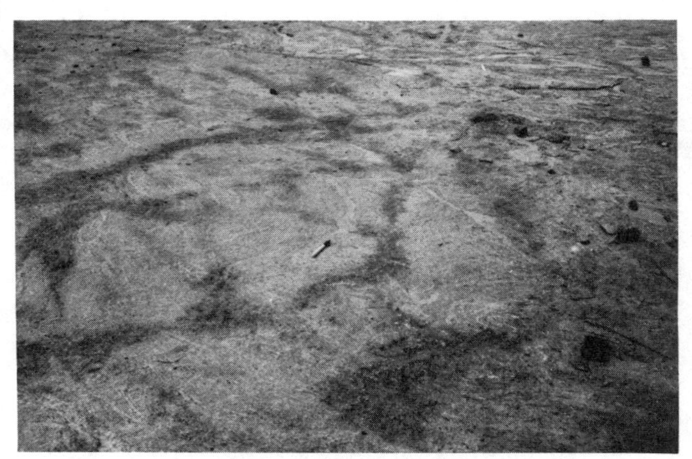

Figure 1. Patchy dark charnockite in migmatized veins in a quarry near Kabbal, Karnataka, south India.

These textures, indicative of metamorphic transformation of amphibolite gneiss to charnockite in the presence of a vapor phase, provide evidence, along with the field relations of simple isograds which cut across complex structures and many lithologies, that many granulite terrains are metamorphic terrains in the ordinary sense. Partial melting and migmatite formation may also be a characteristic part of the process in some gradational terrains; but in others, such as Broken Hill, there is little evidence of migmatite formation (Binns, 1964).

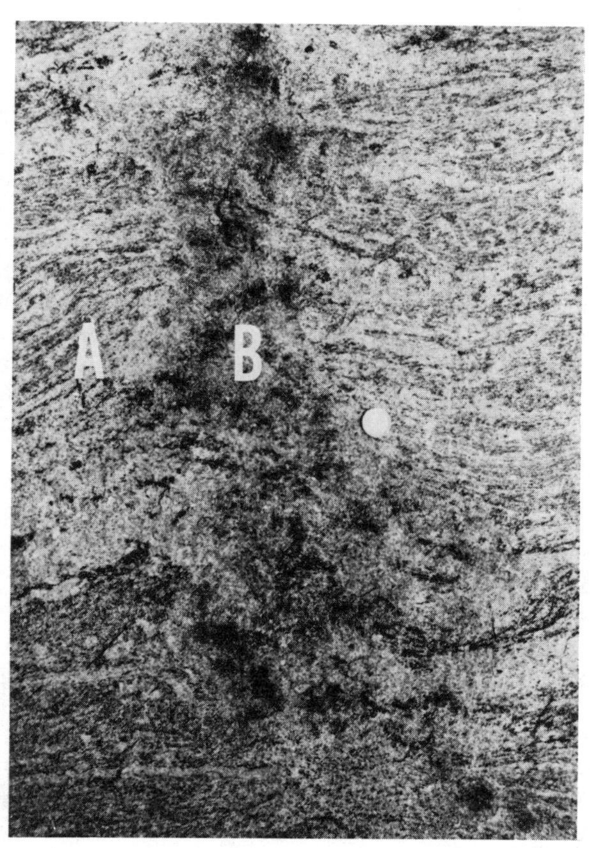

Figure 2. Close-up of a charnockite patch in the Kabbal quarry. Orthopyroxene-bearing vein transgresses gneissic foliation. Analyses of charnockite "B" and gneiss "A" given in Table 1.

TABLE 1. ANALYSES OF SOUTH INDIAN CHARNOCKITES AND GNEISS

wt. %	ppm	Kabbal Amphibolitic Gneiss "A"	Kabbal Charnockite "B"	Avg. Transit. Charnockite,* Karnataka	Avg. Massif Charnockite,* S. India
SiO_2	(F)	70.22 (730)	71.66 (470)	72.23 (268)	70.73 (195)
Al_2O_3	(Cl)	14.06 (120)	13.75 (95)	14.19 (91)	14.69 (118)
TiO_2	(Sr)	0.64 (130)	0.49 (110)	0.22 (183)	0.31 (327)
FeO†	(Ba)	4.09 (500)	3.14 (550)	2.46 (513)	2.91 (475)
MgO	(Zr)	0.79 (310)	0.79 (230)	0.77 (150)	1.42 (120)
MnO	(Cr)	0.06 (152)	0.06 (125)	0.04 (198)	0.04 (323)
CaO	(Rb)	2.50 (70)	1.99 (60)	2.46 (50)	3.36 (16.7)
Na_2O	(U)	3.75 (1.4)	3.77 (1.0)	3.84 (0.6)	4.18 (0.2)
K_2O	(Th)	3.40 (15)	3.68 (15)	3.04 (9.5)	1.70 (6.5)
P_2O_5	(ΣREE)	0.17 (500)	0.12 (450)	0.10 (438)	0.08 (317)
CO_2		0.10	0.10	0.20	
H_2O§		0.48	0.47	0.45	

*Only felsic rocks with 65% < SiO_2 < 75% considered. Four transitional charnockites and six massif charnockites averaged.
†Total Fe as FeO. Totals readjusted to 100%.
§Actual loss on ignition.

The plutonic nature of the most extensive Proterozoic charnockites, notable those of the Adirondack, Grenville, and Rogaland provinces, has suggested to several workers that their granulite-facies mineralogy is the result of slow cooling of acid intrusions at considerable depths (e.g., Martignole and Schrijver, 1977). The model based on the Nain Complex for a shallow-level intrusive origin of the charnockite-anorthosite suite suggests, however, that a metamorphic overprint, not necessarily related to the igneous event, produced the definitive charnockitic character (Morse, 1982). The metamorphic processes were presumably much the same as those that produced the Archean charnockite association.

Chemical features. Numerous analyses of Archean pyroxene gneisses (e.g., Howie, 1955) have shown that they are broadly calc-alkaline in character. However, some charnockitic suites of Proterozoic acid intrusions, associated with anorthosite bodies, have been shown to be mildly alkaline, rather than calc-alkaline, with alkali-lime indices of 48-50 (Emslie, 1978). This chemical distinction, which may constitute a significant difference between Archean and Proterozoic charnockites of ultimate plutonic origin, is likely to have resulted from different provenance of the precursor igneous rocks rather than from their metamorphism.

Recent analyses of the south Indian charnockites bear on the problem of what effect a metamorphic overprint can have on the rock chemistry. Table I shows major element and selected minor element analyses of charnockite and immediately adjacent host gneiss from Kabbal. The analyzed charnockite ("B") and amphibole-bearing gneiss ("A") are shown in Figure 2. The conclusion is that there is almost no chemical distinction between the two rock types, which are so different in texture and mineralogy. The metamorphism is essentially isochemical, and proves that partial melting cannot be the agent of charnockitic segregation because there would be strong partitioning of trace elements like Rb and U between a melt and unmelted host rocks. Table I also gives average analyses of charnockites from the south Indian transition zone and from the Biligirirangan and Nilgiri Hills massifs south of Kabbal. The thorough depletion of incompatible elements and low K_2O contents are typical of granulites from the large Archean high-grade terrains and from the highest-grade zone of the Proterozoic Bamble area (Field and Clough, 1976). The Indian massif charnockites commonly lack primary biotite and show somewhat higher grades of metamorphism. However, the differences between them and the Kabbal-type incipient charnockite may be of degree rather than of kind: the massif charnockites may be the products of intense and prolonged action of anhydrous fluids, which action was just getting started at Kabbal. On the other hand, it is possible that the elevated Mg/Fe and Ca/K ratios of the massif charnockites may require some removal of an anatectic melt.

Abundant migmatite development is a characteristic feature of the transition zones of some granulite terrains, for example, in the Proterozoic Varberg gneisses of

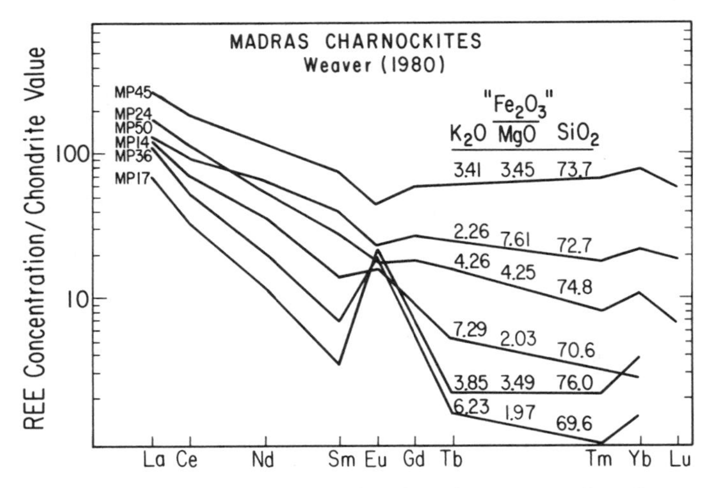

Figure 3. Rare-earth elements in six acid charnockites from Pallavaram, near Madras (Weaver, 1980). Wt. % K_2O, SiO_2, and iron oxide to MgO ratio for the six rocks shows that the element patterns do not result from magmatic processes.

southwestern Sweden (Quensel, 1951). Gneisses and metabasites are shot through with acid veins. Both metabasite and its acid veins may have granulite mineralogy. Some of the migmatization may be metasomatic and some is due to partial melting (rheomorphism). The charnockite type locality at Pallavaram, near Madras, is now recognized as a migmatitic charnockite, on the basis of field relations (Subramaniam, 1959), major-element systematics (Sen, 1974) and trace-element characteristics (Weaver, 1980). Weaver described the Madras occurrence as a high-K charnockite terrain, in contrast to other K-poor charnockite terrains such as the Scourian and south India hill terrains. Weaver's rare-earth element measurements for a number of Madras charnockites are shown in Figure 3. A striking pattern is the change from small negative europium anomalies to large positive values and greater fractionation (La/Yb ratio) with decrease of total rare-earth content. This pattern is interpreted as an anatectic effect in which partial melting leaves residues richer in plagioclase, which sequesters Eu^{2+} (Philpotts, 1970), but lower in total rare earths. In some rocks, the europium anomalies could be quantitatively related to SiO_2 and K_2O contents as indicative of the degree of partial melting. In other Madras rocks, the K_2O contents, SiO_2 contents, and Fe/Mg ratios are not obviously related to Eu anomalies (Fig. 3). This lack of coherence must be explained by some kind of metasomatism rather than igneous processes. Sen (1974) had earlier advocated anatexis and subsequent hybridization as an important agency at Madras on the basis of lack of correlation between K_2O and mafic components in many rocks and petrographic evidence of biotite replacing amphibole. Weaver (1980) concluded that both K-metasomatism and palingenesis immediately preceded granulite metamorphism at Madras.

The evidence from the Indian transitional localities favors a metamorphic origin of charnockite. The process may be profoundly metasomatic with prior introduction of K_2O, as at Madras, or nearly isochemical, as at Kabbal. Commonly, the process is attended by migmatite development. One must be careful to recognize that partial melting is a closely associated, but not causal phenomenon in the first appearance of orthopyroxene. Both basic and acid components of the migmatites have been converted to granulites in southern India. The situation may be similar in the transitional granulite region of the Adirondack Lowlands. Carl (1981) interpreted element redistribution patterns in terms of in situ migmatization with retention of the partial melt phase, and closed system behavior on scales larger than an outcrop. It is not certain yet whether the severe depletions of the incompatible elements, notably U and Rb, seen in the very high-grade, or massif charnockites, demand removal of an anatectic melt or whether these depletions could be achieved by prolonged leaching by a vapor phase.

The highly variable and sometimes exotic nature of the granulite-forming fluids has often been emphasized. Rather low P_{O_2} was deduced for Scourian granulites by Rollinson (1980) from compositions of coexisting oxide minerals, but quite oxidized granulites have also been reported (Dymek, 1983). Some Indian granulites feature biotites, hornblendes, and apatites very rich in F (Leelanandam, 1970; Blattner, 1980). Relatively high SO_4 and CO_3 activities of fluids are indicated by the frequent reports of scapolite from granulite terrains (Blattner, 1976; Von Knorring and Kennedy, 1958). These features have been used to discuss the role of metamorphosed evaporites as essential to the development of the Adirondack anorthosite and associated rocks (Gresens, 1978). Taylor (1969) proposed, from oxygen isotope studies of Adirondack and Grenville charnockites, that CO_2 decarbonated from crustal limestone was heavily involved in metamorphic recrystallization. Thick evaporite sequences with abundant $CaSO_4$ and biogenic graphite have been reported from the Archean of Brazil (Sighinolfi et al., 1980). Anhydrous, low-P_{O_2} vapors might be generated by metamorphism of such deposits.

An important recent contribution is the discovery of very strong local variations in oxygen isotope ratios (Valley and O'Neil, 1981) and oxygen fugacity (Valley et al., 1983) in Adirondack granulites. The extreme values represent relics of biological and diagenetic activity, contact metamorphic effects around shallow anorthosite intrusions, and local mineralogic buffering of the fluid phase, which effects would likely have been erased if the granulite terrain had equilibrated with a pervasive mantle-derived fluid. This evidence again suggests that stratigraphic sources of the volatile phase of granulite metamorphism were, in some cases, important.

Geothermometry-geobarometry. Application of the

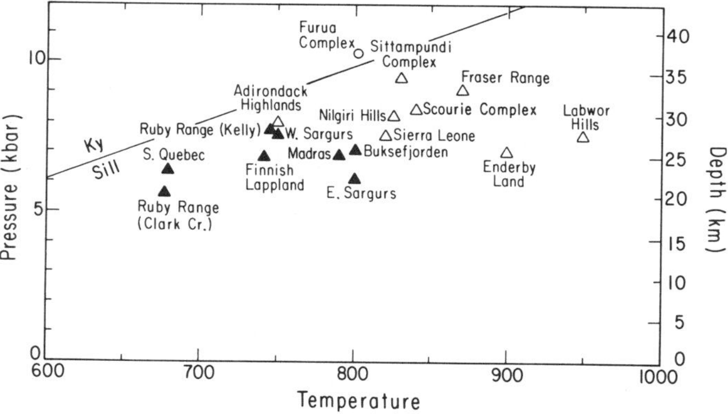

Figure 4. Pressures of metamorphism of Precambrian granulite terrains calculated from thermodynamic data for the assemblage plagioclase-orthopyroxene-garnet-quartz (Newton and Perkins, 1982) and published mineral analyses supplemented by a few personal communications. *Triangular symbols* are from sillimanite terrains. *Circle* is from a kyanite-bearing terrain. *Solid symbols* are from gradational terrains. Madras is so classified because of high K_2O, high-Rb, metasomatic, and migmatitic charnockites. *Open symbols* are from massif terrains. Temperatures are preferred estimates of authors of mineral analyses. Each point is the average of calculations for several rocks. Sources: *Furua Comples, Tanzania:* Coolen (1980). *Sittampundi Complex, Tamil Nadu,* and *Nilgiri Hills, Tamil Nadu, India:* unpublished data of the authors. *W. Sargurs* and *E. Sargurs, Karnataka, India, Scourie Complex, Scotland* and *Sierra Leone:* unpublished data of H. R. Rollinson. *Enderby Land, Antarctica:* Grew (1980). *Labwor Hills, Uganda:* Nixon et al. (1973). *Fraser Range, Australia:* unpublished data of A. F. Wilson. *Madras, Tamil Nadu, India:* Weaver et al. (1978). *Buksefjorden, Greenland:* Wells (1979). *Adirondack Highlands, New York:* Bohlen and Essene (1980). *Ruby Range, Montana:* Dahl (1980). *Finnish Lappland:* Hömann et al. (1980). *S. Quebec:* Perkins (1979). Experimental kyanite-sillimanite boundary from Holdaway (1971).

semiempirical two-pyroxene geothermometer (Wood and Banno, 1973; Wells, 1977) to granulite areas yields temperatures in the range 700-900° C (e.g., Hewins, 1975). Garnet-clinopyroxene Fe, Mg distributions, experimentally calibrated by Ellis and Green (1979) as a geothermometer, commonly give somewhat lower temperatures for the same regions. The alkali feldspar-plagioclase and magnetite-ilmenite thermometers yield the lowest-temperature estimates, running down to 650°C for some Adirondack Highlands granulites (Bohlen and Essene, 1977). Despite the discrepancies, it is clear that temperatures of granulite metamorphism were high enough so that H_2O-rich rocks of a variety of lithologies would have been thoroughly melted during metamorphism. Lack of evidence for extensive melting in many areas is the principal reason for the oft-expressed condition of $P_{H_2O} << P_{total}$ (e.g., Binns, 1964).

Reliable geobarometers for charnockites have been calibrated only recently (Newton and Perkins, 1982; Bohlen et al., 1983). Earlier pressure estimates were based, for the most part, on the aluminum content of orthopyroxene with garnet, which is useful for Mg-rich peridotites but which has poor calibration for the crustal pressure range and complex natures of granulite garnets and pyroxenes. Two new charnockite geobarometers are based on the reactions:

$$\text{A) } \underset{\text{anorthite}}{CaAl_2Si_2O_8} + \underset{\text{enstatite}}{Mg_2Si_2O_8} = \underset{\text{pyrope}}{2/3Mg_3Al_2Si_3O_{12}} + \underset{\text{grossular}}{1/3Ca_3Al_2Si_3O_{12}} + \underset{\text{quartz}}{SiO_2}$$

$$\text{B) } \underset{\text{anorthite}}{CaAl_2Si_2O_8} + \underset{\text{diopside}}{CaMgSi_2O_6} = \underset{\text{pyrope}}{1/3Mg_3Al_2Si_3O_{12}} + \underset{\text{grossular}}{2/3Ca_3Al_2Si_3O_{12}} + \underset{\text{quartz}}{SiO_2}$$

The barometer calibrations (Perkins and Newton, 1981) depend on calorimetric measurements and deductions from high-temperature, high-pressure phase equilibrium work.

All pressure calculations depend on the accuracy of mineral analyses and on independent temperature estimates. Fortunately, the above barometers do not depend sensitively on temperature in the range 700°-950°C. Figure 4 shows pressure calculations for 18 granulite terrains. Each pressure estimate is the average for several different rocks. The average spread for a given terrain is ± 800 bars. Temperatures were taken as the preferred estimates of the authors of the mineral analyses. Sources are given in the caption of Figure 4.

Figure 4 shows two striking features. The granulites classified as transitional show lower pressures than the massif granulites. This effect is even more apparent when it is considered that some of the transitional granulites lack garnet, as the Kabbal specimens, and thus may have formed at pressures below the effective barometric range. The massif granulites cluster in the pressure range of 8.5 ± 1.5 kbar. All of the terrains except one have sillimanite as the regional Al_2SiO_5 polymorph in metapelites. The Proterozoic Furua Complex of the Mozambique mobile belt has kyanite (Coolen, 1980). The calculated pressures satisfy the experimental Al_2SiO_5 diagram (Holdaway, 1971). The narrow pressure range for granulite terrains of a variety of ages (Grenville through late Archean) and a variety of lithologies may require that some oft-repeated mechanism of metamorphism has been operative.

The present pressure calculations of granulite terrains lie between the extreme estimates of other authors. O'Hara and Yarwood (1978) calculated pressures of 15 ± 3 kbar for the Scourian metamorphism, based largely on minimum pressures of garnet stability in basic compositions, a not-well-determined criterion. Saxena (1977) advocated a very low-pressure (~2-3 kbar) and high-temperature (800°-900°C) charnockite geotherm based largely on experimental phase equilibria, but underrating the effect of $P_{H_2O} < P_{total}$.

Experimental evidence for low P_{H_2O}. Figure 5 shows experimental phase equilibrium relations of Luth (1967) bearing on the charnockite problem. Univariant equilibria in the model system K_2O-MgO-Al_2O_3-SiO_2-H_2O intersect near 780°C to limit the upper H_2O pressure for the coexistence of the definitive charnockite assemblage K-feldspar-

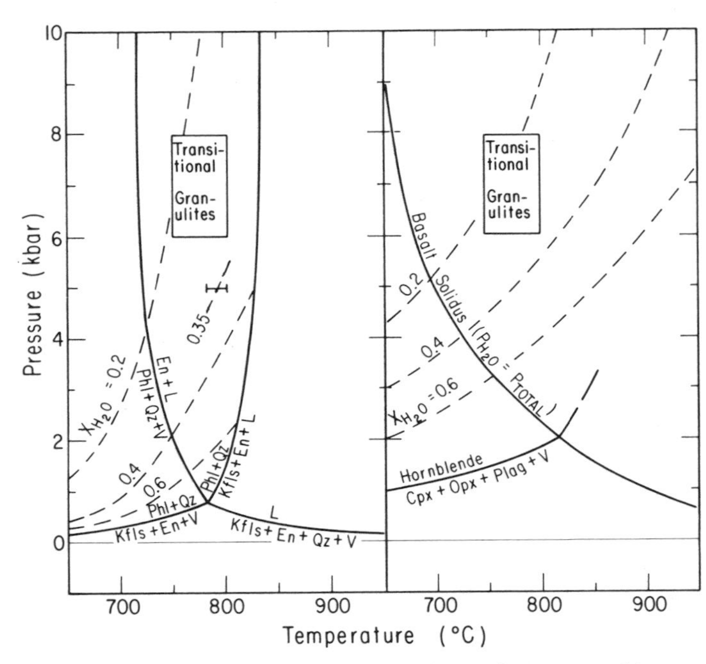

Figure 5. Experimental stability relations of the assemblages phlogopite-quartz in the system K_2O-Al_2O_3-MgO-SiO_2-H_2O (Luth, 1967) and hornblende in a mafic system with $P_{H_2O} = P_{total}$ (Choudhuri and Winkler, 1967). Shown also is the basalt solidus of Lambert and Wyllie (1972) for $P_{H_2O} = P_{total}$. Dashed lines are phlogopite + quartz and hornblende breakdown reactions calculated by the present authors and Wells (1979) for $X_{H_2O} < 1$. The occurrence of the assemblage biotite-quartz-K-feldspar-hypersthene in transitional charnockites and of the assemblage hornblende-clinopyroxene-orthopyroxene-plagioclase in metabasites from the same terrains indicates that the mole fraction of H_2, X_{H_2O} was between 0.3 and 0.1 for the P-T conditions deduced from Figure 4. *Symbols:* Phl = phlogopite, Qz = quartz, Kfls = K-feldspar, En = enstatite, V = vapor, L = liquid, Cpx = clinopyroxene, Opx = orthopyroxene, Plag = plagioclase. The experimental bracket of the phlogopite + quartz reaction at X_{H_2O} = 0.35 of Bohlen et al. (1983) is shown.

orthopyroxene to about 700 bars. Calculated curves for $P_{H_2O} < P_{total}$ in Figure 5 based on ideal CO_2-H_2O mixing (Lewis and Randall Rule), together with the temperture and total pressure ranges for the transitional charnockites from Figure 4, require H_2O in the range 0.1-0.3 mole fraction of a vapor phase. If the slight nonideality of H_2O-CO_2 mixtures at these temperatures and pressures is considered, the results will not be appreciably changed. The major chemical departures from the simple experimental system are FeO, F, and Ti. FeO will be nearly equipartitional between biotite and orthopyroxene, so that the positions of the calculated curves will not shift appreciably. TiO_2 and F in biotite will stabilize it somewhat against reduced P_{H_2O}, so that the critical mole fraction of H_2O for the coexistence of orthopyroxene could be somewhat lower than 0.3. Similar chemographic analysis with experimental phase relations of two pyroxenes + plagioclase versus amphibole (Choudhuri and Winkler, 1967) instead of biotite leads to virtually the same conclusion (Fig. 5) as was demonstrated by Wells (1979) for the Buksefjorden, Greenland charnockites, and mafic granulites. High-grade massif areas, such as the south Indian Highlands, in which charnockites commonly lack primary biotite and amphibole, may have been metamorphosed at still lower P_{H_2O}.

Fluid inclusions. Numerous studies have shown that the dominant fluid inclusion species in quartz and feldspar of many granulite-grade rocks is nearly pure CO_2. Recent application of CO_2 fluid inclusion geobarometry (Coolen, 1981; Hollister, 1982) based on equation of state data of CO_2 (Touret and Bottinga, 1979) has shown that the pressures of entrapment of CO_2 in the granulites studied are compatible with the pressures of granulite metamorphism inferred from mineralogical geobarometry, and thus that the CO_2-rich fluids of the inclusions represent the volatile phase of peak metamorphic conditions. A recent study of the Kabbal rocks from south India (Hansen et al., 1983) revealed that the charnockitic portions of altered gneisses, portion B of Figure 2, differ in fluid inclusions from the host gneisses by having vastly more CO_2-rich fluid inclusions. An occasional irregular inclusion shows a small amount of immiscible H_2O lining its cavity, which probably corresponds to about 30 mole percent H_2O in the bulk fluid, this being near the lower limit of optically detectable H_2O in CO_2-dominated inclusions (Roedder, 1972). The calculated pressure of entrapment is about 5.5 kbar, very near to the pressure inferred by Harris and Jayaram (1982) from mineralogy of metapelites in the Kabbal area. A geobarometric traverse across the south Indian transition zone south of Kabbal showed that the entrapment pressures of CO_2 increased from 5.5 to 8.0 kbar in the high-grade massif areas, in keeping with a continuous increase calculated from geobarometers A and B.

Fluid inclusions from several Adirondack charnockites (Henry, 1978) showed higher levels of H_2O than the Kabbal rocks, with vapors of approximately 50 mole percent H_2O apparently coexisting with orthopyroxene, in contrast with the deduction of an upper limit of X_{H_2O} = 0.3 of the preceding section. The reason for this discrepancy is not known, but it is probably significant that the calculated entrapment pressures average about 3 kbar for the Adirondack charnockites, which is not compatible with the 8 kbar pressures inferred for Adirondack metamorphism from the mineralogy. The CO_2-H_2O fluid inclusions thus may represent fluids that were either entrapped early in the intrusive history, perhaps at the low-pressure igneous intrusive stage, or later, in a retrogressive stage.

PETROGENESIS OF CHARNOCKITES

The present discussion emphasizes a possible origin of charnockite by metamorphism of feldspathic crustal rocks of plutonic, volcanic, and sedimentary origin, in the presence of high-temperature, low-P_{H_2O} volatiles, probably dominantly CO_2. Much of the field evidence for this process comes from transitional amphibolite-to-granulite terrains where charnockite is seen in an arrested state of replacement of pre-existing gneisses. Metasomatism by K-rich, probably hydrous fluids, and anatexis were frequently characteristic associates of the transformation process but were not essential to it. Migmatite formation commonly resulted as hot aqueous fluids purged from deeper crustal rocks rose above a wave of CO_2. Charnockitization followed, converting neosome and paleosome to granulites. Incompatible elements may have been removed in rising partial melt fractions or perhaps by prolonged leaching by high-pressure CO_2 vapors. The observed REE patterns may have been inherited from fractional crystallization of the gneiss precursors.

A conceptual model of the conditions for the creation of crustal charnockitic terrains is given in Figure 6. A deep crustal source of heat and CO_2 is necessary. It has been postulated that CO_2 streaming may be instrumental in transferring heat for crustal metamorphism (Schuiling and Kreulen, 1979). A wave of dehydration spreads from the source as CO_2 permeates outward. The horizon of H_2O purged from the deep crust rises, causing transient migmatization at higher levels. At a given level, partial melting and K-metasomatism are followed by drying and depletion as high CO_2 activity follows the hydrous forerunner. Migmatites and country rock are converted to granulites.

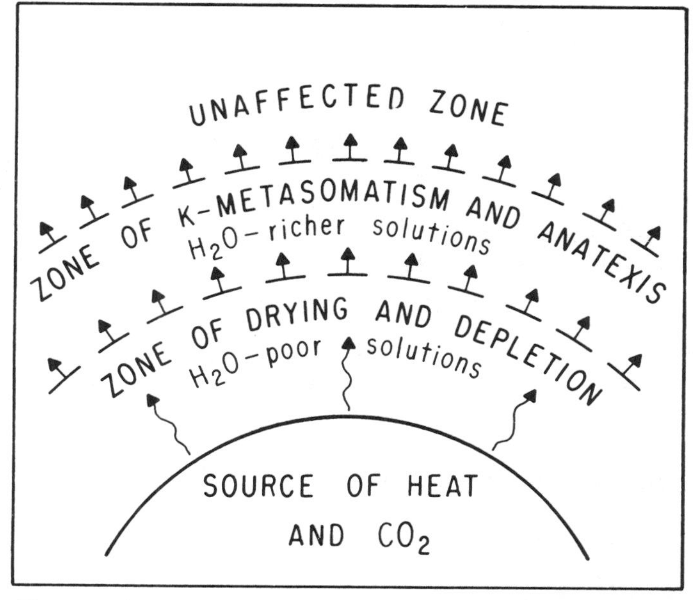

Figure 6. Conceptual model of crustal granulite metamorphism. The deep source of heat and CO_2 could be a mantle diapir, a basalt underplate, or CO_2-rich continental shelf sediment buried under a hot-soled overthrust of continental dimensions. Rising hot CO_2 purges H_2O from the lower crust, promoting transient migmatization at a higher level.

The source of the postulated voluminous CO_2 is the outstanding problem of the origin of the Precambrian charnockite terrains. The major possibilities include decarbonation of a mantle diapir below the crust (Tarney and Windley, 1977), CO_2 exuded from low-crustal basaltic magma underplates (Touret, 1971) or high-crustal tonalitic magma overplates (Wells, 1979), CO_2 devolatilized from subducted limestones (Newton et al., 1980) and carbonate-bearing continental shelf sediments at the interface of a continental collision zone.

Continental collision has been suggested as the tectonic cause of the Adirondack and Grenville late Proterozoic metamorphism (McLelland and Isaachsen, 1980), and for the nearly contemporaneous high-grade metamorphism of southwest Norway (Falkum and Petersen, 1980). The sequence may have begun with rifting of the North American-European continent about 1400 m.y. ago and shallow-level emplacement of the subalkaline anorogenic anorthosite-quartz syenite-rapakivi granite magma suite (Emslie, 1978). Shelf sediments would have accumulated in the widening basin between continental segments. Subsequent closure of the basin may have caused one continental segment to overthrust the other, catching shelf sediments and evaporites at the flat interface of a doubled continent. These stratigraphic sources of CO_2, B, F, and S would have been heated to the temperature prevailing at the base of the overriding continent; this temperature might have been augmented by attendant magmatism. Devolatilization would drive the volatiles into surrounding rocks to leave their imprint on the metamorphism. A stratigraphic volatile source, rather than a subcontinental one has the advantage of explaining strong local gradients in carbon and oxygen isotope ratios and in oxygen fugacity, rather than the monotonous patterns expected to be imparted by equilibration with a mantle-derived fluid. Many rocks may have previously been baked out by proximity to shallow intrusions during the anorogenic phase, and hence were relatively dry to begin with, by analogy with the dry Nain Complex aureoles (Berg, 1977). Subsequent volatile action may have been patchy, leaving widespread igneous textures and incomplete charnockitization, as in the Stark Complex (Brock, 1980). Horizontal structures (nappes and overthrusts), abundant supracrustals, and 8-kbar metamorphism are plausibly explained by the continental doubling model.

The large amount of CO_2 necessary to produce granulite metamorphism of a major portion of the crust is a problem of most of the models of granulite metamorphism. The continental collision model has the advantage that it predicts granulite metamorphism only in the vicinity of the suture zone (i.e., near the continent-continent interface), and this restriction would greatly reduce the amount of CO_2 ultimately required. The common supposition that exposed granulite terrains are underlain by granulite-facies rocks through the entire crustal column is not a necessary consequence of the continental collision model. From this point of view, the granulite terrain model of the deep continental crust (Fountain and Salisbury, 1981) loses some of its appeal.

Many features of Archean high-grade terrains are analogous to the Proterozoic high-grade terrains, including nappe structures, supracrustals, and transition zones with mappable isograds. The calc-alkaline nature of many Archean charnockites, contrasting with the subalkaline character of many Proterozoic charnockites, indicates that igneous gneiss precursors had somewhat different origins. However, the metamorphic overprint of the Archean charnockites implies, in its similarities to Proterozoic high-grade metamorphism, that if the continental collision model applies to Proterozoic granulites, some similar form of plate tectonics was operative at least back to 2.7 billion years ago.

ACKNOWLEDGMENTS

A National Science Foundation grant, EAR 78-15939 (RCN), provided funds for field work in India, from which much of the present discussion results. Another NSF grant, EAR 79-95723 (RCN), provided funds for microanalysis of the Indian rocks and minerals, which is the basis for some of the geothermometry-geobarometry discussed here. Fluid inclusion studies were supported by NSF EAR 81-07110.

Helpful discussions with C. S. Pichamuthu, B. P. Radhakrishna, A. S. Janardhan, J. Martignole, D. Perkins III, B. S. Brock, J. W. Valley, L. D. Ashwal, and W. Glassley are acknowledged.

We especially thank an anonymous reviewer whose well-taken comments diverted this paper from the larger original topic of the origin of granulite terrains in general to the more tractable topic of the origin of charnockites.

REFERENCES CITED

Berg, J. H., 1977, Regional geobarometry in the contact aureoles of the anorthositic Nain Complex, Labrador: J. Petrol., v. 18, p. 399–430.

Binns, R. A., 1964, Zones of progressive regional metamorphism in the Williyama complex, Broken Hill district, New South Wales; J. Geol. Soc. Australia, v. 11, p. 283–330.

Blattner, P., 1976, Replacement of hornblende by garnet in granulite facies assemblages near Milford Sound, New Zealand: Contr. Min. Pet., v. 55, p. 181–190.

—— 1980, Chlorine and fluorine in apatite, biotite and hornblende of basic charnockites from Kondapalli, India: N. Jb. Miner. Mh., 1980, p. 283–288.

Bohlen, S. R., Boettcher, A. L., and Wall, V. J., 1983, Biotite-quartz, sanidine-quartz dehydration and melting: GSA Abstr. w/Prog., v. 14, p. 446–447.

Bohlen, S. R., and Essene, E. J., 1977, Feldspar and oxide thermometry of granulites in the Adirondack Highlands; Contr. Min. Pet., v. 62, p. 153–169.

—— 1980, Evaluation of coexisting garnet-biotite, garnet-clinopyroxene, and other Mg-Fe thermometers in Adirondack granulites; Geol. Soc. Amer. Bull., v. 91, (Pt. II), p. 685–719.

Bohlen, S. R., Wall, V. J., and Boettcher, A. L., 1983, Experimental investigation and application of garnet granulite equilibria: Contr. Min. Pet. (in press).

Brock, B. S., 1980, Stark complex (Dexter Lake area): Petrology, chemistry, structure, and relation to other green rock complexes and layered gneisses, northern Adirondacks, New York; Geol. Soc. Amer. Bull., v. 91 (Pt. I), p. 93–97.

Brown, G. C., and Fyfe, W. S., 1970, The production of granitic melts during ultrametamorphism: Contr. Min. Pet., v. 28, p. 310–318.

Buddington, A. F., 1963, Isograds and the role of H_2O in metamorphic facies of orthogneisses of the northwest Adirondack area, New York: Geol. Soc. Amer. Bull., v. 74, p. 1155–1182.

Carl, J. D., 1981, Alkali metasomatism in the major gneiss, northwest Adirondacks, New York: open system or closed?: Geochim. et Cosmochim. Acta, v. 45, p. 1603–1607.

Choudhuri, A., and Winkler, H.G.F., 1967, Anthophyllit und Hornblende ineingen Metamorphosen Reaktionen: Contr. Min. Pet., v. 14, p. 293–315.

Clemens, J. D., and Wall, V. J., 1981, Origin and crystallization of some peraluminous (S-type) granitic magmas: Canad. Mineral., v. 19, p. 111–131.

Collerson, K. D., and Fryer, B. J., 1978, The role of fluids in the formation and subsequent development of early continental crust: Contr. Min. Pet., v. 67, p. 151–167.

Compton, R. R., 1960, Charnockitic rocks of the Santa Lucia Range, California; Amer. J. Sci., v. 258, p. 609–639.

Coolen, J.J.M.M.M., 1980, Chemical petrology of the Furua granulite complex, southern Tanzania: GUA (Amsterdam) papers, v. 13, (Ser. 1), p. 1–258.

—— 1981, Carbonic fluid inclusions in granulites from Tanzania—a comparison of geobarometric methods based on fluid density and mineral chemistry; Chem. Geol., v. 37, p. 59–77.

Cooray, P. G., 1962, Charnockites and their associated gneisses in the Pre-cambrian of Ceylon: Quart. J. Geol. Soc. Lond., v. 118, p. 239–266.

—— 1969, Charnockites as metamorphic rocks: Amer. J. Sci., v. 267, p. 969–982.

Dahl, P. S., 1980), The thermal-compositional dependence of Fe^{2+} -Mg^{2+} distributions between coexisting garnet and pyroxene: applications to geothermometry: Amer. Mineral, v. 65, p. 852–866.

DeWaard, D., 1969, The occurrence of charnockite in the Adirondacks: a note on the origin and definition of charnockite: Amer. J. Sci., v. 267, p. 983–987.

Drury, S. A., 1973, The geochemistry of Precambrian granulite facies rocks from the Lewisian Complex of Tiree, Inner Hebrides, Scotland: Chem. Geol. v. 11, p. 167–188.

—— 1980, Lewisian pyroxene gneisses from Barra and the geochemistry of the Archaean lower crust: Scott J. Geol., v. 16, p. 199–207.

Dymek, R. F., 1983, Fe-Ti oxides in the Malene supracrustals and the occurrence of Nb-rich rutile: Geol. Surv. of Greenland Bull. (in press).

Ellis, D. J., and Green, D. H., 1979, An experimental study of the effect of Ca upon garnet-clinopyroxene Fe-Mg exchange equilibria: Contr. Min. Pet., v. 71, p. 13–22.

Emslie, R. F., 1978, Anorthosite massifs, rapakivi granites, and late Proterozoic rifting of North America: Precam. Res., v. 7, p. 61–98.

Falkum, T., and Petersen, J. S., 1980, The Sveconorwegian Orogenic Belt, a case of Late-Proterozoic plate-collision: Geol. Rundschau, v. 69, p. 622–647.

Field, D., and Clough, P.W.L., 1976, K/Rb ratios and metasomatism in metabasites from a Precambrian amphibolite-granulite transition zone: J. Geol. Soc. Lond., v. 132, p. 277–288.

Field, D., Drury, S. A., and Cooper, D. C., 1980, Rare-earth and LIL element fractionation in high-grade charnockitic gneisses, south Norway: Lithos, v. 13, p. 281–289.

Fountain, D. M., and Salisbury, M. H., 1981, Exposed cross-sections through the continental crust: implications for crustal structure, petrology and evolution: Earth, Plan. Sci. Lett., v. 56, p. 263–277.

Friend, C.R.L., 1981, The timing of charnockite and granite formation in relation to influx of CO_2 at Kabbaldurga, Karnataka, South India: Nature, v. 294, p. 550–552.

Fyfe, W. S., 1973, The generation of batholiths: Tectonophysics, v. 17, p. 273–283.

Green, T. H., 1969, Experimental fractional crystallization of quartz diorite and its application to the problem of anorthosite origin: N.Y. State Mus., Sci. Serv. Mem., v. 18, p. 23–29.

Gresens, R. L., 1978, Evaporites as precursors of massif anorthosites: Geology, v. 6, p. 46–50.

Grew, E. S., 1980, Sapphirine + quartz association from Archean rocks in Enderby Land, Antarctica: Amer. Mineral, v. 65, p. 821–836.

Hamilton, P. J., Evensen, N. M., and O'Nions, R. K., 1979, Sm-Nd systematics of Lewisian gneisses: implications for the origin of granulites: Nature, v. 277, p. 25–28.

Hansen, E. C., Newton, R. C., and Janardhan, A. S., 1983, Pressures, temperatures and metamorphic fluids across an unbroken amphibolite-facies to granulite-facies transition in southern Karnataka, India, *in* A. Kroener, A. M. Goodwin, and G. N. Hanson, eds., Project 92, IGCP, Final Volume (in press).

Harris, N.B.W., and Jayaram, S., 1982, Metamorphism of cordierite gneisses from the Bangalore region of the Indian Archean: Lithos, v. 15, p. 89–98.

Heier, K. S., 1973, Geochemistry of granulite facies rocks and problems of their origin: Phil. Trans. R. Soc. Lond., A-273, p. 429–442.

—— 1976, Chemical composition and origin of Archean granulites and charnockites, *in* B. F. Windley, ed., The Early History of the Earth, New York, John Wiley, Interscience, p. 159–164.

Henry, D. L., 1978, A study of metamorphic fluid inclusions in granulite facies rocks of the eastern Adirondacks. [Senior Thesis]: Dept. of Civil Eng., Princeton Univ., 76 p.

Hewins, R. H., 1975, Pyroxene geothermometry of some granulite facies rocks: Contr. Min. Pet., v. 50, p. 205–209.

Holdaway, M. J., 1971, Stability of andalusite and the aluminum silicate phase diagram: Amer. J. Sci., v. 271, p. 97–131.

Holland, J. G., and Lambert, R. St. J., 1975, The chemistry and origin of the Lewisian gneisses of the Scottish mainland: the Scourie and Inver assemblages and subcrustal accretion: Precamb. Res., v. 2, p. 161–188.

Hollister, L. S., 1982, Metamorphic evidence for rapid (2 mm/yr) uplift of a portion of the Central Gneiss complex, Coast Mountains, B.C.: Canad. Mineral, v. 20, p. 319–332.

Hörmann, P. K., Raith, M., Raase, P., Ackermand, D., and Seifert, F., 1980, the granulite complex of Finnish Lappland: petrology and metamorphic conditions in the Ivalojoki-Inarijärvi area: Geol. Surv. Finland Bull., v. 308, p. 1–95.

Howie, R. A., 1955, The geochemistry of the charnockite series of Madras, India: Trans. Roy. Soc. Edinburgh, v. 62, p. 725–768.

Howie, R. A., 1967, Charnockites and their colour: J. Geol. Soc. Ind., v. 8, p. 1–7.

Hubbard, F. H., 1978, Geochemistry of the Varberg granite gneisses: Geol. För. Stock. Föhr., v. 100, p. 31–38.

Hubbard, F. H., and Whitley, J. E., 1979, REE in charnockite and associated rocks, southwest Sweden: Lithos, v. 12, p. 1–11.

Hubregtse, J.J.M.W., 1980, The Archaean Pikwitonei granulite domain and its position at the margin of the northwestern Superior Province (Central Manitoba): Manitoba Geol. Surv. Pap. GP80–3, p. 1–16.

Hynes, A., 1980, Carbonization and mobility of Ti, Y, and Zr in Ascot Formation metabasalts, SE Quebec: Contr. Min. Pet., v. 75, p. 79–88.

Janardhan, A. S., Newton, R. C., and Smith, J. V., 1979, Ancient crustal metamorphism at low P_{H_2O}: charnockite formation at Kabbaldurga, south India: Nature, v. 278, p. 511–514.

Lambert, I. B., and Wyllie, P. J., 1972, Melting of gabbro (quartz eclogite) with excess water to 35 kilobars, with geological implications: J. Geol., v. 80, p. 693–708.

Leelanandam, C., 1980, Chemical mineralogy of hornblendes and biotites from the charnockitic rocks of Kondapalli, India: J. Petrol. v. 11, p. 475–505.

Luth, W. C., 1967, System $KAlSiO_4$-SiO_4SiO_2-H_2O. I. Inferred phase relations and petrologic applications: J. Petrol., v. 8, p. 372–416.

Madsen, J. K., 1977, Fluid inclusions in the Kleivan granite, South Norway, I: Microthermometry: Amer. J. Sci., v. 277, p. 673–696.

Martignole, J., and Schrijver, K., 1977, Anorthosite-farsundite complexes in the southern part of the Grenville Province: Geosci. Canada, v. 4, no. 3, p. 137–143.

Mason, R., 1973, The Limpopo mobile belt—southern Africa: Phil. Trans. Roy. Soc. Lond., A-273, p. 463–485.

McCarthy, T. S., 1976, Chemical interrelationships in a low-pressure granulite terrain in Namaqualand, South Africa, and their bearing on granite genesis and the composition of the lower crust: Geochim. Cosmochim. Acta, v. 40, p. 1057–1068.

McLelland, J., and Isaachsen, Y., 1980, Structural synthesis of the southern and central Adirondacks: A model for the Adirondacks as a whole and plate-tectonics interpretations: Geol. Soc. Amer. Bull., v. 91 (Pt. I), p. 68–72.

Morse, S. A., 1982, A partisan review of Proterozoic anorthosites: Amer. Mineral, v. 67, p. 1087–1100.

Nesbitt, H. W., 1980, Genesis of the New Quebec and Adirondack granulites: evidence for their production by partial melting: Contr. Min. Pet., v. 72, p. 303–310.

Newton, R. C., and Perkins, D., 1982, Thermodynamic calibration of geobarometers based on the assemblage garnet-plagioclase-orthopyroxene (clinopyroxene)-quartz: Amer. Mineral 67, p. 203–222.

Newton, R. C., Smith, J. V., and Windley, B. F., 1980, Carbonic metamorphism, granulites and crustal growth: Nature, v. 288, p. 45–50.

Nixon, P. H., Reedman, A. J., and Burns, L. K., 1973, Sapphirine-bearing granulites from Labwor, Uganda: Min. Mag., v. 39, p. 420–428.

O'Hara, M. J., and Yarwood, G., 1978, High pressure-temperature point on an Archaean geotherm, implied magma genesis by crustal anatexis and consequences for garnet pyroxene thermometry and barometry: Phil. Trans. Roy. Soc. Lond., A-228, p. 441–456.

O'Nions, R. K., and Pankhurst, R. J., 1978, Early Archaean rocks and geochemical evolution of the earth's crust: Earth, Plan. Sci. Lett., v. 38, p. 211–236.

Perkins, D., 1979, Application of new thermodynamic data to mineral equilibria. [Unpub. Ph.D. thesis]: Univ. of Michigan, 214 p.

Perkins, D., and Newton, R. C., 1981, Charnockite geobarometers based on coexisting garnet-pyroxene-plagioclase-quartz: Nature, v. 292, p. 144–146.

Petersen, J. S., 1980, Rare-earth element fractionation and petrogenetic modelling in charnockitic rocks, southwest Norway: Contr. Min. Pet., v. 73, p. 161–172.

Philpotts, J. A., 1970, Redox estimation from a calculation of Eu^{2+} and Eu^{3+} concentrations in natural phases: Earth, Plan. Sci. Lett., v. 9,

p. 257–268.
Pichamuthu, C. S., 1953, "The charnockite problem": Spec. Publ., Mysore Geologists' Assoc.
—— 1960, Charnockite in the making: Nature, v. 188, p. 135–136.
—— 1961, Transformation of peninsular gneiss into charnockite in Mysore State, India: J. Geol. Soc. India, v. 2, p. 46–49.
—— 1965, Regional metamorphism and charnockitization in Mysore State, India: Ind. Mineral, v. 6, p. 119–126.
Pride, C., and Muecke, G. K., 1980, Rare earth element geochemistry of the Scourian Complex, N.W. Scotland—evidence for the granite-granulite link: Contr. Min. Pet., v. 73, p. 403–412.
Quensel, P., 1951, The charnockite series of the Varberg area on the southwest coast of Sweden: Arkiv. for Min. Geol., v. 1, p. 229–232.
Ramiengar, A. S., Ramakrishnan, M., and Viswanatha, M. ., 1978, Charnockite-gneiss-complex relationship in southern Karnataka: J. Geol. Soc. of India, v. 19, p. 411–419.
Roedder, E., 1972, The composition of fluid inclusions: U.S. Geol. Surv. Prof. Pap. 440JJ, 164 p.
Rollinson, H. R., 1980, Iron titanium oxides as an indicator of the role of the fluid phase during the cooling of granites metamorphosed to granulite grade: Min. Mag., v. 43, p. 623–631.
Rollinson, H. R., and Windley, B. F., 1980, Selective elemental depletion during metamorphism of Archaean granulites, Scourie, NW Scotland: Contr. Min. Pet., v. 72, p. 257–263.
Saxena, S. K., 1977, The charnockite geotherm: Science, v. 198, p. 614–617.
Schmid, R., 1978, Are the metapelites of the Ivrea-Verbano Zone restites?: Memorie di Scienze Geologiche, v. 33, p. 67–69.
Schuiling, R. D., and Kruelen, R., 1979, Are thermal domes heated by CO_2-rich fluids from the mantle?: Earth, Plan. Sci. Lett., v. 43, p. 298–302.
Sen, S. K., 1974, A review of some geochemical characters of the type area (Pallavaram, India) charnockites: J. Geol. Soc. India, v. 15, p. 413–420.
Sheraton, J. W., Skinner, A. C., and Tarney, J., 1973, The geochemistry of the Scourian gneisses of the Assynt district, *in* R. G. Park and J. Tarney, eds., The Early Precambrian Rocks of Scotland and Related Rocks of Greenland: Univ. Keele, p. 13–30.
Sighinolfi, G. P., Kronberg, B. I., Gorgoni, C., and Fyfe, W. S., 1980, Geochemistry and genesis of sulphide-anhydrite-bearing Archaean carbonate rocks from Bahia (Brazil): Chem. Geol., v. 29, p. 323–331.
Subramanian, A. P., 1959, Charnockites of the type area near Madras—a reinterpretation: Amer. J. Sci., v. 257, p. 321–353.
Tarney, J., and Windley, B. F., 1977, Chemistry, thermal gradients and evolution of the lower continental crust: J. Geol. Soc. Lond., v. 134, p. 153–172.
Taylor, H. P., 1969, Oxygen isotope studies of anorthosites with particular reference to the origin of bodies in the Adirondacks Mountains, New York: N.Y. State Mus., Sci. Serv. Mem., v. 18, p. 111–134.
Touret, M. J., 1970, Le faciès granulite, métamorphisme en milieu carbonique: C. R. Acad. Sci. Paris, v. 271, Ser. D., p. 2228–2231.
—— 1971, Le faciès granulite en Norwege Meridionale. I. âssociations mineralogiques: Lithos, v. 4, p. 239–249.
Touret, M. J., and Bottinga, Y., 1979, Équation d'état pour le CO_2; application aux inclusions carboniques: Bull. Minèral, v. 102, p. 577–583.
Valley, J. W., McLelland, J., Essene, E. J., and Lamb, W., 1983, Metamorphic fluids in the deep crust: evidence from the Adirondacks: Nature, v. 301, p. 226–228.
Valley, J. W., and O'Neil, J. R., 1981, $^{13}C/^{12}C$ exchange between calcite and graphite: a possible thermometer in Grenville marbles: Geochim. et Cosmochim. Acta, v. 45, p. 411–419.
von Knorring, O., and Kennedy, W. Q., 1958, The mineral paragenesis and metamorphic status of garnet-hornblende-pyroxene-scapolite gneiss from Ghana (Gold Coast): Mineral Mag., v. 31, p. 846–859.
Weaver, B. L., 1980, Rare-earth element geochemistry of Madras granulites: Contr. Min. Pet., v.71, p. 271–279.
Weaver, B. L., Tarney, J., Windley, B. F., Sugavanam, E. B., and Venkata Rao, V., 1978, Madras granulites: Geochemistry and P-T conditions of crystallization, *in* B. F. Windley, and S. M. Naqvi, eds., Archaean Geochemistry, Amsterdam, Elsevier, p. 177–204.
Wells, P.R.A., 1977, Pyroxene thermometry in simple and complex systems: Contr. Min. Pet., v. 62, p. 129–139.
—— 1979, Chemical and thermal evolution of Archaean sialic crust, southern West Greenland: J. Petrol., v. 20, p. 187–226.
Wheeler, E. P., 1960, Anorthosite-adamellite complex of Nain, Labrador: Geol. Soc. Amer. Bull., v. 71, p. 1755–1762.
Wilson, A. F. 1978, Comparison of some of the geochemical features and tectonic settings of Archaean and Proterozoic granulites, with particular reference to Australia, *in* B. F. Windley, and S. M. Naqvi, eds., Archaean Geochemistry: Amsterdam, Elsevier, p. 241–268.
Winkler, H.G.F., and von Platen, H., 1961, Experimentalle Gesteinsmetamorphose IV—Bildung anatektischer Schmelzen aus metamorphisierten Grauwacken: Geochim. et Cosmochim. Acta, v. 24, p. 48–69.
Wood, B. J., and Banno, S., 1973, Garnet-orthopyroxene and orthopyroxene-clinopyroxene relationships in simple and complex systems: Contr. Min. Pet., v. 42, p. 109–124.

Manuscript Accepted by the Society April 14, 1983

Geological Society of America
Memoir 161
1983

Tectonic controls of the time-space distribution of some Proterozoic metal deposits

Frederick J. Sawkins
Department of Geology and Geophysics
University of Minnesota
Minneapolis, Minnesota 55455

ABSTRACT

A brief review of some major types of Proterozoic metal deposits indicates that each type is characterized by a distinctive lithologic and tectonic setting. The main types of metalliferous ores considered are: volcanic-hosted massive sulfide deposits, sediment-hosted massive sulfide deposits, stratiform copper deposits, carbonate-hosted lead-zinc deposits, magmatic copper-nickel deposits, and banded iron formations.

Metal deposits in sedimentary and volcanic rocks dominate Proterozoic metallogeny, and it can be demonstrated that most formed in tectonic environments characterized by rifting. This association is reinforced by the time-space relationship between specific tectonic environments and metal deposits during Proterozoic time.

Although Proterozoic metal deposits are distinctly different from the dominant types of late Phanerozoic deposits, these differences are considered to be primarily a function of erosion levels, and initial deep burial of syngenetic-type deposits. Finally, there seems to be no compelling evidence that tectonic styles or ore-generating systems were markedly different in the Proterozoic versus those of the Phanerozoic.

INTRODUCTION

At the most fundamental level, plate tectonic activity can be viewed as a mechanism by which the earth rids itself of excess internal heat. The extent to which Phanerozoic-type plate tectonics operated during the Proterozoic is still a matter of some debate, but the requirements of mantle heat dissipation must have been equally potent during Proterozoic time. I would argue that any unique aspects of the Proterozoic geologic record are more a function of Proterozoic continental geography and preservation of intracontinental geologic terrains than of any major evolutionary changes in crust-mantle interactions.

Tectonics exert a fundamental control on igneous activity, sedimentation, and thermal activation of the upper crust; and these factors in turn determine where economic concentrations of metals will tend to form. It follows that any survey of Proterozoic metal deposits is best attempted within the framework of tectonics. Another important factor that must be considered is the evolutionary change in earth atmospheres that occurred during Proterozoic time.

The recognition of tectonic environments in ancient geologic terrains must of necessity be based on analogies to modern environments. Accordingly, bimodal magmatism (Martin and Piiwinski, 1972), anorogenic granitic ring complexes, and very thick, intracontinental sedimentary sequences are taken to indicate rifting, whereas calc-alkaline magmatism is taken to suggest plate convergence.

MAJOR TYPES OF PROTEROZOIC METAL DEPOSITS

With a few notable exceptions, Proterozoic metal deposits occur within bedded sedimentary or volcanic rocks, or their metamorphic equivalents, and are manifestly conformable with their host rocks. This conformable aspect of Proterozoic metal deposits is in sharp contrast to the majority of late Phanerozoic deposits and has led to the suggestion of fundamental changes in the nature of ore-generating systems with geologic time (Pereira and Dixon,

TABLE 1. PROTEROZOIC VOLCANICS-HOSTED MASSIVE SULFIDE ORES

District	Deposits	Host rock lithology	Composition	Age (by)	Reference
central Arizona	Jerome, Iron King & others	felsic pyroclastics	Cu, Zn, Pb	∿1.8	Anderson and Guilbert, 1978
Flin Flon Snow Lake Canada	24 deposits	minor felsic volc. major mafic volc.	Cu, Zn	∿1.8	Koo and Mossman, 1975
Outokumpu district Finland	Outokumpu	felsic volcanics black shales	Cu, Zn (Pb)	∿2.2	Huhtala, 1979
Skellefte district Sweden	many ore bodies	lepitites (felsic metavolcanics)	Cu, Zn	∿2.0	Rickard and Zweifle, 1975
Bergslagen district Sweden		leptites	Cu, Zn, Pb	∿1.9	Korak, 1973
Orijarvi district Finland	Atjala Metsamonttu Orijarvi	leptites	Cu, Zn, Pb	∿1.8	Latvalahti, 1979
northern Wisconsin	Crandon	felsic volc. mafic volc.	Cu, Zn	∿1.8	Schmidt et al,. 1978
Arabian Shield	Jabal Sayid Nugrah	felsic pryoclastics	Cu, Zn, Pb	∿0.7	Sabir, 1979

1965; Laznicka, 1973). I reject this concept. Late Phanerozoic deposits of Cordilleran-type (e.g., porphyry copper, skarn, and vein-type deposits) are emplaced at shallow levels in subaerial convergent arc environments (Sawkins, 1972), and their increasing scarcity in progressively older terrains is more logically viewed as a result of erosion of these shallow levels of arc systems.

Rigorous classification of natural phenomena is never straightforward and always time consuming. Thus, in this paper, the primary emphasis will be restricted to nonferrous sulfide metal deposits; some consideration, however, will also be given to ferrous metal deposits. Of these deposits, the following types have significant representation in Proterozoic terrains:

(1) Volcanic-hosted massive sulfide deposits;

(2) Sediment-hosted massive sulfide deposits;

(3) Stratiform copper deposits;

(4) Carbonate-hosted lead-zinc deposits;

(5) Copper-nickel and other deposits associated with mafic intrusives; and

(6) Banded iron formations.

In addition, there are isolated examples of Proterozoic hydrothermal tin and copper deposits.

It is significant that examples of virtually all these types of metal deposits are also known from Phanerozoic terrains and several are represented in Archean terrains. This would indicate that Proterozoic ore-generating systems were not uniquely distinctive and should be as amenable to interpretation of their tectonic setting as ore-generating systems of younger age.

Volcanic-hosted massive sulfide deposits

Significant districts of volcanic-hosted massive sulfide deposits of Proterozoic X age occur in Canada, Arizona, Sweden, and Finland (Table 1). In most instances, the deposits occur in greenstone terrains that appear to be closely analogous to those of Archean age. Currently favored models of greenstone belt formation (Tarney et al., 1976) envisage an environment of backarc extension similar to the Miocene events that produced the green-tuff region of Japan and its associated Kuroko massive sulfide deposits (Cathles et al., 1980).

It appears that the inception or overlapping of tensional environments on subduction-related calc-alkaline magmatic arcs somehow critically controls the generation

TABLE 2. PROTEROZOIC SEDIMENT-HOSTED MASSIVE SULFIDE DEPOSITS

Deposit	Host Rocks	Age m.y.	Composition	Assoc. Igneous Rocks	Tonnage x 10^6	Reference
Sullivan Canada	Aldridge argillite	∿ 1,400	Zn, Pb, Ag	Moyie sills, basaltic	155	Freeze, 1966
Mt. Isa Aust.	Urquhart Shale	∿ 1,600	Zu, Pb, Ag, Cu	Numerous, but volumetrically minor tuffite bands	88 Pb, Zn ore 181 Cu ore	Dunnet, 1976
Lady Lorretta Aust.	Paradise Creek carbonaceous shale	∿ 1,600	Zn, Pb, Ag	but volumetrically minor tuffite bands	8.6	London et al., 1975
McArthur River Aust.	HYC pyritic shale	∿ 1,600	Zn, Pb (Ag)	very minor Tuffite	190	Walker et al., 1977
Ducktown, Tenn.	Great Smoky greywackes and schists	∿ 800	Cu, Zn	Amphibolite (metabasalt?)	75	Feiss and Hauck, 1980
Otjihase Namibia	Khomas schists	∿ 700	Cu, Zn	Amphibolite (metabasalt?)	?	Anhausser and Button, 1974
Gamsberg S. Africa	Al-rich metapellites	∿ 1,300	Zn (Pb)	Amphibolite	143	Rozendaal, 1980
Aggenuys S. Africa	Al-rich metapellites	∿ 1,300	Cu, Zn, Pb, Ag	Amphibolite	200	Van Biljon, 1980a
Broken Hill Aust.	metapellites metavolcanics?	∿ 1,700	Zn, Pb, Ag	Amphibolite some metam. felsic volcanic rocks as well	>200	Johnson and Klinger, 1975 Laing et. al., 1978

of these volcanic-hosted massive sulfide deposits (Sillitoe, in press).

This scheme is appropriate perhaps for the Flin Flon-Snow Lake districts of Manitoba, the massive sulfide deposits of Wisconsin and those of Arizona and New Mexico. However, the massive sulfide deposits of Uihanti, Pyhasalmi, and the Outokumpu district in the Karelides of central Finland appear to overlie rifted Archean basement.

The series of younger Proterozoic volcanic-hosted massive sulfide deposits of the Arabian Shield (Sabir, 1979) are associated with typical arc volcanic sequences that are considered to record late Proterozoic (~660 m.y.) continental accretion (Al-Shanti and Mitchell, 1976) in this area.

Sediment-hosted massive sulfide deposits

Sediment-hosted massive sulfide deposits represent an important facet of Proterozoic metallogeny for many deposits contain tens, and some hundreds, of millions of tons of high-grade base metal ore (Table 2). Deposits of this type typically exhibit well-defined banding of their constituent sulfides and are generally accepted as being of exhalative origin.

The term *sediment-hosted massive sulfides* has gained wide usage with respect to these deposits, but, in fact, some occur in siltstones (e.g., Sullivan); and dolomitic units or even tuff horizons (e.g., Mt. Isa) may occur in close association with the bedded ores.

Assignment of many metamorphosed massive sulfide deposits to this category involves a certain degree of geopoetic license. However, the high alumina contents of the gneisses that enclosed the Broken Hill, N.S.W. ores (Johnson and Klingner, 1975) and those of the Northern Cape, S. Africa (Moore, 1980) imply that these rocks are metapelites.

One notable aspect of the Mt. Isa and McArthur River deposits is the considerable stratigraphic interval over which conformable mineralization occurs, 650 and 130 meters, respectively. Similarly, at Sullivan, massive sulfides occur over a vertical interval of 90 meters. The host sediments in all of these deposits must have accumulated relatively slowly, and thus time periods of intermittent mineralization of millions of years are indicated. This extended time frame is in strong contrast to volcanic-hosted massive sulfide deposits which probably form over time periods involving only tens or hundreds of years (Henley and Thornley, 1979).

We still have to learn about the genesis of these ores, but an environment of extensional tectonics, high heat flow, rift basin sedimentation, and penecontemporaneous faulting (Large, 1980) appears to be an important common denominator for the ore-generating systems involved

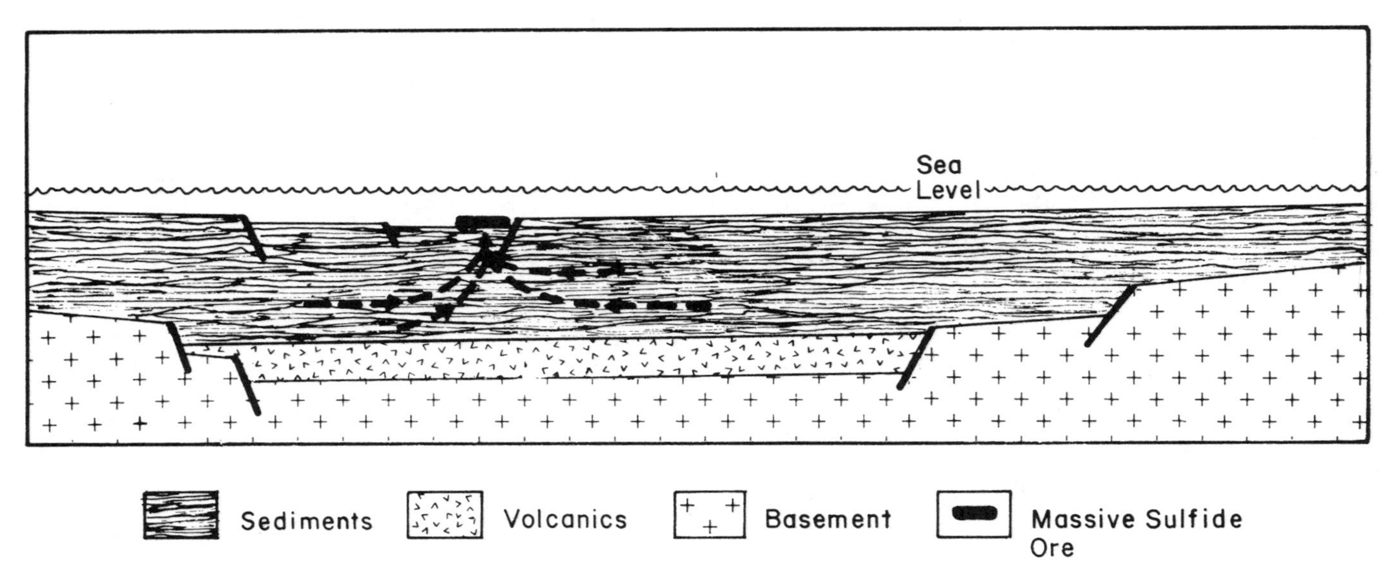

Figure 1. Conceptual model for the generation of sediment-hosted massive sulfide deposits. Metal-bearing fluids are thought to derive from the rift sediments and to precipitate metal sulfides at or very close to the sediment-seawater interface.

(Fig. 1). Analogous sediment-hosted massive sulfide deposits are well represented in certain Paleozoic terrains (Sawkins and Burke, 1980; Large, 1980), but no deposits of Archean age are known.

Stratiform copper deposits

Copper deposits in which the ore minerals are disseminated within specific shale or sandstone horizons represent an important class of Proterozoic metal deposits (Table 3). Most prominent are the ores of the Zambian copper belt, but examples are widespread. In many cases, a clear-cut association with intracontinental rifting events is apparent (Sawkins, 1976a).

The deposits typically occur within shallow marine dark shale or siltstone units that are separated from the underlying basement by fluviatile arkoses, sandstones, and conglomerates. Basaltic volcanics are commonly present. The basalts that occur in continental rift and hotspot environments tend to exhibit significant primary enrichments in copper (see Sawkins, 1976a; Table 2) and are a logical source of the copper in these stratiform deposits.

Based on his studies of the White Pine deposit, Michigan, Brown (1971, 1980) has suggested that stratiform copper deposits are formed by replacement of original syngenetic pyrite, by flushing of copper-rich groundwaters through reduced shales. However, the zoning of copper, copper-iron, and iron sulfides in the various deposits of the Zambian copper belt is more suggestive of syngenetic mineralization related to various near-shore depositional environments (Fleisher et al., 1976).

Stratiform copper deposits appear to be generated either during the early stages of rifting or in the inner zones of aulacogens (Fig. 2). Examples of similar deposits are known from Phanerozoic terrains (e.g., Kupferschiefer in central Europe, Jung and Knitzschke, 1976), whereas their absence in the Archean presumably reflects the paucity of continental environments during that period of earth history.

Stratiform copper deposits exhibit a strong concentration during Proterozoic Y time (~1 b.y., see Table 3). This may simply result from the widespread continental rifting events that occurred then (Sawkins, 1976b), but it may also reflect atmospheric evolution. The solubility of copper in natural waters, especially chloride and sulfate brines, is controlled by redox reactions; and prior to Precambrian Y time, circulating groundwaters may not have been sufficiently oxidizing to effect significant redistribution of copper.

Carbonate-hosted Pb-Zn (±Cu) deposits

Replacement deposits of lead-zinc sulfides in carbonate rocks, unrelated to magmatism (i.e., Mississippi Valley-type deposits) are an important facet of Phanerozoic metallogeny. A number of apparently similar Proterozoic deposits are known (Table 4). The designation of certain of these deposits, especially those that have undergone metamorphism (Black Angel, Balmat-Edwards), as Mississippi Valley-type is rather speculative. Nevertheless, the low silver contents of the ores, their dolomitic marble host rocks, and the absence of nearby intrusives all suggest mineralization of this type.

Recent work on the important carbonate-hosted deposits in northern Namibia (e.g., Tsumeb, M. Hughes, written communication) has indicated that they formed by

TABLE 3. PROTEROZOIC STRATIFORM COPPER DEPOSITS

Deposit/district	Age	Host rocks	Lithology	Evidence for Rifting	Reference
Aynak copper dep. N.E. Afghanistan	Proterozoic Z	Aynak Series	metasandstone metadolomite	assoc. with formation of Tethys	Sillitoe, 1980
White Pine, Michigan	1.0 b.y.	Nonesuch shale	gray-maroon shale siltstone and sandstone	Keweenawan basalts	White, 1968
Belt copper prospects, Montana	Proterozoic Y	Revett Formation	white quartzite and siltite	thick sedimentary sequence, basalts	Harrison, 1972
Seal Lake Labrador, Canada	Proterozoic Y	Adeline Island Formation	gray-green shales	thick clastics, assoc. basalts	Gandhi and Brown, 1975
Coppermine River N.W.T., Canada	Proterozoic Y	Rae Group	gray-green glauconitic sandstone	thick clastics, assoc. basalts	Kindle, 1972
Redstone Copper Belt, N.W.T.,Canada	Proterozoic Y	Redstone River Formation	siltstones and carbonates	normal faulting, assoc. basalts	Ruelle, 1978
Zambian Copper Belt, Central Africa	Proterozoic Y	Ore shale Lower Roan Fm	argillite and impure dolomite	sediment thickness changes, time equiv. Bukoban basalts	Mendelsohn, 1961
Witvlei and Klein Aus mines, Namibia	Proterozoic Y	Wituki Formation Nosib group	greenish-grey argillite	thick clastics, underlying basalts	Toens, 1975
Adelaidean copper province, South Australia	Proterozoic Y	lower Willouran Adelaidean	dolo-siltstones carbonaceous dolo-arenites	thick clastics underlying basalts	Rowlands, 1973
Kilembe Mine Uganda	Proterozoic X	Kilembe Series	meta-siltites	thick meta-clastics, meta-basalts	Davis, 1967

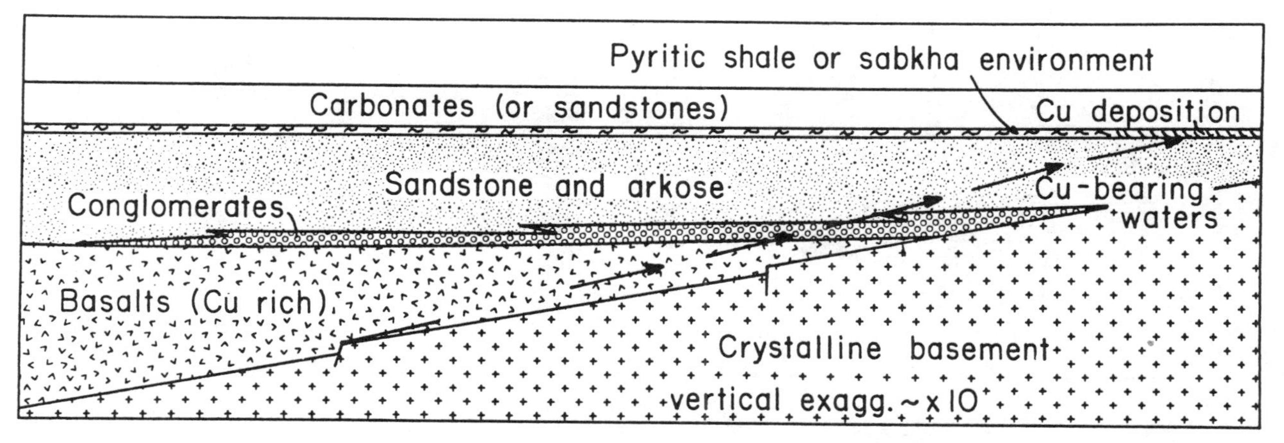

Figure 2. Conceptual model for the generation of stratiform copper deposits. View represents a longitudinal section along a continental rift.

TABLE 4. CARBONATE-HOSTED Pb-Zn DEPOSITS

Deposit(s)	Host rocks	Composition	Age	Reference
Tsumeb, Kombat Namibia	Otavi dolomites	Pb, Zn, Cu	∿600 m.y.	Sohnge, 1964
Berg Aukus Namabia	Otavi dolomites	Pb, Zn	∿600 m.y.	Sohnge, 1964
Nanisivik N. Baffin Island	Society Cliffs dolomites	Pb, Zn	Proterozoic Z	Olson, 1977
Black Angel W. Greenland	Marmorilik marbles	Pb, Zn	Proterozoic X	Pedersen, 1980
Cooley II Queensland	Cooley dolomite	Pb, Zn	Proterozoic X	Williams, 1978
Balmat-Edwards N.Y.	Grenville dolomitic marbles	PB, Zn	Proterozoic Y	Lea and Dill, 1968

TABLE 5. PROTEROZOIC MAGMATIC ORE DEPOSITS

Deposit/ District	Host rocks	Composition	Age	Reference
Thompson-Moak Lake, Canada	serpentinites ultramafics	Cu-Ni	Proterozoic X	
Cape Smith-Wakeham Bay Canada	mafic-ultramafic intrusives	Cu-Ni	Proterozoic X	Wilson et. al., 1969
Petsamo Belt, Finland	mafic-ultramafic intrusives	Cu-Ni	Proterozoic X	Haapala, 1969
Sudbury, Ontario	norite, quartz dorite ultramafics	Cu-Ni	2.0 b.y.	Souch et al., 1969
Duluth Complex Minnesota	layered mafic intrusive	CU-Ni	1.1 b.y.	Weiblen and Morey, 1975
Bushveld Igneous Complex	layered mafic intrusive	Pt, Cr, Fe, V	∿2.0 b.y.	Willemse, 1969

regional movement of fluids through the permeable Mulden sandstones and the underlying karst surface developed in Otavi dolomites. This scenario is typical of those suggested for many Mississippi Valley-type deposits. Furthermore, certain minor lead-zinc replacement bodies in the McArthur River area appear to be typical examples of this class of carbonate-hosted deposit (Williams, 1978).

Based on regional geologic settings, an environment of rifting can be tentatively postulated for many of these deposits, especially those in the McArthur River area, the Nanisivik deposit, and those in northern Namibia. Sawkins (1976a) has noted similar tectonic settings for at least some Phanerozoic Mississippi Valley-type deposits. Derivation of the ore fluids and metals from adjacent basinal sedimentary sequences appears likely (Fig. 3), but precise genetic models for these deposits remain to be formulated.

Mafic-ultramafic-hosted copper-nickel deposits

Mafic and ultramafic igneous rocks that contain economic concentrations of copper-nickel sulfides occur in geologic terrains of all ages. Two relatively distinctive geologic environments are included in this spectrum: stable intracratonic regions subjected to mantle hotspot activity, and intracratonic mobile belts.

Proterozoic deposits of this type occur in Canada, the United States, and Finland (Table 5). The copper-nickel sulfides typically occur as massive and/or disseminated zones, at or near the base of layered mafic-ultramafic intrusives, and are clearly magmatogenic although incorporation of sulfur from host-rock sources has been demonstrated for the ores in the Duluth Complex (Mainwaring and Naldrett, 1977).

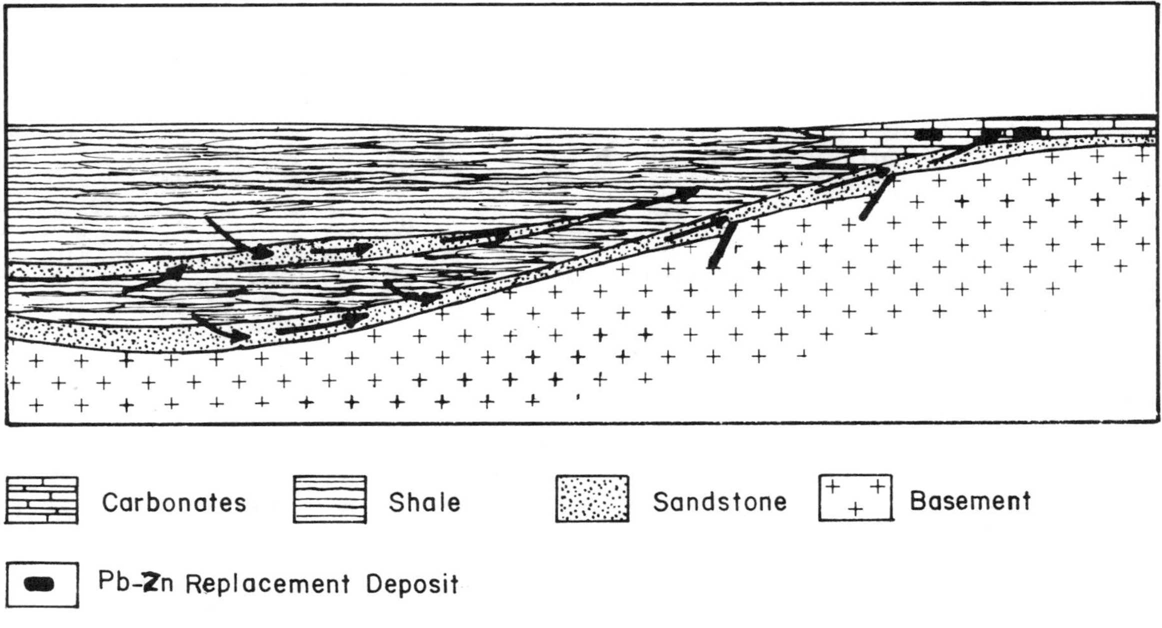

Figure 3. Conceptual model for the generation of stratabound lead-zinc deposits in carbonate rocks. Fluids moving outwards from a sedimentary basin transport lead and zinc to depositional sites in adjacent platform carbonates.

Layered mafic-ultramafic complexes in intracratonic settings and those in mobile belts both originate from episodes of mantle melting in either hotspot or tensional tectonic environments (Sawkins, 1976a). The Sudbury Irruptive, however, has been related to a meteorite impact (French, 1970). Whether this postulated origin is correct or not, it clearly represents a major mantle melting event. The Duluth Complex, on the other hand, is unequivocally related to Keweenawan rifting events (Weiblen and Morey, 1975).

The Bushveld Igneous Complex does not contain known copper-nickel deposits but is an important repository of magmatic ores (chrome, platinum, iron, vanadium; Willemse, 1969). Early events associated with the Bushveld Complex; initial doming, volcanism, Cu-bearing alkali magmatism (Palabora) and aulacogen formation (see Hunter, 1976; Jansen, 1975), and the huge volume of the complex itself all suggest mantle hotspot activity.

Banded Iron Formations

The major period of deposition of banded iron formations that occurred on most continents during Proterozoic X time can be considered as a unique event in earth history. However, Cole and Klein (1981) have challenged this concept, emphasizing that early Proterozoic iron formations span a time period of at least 400 m.y. and noting the similarities in textures of many Archean and Proterozoic iron formations.

The lithologic setting of early Proterozoic iron formations suggests that the deposition of iron and accompanying chert occurred in shallow marine environments, and in this respect they differ from Archean iron formations. The extent of Proterozoic iron formations and their broad contemporaneity argue against specific sources of iron in each case (i.e., continental or volcanic derivation). Rather, it appears that oxygen levels in these environments caused precipitation of a significant amount of the oceanic budget of ferrous iron (Holland, 1973). It has also been suggested that evaporation may have aided this process of local iron enrichment (Button, 1976).

The Hamersley Range iron formations in western Australia are the most impressive example of this type of iron deposit; and here thicknesses of sediment accumulation, bimodal volcanism, and flanking Archean cratonic blocks strongly suggest a tectonic setting dominated by rifting and crustal thinning (Trendall and Blockley, 1970; Horwitz and Smith, 1976). In other areas of similar age banded iron formation, the tectonic framework of basin development is less clear; but it seems possible that all Proterozoic basins of iron accumulation were related to extensional tectonics. For example, the Animikie basin, which contains the iron formations of Minnesota and Michigan (Van Schmus et al., 1975), and the massive sulfide deposits of the Crandon district (see earlier) apparently formed within an area of older continental crust and thus are logically related to a rifting event.

There are also a number of late Proterozoic iron formations known. These include the Rapitan iron formation, northwest Canada, the Braemar/Holowilena iron formation in the Adelaide Geosyncline, and the Banda Alta iron formation in western Brazil and adjacent Bolivia (see Young, 1976). In all cases, a strong association with glaciogenic sediments is apparent, as well as evidence for low paleolatitudes and evaporite conditions. This juxtaposition of contrasting paleoclimatic indicators is puzzling, but it is of some interest that both the Canadian and Australian examples occur in well-defined rift settings.

Hydrothermal metal deposits of Proterozoic age

Although heated aqueous fluids have almost certainly played a role in the formation of many of the metal deposits discussed above, I plan to discuss here certain deposits or districts of more definitive hydrothermal aspect. The tin deposits of Rhondonia, western Brazil, are closely associated with a series of 1.1 b.y. anorogenic granites (Kloosterman, 1970) that have high initial strontium ratios (Priem et al., 1971). Sillitoe (1974) has emphasized that such tin deposits are one manifestation of mantle hotspot activity and that similar deposits of Jurassic age occur in west Africa.

The copper-bearing breccia pipes of the Tribag area, Ontario (Norman, 1978), exhibit a space-time relationship to Keweenawan rifting events, and as such are distinctive from the vast majority of hydrothermal copper deposits. The Mesozoic Messina copper-bearing breccia pipes in South Africa (Sawkins, 1977), however, formed in a tectonic setting that has close analogies to the Keweenawan rift province.

Porphyry copper-type mineralization has been reported from the Haib area, southwestern Africa. Detailed petrologic and geochemical studies of the volcanic and intrusive rocks of this area (Reid, 1977) demonstrate that it is part of a typical calc-alkaline volcanoplutonic arc, formed approximately 2.0 b.y. ago. For some reason, the crustal thickening associated with volcanoplutonic arc formation must have been less effective in this area, allowing for preservation from erosion of its upper (mineralized) portions. The mineralization is of disseminated type and occurs within and around a porphyritic to equigranular adamellite-granodiorite pluton. Associated alteration consists of sericite-quartz-pyrite. Overall, the similarities in lithologic setting, mineralization, and alteration suggest this is a typical example of porphyry copper mineralization.

Hydrothermal uranium deposits related to major unconformities form a distinctive class of Proterozoic metal deposits (Robertson et al., 1978). These deposits are covered elsewhere in this volume and will not be discussed further here.

DISCUSSION

This brief review of Proterozoic metal deposits is obviously not an exhaustive one. The primary intent has been to define certain types of ore deposits that have significant representation in Proterozoic terrains and to provide major examples of these. Further, it has been emphasized that in almost all instances the ore types involved are not unique to the Proterozoic, either in themselves or in the geologic settings in which they occur. This lack of uniqueness further indicates that the respective tectonic frameworks that controlled these environments were not necessarily restricted to the Proterozoic period.

Despite the foregoing, there are some aspects of Proterozoic geology and metallogeny that can be considered distinctive. Earth atmospheres and the oxygen content of the hydrosphere clearly underwent critical evolution from the beginning of Proterozoic time until its end. Not only is the cessation of major iron deposition by 1.8 b.y. a major consequence of this change, but also the very low oxygen levels prior to this time permitted the survival and concentrations of uraninite in surficial environments. The results include the formation of the Blind River deposit in the lowermost conglomerates of the Huronian Supergroup, Canada (Frarey, 1977), and the uranium (+ gold) deposits of the Witwatersrand Basin in South Africa (Pretorius, 1975). A strong case for a rift setting for deposition of the Huronian Supergroup, based on thickness, early bimodal mafic-felsic volcanism, and contemporaneous faulting, can be made. Many of the same considerations apply to the essentially time-equivalent Witwatersrand succession, which has also been suggested to be related to rifting (von Biljon, 1980b).

Overall, it is apparent that most of the metal deposits formed during Proterozoic time were generated in tectonic environments characterized by rifting. Many of the remaining deposits occur in the high-grade metamorphic terrains of Proterozoic orogenic belts. There is still disagreement as to whether such belts mark the sites at which Wilson Cycles operated (Burke et al., 1976) or whether they resulted from ensialic orogeny (Kroner, 1977). The important point is that the metal deposits in question almost certainly formed prior to folding and metamorphism and that both types of orogeny are preceded by rifting events. The orogenic events that eventually follow many rift cycles are extremely important in terms of the exhumation of the metal deposits that form during these cycles, for they tend initially to become deeply buried under thick sequences of postrift sediments (Fig. 4). This explains why, apart from the contemporary Red Sea deposits, virtually no major sediment-hosted massive sulfide deposits nor stratiform copper deposits of post-

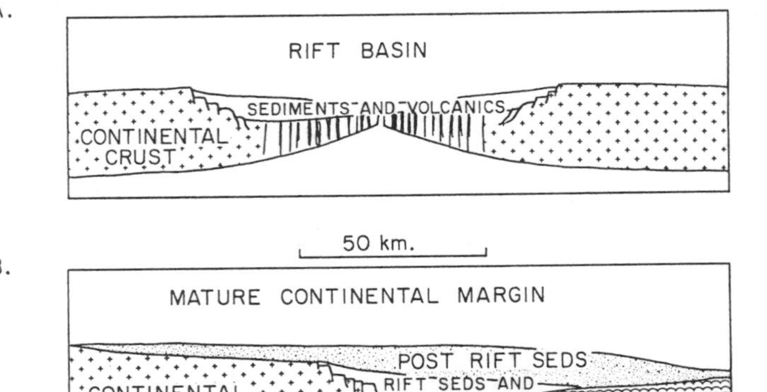

Figure 4. Sketch to illustrate that rift sediments and volcanics that may contain metal deposits (A) tend to become deeply buried by postrift continental sediments along passive continental margins (B). Such potential deposits will only become 'unearthed' subsequent to major tectonism.

Paleozoic age are known, despite the evidence for considerable rifting activity during the Mesozoic and Cenozoic.

Although continental rifting and hotspot activity manifestly similar to that of Phanerozoic time did obviously occur broadly during the Proterozoic, the question of plate tectonic activity at this time is still under debate. Detractors of plate movements during the Proterozoic cite the absence of ophiolites and of identifiable continental margin sedimentary sequences in support of their skepticism. The validity of these objections is, I believe, questionable. Most undeformed Phanerozoic ophiolite complexes (e.g., Cyprus, Oman, Bay of Islands, Newfoundland; Zambales Range, Philippines) are currently undergoing erosion, and much the same applies to deformed ophiolite suites in mountain belts. This observation, plus the fact that so much of the preserved Proterozoic record represents intracontinental geologic terrains, may be adequate to explain the apparent absence of ophiolites prior to Proterozoic time.

Support, at least by inference, for the operation of plate tectonics during the Proterozoic comes from distinctive polar wander curves for various continental segments (Irving and McGlynn, 1976), and from calc-alkaline volcanoplutonic terrains in southern Africa (Haib, see above) and northwest Canada (Wopmay orogen, Hoffman, 1973). The status of greenstone belts vis-à-vis plate tectonics is still controversial; but if they do form in relation to plate activity, then the Proterozoic greenstone belts of Canada, Arizona, Guiana, Africa, and Saudi Arabia provide additional evidence of plate activity during that period of earth history. It is also conceivable that at least some of the high-grade terrains of the Pan African and Baikalian orogenies may represent the root zones of Andean-type continental margins. Despite these examples, the dominance of rift-

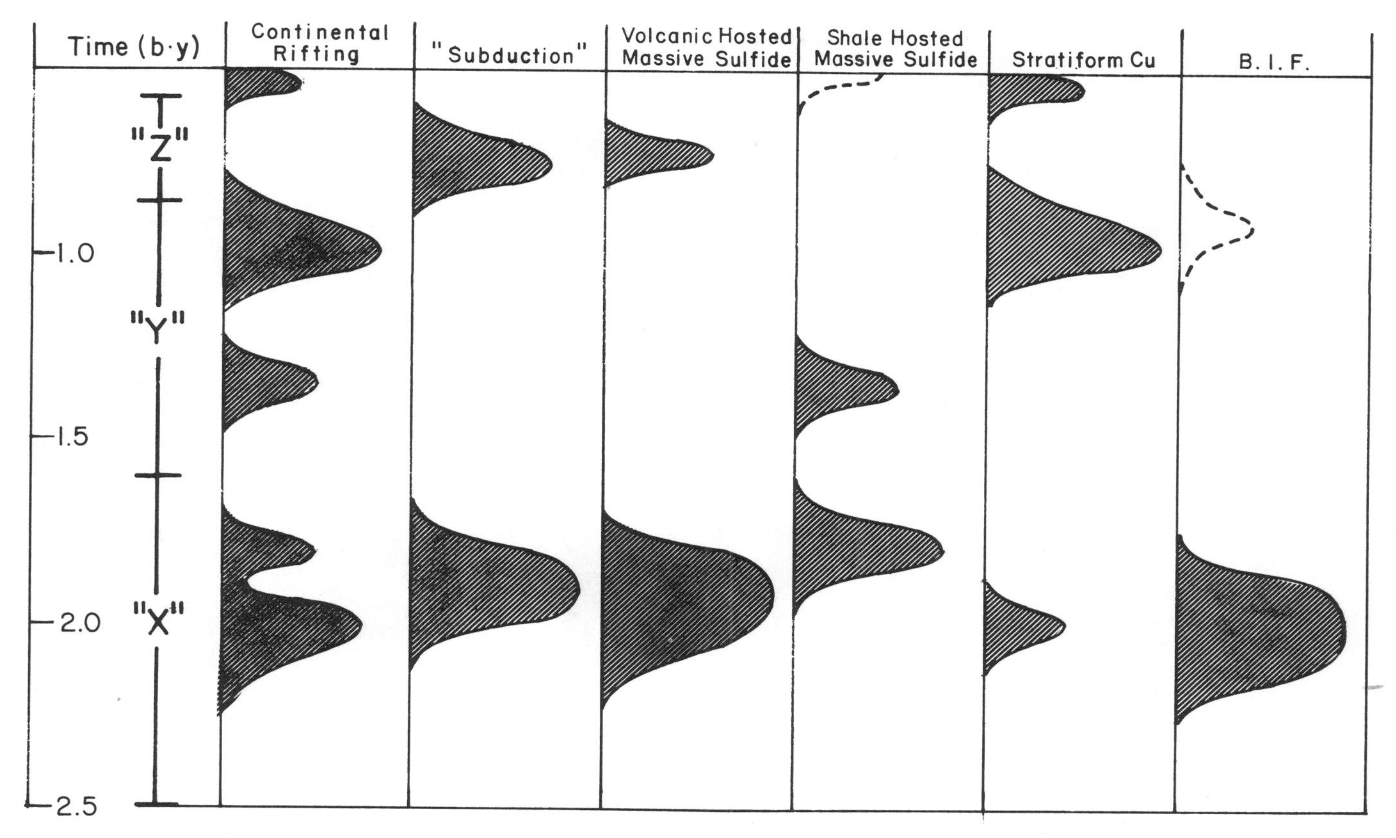

Figure 5. Diagram to illustrate tectonic and metal deposit-forming events as a function of Proterozoic time.

related terrains and the paucity of demonstrable subduction-related terrains in this part of the Precambrian historical record are puzzling.

The age distribution of Proterozoic metal deposits is of some interest (Fig. 5), for there were specific periods during which certain types of ore-generating systems were concentrated. Furthermore, these periods coincide with periods during which specific types of tectonic activity were prevalent. Although Figure 5 can be regarded only as a crude attempt to quantize tectonic activity and ore deposition during the Proterozoic with respect to the *preserved* record, it does serve to emphasize the strong interdependence of ore deposition events and tectonics, and their sporadic nature.

The ultimate drive of crustal tectonics is the generation of excess heat in the earth's mantle. This heat flux cannot be subject to short-term fluctuations, suggesting that build-up of this heat over significant time periods (tens to hundreds of millions of years) is required before it is dissipated as magmatism and tectonic activity. As I have attempted to demonstrate, the generation of metal deposits is closely linked to such activity, and thus variations in age of Proterozoic metal-deposit types are understandable.

CONCLUSIONS

An analysis of major Proterozoic metal-deposit types and their geological settings demonstrates a strong correlation of such types to the tectonic frameworks in which they formed. The majority of these deposits are not unique to Proterozoic time, although their representation in Proterozoic terrains may be unduly strong. This apparent concentration of specific ore types during the Proterozoic is thought to be largely a function of both preservation and continental geography during the latter portion of Proterozoic time.

Although there are certain unique aspects of the Proterozoic geological record, it varies more in degree than in kind from the Phanerozoic record. Thus, it seems possible that essentially similar plate tectonic activity was taking place in both Phanerozoic and Proterozoic time.

REFERENCES CITED

Al-Shanti, A. M., and Mitchell, A. H., 1976, Late Precambrian subduction and collision in the Al-Amor-Idsas region, Arabian Shield, Kingdom of Saudi Arabia: Tectonophysics, v. 30, p. 41–47.

Anderson, P., and Guilbert, J. M., 1978, The Precambrian massive sulfide deposits of Arizona—A distinct metallogenic epoch and province [abs.]: 5th IAGOD Symposium, Snowbird, Utah, p. 39.

Anhaeusser, C. R., and Button, A., 1974, A review of southern African stratiform ore deposits—their position in time and space: Econ. Geol. Research Unit, Univ. of the Witwatersrand, Inform. Circ., No. 85, p. 48.

Brown, A. C., 1971, Zoning in the White Pine copper deposit, Ontonagon County, Michigan: Econ. Geol., v. 65, p. 543–573.

—— 1980, The diagenetic origin of stratiform copper deposits: Proc. 5th IAGOD Symposium, Snowbird, Utah, p. 81–90.

Burke, K., Dewey, J. F., and Kidd, W.S.F., 1976, Precambrian paleomagnetic results compatible with contemporary operation of the Wilson Cycle: Tectonophysics, v. 33, p. 287–299.

Button, A., 1976, Iron formations as an end-member in carbonate sedimentary cycles in the Transvaal Supergroup, South Africa: Econ. Geol., v. 71, p. 193–201.

Cole, M. J., and Klein, C., 1981, Banded iron-formation through much of Precambrian time: Jour. Geology, v. 89, p. 163–183.

Davis, G. R., 1969, Aspects of the metamorphosed sulfide ores at Kilembe, Uganda: Sedimentary Ores, Proc. 15th Inter-University Geol. Cong. Spec. Pub. No. 1, Univ. of Leicester, p. 273–296.

Dunnet, D., 1976, Some aspects of the Panantarctic craton margin in Australia: Phil. Trans. R. Soc. Lond. Ser. A., v. 273, p. 641–654.

Feiss, P. G., and Hauck, S. H., 1980, Tectonic setting of massive-sulfide deposits in the Southern Appalachians, U.S.A.: Proc. 5th IAGOD Symposium, Snowbird, Utah, p. 567–580.

Fleischer, V. D., Garlick, W. G., and Haldane, R., 1976, Geology of the Zambian Copperbelt: Handbook of Stratabound and Stratiform Ore Dep. (ed. K. H. Wolfe), v. 6, p. 223–352.

Frarey, M. J., 1977, Geology of the Huronian belt between Sault Ste. Marie and Blind River, Ontario: Geol. Survey Canada Mem. 383, 87 p.

Freeze, A. C., 1966, On the origin of the Sullivan orebody, Kimberley, B. C.: Can. Inst. Min. and Metall. Spec. Vol., No. 8, p. 263–294.

French, B. M., 1970, Possible relationship between meteorite impact and igneous petrogenesis as indicated by the Sudbury structure, Ontario, Canada: Bull. Volcanol., v. 34, p. 466–517.

Gandhi, S. S., and Brown, A. C., 1975, Cupriferrous shales of the Adeline Island Formation, Seal Lake Group, Labrador: Econ. Geol., v. 70, p. 145–163.

Haapala, P. S., 1969, Fennoscandian Nickel Deposits: Econ. Geol. Mono. No. 4, Magmatic ore deposits, p. 262–275.

Harrison, J. E., 1972, Precambrian belt basin of northwestern United States: its geometry, sedimentation and copper occurrences: Geol. Soc. Am. Bull., v. 83, p. 1215–1240.

Henley, R. W., and Thornley, P., 1979, Some geothermal aspects of polymetallic massive sulfide formation: Econ. Geol., v. 74, p. 1600–1612.

Hoffman, P., 1973, Evolution of an early Proterozoic continental margin: the Coronation Geosyncline and associated aulacogens of the northwestern Canada Shield: Phil. Trans. Royal Soc. Lond., v. A273, p. 547–581.

Holland, H. D., 1973, The oceans: a possible source of iron in iron-formations: Econ. Geol., v. 68, p. 1169–1172.

Horwitz, R. C., and Smith, R. E., 1976, Bridging the Yilgarn and Pilbara Blocks, western Australian Shield: I.G.C. abs., Sydney, p. 12.

Huhtala, T., 1979, The geology and zinc-copper deposits of the Pyhasatmi-Piclavesi District, Finland: Econ. Geol., v. 74, p. 1069–1083.

Hunter, D. R., 1976, Some enigmas of the Bushveld Complex: Econ. Geol., v. 71, p. 229–248.

Irving, E., and McGlynn, J. C., 1976, Proterozoic magnetostratigraphy and the tectonic evolution of Laurentia: Phil. Trans. Royal Soc. Lond., v. A280, p. 433–468.

Jansen, H., 1975, The Southpansberg Trough (Northern Transvaal)—an aulacogen: Trans. Geol. Soc. S. Africa, v. 78, p. 129–136.

Johnson, I. R., and Klingner, G. D., 1975, Broken Hill ore deposit and its environment: Economic Geology of Australia and Papua-New Guinea Aust. Inst. Min. and Metall. Mono. No. 5, v. 1, p. 476–491.

Jung, W., and Knitzschke, G., 1976, Kupferschiefer in the German Democratic Republic with specific reference to the Kupferschiefer deposit in the southeastern Harz foreland: Handbook of Stratabound and Statiform Ore Dep. (ed. K. H. Wolfe), v. 6, p. 353–406.

Kindle, E. E., 1972, Classification and description of copper deposits, Coppermine River area, District of Mackenzie: Geol. Surv. Canada Bull. v. 214, p. 198.

Kindle, E., Dahlgrun, F., Ramdohr, P., and Wilke, A., 1955, Die ERzlager des Rammelsberges bei Goslar: Hannover, Monographien der Deutschen Blei-Zink Erzlagerstatten, No. 4, 394 p.

Kloosterman, J. B., 1970, A two fold analogy between the Nigerian and Amazonian tin provinces: Second Intern. Tin Conf. Bangkok, v. 1, p. 197–222.

Koark, H. J., 1973, Zur entstehung des tektonischen Stengelbaus an prakambrischen Eisen- und Sulfiderzkorpen der zentralschwedischen Leptitserie: Mineralium Deposita, v. 8, p. 19–34.

Koo, J., and Mossman, D. J., 1975, Origin and metamorphism of the Flin Flon Stratabound Cu-Zn deposits, Saskatchewan and Manitoba: Econ. Geol, v. 70, p. 48–62.

Kroner, A., 1977, Precambrian mobile belts of southern and eastern Africa—Ancient sutures or sites of ensialic mobility? A case for crustal evolution towards plate tectonics: Tectonophysics, v. 40, p. 101–135.

Laing, W. P., Marjoribanks, R. W., and Rutland, R. W., 1978, Structure of the Broken Hill Mine area and its significance for the genesis of the orebodies: Econ. Geol., v. 72, p. 1112–1136.

Large, D. E., 1980, Geologic parameters associated with sediment-hosted submarine exhalative Pb-Zn deposits: an empirical model for mineral exploration: Geol. Jahrb., v. 40, p. 59–129.

Latvalahti, U., 1979, Cu-Zn-Pb ores of the Aijala-Orijarvi area, southwest Finland: Econ. Geol. v. 74, p. 1035–1059.

Laznicka, P., 1973, Development of nonferrous metal deposits in geological time: Can. J. Earth Sci., v. 10, p. 18–25.

Lea, E. R., and Dill, D. B., 1968, Zinc deposits of the Balmat-Edwards District, New York: AIME Graton-Sales Volume 1, p. 20–48.

London, A. G., Lee, M. K., Dowling, J. F., and Bourn, R., 1975, Lady Loretta silver-zinc deposit: Economic geology of Australia and Papua-New Guinea, Australasian Inst. Min. and Metall. Mono. No. 5, p. 377–382.

Mainwaring, P. R., and Naldrett, A. J., 1977, Country rock assimilation and the genesis of Cu-Ni sulfides in the Water Hen Intrusion, Duluth Complex, Minnesota: Econ. Geol., v. 72, p. 1269–1284.

Martin, R. F., and Piiwinski, A. J., 1972, Magmatism and tectonic setting: Jour. Geophys. Res., v. 77, p. 4966–4975.

Mendelsohn, F., 1961, The geology of the Northern Rhodesian Copper Belt: MacDonald and Co., Ltd., London, p. 523.

Moore, J. M., 1980, Paleo-environmental implications of sillimanite-rich rocks in the North-West Cape, South Africa and their relation to the sulfide deposits of the area: Proc. 5th IAGOD Symposium, Snowbird, Utah, p. 209–216.

Norman, D. I., 1978, Ore deposits related to the Keweenawan Rift: *in* Petrology and Geochemistry of Continental Rifts (eds. E. R. Neu-

mann and I. B. Ramberg), Reidel Pub. Co., p. 245–254.
Olson, R. A., 1977, Geology and genesis of zinc-lead deposits within a late-Precambrian dolomite, northern Baffin Island, N.W.T.: Univ. British Columbia, [unpubl. Ph.D. thesis]: 371 p.
Pedersen, F. D., 1980, Remobilization of the massive sulfide ore of the Black Angel Mine, Central West Greenland: Econ. Geol., v. 75, p. 1022–1041.
Pereira, J., and Dixon, C. J., 1965, Evolutionary trends in ore deposition: Trans. I.M.M., v. 74, p. 505–527.
Pretorius, D. A., 1975, The depositional environment of the Witwatersrand goldfields: a chronological review of speculations and observations: Minerals Sci. Engin., v. 7, p. 18–47.
Priem, H., Boetrijk, N., Hebeda, E., Verdusmen, E., Verschure, R., and Bon, E., 1971, Granitic complexes and associated tin mineralizations of 'Grenville' age in Rondonia, western Brazil: Geol. Soc. Am. Bull., v. 82, p. 1095–1102.
Reid, D. L., 1977, Geochemistry of Precambrian igneous rocks in the lower Orange River region: Precam. Research Unit, Univ. of Cape Town Bull. 22, 397 p.
Rickard, D. T., and Zweifel, H., 1975, Genesis of Precambrian sulfide ores, Skellefte district, Sweden: Econ. Geol., v. 70, p. 225–274.
Robertson, D. S., Tilsley, J. E., and Hogg, G. M., 1978, The time-bound character of uranium deposits: Econ. Geol., v. 73, p. 1409–1419.
Rowlands, N. J., 1973, The Adelaidean system of South Australia: A review of its sedimentation, tectonics and copper occurrences: Belt Symposium Volume, Idaho Bureau of Mines and Geology, p. 80–112.
Rozendaal, A., 1980, The Gamsberg Zinc deposits, South Africa: A banded stratiform base-metal sulfide ore deposit: Proc. 5th IAGOD Symposium, Snowbird, Utah, p. 619–634.
Ruelle, J. C., 1978, Depositional environment and genesis of stratiform copper deposits of the Redstone Copper Belt, Mackenzie Mountains, N.W.T. [abs.]: Geol. Soc. Am. Ann. Mtgs., Toronto, p. 482–483.
Sabir, H., 1979, Precambrian polymetallic sulfide deposits in Saudi Arabia and their metallogenic significance: Evolution and Mineralization of the Arabian-Nubian Shield (ed. Al-Shanti) Pergammon Press, v. 2, p. 83–92.
Sawkins, F. J., 1972, Sulfide ore deposits in relation to plate tectonics: Jour. Geol., v. 80, p. 1028–1041.
——1976a, Metal deposits related to intracontinental hot-spot and rifting environments: Jour. Geol., v. 84, p. 653–671.
——1976b, Widespread continental rifting: some consideration of timing and mechanism: Geology, v. 4, p. 427–430.
——1977, Fluid inclusion studies of the Messina copper deposits, Transvaal, South Africa: Econ. Geol., v. 72, p. 619–631.
Sawkins, F. J., and Burke, K., 1980, Were the Rammelsberg, Meggen, Rio Tinto and related ore deposits formed in a Devonian rifting event? Geol. Rundschau, v. 69, p. 349–360.
Schmidt, P. G., Dolence, J. D., Lluria, M. R., and Parsons, G., 1978, Geology of Crandon massive sulfide deposit in Wisconsin: Skilling Mining Rev., May 6th, p. 8–11.
Sillitoe, R. H., 1974, Tin mineralization above mantle hotspots: Nature, v. 248, p. 497–499.
——1980, Strata-bound ore deposits related to Infracambrian rifting along northern Gondawanaland: Proc. 5th IAGOD Symposium, Snowbird, Utah, p. 163–172.
Sohnge, P. G., 1964, The geology of the Tsumeb Mine: *in* S. H. Haughton (ed.), The Geology of Some Ore Deposits in Southern Africa, v. II, p. 367–382.
Souch, B. E., Podolsky, T., and Geological Staff, 1969, The sulfide ores of Sudbury: Their particular relationship to a distinctive inclusion-bearing facies of the Nickel Irruptive: Econ. Geol. Mono. No. 4, Magmatic ore deposits, p. 252–261.
Tarney, J., Dalziel, I. W., and DeWit, M. J., 1976, Marginal basin 'Rocas Verdes' complex from S. Chile: a model for Archean greenstone belt formation: *in* B. F. Windley (ed.), The Early History of the Earth, Wiley, London, p. 131–146.
Toens, P. D., 1975, The geology of part of the southern foreland of the Damara Orogenic Belt in S.W.A. and Botswana: Geol. Rundschau, v. 64, p. 175–192.
Trendall, A. F., and Blockley, J. G., 1970, The iron formations of the Precambrian Hamersley Group, Western Australia: Bull. 119, Geol. Surv. W. Aust., p. 366.
Van Biljon, W. J., 1980a, The distribution in space and time of the Precambrian metal deposits in Southern Africa: 25th Internat. Geol. Cong. Coll. C.I. Mineral Resources, p. 25–37.
——1980b, Plate tectonics and the origin of the Witwatersrand Basin: Proc. 5th IAGOD Symposium, Snowbird, Utah, p. 217–226.
Van Schmus, W. R., Thurman, E. M., and Peterman, Z. E., 1975, Geology and Rb-Sr chronology of middle Precambrian rocks in eastern and central Wisconsin: Geol. Soc. Am. Bull., v. 86, p. 1255–1265.
Walker, R. N., Logan, R. G., and Binnekamp, J. G., 1977, Recent geological advances concerning the H.Y.C. and associated deposits, MacArthur River, N.T.: Jour. Geol. Soc. Australia, v. 24, p. 365–380.
Weiblen, P. W., and Morey, G. B., 1975, The Duluth Complex—a petrologic and tectonic summary: Minn. Geol. Surv. Reprint Series #28, p. 28.
White, W. S., 1968, The native copper deposits of northern Michigan: *in* Ore Deposits of the United States, 1933/1967 (Graton-Sales Volume): New York Am. Inst. Min. and Metall. Engineers, p. 303–325.
Willemse, J., 1969, The geology of the Bushveld Igneous Complex, the largest repository of magmatic ore deposits in the world: Econ. Geol. Mono. NO. 4, Magmatic Ore Deposits, p. 1–22.
Willemse, J., Schwellnus, C. M., Brandt, J. W., Russell, H. D., and Van Rooyen, D. P., 1944, Lead deposits in the Union of South Africa and South West Africa with some notes on associated ores: Mem. Geol. Surv. S. Africa, v. 39, 177 p.
Williams, N., 1978, Studies of the base metal sulfide deposits at McArthur River, Northern Territory, Australia: 1. The Cooley and Ridge deposits: Econ. Geol., v. 73, p. 1005–1035.
Wilson, H.D.B., Kilburn, L. C., Graham, A. R., and Ramlal, K., 1969, Geochemistry of some Canadian nickeliferous ultrabasic intrusions: Econ. Geol. Mono. No. 4, Magmatic ore deposits, p. 294–309.
Young, G. M., 1976, Iron-formation and glaciogenic rocks of the Rapitan Group, Northwest Territories, Canada: Precam. Research, v. 3, p. 137–158.

Manuscript Accepted by the Society April 14, 1983
University Of Minnesota School of Earth Sciences Publication No. 1039

Printed in U.S.A.

Geological Society of America
Memoir 161
1983

Proterozoic exhalative massive sulphide deposits

G. H. Gale
Mineral Resources Division
993 Century Street
Winnipeg, Manitoba R3H OW4
Canada

ABSTRACT

Proterozoic massive sulphide deposits occur in a wide variety of geologic settings that range from those composed of volcanic flow rocks to those composed of clastic sedimentary rocks. Evidence of volcanism, contemporaneous with the mineralizing event, can be found in the host rocks to most of the deposits, including a number of those occurring in thick sedimentary sequences. Proterozoic massive sulphide deposits in volcanic terranes have metal ratios similar to those of Archean, Phanerozoic, and younger deposits when compared to deposits in similar geologic settings. Deposits found in sedimentary terranes are more lead-rich and copper-poor than those in volcanic terranes. Stratabound nickeliferous sulphide deposits at Outokumpu, Finland, and Thompson, Manitoba, are examples of exhalative massive sulphide mineralization.

A genetic model that appears to be compatible with empirical observations and recent isotopic studies on massive sulphide deposits involves the generation of magmatic 'ore-fluids' during the crystallization of a magma and the mixing of this fluid with connate water and/or seawater in the upper portions of the volcanic rock pile.

INTRODUCTION

This paper reviews the types and variety of geologic settings of exhalative massive sulphide deposits associated with volcanic rocks of Proterozoic age. Stratabound exhalative massive sulphide deposits are present in Proterozoic terranes throughout the world. These deposits are important sources of copper, zinc, lead, silver, gold, cadmium, and tin. Several Proterozoic nickel-bearing massive sulphide deposits probably belong to this class of deposit. Examples of the deposit type used as illustrations are drawn from North American, Australian, South African, Scandinavian, and Finnish deposits; however, deposits of this type are also known from other Proterozoic terranes such as those of the Soviet Union and India.

The metal ratios of Proterozoic exhalative massive sulphide deposits vary from copper-rich and lead- and zinc-poor, to lead- and zinc-rich and copper-poor. Host rocks associated with these deposits can be predominantly volcanic rocks, predominantly sedimentary rocks, or mixtures of both volcanic and sedimentary rocks.

'Massive sulphide' as used here refers to a *deposit type* not an ore type, since 'Massive' ore can contain up to 50% silicate and/or oxide minerals and a sulphide lens in these deposits may in some parts contain as little as 10% sulphide (by volume). The use of 'solid sulphide' for 90% to 100% sulphide minerals and 'near-solid sulphide' for 50% to 90% sulphide minerals is adopted in this paper, thereby avoiding the common confusion between the deposit type and the sulphide mineralization type present in a deposit.

Exhalative massive sulphide deposits consist of either a strata-bound lens of sulphide mineralization together with a discordant zone of alteration representing the exhalative vent (i.e., a proximal deposit) or a stratabound lens of sulphide mineralization without a closely associated zone (i.e., a distal deposit). In this paper massive sulphide depos-

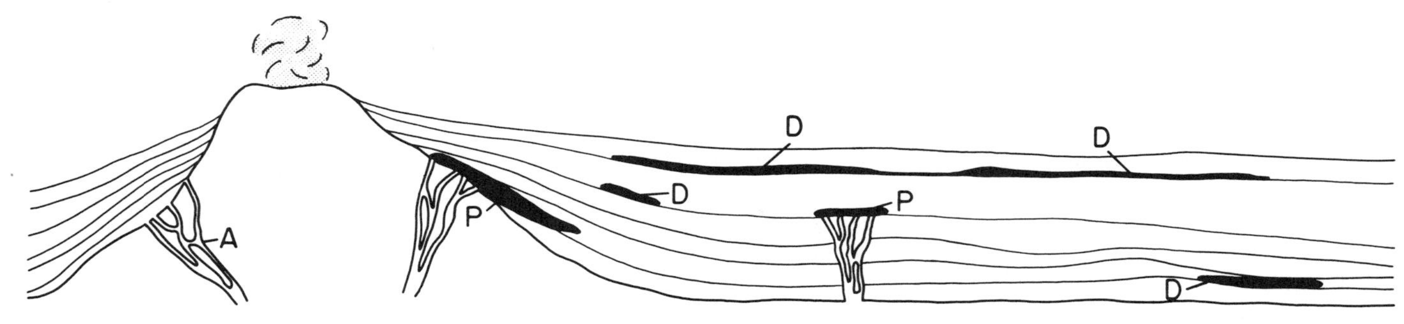

Figure 1. Schematic illustration of exhalative massive sulphide deposit types. P, proximal massive sulphide deposit; D, distal massive sulphide deposit; A, stringer zone.

its are classified on the basis of proximity to an exhalative vent rather than proximity to a volcanic edifice (Large, 1977), since (1) it is the exhalative process that generates a deposit regardless of whether it is contained within volcanic or sedimentary rocks; (2) in the classification of Large (1977), a deposit may be distal to a volcanic vent with respect to the stratigraphically underlying rocks but immediately overlain by volcanic flow rocks; and (3) alteration products are readily determined by visual examination and geochemical methods, thereby permitting ease of recognition of deposit types in both field mapping and geochemical exploration programs. Consequently, a *proximal* massive sulphide deposit (Fig. 1) is defined as composed of one or more lenses (masses) of sulphide mineralization together with the exhalative zone through which the mineralizing fluids traveled to the rock surface. The sulphide lens may have been deposited as a sediment on the ocean floor where it filled available depressions in the topographic surface or as a silica + sulphide mass on a topographically high area such as a rhyolite dome; consequently, in deposits that have not been modified by later tectonic events the stratigraphically lower content of a lens may be an irregular surface, whereas the upper contact is generally conformable with the overlying stratum. In contrast, the alteration zone or 'feeder zone' is generally characterized by silicate minerals produced by the reactions of mineralizing fluids with the rocks stratigraphically underlying the massive sulphide lens. This zone of alteration may commonly have a funnel-like shape that is discordant to the strata. Sulphide minerals, generally a few tens of per cent, but locally up to 90%, are deposited in a vein network below the rock-water interface to form a stockwork or 'stringer' zone of mineralization (Fig. 1).

A *distal* deposit may occasionally have an irregular but roughly concordant layer of silicate alteration products associated with it; however, it is the absence of a discordant silicate alteration zone that distinguishes a distal from a proximal deposit (Fig. 1). The sulphide lens of a distal massive sulphide deposit is indistinguishable from that of a proximal deposit. The sulphide lens and associated silicate alteration products, if any, in distal deposits may result from (1) deposition away from the site of exhalation (Sato, 1972) or (2) transportation of consolidated material away from the site of exhalation by slumping or gravity slides prior to deposition of the stratigraphically overlying rocks (Horikoshi, 1969).

DISTRIBUTION OF PROTEROZOIC MASSIVE SULPHIDE DEPOSITS

Selected massive sulphide deposits of Proterozoic age in North America are shown in Figure 2. Major districts include the Flin Flon and Snow Lake districts of Manitoba and Saskatchewan, the Balmat-Edwards district of New York, the Ducktown district of Tennessee, the Jerome and Bagdad districts of Arizona, the Wisconsin district, and the Sullivan district of British Columbia.

Major deposits outside North America include those of the Broken Hill, Mount Isa, and McArthur River districts of Australia; the Copperton and Gams district of South Africa; the Skellefte district of Sweden; and the Outokumpu district of Finland.

Exhalative massive sulphide deposits occur in all three major time periods of the Proterozoic. For example, deposits in the Flin Flon, Jerome, and Skellefte districts are of Proterozoic X age (2500 to 1600 Ma), the Sullivan, Gams,a nd Mount Isa districts contain deposits of Proterozoic Y age (1500 to 800 Ma), and those of the Ducktown district are of Proterozoic Z age (800 to 570 Ma).

Since exhalative massive sulphide deposits are regarded as having been deposited contemporaneously with volcanic and sedimentary rocks, it is useful to group deposits according to their dominent host rock (cf. Sangster and Scott, 1976; Gilmour, 1976). A classification of the environments of deposition of massive sulphide deposits is illustrated in Figure 3. This classification is similar to that of Gilmour (1976) and Sangster and Scott (1976) and attempts to distinguish a volcanic from a sedimentary environment in which there is little, if any, evidence of volcanic rocks contributing directly to the sedimentary rock units.

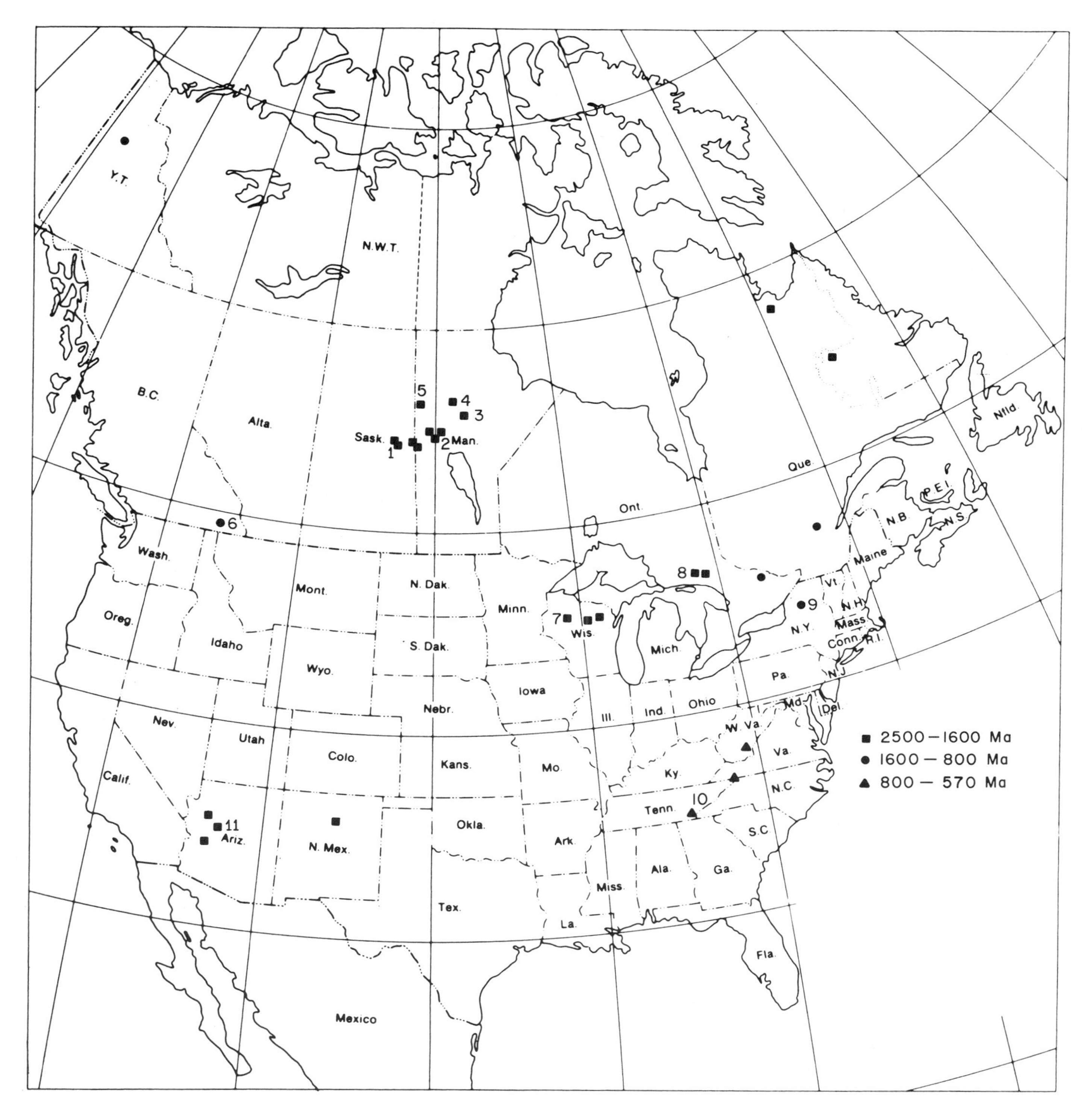

Figure 2. Distribution of Proterozoic massive sulphide districts of North America, after Sangster (1980). 1, Flin Flon; 2, Snow Lake; 3, Thompson; 4, Ruttan; 5, Fox Lake; 6, Sullivan; 7, Crandon; 8, Vermillion; 9, Balmat-Edwards; 10, Ducktown; 11, Jerome.

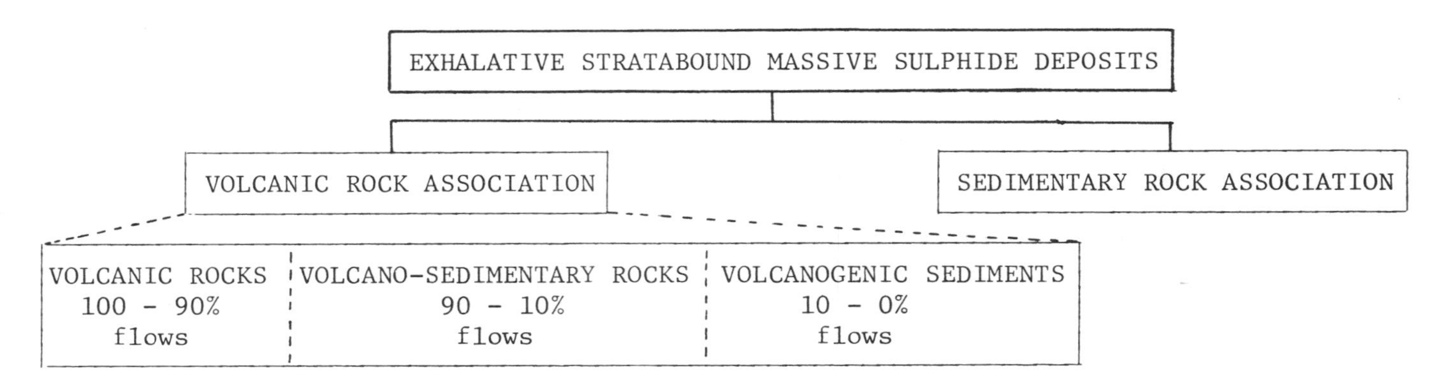

Figure 3. Classification of geologic settings hosting massive sulphide deposits.

The volcanic association includes all lithologies from flow rocks to volcanogenic sedimentary rocks where volcanic activity can be shown to be contemporaneous with the deposition of some or all of the rocks. A convenient subdivision of this association is made according to the relative proportions of extrusive volcanic-flow rocks present (Fig. 3). Massive sulphide deposits are also hosted by a variety of sedimentary rocks (e.g., shale, siltstone, calcareous sedimentary rocks) that contain only minor amounts of volcanic material. These rocks are referred to here as the sedimentary association. Although some degree of uncertainty exists in establishing firm boundaries between the subdivisions, this is a reasonable representation of the rock associations found in nature (Gilmour, 1976).

Volcanic Rock Association

Deposits Associated with Volcanic Flows. The Flin Flon deposits in Manitoba and the United Verde deposit in Arizona are good examples of proximal, volcanic rock–hosted massive sulphide deposits (Fig. 4). Basaltic pillow lava and flow breccia form a thick sequence stratigraphically underlying the Flin Flon deposit. A locally derived polymictic volcaniclastic unit of dominantly mafic composition overlies the lava sequence. Locally, the uppermost member of this volcaniclastic rock is a breccia ('mill rock' of Sangster, 1972). This breccia, composed of quartz-porphyry fragments in a matrix of mafic fragmental rocks, occurs at approximately the same stratigraphic position as the ore lenses and probably predates the mineralizing activity by a short time. Quartz porphyritic felsic flows and flow breccia overlie the solid sulphide lenses. A younger sequence of extensive mafic volcanic rocks overlies the sulphide deposits. An extensive alteration pipe has been documented from both underground workings (Sangster, 1972) and surface exposures (Gale et al., 1980). It appears from present reconstructions that the Flin Flon deposit formed during or immediately preceding an episode of felsic volcanism; however, this is difficult to ascertain in the immediate vicinity of the deposit due to extensive footwall alteration. Although felsic rocks are volumetrically a minor constituent of the volcanic pile in the Flin Flon mine area, they are present.

The United Verde deposit at Jerome, Arizona, differs from the Flin Flon deposit mainly in its association with a thick felsic, rather than mafic, volcanic rock sequence. This deposit is hosted by the 1200-m-thick rhyolitic rock unit that is overlain by clastic sedimentary rocks and underlain by a thick sequence of dacite, andesite, and basalt (Anderson and Nash, 1972). The lower part of the rhyolitic unit is a generally massive fine grained rock in which flow, breccia, and tuff can be distinguished where relict textures are present. The upper part of the rhyolite unit is an intertongueing complex of massive rhyolitic rocks, flow-banded quartz porphyry, coarse breccia, and crystal tuff; both flow rocks and near-surface intrusions may be represented by the massive rhyolitic rocks. Anderson and Nash (1972) considered some of the rhyolitic rocks to have been emplaced largely as subaqueous pyroclastic flows or debris flows resulting from violent phreatic eruptions. The rhyolitic rocks are overlain by a well-bedded clastic unit consisting of layers of coarse volcaniclastic rocks, well-bedded tuffaceous rocks, cherty shale, and chert. A conformable 'gabbro' overlying these clastic sedimentary rocks is now considered to be a basaltic flow since Ei Horikoshi recognized pillow structures in it (pers. comm. *in* Gilmour, 1976). The ore deposit consists of solid to near-solid sulphide lenses which are stratigraphically underlain by a zone of chloritic alteration and stringer ore ('black schist'). Lenses of chert ('white quartz') stratigraphically overlie the deposit.

The Coronation deposit (Fig. 4), immediately west of Flin Flon, is a copper-rich deposit of near-solid sulphide in tholeiitic flows and flow breccias of island-arc composition (Froese, 1969; Fox, 1976). Felsic flow rocks have not been identified in the area. Cordierite-anthophyllite rocks, representing the metamorphosed alteration zone, occur immediately adjacent to the ore deposit.

The Fox Lake deposit (Fig. 4) is an example of a distal deposit in volcanic flow rocks. The footwall rocks are a thick sequence of basaltic flow and flow breccia. Minor

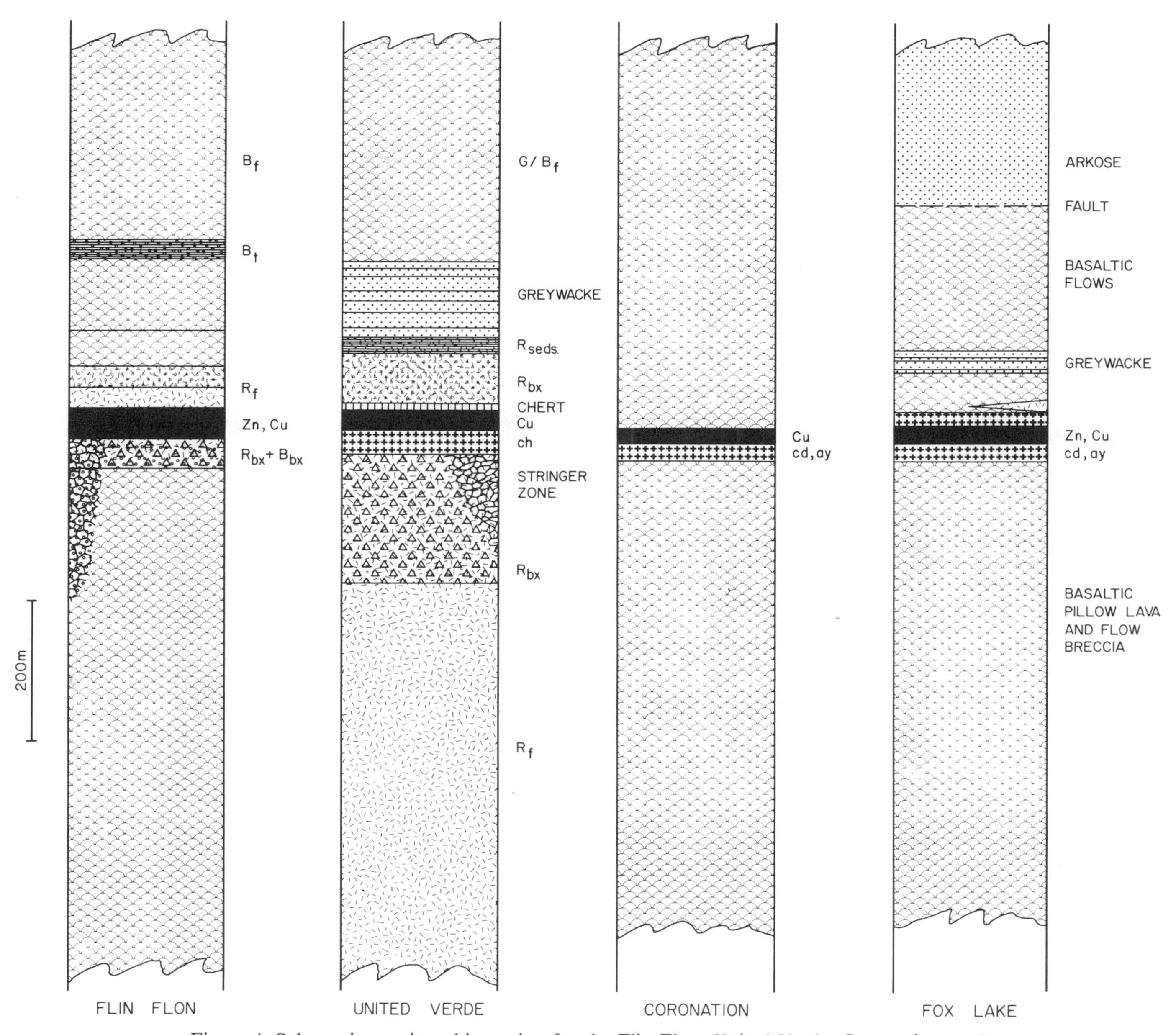

Figure 4. Schematic stratigraphic section for the Flin Flon, United Verde, Coronation, and Fox Lake deposits, after Gale et al. (1980), Anderson and Nash (1972), Froese (1969), and Lustig (1979), respectively. Scale bar represents approximately 200 m. Abbreviations (Figs. 4–7): ay, anthophyllite; B, basaltic rocks; Blk. S, black shale; bx, breccia (mostly debris flows); cd, cordierite; ch, chert; Cu, copper; f, F, flow rocks; G, gabbroic rocks; K, potassium; Ni, nickel; Pb, lead; R, rhyolitic and/or rhyodacitic rocks; t, tuffaceous rocks; Zn, zinc.

amounts of felsic volcanic rocks stratigraphically overlie the massive sulphide deposits. The near-solid sulphide lens is contained within a silicate rock unit with abundant cordierite ± muscovite ± phlogopite ± sericite (Lustig, 1979) that is considered to be an exhalative product (chert and clay minerals) deposited some distance from the exhalative vent (Gale et al., 1980).

Deposits Hosted by Volcano-Sedimentary Rocks. Deposits in this geologic setting are represented by several massive sulphide deposits in the Snow Lake area of Manitoba that are hosted by a thick sequence of mainly felsic volcaniclastic rocks and volcanogenic sedimentary rocks which are in turn overlain by a thick sequence of both mafic and felsic subaqueous lava flows. The volcaniclastic rocks are composed of debris flow and laharic breccia representing reworked felsic material that may originally have been deposited as pyroclastic rocks or lava flows; however, their subaqueous deposition was at a site different from that of

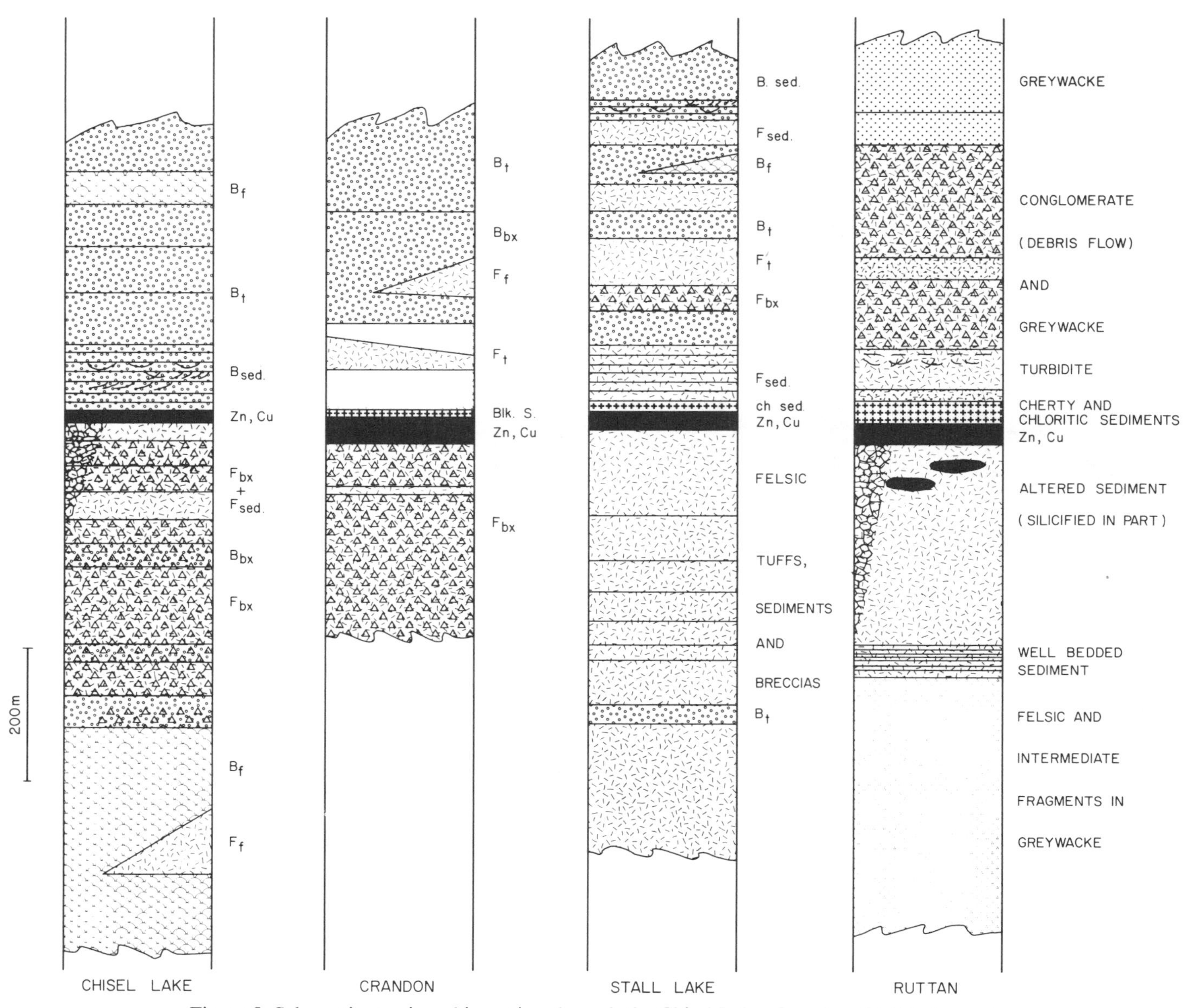

Figure 5. Schematic stratigraphic section through the Chisel Lake, Crandon, Stall Lake, and Ruttan deposits, after Gale (1977), Schmidt et al. (1978), Studer (1982), and Baldwin (1982), respectively. Scale bar and abbreviations as in Figure 4.

the volcanic rocks from which the clasts and the matrix were derived. The thin units of volcanogenic sedimentary rocks are mafic to felsic in composition, exhibit well-defined bedding, and commonly have internal sedimentary structures. Flow and pyroclastic rocks are commonly interlayered with the volcaniclastic rocks and volcanogenic sedimentary rocks on the 'volcanic' end of this spectrum. Flow rocks are rarely present, and the volcaniclastic rocks decrease in clast size and become the least dominant rock type towards the 'sedimentary' end of this suite.

The Chisel Lake deposit (Fig. 5) occurs at the top of a sequence of dominantly volcaniclastic rocks in which large-scale layering is common (Fig. 5). The fragments and the matrix are generally felsic; however, several layers contain large felsic fragments (greater than 30 cm in diameter) in a mafic matrix, and in others both felsic and mafic fragments are present. Arenaceous sedimentary rocks with graded beds are scattered throughout the upper part of the volcaniclastic sequence. The felsic matrix and rock fragments appear to have been derived from a thick sequence of felsic flows and pyroclastic rocks, probably a felsic dome, located immediately east of the mine area. The geologic setting of this deposit represents the volcanic end of this spectrum. The Crandon deposit (Fig. 5), which is contained within a

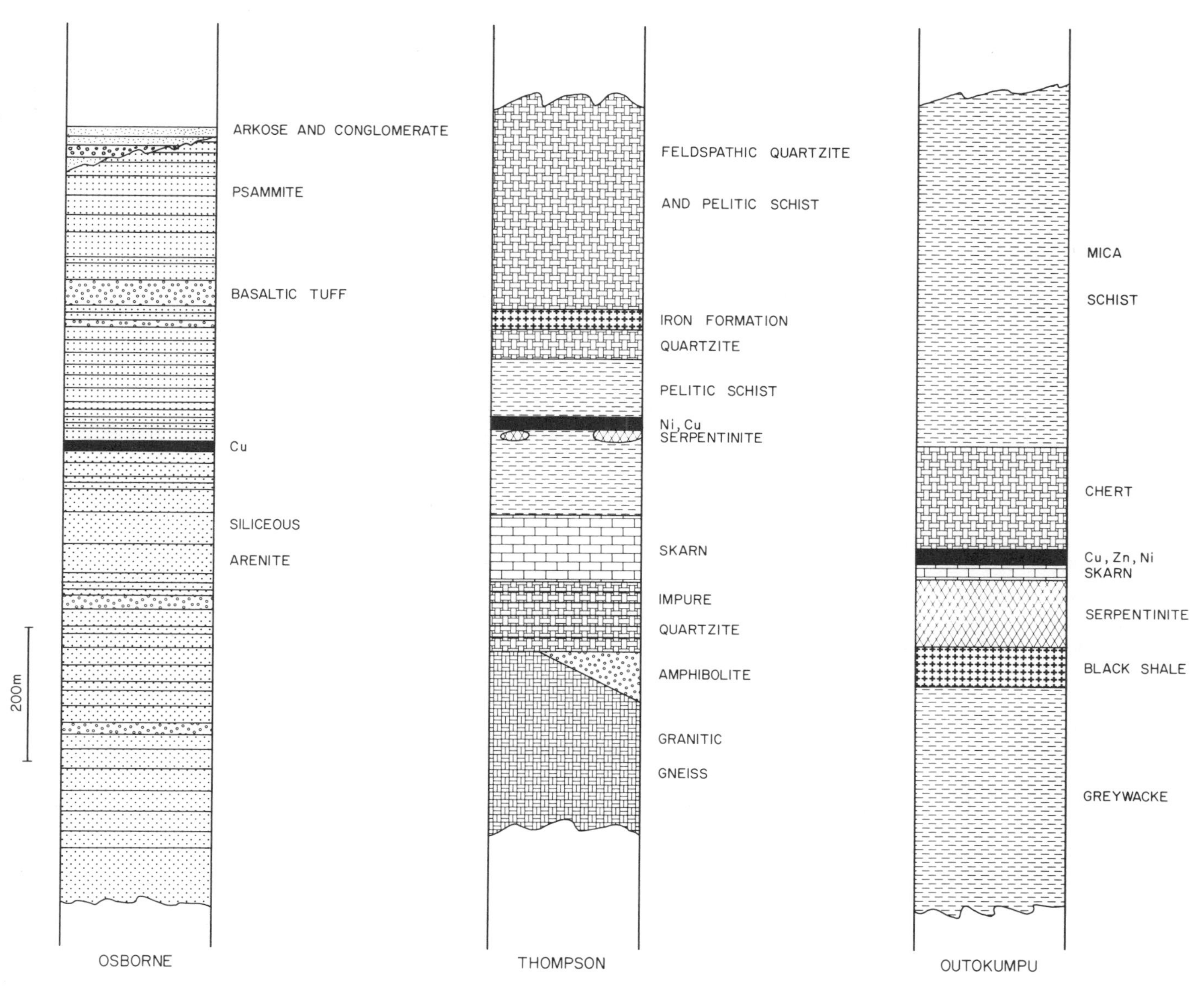

Figure 6. Schematic stratigraphic section through the Osborne, Thompson, and Outokumpu deposits, after Gale et al. (1980), Peredery and Geological Staff (1982), and Gaal et al. (1975). Scale bar and abbreviations as in Figure 4.

sequence of volcanic and associated sedimentary rocks, and the Prieska deposit, South Africa, which occurs in a thick unit of volcanogenic sedimentary rocks associated with dacitic lavas (Wagener, 1980), are other examples of deposits occurring in this geologic setting.

The Ruttan deposit in Manitoba is situated in a 900-m-thick sequence of well-layered intermediate and felsic volcaniclastic rocks, fragments averaging 2 cm in diameter, and well-layered turbidites of greywacke composition. Basaltic flows are present at the base of the epiclastic rocks; however, felsic flows and pyroclastic rocks have not been identified in the sequence of epiclastic rocks that host the massive sulphide deposit. The geologic setting of this deposit exemplifies the sedimentary end of this volcano-sedimentary spectrum.

Deposits Hosted by Volcanogenic Sedimentary Rocks. This geologic setting is characterized by volcano-derived sedimentary rocks. Material indicative of continuing volcanism (for example, lavas, volcaniclastic rocks, tuffaceous rocks) are generally present but constitute an infinitely small proportion of the stratigraphic sequence by volume.

The Wim, Osborne Lake (Fig. 6), and Sherridon deposits in Manitoba occur in this geologic setting. The Wim deposit is a proximal exhalative stratabound, near-solid to solid sulphide lens composed of coarsely recrystallized pyrite, pyrrhotite, chalcopyrite, and minor sphalerite. The host rocks are an alternating sequence of sedimentary rocks characterized by quartzofeldspathic-biotite-garnet gneiss and white- to buff-coloured, delicately laminated quartzofeldspathic hornblende gneiss, both derived from a volcanic source (Bailes, 1975). At Osborne Lake, a proximal exhalative copper-rich deposit is contained in a well-layered felsic gneiss. The stratigraphically overlying rocks are quartz-biotite-muscovite gneiss and contain argillitic(?) and siliceous layers. The underlying rocks are siliceous quartz-biotite gneiss that appear from geochemical studies to have been derived from felsic volcanic rocks. The Sherridon deposits are copper-zinc-bearing pyritic bodies within a sequence of quartzite, well-layered quartz-rich gneiss, marble, semipelitic gneiss, and amphibolite. A volcanic origin has been proposed for some of the amphibolitic rocks (Froese and Goetz, 1976), and some of the quartzofeldspathic rocks may be of volcanic origin; however, the presence of volcanic material has not been established with any degree of certainty (Gale et al., 1980). The Sherridon deposits are distal exhalative deposits that contain a cordierite-garnet-anthophyllite rock interpreted to have been an exhalative mud that was deposited with the sulphides.

It has been proposed (Gale et al., 1980) that the stratiform nickel-copper-bearing solid sulphide deposit at Thompson (Zurbrigg, 1963), Manitoba, is an exhalative massive sulphide deposit. The Thompson deposit (Fig. 6) occurs in a metasedimentary assemblage of siliceous, calcareous, pelitic, and ferruginous rocks that underlie an area of 2 km by 12 km. A typical section through the sedimentary band includes biotite gneiss, quartzite, a calc-silicate rock, pelitic schist, greywacke containing stratabound sulphides, banded 'iron-formation', and quartzite. Small ultramafic lenses are present locally within the massive sulphide deposit and the greywacke host rocks. Stratigraphic tops in the mine are uncertain, but in a similar succession at the Pipe Mine, about 35 km southwest of the Thompson Mine, the iron-formation occurs near the stratigraphic top of the sedimentary succession (Peredery et al. 1982).

The Thompson deposit is a thin, conformable, sheet-like body with a strike length of over 5 km, within the pelitic schist member of the sedimentary sequence. The higher grade portions of the deposit occur mainly in the thickened hinge zones of drag folds. Ultramafic rocks are intimately associated with the sulphide deposit; however, the ratio of ultramafic rock to sulphides is only 1:4 (Peredery et al., 1982).

At the Pipe Mine, 30 km along strike from the Thompson deposit, sulphides are found as a sulphide network within the ultramafic rock and as a solid sulphide layer in graphitic sedimentary rocks. Mafic sedimentary rocks observed at the top of the Pipe Mine ultramafic rock may represent erosional products derived from weathering of the ultramafic rock. Although the ultramafic rocks associated with nickel mineralization in the Thompson Nickel Belt of Manitoba are considered by Peredery et al. (1982) to have been emplaced as sills, I consider the restriction of the nickel-sulphide-bearing ultramafic rocks to a pelitic schist unit that is similar to the sedimentary rocks containing the Thompson deposit to be indicative of extrusive rather than intrusive, igneous activity. The conformability of the massive sulphide sheet at the Thompson deposit within a sedimentary unit (the pelitic schist), the close association of the nickel-copper ores with a graphitic sulphide layer of more than 10-km strike length, the presence of graphite within the ore, and the presence of interbanded sulphides and silicates near the margins of the deposit are all features commonly observed in exhalative massive sulphide deposits (see also Lusk, 1976).

The copper-zinc exhalative massive sulphide deposits in the Outokumpu district, Finland, are associated with serpentinite, siliceous schist, and carbonaceous black schist (Fig. 6) of the 240-km-long Outokumpu zone (Peltola, 1978). These deposits occur in a 3-km-thick sequence of mainly phyllite and micaceous schist (flysch) with a basal unit of conglomerate and arkosic quartzite. The serpentinite occurs as conformable, elongate lenses parallel to bedding; dolomite and skarn form reaction products around the serpentinite. Siliceous quartzite, identified as chert by Peltola (1978), overlies the serpentinite and contains 0.1% to 0.2% Ni as pentlandite. The copper ore bodies contain as much as 0.5% Ni (Gaal et al., 1975) but have an average content of 0.12% Ni and 0.24% Co (Peltola, 1978).

The stratabound Outokumpu massive sulphide deposit is an example of a nickeliferous copper-zinc exhalative massive sulphide deposit, whereas I consider the Thompson deposit to be a stratabound nickel-copper exhalative massive sulphide deposit.

Sedimentary Rock Association

This geologic setting is characterized by a thick sequence of clastic and/or chemical sedimentary rocks. Although volcanic rocks are not present and it does not appear from the geological record that active volcanism contributed significantly to the buildup of the sedimentary sequence, it is common to find evidence of contemporaneous volcanic activity either in the immediate host rocks of the massive sulphide deposit or in the stratigraphically younger rocks. For example, air-fall glass shards are present in the McArthur River deposit (Lambert, 1976); metamorphosed rocks in the Balmat-Edwards district (Gilmour, 1976) and Broken Hill (Stevens et al., 1979) district are interpreted to be of volcanic origin. Admittedly, it is not always easy to establish a boundary between this geologic setting and the volcanogenic sedimentary rock setting.

The Sullivan deposit (Freeze, 1966; Morris, 1972) at Kimberley, British Columbia, occurs in a thick (greater than 10 km) sequence of Middle Proterozoic fine-grained clastic sedimentary rocks at the transition from the Lower to the Middle Aldridge Formations. The footwall rocks, the Lower Aldridge Formation, are characterized by a rhythmic succession of thin-bedded, graded, fine-grained argillite and siltstone and some impure quartzite. The Middle Aldridge Formation, stratigraphically overlying the ore deposit, is more thickly bedded and arenaceous than the footwall sedimentary rocks. Intraformational conglomerate is present in the immediate footwall of the mine and in several places in the immediate hanging wall. A distinctive feature of this deposit is the presence of a brecciated zone with hydrothermal alteration characterized by extensive tourmalinization and disseminated sulphide mineralization that occurs stratigraphically below the ore. Albititic alteration in the immediate hanging wall of the ore deposit is probably related to exhalations associated with the mineralizing event. The only known volcanic rocks are thin basaltic flows that occur approximately 6 km stratigraphically above the ore zone. Sills and dykes of quartz diabase, the Moyie intrusions, intruded the Aldridge at 1100 to 1500 Ma (K-Ar dates), whereas single-stage lead isotope ages on galena from the ore deposits give ages between 1200 and 1400 Ma (Leech and Wanless, 1962; see Thompson and Panteleyev, 1976, for discussion). The Moyie sills and dykes may be genetically relatable to the ore-forming processes.

Other well-known North American examples in this setting are the copper-zinc-bearing massive sulphide deposits in Late Precambrian greywacke conglomerate, mica-schist, quartzite, chlorite-garnet schist, and chlorite-garnet-staurolite schist of the Great Smokey Group in the Ducktown district, Tennessee (Magee, 1968). The area is structurally complex and has been metamorphosed to the middle-amphibolite grade (Nesbitt and Kelly, 1980). Metamorphosed alteration zones adjacent to the ore deposits contain garnet, staurolite, tremolite, and kyanite. Some of the chloritic rocks may represent tuffaceous sedimentary rocks. Igneous rocks are represented by a stratiform amphibolite sill (altered gabbro?) that has a strike length of 20 km; some of the small occurrences of amphibolite near the orebodies are metamorphosed alteration products. The ore averages 60% pyrrhotite, 30% pyrite, 4% chalcopyrite, 4% sphalerite, 2% magnetite, and minor galena. Many of the deposits can be interpreted to have formed at one stratigraphic level (Magee, 1968).

In the Balmat-Edwards district, New York, the host rocks to the massive sulphide deposits are interlayered with calcitic and dolomitic marble, silica-rich layers of marble, quartzose and biotitic gneiss, serpentinite, and calc-silicate gneiss (Lea and Dill, 1968). Gilmour (1976) suggested that some of the rocks, especially the quartz-mica-feldspar gneiss, lamprophyre, impure marble, and amphibolite described by Lea and Dill (1968), may be of volcanic origin. Carl and Van Diver (1975) interpreted the basal quartz-biotite-oligoclase gneiss underlying the marble unit to be ash-flow tuffs.

The Sullivan deposit is unusual in some respects as an example of deposits in this geologic setting in that there is no evidence of ongoing volcanism at the time of mineralizing activity. In contrast, the unmetamorphosed sedimentary rocks that host the massive sulphide deposit at McArthur River, Australia, contain ample evidence that at the time of sulphide deposition there was volcanic activity some distance away, probably at the margins of the sedimentary basin (Lambert, 1976). The McArthur deposit occurs in a sequence of dolomite, siltstone, shale, and tuffite that attains a thickness of up to 5.5 km. The greatest concentration of tuff in the McArthur Group is in the rocks that host the sulphide deposits, the H.Y.C. Pyritic Shale Member, where six major tuffite beds, 8 to 30 cm thick, have been recognized.

The Broken Hill deposit (Fig. 7) occurs in granulite facies metasedimentary rocks of the Willyama Complex. Well-bedded quartzofeldspathic sedimentary rocks underlie the 'Mine Sequence' that is in turn stratigrpahically overlain by pelitic and psammopelitic gneiss having well-bedded turbidite-like deposits, impure quartzites, and minor calcareous sedimentary rock layers. The Mine Sequence contains, in addition to the ore deposits, sillimanite gneiss, quartzite, garnetiferous quartzite, sillimanite-garnet-biotite gneiss, mica schist, amphibolite, and banded iron-formation (Laing et al., 1978). Although volcanic textures have not been recognized, some of the gneiss is chemically similar to dacitic and rhyodacitic tuff (Stanton, 1976). The thick amphibolite layers are either basaltic flows or sills, and some of the thinner bodies of amphibolite probably represent air-fall ash deposits (Stevens, et al., 1979). The bulk of the Mine Sequence is well-layered sedimentary rock.

Stratigraphic Control of Deposits

A number of review articles have been presented recently that deal with the main features of massive sulphide deposits in general (Sangster, 1972; Sangster and Scott, 1976; Gilmour, 1976) and North American Precambrian massive sulphide deposits in particular (Sangster and Scott, 1976; Sangster, 1980). The general features of Archean and Proterozoic massive sulphide deposits discussed by Sangster and Scott (1976) include ore types, composition, mineralogy, morphology, zoning, alteration, and metamorphic effects. Deposits in Manitoba, described by Gale et al. (1980), indicate that Proterozoic deposits in general have correlatives in Archean, Phanerozoic, and younger deposits when comparisons are made of deposits in similar geologic settings that have been metamorphosed under similar conditions.

Proterozoic massive sulphide deposits in volcanic

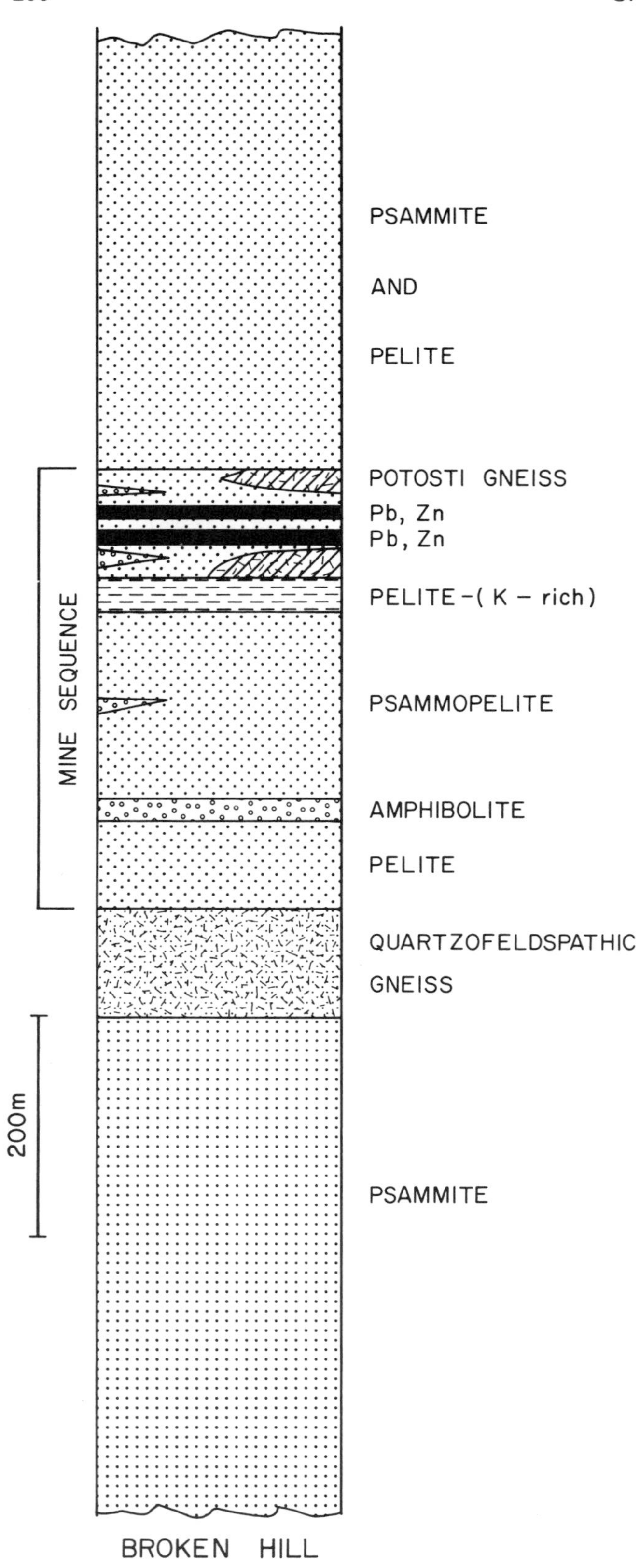

Figure 7. Schematic stratigraphic section through the Broken Hill deposit, after Barnes (1979). Scale bar and abbreviations as in Figure 4.

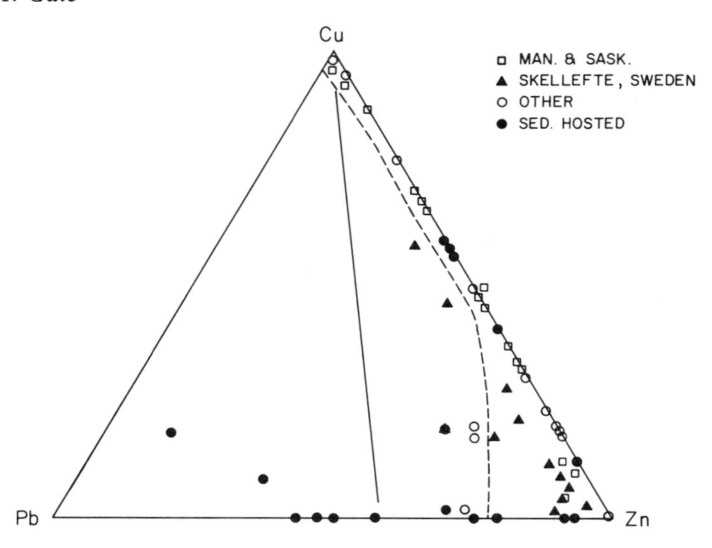

Figure 8. Metal ratios in selected Proterozoic massive sulphide deposits. Data for Skellefte district from Rickard and Zwiefel (1975); for Manitoba, Saskatchewan, and other areas from Table 1. Righthand side of dashed line is the field for Archean massive sulphide deposits (Sangster, 1980); on the right side of solid line is the field for Phanerozoic deposits (Sangster and Scott, 1976).

rocks are shown to be lead-poor relative to Phanerozoic deposits in volcanic settings (Sangster and Scott, 1976, Fig. 26B). A few Precambrian deposits in association with volcanic rocks have zinc-rich ore zones that also contain relatively high lead contents; for example, the Chisel Mine in Manitoba and the Mons Cupri deposit of Archean age in Australia which has a one-million-tonne solid sulphide ore lens containing 2.5% Pb and 3.5% Zn (Miller and Gair, 1975).

The apparent increase in lead content of Proterozoic massive sulphide deposits in comparison to Archean deposits occurs in those deposits found in thick sedimentary sequences; however, there are no known Archean deposits in this setting. In addition, lead-rich Proterozoic deposits associated with volcanic rocks have no more lead (Fig. 8) than some Archean deposits (Sangster, 1980). Deposits occurring within or at the end of essentially mafic volcanic sequences are usually lead-poor and contain more copper than zinc (e.g., Coronation Mine). Deposits that occur at the stratigraphic top of a thick and extensive felsic volcanic sequence generally contain more zinc than copper and are relatively lead-rich (e.g., Chisel Lake, Errington, and Vermillion Lake Mines).

A common feature of volcanic-hosted massive sulphide deposits, including those of Proterozoic age, is their apparent time and spatial equivalence sometimes over distances of several hundred kilometres (cf. Ueno, 1975); most of the deposits in any one district are located within one volcanic sequence or close to the same paleosubaqueous surface. This feature has been observed in the Snow Lake district of Manitoba (Gale, 1977), the Jerome district of Arizona (Anderson and Guilbert, 1979), and the Skellefte district of Sweden (Rickard and Zwiefel, 1975).

The nickel-copper deposits and associated ultramafic rocks (lavas?) of the Thompson Nickel Belt ocur within a thin pelitic schist unit over a distance of more than 65 km. The pelitic rock unit maintains the same stratigraphic position relative to the calcareous sedimentary rocks (skarn) and the iron-formation over their exposed strike length (Peredery et al., 1982). Known stratabound massive sulphide deposits in the Outokumpu district occur within the Outokumpu zone over a strike length of 240 km (Peltola, 1978). This zone is about several hundred metres thick and consists mainly of carbonaceous black schists, serpentinites (lavas?), and siliceous quartz-rich schists.

Massive sulphide deposits in a sedimentary basin may also occur at or near the same stratigraphic position. Magee (1968) presented an interpretation of ore deposits in the Ducktown area that placed all of the known deposits in that area on or close to the same stratigraphic position. The Mount Isa and Hilton Mines occur at about the same position within the Urquhart Shale, although separated along strike by a distance of 20 km. The 28 separate stratiform orebodies at Mount Isa (Finlow-Bates and Stumpfl, 1979) and the seven separate orebodies at Hilton (Lambert, 1976) indicate that considerable clastic sedimentation was added to the sequence during the period of exhalative activity. The sedimentary rocks and ore deposits at McArthur River and those at Mount Isa are lithologically similar (Plumb and Derrick, 1975); however, they cannot be traced uninterrupted over the intervening 450-km distance. The presence of volcanic debris in rocks adjacent to the sulphides in both areas may be indicative of contemporaneous deposition of mineralization in both areas.

In the Broken Hill Block of the Willyama Complex, Australia, the lead-silver-zinc mineralization of the Broken Hill–type occupies a restricted stratigraphic interval within the Mine Sequence suite of rocks (Willis, 1979; Laing, 1979) and is often associated with quartz-gahnite-garnet rock and banded iron-formation, derived from chemical sediments that locally can be traced for several tens of kilometres along strike and were originally deposited over areas of several hundred square kilometres (Barnes, 1979). The Mine Sequence suite not only hosts the Broken Hill deposit but virtually all Broken Hill–type mineralization in the approximately 4,000-km^2 area of the Broken Hill Block (Stevens et al., 1979). This apparent stratigraphically controlled stratiform mineralization throughout the Broken Hill Block suggests that the metal-bearing hydrothermal solutions were debouched onto the ocean floor at approximately the same time. Barnes (1979) suggested that the episode of mineralization took place at the end of an episode of felsic-mafic volcanism.

Although detailed stratigraphic correlations in many mining districts are not complete, there is an increasing geologic data base suggesting that mineral deposits of the stratabound exhalative type exhibit a marked stratigraphic control and probably formed on the ocean floor in a relatively short interval of time in any one district or region regardless of whether the deposits are found in volcanic, volcanosedimentary, or sedimentary rocks. In addition to the examples of Proterozoic deposits presented here, there are many other examples, in rocks of various ages, of massive sulphide deposits located within a 'favourable' stratigraphic interval. For example, most of the Archean deposits in the Noranda area are found within the Amulet Andesite formation (Spence and de Rosen-Spence, 1975). Most of the massive sulphide deposits in the Bathurst area, New Brunswick, appear to occur within a narrow stratigraphic interval in close proximity to the upper contact (Holyk, 1957) of a thin layer of porphyritic ash-flow tuff. Davies and McAllister (1980) suggested that all of the sulphide deposits may be assigned to one relatively wide stratigraphic level. Many of the deposits can be related to a resurgent Ordovician caldera structure (Harley, 1979). Most of the Kuroko deposits in the Green Tuff region of Japan occur within a narrow stratigraphic interval in middle Miocene volcanic rocks (Takahashi and Suga, 1974) and appear to have formed in less than 200,000 years over a strike length of more than 300 km (Ueno, 1975).

It is readily apparent that most of the deposits in any one district, regardless of geologic age, will occur within a narrow stratigraphic interval within a 'favourable stratigraphic unit'; however, it is well established that not all deposits in a district occur at one 'horizon'. This implies that the massive sulphide depositional environment in volcanic terranes has not changed significantly since the formation of Archean massive sulphide deposits and that conditions favourable for the formation of massive sulphide deposits were generated by geologic events of a regional rather than a local nature.

Origin of Deposits

Proterozoic massive sulphide deposits exhibit marked similarities with Archean, Phanerozoic, and younger deposits when 'volcanic-hosted' and 'sedimentary-hosted' deposits are compared separately. The appearance of a number of large sedimentary-hosted deposits in the Proterozoic is probably a reflection of more stable global crustal conditions, in comparison to Archean time, rather than any change or difference in the genesis of massive sulphide deposits; Archean crustal conditions may not have been conducive to the formation or preservation of thick sequences of Archean sediment in major sedimentary basins.

Many authors have discussed the problem of ore genesis in massive sulphide deposits (cf. Ridge, 1976; King, 1976; Bernard and Samama, 1976), and many areas have seen 'full-circle' changes in ideas as illustrated for the Caledonian massive sulphide deposits by Vokes (1976, Fig. 7). Detailed discussions based upon individual models are excluded from this paper, except to note some of the problems associated with current ore-genesis models. A review of the shortcomings of these models becomes necessary if the origins of Cu-Zn ± Pb, Zn-Pb ± Cu, and Ni-Cu deposits are to be explained. A detailed examination of the problem of massive sulphide deposit genesis is given by Lydon (1981) and Lydon *in* Franklin et al. (1981).

It has been generally accepted that 'volcanogenic massive sulphide deposits' are not only related to volcanic processes (e.g., Sangster, 1972; Large, 1977) but also that their probable mode of formation was related to the exhalation of brines onto the seafloor (Sato, 1972). The exhalative process has also been established for deposits in sedimentary terranes where the deposit occurs immediately overlying an exhalative vent (Sullivan; Thompson and Pantelayev, 1976) or has been transported from the exhalative site to a slight depression on the ocean floor (McArthur River; Lambert, 1976). The 'volcanic' influence on the origin of the deposits in thick sedimentary sequences is unknown or even highly questionable even though some (e.g., Mount Isa and McArthur River) were deposited at approximately the same time as volcanic activity outside the sedimentary basin.

The origins of the meta-bearing fluids being exhaled onto the ocean floor to form the massive sulphide deposits are still a source of controversy. They may have been generated from seawater circulating through the underlying rock pile, from connate waters, or from 'aqueous fluids' during crystallization of a magma.

The model that appears to be most popular at this time involves (1) sea-water leaching of metals from the rocks during circulation through the footwall rocks; (2) heating of these waters by a synvolcanic intrusive rock mass or a high geothermal gradient; and (3) subsequent ejection of hot fluids through one or more, probably fault-controlled, orifices where the metals are precipitated upon mixing with cooler ocean water at or near the ocean floor (cf. Spooner and Fyfe, 1973; Solomon, 1976). This model is supported mainly from oxygen-isotope studies on fluid inclusions in some of the Japanese Kuroko deposits where it has been shown that a high proportion of the water in the inclusions originated as seawater (Ohmoto and Rye, 1974), as well as from studies of alteration (Spooner, 1977). Solomon (1976), in arguing the merits of the convecting sea-water model, noted the difficulty in explaining the tendency for many of the deposits in a district to occur within a narrow stratigraphic interval and the common association of deposits and felsic volcanic rocks. Solomon (1976) considered the necessity of replacing the pore fluids 600 times to produce a medium-sized deposit on Cyprus. If the hydrothermal fluids are extremely low in metals, then it would probably take several tens of thousands of years to form a deposit on the ocean floor (cf. Solomon, 1976; Spooner, 1977), which represents a significantly long period of time to expect nondeposition of rock material in an active volcanic terrane. This problem is resolved, however, if the fluids being expelled onto the ocean floor contained concentrations of several thousand parts-per-million metal such as those found in fluid inclusions by Sawkins and Scherkenback (1981). Theoretically, these problems can be surmounted by ponding the fluids under an impermeable layer (e.g., a sill) until they have been saturated in metals with respect to the host-rock minerals and then released onto the sea floor by fracturing of the cap rock (Hodgson and Lydon, 1977). For details of this model, the reader is referred to the review by Solomon (1976) and articles by Spooner (1977, 1980).

Connate waters with high metal contents, especially lead and zinc, have been recorded in oil-field brines (e.g., Carpenter et al., 1974). Interstitial fluids of this type have been considered as the mineralizing fluids for some ore deposits (Roedder, 1971; Doe and Delevaux, 1972). A number of massive sulphide deposits in sedimentary terranes that are lead- and zinc-rich but copper-poor (e.g., Sullivan and McArthur River) could conceivably have been generated by connate waters trapped in thick sequences of sediments leaching metals from the host strata (Badham, 1981).

In general, the sulphur isotopic compositions of deposits in volcanic terranes are similar to those of sulphur derived from magmatic sources, whereas sulphur in the sedimentary rock–hosted deposits appears to have been derived from seawater (Sangster, 1980). This can be considered as indirect support for a connate water model, since leaching of metals from a volcanic and a sedimentary host rock should provide different sulphur isotopic values to the exhaled hydrothermal fluids and the resulting ore deposits.

Contemporaneous volcanism at the time of some mineralizing activity in sedimentary basins could be an indication that (1) volcanic activity, although distal, provided geothermal gradients to move connate water out of the basin; (2) tectonic activity associated with the volcanism provided structural breaks to permit escape of metal-bearing brines to the seafloor; and (3) tectonic activity accompanying the volcanism could produce changes on a regional scale that would be reflected in a different sedimentary environment (usually higher energy) after deposition of the sulphide deposits (e.g., Sullivan).

Deposits in volcanic terranes could also have been derived from connate waters if entrapped seawater were raised to temperatures of several hundred degrees centigrade by an increased geothermal gradient resulting from later intrusions, leached metals from the volcanic rock pile, and subsequently released onto the ocean floor through fractures and faults resulting from later tectonic activity.

TABLE 1. TONNAGE AND METAL GRADE FOR SELECTED PROTEROZOIC MASSIVE SULPHIDE DEPOSITS

Name	Size ($x10^6$ tons)	%Cu	%Zn	%Pb	Source	Age (Ga)
UNITED STATES						
1. Crandon, Wis	70.0	1	5		Schmidt et al, (1978)	1.8
2. Pelican River, Wis.	2.3	1.0	4.5			1.82
3. Flambeau, Wis.	6	3.5	1			
4. United Verde, Ariz.	34* (80)	5.0			Anderson and Guilbert (1979), Gilmour (1976)	1.73
5. Iron King, Ariz.	5	0.19	7.34	2.50	Gilmour and Still, (1968)	
6. Old Dick, Ariz.	0.6	3.36	10.6		Baker and Clayton (1968)	1.7
7. Copper Queen, Ariz.	0.14	4.7	14.4			
8. Burra Burra, Tenn.	19	1.6	1.2		Magee (1968)	?
9. London, Tenn.	1.6	1.8	1.2		Magee (1968)	
10. East Tennessee, Tenn.	0.25	7.5	1.2		Magee (1968)	
11. Eureka, Tenn.	?	0.7	0.5		Magee (1968)	
12. Boyd, Tenn.	?	0.7	0.5		Magee (1968)	
13. Cherokee, Tenn.	0.7	0.5			Magee (1968)	
14. Calloway, Tenn.	1.7	1.7			Magee (1968)	
15. Mary-Polk County, Tenn	1.7	1.2			Magee (1968)	
16. Edwards, N.Y.	4.5		11.25		Lea and Dill (1968)	1.2-1.5
17. Hyatt, N.Y.	0.22		7.0			
18. Balmat No. 2, N.Y.	10.6		9.65	0.73		
19. Balmat No. 3, N.Y.	2.1		10.35			
AUSTRALIA						
20. McArthur River	200	0.2	10	4	Lambert (1976)	1.6
21. Mt. Isa (Cu zone)	140	3.0			Finlow-Bates (1979) Plumb and Derrick (1975)	1.4-1.6
22. Mt. Isa (Pb-Zn zone)	100+		6.0	7.8	Lambert (1976)	
23. Hilton	35+		9.6	7.7		
24. Broken Hill	200		12	12		1.8
SOUTH AFRICA						
25. Prieska	47	1.7	3.8		Anhaeusser and Button (1976)	
26. Black Mountain	30	0.6		2.3	Anhaeusser and Button (1976)	1.0
	48+	0.8	0.6	2.9	Anhaeusser and Button (1976)	
27. Broken Hill	38	0.4	2.3	4.5	Anhaeusser and Button (1976)	
	25+	0.36	2.2	3.0	Anhaeusser and Button (1976)	
28. Gamsberg	143		7.41	0.55	Koeppel (1980) Rozendaal (1980)	1.3
SWEDEN						
29. Skellefte district (average grade of 20 mines)	?	0.8	2.3	0.8	Rickard and Zweifel (1975)	2.0
FINLAND						
30. Outokumpu	28	3.8	1.0	(0.12% Ni) +(0.24% Co)	Gaal et al. (1975) Peltola (1978)	2.25
CANADA						
31. Sullivan, B.C.	175		5.5	6.4	Sangster and Scott (1976) Thompson and Pantelayev (1976)	1.0
32. Tetreault-Anacon, Que.	2.6		4.53	1.54	Gauthier and Brown (1980)	1.0-1.4
33. New Calumet, Que.	3.7		5.9	1.65	Sangster (1980)	
34. Errington, Ont.	7.5	1.02	3.24	0.75	Martin (1957)	1.7-1.9
35. Vermilion Lake, Ont.	2.8	1.43	4.50	1.10	Sangster (1980)	
36. Flin Flon, Man.	64	2.2	4.4		Gale et. (1980)	1.8
White Lake, Man.	0.4	2.15	4.48			
Cuprus, Man.	0.5	3.25	6.4			
Centennial, Man.	1.2	2.6	2.6			
North Star, Man.	0.25	6.11				
Embury Lake, Man.	3.6	2.6	4.3			
Chisel Lake, Man.	5.5	0.53	11.7	0.8		
Ghost Lake, Man.	0.49	1.85	12.6	0.3		
Dickstone, Man.	1.0	2.58	3.1			
Schist Lake, Man.	2.0	4.22	7.0			
West Arm, Man.	0.7	4.63	0.6			
Spruce Point, Man.	0.9	2.0	4.0			
Reed Lake, Man.	1.3	2.09				
Rod, Man.	0.7	5.38	2.53			
Stall Lake, Man.	5.0	4.79	0.6			
Anderson Lake, Man.	3.0	3.81	0.1			
Osborne Lake, Man.	3.2	3.75	2.78			
Sherridon, Man.	7.7	2.37	2.78			
Wim, Man.	0.98	2.91				
Fox Lake, Man.	10.6	2.03	2.15			
Ruttan, Man.	45.9	1.45	1.61			
Coronation, Sask.	1.5	4.2			Whitmore (1969)	
Flexar, Sask.	0.37	3.77	0.27			
Birch Lake, Sask.	0.3	6.2				
Thompson, Man.	25+	(2.97%Ni+Cu)			Zurbrigg (1963	2.32

*Average grade of production.

This model can be used to explain the regional stratigraphic control of massive sulphide deposits in both volcanic and sedimentary terranes, since major crustal adjustments in response to a particular volcanic-tectonic event could affect a large region and thus provide an abundance of conduits for debouching fluids onto the ocean floor. The connate-water model does not, however, appear to provide a satisfactory explanation of the association of massive sulphide deposits with felsic volcanic rocks or ultramafic volcanic rocks. In addition, the sedimentary rocks that stratigraphically underlie the Outokumpu and Thompson mines are unlikely sources of nickel to form exhalative massive sulphide deposits by this model.

Although the generation of ore fluids during the crystallization of fractionating magmas had been standard fare for many years after the work of Lindgren, the idea appears to have fallen into disfavour or has been largely ignored in recent years with respect to the formation of massive sulphide deposits. Some authors refrain from endorsing the magmatic source for the ore fluids and metals but do caution against the preclusion of this source (e.g., Addy and Ypma, 1977). Lambert and Sato (1974) indicated that their observations on the Kuroko deposits could be explained either from leaching by circulating seawater or by the separation of an aqueous ore fluid during the final stages of fractionation and solidification of felsic magmas. Any magmatic fluids involved would have had ample opportunity to mix with seawater, especially in the upper, porous levels of the rock pile, to produce deposits from fluids that were essentially of seawater or meteoric origin but which derived most of their metals from a magmatic source. Magmatic fluids with several thousand parts-per-million metal ions (Sawkins and Scherkenback, 1981) could be diluted by meteoric waters several times and still be metal-rich ore-forming fluids; however, their original magmatic signature would be lost or difficult to detect. Ohomoto and Rye

(1974) indicated from oxygen-isotopic evidence that no more than 25% magmatic water was involved in the formation of some Kuroko deposits. Hattori and Muchlenbacks (1980) have established, from isotope studies of alteration minerals around a Kuroko deposit, that the hydrogen-isotope variations are best explained if the ore fluids contained up to one-third magmatic water. In addition, Urabe and Sato (1978) favoured derivation of the Kuroko ore fluids from an acidic magma.

A magmatic source for the ore-bearing fluids not only provides an explanation of the common observation of Cu-Zn deposits associated with acidic magmas but also of the source of stratabound nickeliferous massive sulphide deposits, such as Thompson and Outokumpu, that are associated with ultramafic magma. It is readily apparent that the ultramafic magma associated with and considered the source of the Thompson-type sulphide mineralization was metal-rich, since contemporaneous ultramafic rocks emplaced at the same stratigraphic level as that at Thompson contain disseminated nickeliferous sulphide, that is, the Pipe Mine (Peredery et al., 1982).

Magma chambers emplaced 5 to 10 km below the ocean floor are envisaged as producing during crystallization metal-rich magmatic fluid or vapour phases. Faulting of the overlying rocks as a result of tectonic activity related to magmatic intrusions (Roberts, 1970) could provide channelways for the ore-bearing fluids to produce either a number of deposits within a narrow stratigraphic interval in a district if a number of faults were produced or one or two large deposits if a single fault zone tapped the metal-rich phase. A fault tapping the fluid or vapour phase adjacent to another fault simultaneously tapping the magma chamber could account for the stacking of ore deposits observed in some districts. Furthermore, if massive sulphide deposits are generated in response to large-scale regional tectonic events, such as plate tectonics (Hutchinson, 1973), then magma production and emplacement would be more or less contemporaneous over extensive areas, and thus fractionation of the magmas could account for the deposition of sulphide deposits within a narrow stratigraphic interval over distances of several hundred kilometres; for example, the Kuroko deposits of Japan.

A deeply buried magmatic source may also be evoked to explain the massive sulphide deposits in some sedimentary basins (Badham, 1981); however, with the possible exception of the Sullivan deposit, this merely puts the source 'out of sight' within the earth's crust. It could conceivably account for the association of mineralization and volcanic products in some deposits; however, the volcanic centres would have to be several hundred kilometres away from the site of ore deposition; for example, McArthur River. The change to a higher energy type of sedimentation on a regional scale following the local deposition of a massive sulphide deposit (e.g., Sullivan, Broken Hill, McArthur River) might reflect isostatic readjustment after the intrusion of a deep-seated magma chamber.

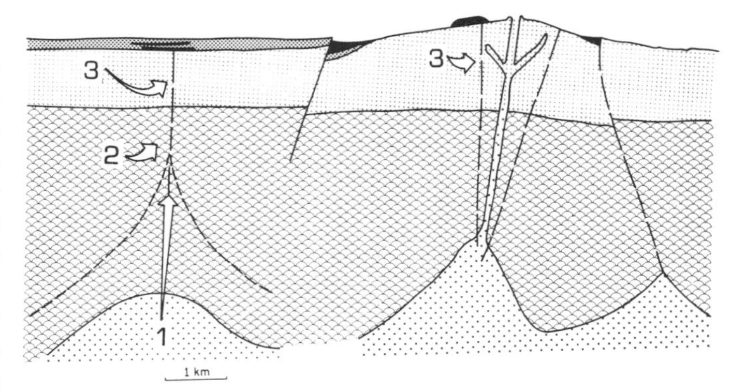

Figure 9. Hypothetical model illustrating the origin of massive sulphide deposits. Short dashed line indicates probable configuration of geotherm above intrusion. Heavy dashed lines indicate geofractures. Solid arrows indicate movement of fluids—magmatic (1), connate (2), and seawater (3).

A model involving magmatic water does not preclude circulating seawater or connate water as part of the ore-forming process. Although some authors favour seawater (e.g., Spooner, 1977) or connate waters and seawater (e.g., Hodgson and Lydon, 1977; Lydon, 1981), a model (Fig. 9) emerging from recent oxygen and hydrogen isotopic studies (e.g., Ohmoto and Rye, 1974; Hattori and Muchlenbachs, 1980) that appears to be consistent with empirical observations involves (1) emplacement of a broad-based magmatic body into the lower portions of a volcanic pile; (2) an increase in the geothermal gradients during crystallization of this magma; (3) separation of metal-rich fluids during fractionation and crystallization of the magma; (4) release of the ore fluids along fractures and fault zones; (5) mixing of the magmatic fluids with waters of sea-water derivation (connate water and/or circulating seawater) in the upper portions of the volcanic/sedimentary pile; and (6) formation of sulphide mineral deposits on or near the ocean floor by thorough mixing of already diluted magmatic fluids with abundant seawater.

CONCLUSION

Proterozoic massive sulphide deposits occur in a wide variety of geologic settings that are similar to those in which younger deposits are found. Although the lead-zinc deposits in sedimentary terranes do not appear to have Archean counterparts, the geologic setting of deposits in Proterozoic volcanic rocks are similar to deposits in Archean rocks. Likewise, the size, grade, and metal ratios of massive sulphide deposits associated with Proterozoic volcanic rocks are similar to Archean, Proterozoic, and younger deposits. Therefore, the processes that controlled the formation of Proterozoic massive sulphide in volcanic terranes must have been active in the Archean volcanic terranes, and there is no evidence of any profound differences between Archean and Proterozoic geologic conditions to be drawn from the volcanic-hosted massive sulphide deposits.

ACKNOWLEDGMENTS

Don Sangster, Robert Lambe, Mark Fedikow, and Peter Theyer critically reviewed an early draft of the manuscript and provided many helpful comments. The diagrams were drafted by the Mineral Resources Division drafting personnel, and the manuscript was typed by Barbara Thakrar and Leah Chudy.

REFERENCES CITED

Addy, S. K., and Ypma, P.J.M., 1977, Origin of massive sulfide deposits at Ducktown, Tennessee: An oxygen, carbon, and hydrogen isotope study: Economic Geology, v. 72, p. 1245–1268.

Anderson, C. A., and Nash, J. T., 1972, Geology of the massive sulfide deposits at Jerome, Arizona—A reinterpretation: Economic Geology, v. 67, p. 845–863.

Anderson, P., and Guilbert, J. M., 1979, the Precambrian massive sulfide deposits of Arizona—A distinct metallogenic epoch and province, *in* International Association on the Genesis of Ore Deposits (IAGOD), 5th Symposium, Snowbird, Utah, volume II: Nevada Bureau of Mines and Geology, Report 33, p. 39–48.

Anhaeusser, C. R., and Button, A., 1976, A review of southern African stratiform ore deposits—their position in time and space, *in* Wolf, K. H., ed., Handbook of stratabound and stratiform ore deposits: Elsevier, New York, v. 5, p. 257–319.

Badham, J.P.N., 1981, Shale-hosted Pb-Zn deposits: Products of exhalation of formation waters?: Transactions of the Institution of Mining and Metallurgy, London, Section B, v. 90, p. B70–B75.

Bailes, A. H., 1975, Geology of the Guay-Wimapedi Lakes area: Manitoba Mineral Resources Division, Publication 75-2, 104 p.

Baldwin, D. A., 1982, Mineral deposits in the Ruttan Lake, Karsakuwigamak Lake, Muskayak Lake areas, Manitoba: Manitoba Mineral Resources Division, Open File Report 81-4, 60 p.

Baker, A. III, and Clayton, R. L., 1968, Massive sulfide deposits of the Bagdad District, Yavapai County, Arizona, *in* Ridge, J. D., ed., Ore deposits of the United States, 1933–1967: American Institute of Mining, Metallurgical and Petroleum Engineers, p. 1311–1327.

Barnes, R. G., 1979, Types of mineralization and their relationship to stratigraphy, *in* A guide to stratigraphy and mineralization of the Broken Hill Block: Geological Survey of New South Wales, Department of Mineral Resources and Development, G. S. 1979/062, p. 31–66.

Bernard, A. J., and Samama, J. C., 1976, Summary of the French School of studies of ores in sedimentary and associated volcanic rocks—Epigenesis versus syngenesis, *in* Wolf, K. H., ed., Handbook of stratabound and stratiform ore deposits: Elsevier, New York, v. 1, p. 299–338.

Bernard, A. J., and Samama, J. C., 1976, Summary of the French School of studies of ores in sedimentary and associated volcanic rocks—Epigenesis versus syngenesis, *in* Wolf, K. H., ed., Handbook of stratabound and stratiform ore deposits: Elsevier, New York, v. 1, p. 299–338.

Carl, J. D., and Van Diver, B. B., 1975, Precambrian Grenville alaskite bodies as ash-flow tuffs, north-west Adirondacks, New York: Geological Society of America Bulletin, v. 86, p. 1691–1707.

Carpenter, A. B., Trout, M. L., Pickett, E. E., 1974, Preliminary report on the origin and chemical evolution of lead- and zinc-rich oil field brines in central Mississippi: Economic Geology, v. 69, p. 1191–1206.

Davies, J. L., and McAllister, A. L., 1980, Geology and massive sulphides of the Bathurst area, New Brunswick: Geological Association of Canada, Halifax Annual Meeting, May 1980, Field Trip Guidebook 16, p. 1–16.

Doe, B. R., and Delevaux, M. H., 1972, Source of lead in southeast Missouri galena ores: Economic Geology, v. 67, p. 409–425.

Finlow-Bates, T., 1979, Cyclicity in the lead-zinc-silver-bearing sediments at Mount Isa Mine, Queensland, Australia, and rates of sulfide accumulation: Economic Geology, v. 74, p. 1408–1419.

Finlow-Bates, T., and Stumpfl, E. F., 1979, The copper and lead-zinc-silver orebodies of Mt. Isa Mine, Queensland: Products of one hydro-thermal system: Annales de la Societe Geologique de Beligique, v. 102, p. 497–517.

Fox, J. S., 1976, Some comments on the volcanic stratigraphy and economic potential of the west Amisk Lake area, Saskatchewan [abs.]: Geological Association of Canada, Annual Meeting, Edmonton.

Franklin, J. M., Lydon, J. W., and Sangster, D. F., 1981, Volcanic-associated massive sulphide deposits: Economic Geology, 75th Anniversary v., p. 485–627.

Freeze, A. C., 1966, On the origin of the Sullivan ore body, Kimerley, B. C., *in* Tectonic history and mineral deposits of the western Cordillera: Canadian Institute of Mining and Metallurgy, Special v. 8, p. 263–294.

Froese, E., 1969, General geology of the Coronation Mine area, *in* Byers, A. R., ed., Symposium on the Geology of the Coronation Mine, Saskatchewan: Geological Survey of Canada, Paper 68-5, p. 7–36.

Froese, E., and Goetz, P. A., 1976, Petrological studies in the Sherridon area, Manitoba: Report of activities Part A, Geological Survey of Canada, Paper 76-1A, p. 171–172.

Gaal, G., Koistinen, T., Mattila, E., 1975, Tectonics and stratigraphy in the vicinity of Outokumpu, North Karelia, Finland: Geological Survey of Finland, Bulletin 271, 67 p.

Gale, G. H., 1977, Investigation of massive sulphide environments in the Flin Flon–Snow Lake greenstone belt, *in* Report of field activities, 1976: Manitoba Mineral Resources Division, p. 17–22.

Gale, G. H., and Koo, J., 1977, Evaluation of massive sulphide environments, 2nd annual report 1976–1977, Non-Renewable Resource Evaluation Program: Manitoba Department of Mines, Resources and Environmental Management, p. 43–62.

Gale, G. H., Baldwin, D. A., and Koo, J., 1980, A geological evaluation of Precambrian massive sulphide deposit potential in Manitoba: Manitoba Mineral Resources Division, Economic Geology Report ER 79-1, 137 p.

Gauthier, M., and Brown, A. C., 1980, Lithologic and stratigraphic setting of zinc mineralization in Granville metasediments, Quebec: Mineralium Deposita, v. 15, p. 163–174.

Gilmour, P., 1976, Some transitional types of mineral deposits in volcanic and sedimentary rocks, *in* Wolf, K. H., ed., Handbook of stratabound and stratiform ore deposits: Elsevier, New York, v. 1, p. 111–160.

Gilmour, P., and Still, A. R., 1968, The geology of the Iron King Mine, *in* Ridge, J. D., ed., Ore deposits in the United States, 1933–1967: Graton-Sales Volume, American Institute of Mining, Metallurgical and Petroleum Engineers, p. 1239–1257.

Harley, D. N., 1979, A mineralized Ordovician resurgent caldera complex in the Bathurst-Newcastle mining district, New Brunswick, Canada: Economic Geology, v. 74, p. 786–796.

Hattori, K., and Muchlenbachs, K., 1980, Marine hydrothermal alteration at a Kuroko ore deposit, Kosaka, Japan: Contributions to Mineralogy and Petrology, v. 74, p. 285–292.

Hodgson, C. J., and Lydon, J. W., 1977, Geological setting of volcanogenic massive sulphide deposits and active hydrothermal systems: Some implications for exploration: Canadian Institute of Mining and Metallurgy, Bulletin, v. 70, p. 95–106.

Holyk, W., 1957, Structure of northern New Brunswick, *in* Structural geology of Canadian ore deposits, volume 2: Canadian Institute of Mining and Metallurgy, Montreal, p. 485–492.

Horikoshi, E., 1969, Volcanic activity related to the formation of Kuroko-type deposits in the Kosaka district, Japan: Mineralium Deposita, v. 4, p. 321–345.

Hutchinson, R. W., 1973. Volcanogenic sulphide deposits and their metallogenic significance: Economic Geology, v. 68, p. 1223–1246.

King, H. F., 1976, Development of syngenetic ideas in Australia, *in* Wolf, K. H., ed., Handbook of stratabound and stratiform ore deposits: Elsevier, New York, v. 1, p. 161–182.

Koeppel, V., 1980, Lead isotope studies of stratiform ore deposits of the Namaqualand, N.W. Cape Province, South Africa, and their implications on the age of the Bushmanland Sequence, *in* Ridge, J. D., ed., Proceedings of the Fifth Quadrennial IAGOD Symposium: Schweizerbart'sche, E., Verlagsbuchhandlung, Stuttgart, v. 1, p. 195–208.

Laing, W. P., 1979, Stratigraphic interpretation of the Broken Hill Area, *in* A guide to stratigraphy and mineralization of the Broken Hill Block: Geological Survey of New South Wales, Department of Mineral Resources and Development, G. S. 1979/062, p. 31–66.

Laing, W. P., Marjoribanks, R. W., and Rutland, R.W.R., 1978, Structure of the Broken Hill Mine area and its significance for the genesis of the orebodies: Economic Geology, v. 73, p. 1112–1136.

Lambert, I. B., 1976, The McArthur zinc-lead-silver deposit: Features, metallogenesis and comparisons with some other stratiform ores, *in* Wolf, K. H., ed., Handbook of stratabound and stratiform ore deposits: Elsevier, New York, v. 6, p. 535–585.

Lambert, I. B., and Sato, T., 1974, The Kuroko and associated ore deposits of Japan: A review of their features and metallogenesis: Economic Geology, v. 69, p. 1215–1236.

Large, R. R., 1977, Chemical evolution and zonation of massive sulphide deposit in volcanic terrains: Economic Geology, v. 72, p. 549–572.

Lea, E. R., and Dill, D. B., 1968, Zinc deposits of the Balmat-Edwards District, New York, *in* Ridge, J. D., ed., Ore deposits in the United States, 1933–1967: Graton-Sales Volume, American Institute of Mining, Metallurgical and Petroleum Engineers, p. 20–48.

Leech, G. B., and Wanless, R. K., 1962, Lead isotope and potassium argon studies in the East Kootanay district of British Columbia, *in* Petrologic studies—A volume in Honour of A. F. Buddington: Geological Society of America, New York, N.Y., p. 241–279.

Lusk, J., 1976, A possible volcanic-exhalative origin for lenticular nickel sulfide deposits of volcanic association with special reference to those in Western Australia: Canadian Journal of Earth Science, v. 13, p. 451–458.

Lustig, G., 1979, Geology of the Fox orebody, northern Manitoba [M.Sc. thesis]: University of Manitoba.

Magee, M., 1968, Geology and ore deposits of the Ducktown district, Tennessee, *in* Ridge, J. D., ed., Ore deposits of the United States, 1933–1967: Graton-Sales Volume, American Institute of Mining, Metallurgical and Petroleum Engineers, p. 297–241.

Martin, W. C., 1957, Errington and Vermilion Lake Mines, *in* Structural geology of Canadian ore deposits, volume II: Sixth Commonwealth Mining and Metallurgical Congress, Mercury Press, Montreal, Canada, p. 363–376.

Miller, L. J., and Gair, H. S., 1975, Mons Cupri copper-lead-zinc-silver deposit, *in* Knight, C. L., ed., Economic geology of Australia and Papua New Guinea: The Australian Institute of Mining and Metallurgy, v. 1, Metals, p. 195–202.

Morris, H. C., 1972, An outline of the geology of the Sullivan Mine, Kimberley, British Columbia, *in* Irvine, W. T., et al., eds., Major lead-zinc deposits of Western Canada: International Geological Congress, 24th, Guide Excursions A24 and C24, p. 26–34.

Nesbitt, B. E., and Kelly, W. C., 1980, Metamorphic zonation of sulfides, oxides and graphite in and around the orebodies at Ducktown, Tennessee: Economic Geology, v. 75, p. 1010–1021.

Ohmoto, H., and Rye, R. O., 1974, Hydrogen and oxygen isotopic compositions of fluid inclusions in the Kuroko deposits, Japan: Economic Geology, v. 69, p. 947–953.

Peltola, E., 1978, Origin of Precambrian copper sulfides of the Outokumpu District, Finland: Economic Geology, v. 74, p. 461–477.

Peredery, W. V., and Geological Staff, 1982, Geology and nickel sulphide deposits of the Thompson Belt, Manitoba, *in* Hutchinson, R. W., Spence, C. D. and Franklin, J. M., eds., Precambrian sulphide deposits—H. S. Robinson Memorial Volume: Geological Association of Canada, Special Paper 25, p. 165–209.

Plumb, K. A., and Derrick, G. M., 1975, Geology of the Proterozoic rocks of the Kimberley to Mount Isa Region, *in* Economic geology of Australia and Papua, New Guinea: The Australian Institute of Mining and Metallurgy, v. 1, Metals, p. 217–252.

Rickard, D. T., and Zweifel, H., 1975, Genesis of Precambrian sulfide ores, Skellefte District, Sweden: Economic Geology, v. 70, p. 255–274.

Ridge, J. D., 1976, Origin, development and changes in concepts of syngenetic ore deposits as seen by North American geologists, *in* Wolf, K. H., ed., Handbook of stratabound and stratiform ore deposits: Elsevier, New York, v. 1, p. 183–298.

Roberts, J. L., 1970, The intrusion of magma into brittle rocks, *in* Newall, G., and Rast, N., eds., Mechanism of igneous intrusion: Gallery Press, Liverpool, p. 187–366.

Roedder, E., 1971, Fluid inclusion evidence on the environment of formation of mineral deposits of the southern Appalachians: Economic Geology, v. 66, p. 777–791.

Rozendaal, A., 1980, The Gamsberg zinc deposit, South Africa: A banded stratiform base metal sulfide ore deposit, *in* Ridge, J. D., ed., Proceedings of the Fifth Quadrennial IAGOD Symposium: Schweizerbart'sche, E., Verlagsbuchhandlung, Stuttgart, p. 619–634.

Sangster, D. F., 1972, Precambrian volcanogenic massive sulphide deposits in Canada, A review: Geological Survey of Canada, Paper 72-22, 44 p.

—— 1980, Distribution and origin of Precambrian massive sulphide deposits of North America, *in* Strangway, D. W., ed., The continental crust and its mineral deposits: Geological Association of Canada, Special Paper 20, p. 723–739.

Sangster, D. F., and Scott, S. D., 1976, Precambrian stratabound, massive Cu-Zn-Pb sulfide ores of North America, *in* Wolf, K. H., ed., Handbook of stratabound and stratiform ore deposits: Elsevier, New York, v. 6, p. 129–222.

Sato, T., 1972, Behaviours of ore-forming solutions in seawater: Mining Geology, v. 22, p. 31–42.

Sawkins, F. J., and Scherkenback, D. A., 1981, High copper content of fluid inclusions in quartz from Northern Sonora: Implications for ore-genesis theory: Geology, v. 9, p. 37–40.

Schmidt, P. G., Dolence, J. D., Lluria, M. R., and Parsons III, G., 1978, Geology of Crandon massive sulfide deposit in Wisconsin: Skillings Mining Review, May 6, p. 8–11.

Solomon, M., 1976, "Volcanic" massive sulphide deposits and their host rocks—A review and explanation, *in* Wolf, K. H., ed., Handbook of stratabound and stratiform ore deposits: Elsevier, New York, v. 6, p. 21–54.

Spence, C. D., and de Rosen-Spence, A. F., 1975, The place of sulphide mineralization in the volcanic sequence at Noranda, Quebec: Economic Geology, v. 70, p. 90–101.

Spooner, E.T.C., 1977, Hydrodynamic model for the origin of the ophiolitic cupriferous pyrite ore deposits of Cyprus: Geological Society of

London, Special Publication No. 7, p. 58–71.

—— 1980, Cu-pyrite mineralization and seawater convection in oceanic crust—The ophiolitic ore deposits of Cyprus, *in* Strangway, D. W., ed., The continental crust and its mineral deposits: Geological Association of Canada, Special Paper 20, p. 685–704.

Spooner, E.T.C., and Fyfe, W. S., 1973, Sub-sea-floor metamorphism, heat and mass transfer: Contributions to Mineralogy and Petrology, v. 42, p. 287–304.

Stanton, R. L., 1976, Petrochemical studies of the ore environment at Broken Hill, New South Wales, 4–Environmental synthesis: Transactions of the Institution of Mining and Metallurgy, London, Section B, Applied Earth Sciences, p. B221–B223.

Stevens, B.P.J., Stroud, W. J., Willis, I. L., Bradley, G. M., Brown, R. E., and Barnes, R. G., 1979, A stratigraphic interpretation of the Broken Hill Block, *in* A guide to the stratigraphy and mineralization of the Broken Hill Block: Geological Survey of New South Wales, Department of Mineral Resources and Development, G.S. 1979/062, p. 7–30.

Studer, R. D., 1982, Geology of the Stall Lake copper deposit, Snow Lake, Manitoba: Canadian Institute of Mining, v. 75, p. 66–72.

Takahashi, T., and Suga, K., 1974, Geology and ore deposits of the Hanaoka Kuroko Belt, Akita Prefecture, *in* Geology of Kuroko deposits: The Society of Mining Geologists of Japan, Tokyo, Mining Geology Special Issue No. 6, p. 101–113.

Thompson, R. I., and Pantelayev, A., 1976, Stratabound mineral deposits of the Canadian Cordillera, *in* Wolf, K. H., ed., Handbook of stratabound and stratiform ore deposits: Elsevier, New York, v. 5, p. 37–108.

Ueno, H., 1975, Duration of the Kuroko mineralization episode: Nature, v. 253, p. 428–429.

Urabe, T., and Sato, T., 1978, Kuroko deposits of the Kosaka mine, Northeast Japan—products of submarine hot springs on Miocene seafloor: Economic Geology, v. 73, p. 161–179.

Vokes, F. M., 1976, Caledonian massive sulfide deposits in Scandinavia: A comparative review, *in* Wolf, K. H., ed., Handbook of stratabound and stratiform ore deposits: Elsevier, New York, v. 6, p. 79–128.

Wagener, J.H.F., 1980, The Prieska zinc-copper deposit, Cape Province, South Africa, *in* Ridge, J. D., ed., Proceedings of the Fifth IAGOD Symposium: Schweizerbart'sche, E., Verlagsbuchhandlung, Stuttgart, p. 635–652.

Whitmore, D.R.E., 1969, Geology of the Coronation Copper Deposit *in* Byers, A. R., ed., Symposium on the Geology of the Coronation Mine, Saskatchewan: Geological Survey of Canada, p. 68-5, p. 37–54.

Willis, I. L., 1979, Stratigraphic interpretation of the Silverton-Thackaringa area, *in* A guide to the stratigraphy and mineralization in the Broken Hill Block: Geological Survey of New South Wales, Department of Mineral Resources and Development, G.S. 1979/062, p. 129–138.

Zurbrigg, H. F., 1963, Thompson Mine geology: Canadian Institute of Mining and Metallurgy, v. 56, p. 451–560.

Manuscript Accepted by the Society April 14, 1983

Printed in U.S.A.

Geological Society of America
Memoir 161
1983

The major stratiform lead-zinc deposits of the Proterozoic

I. B. Lambert
CSIRO, Baas Becking Laboratory
P.O. Box 378, Canberra City
A.C.T. 2601 Australia

ABSTRACT

Numerous Pb-Zn deposits formed during the Proterozoic, in contrast with the situation in the Archean. The largest examples, which are reviewed here, are McArthur, Mount Isa–Hilton, Sullivan, Gamsberg, and Broken Hill.

These huge stratiform deposits occur well above the bases of thick, predominantly sedimentary sequences which accumulated in major ensialic troughs. The sequences are dominated by carbonates or clastics, but the mineralization is localized within distinctive chemo-clastic facies which were deposited in basins of restricted extent. There is commonly evidence for synsedimentary faulting and for distal igneous activity. Biogenic sulfide was probably incorporated into some of the pyrite but is unlikely to have precipitated the bulk of the Pb and Zn. The base metals are of crustal derivation; they could have been supplied by ascending basinal brines and/or hydrothermal fluids migrating from distant centres of igneous activity.

There is active debate, focussed on the relatively pristine McArthur deposit, as to whether the mineralization formed at or beneath the sediment-water interface. It is maintained here that all features are consistent with syngenetic accumulation of the great bulk of the sphalerite, galena, and some of the pyrite, complemented by growth of biogenic pyrite and other diagenetic minerals within the sulfidic muds.

INTRODUCTION

General patterns for the relative abundances of different types of mineral deposits through geological time are summarized in Figure 1, along with other major evolutionary trends.

Archean base metal sulfide deposits formed largely as a result of high levels of igneous activity. They constitute important resources of Ni, Cu, and Zn, but Pb contents are very low except in a few minor examples, such as the ca. 3.45-b.y.-old Big Stubby Ag-Pb-Zn-Cu-Ba mineralization of Western Australia (Reynolds and others, 1975; Sangster and Brook, 1977; Lambert and others, 1978).

In marked contrast, numerous Pb-Zn deposits formed in predominantly sedimentary environments during the Proterozoic (Stanton, 1972; Lambert, 1976; Large, 1980; Rutland and Both, 1983). The largest known are the stratiform deposits at Broken Hill (New South Wales), Mount Isa–Hilton (Queensland), McArthur (Northern Territory; also known as H.Y.C. and McArthur River), Sullivan (British Columbia), and Gamsberg (Cape Province). The locations of these are shown on a reconstruction of Pangea in Figure 2, where it can be seen that they formed close to contemporaneous continental margins.

This paper is concerned with these major Proterozoic Pb-Zn deposits. It succinctly reviews their geological, mineralogical, and geochemical features, and then addresses the syngenetic versus epignetic controversy centered on the McArthur deposit.

GENERAL FEATURES

Table 1 lists the sizes, metal grades, mineralogies, metamorphic grades, and ages of the major Proterozoic

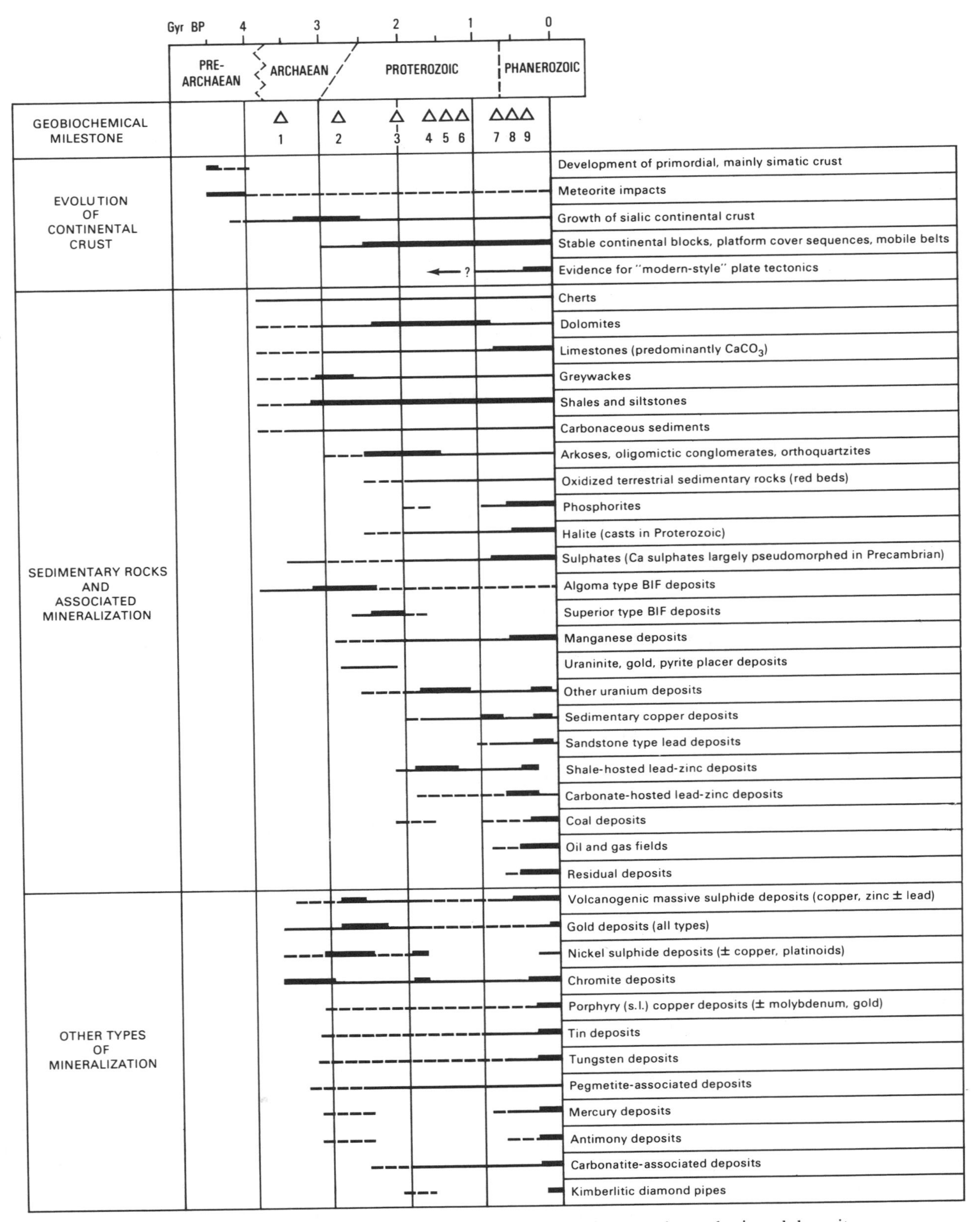

Figure 1. General evolutionary trends for the crust, sedimentary rocks, and mineral deposits. Note that the Proterozoic was an important era for formation of major "shale-hosted" Pb-Zn deposits (from Lambert and Groves, 1981).

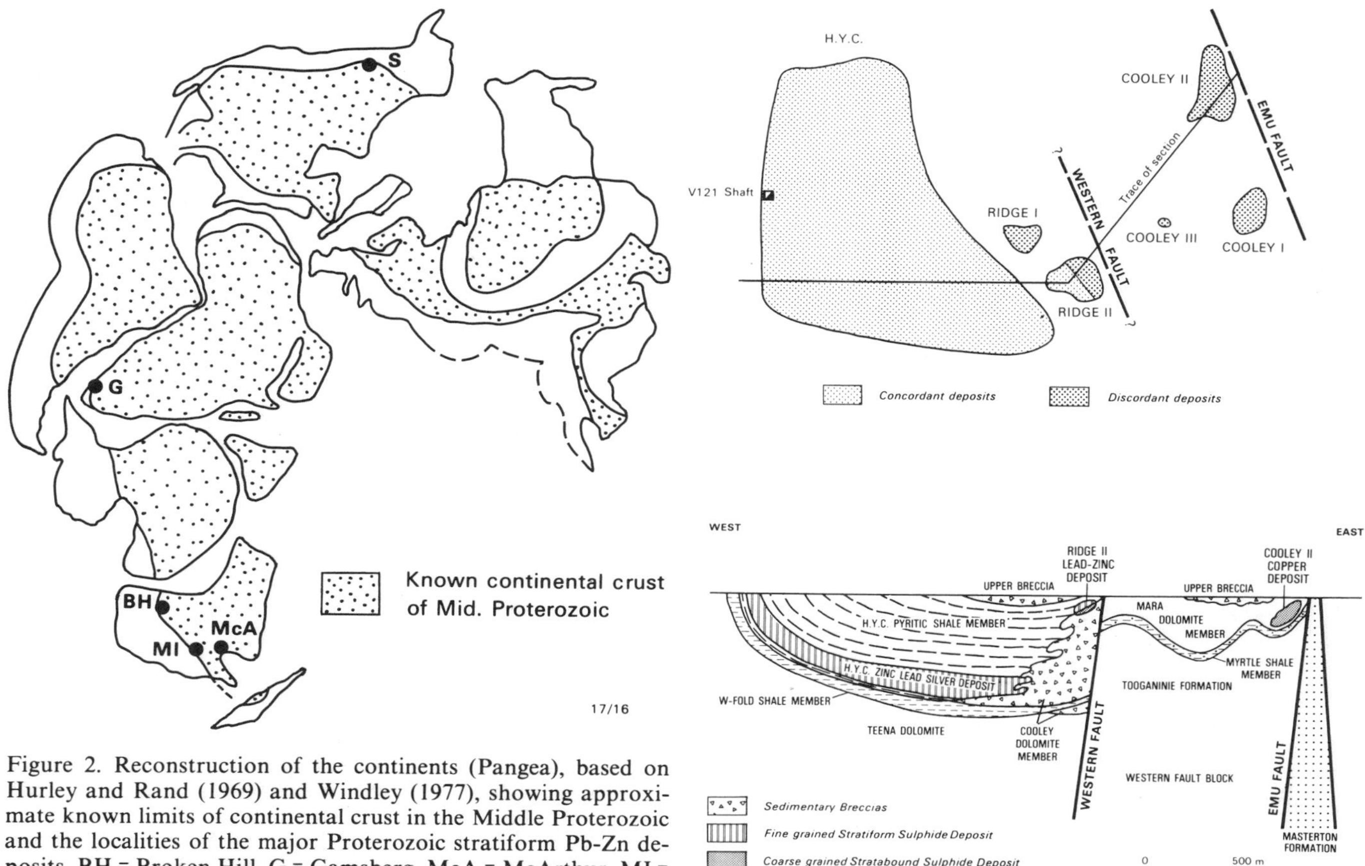

Figure 2. Reconstruction of the continents (Pangea), based on Hurley and Rand (1969) and Windley (1977), showing approximate known limits of continental crust in the Middle Proterozoic and the localities of the major Proterozoic stratiform Pb-Zn deposits. BH = Broken Hill, G = Gamsberg, McA = McArthur, MI = Mount Isa, S = Sullivan.

Figure 3. Sketch map and section through the stratiform McArthur (H.Y.C.) Pb-Zn deposit and nearby discordant mineralization (after Walker and others, 1977; Williams, 1978a).

Pb-Zn deposits, and other features are reviewed below. The deposits are considered in order of increasing metamorphic grade which, naturally, corresponds with a general increase in difficulty of ascertaining original features.

McArthur

General References. Croxford and Jephcott, 1972; Murray, 1975; Lambert, 1976; Walker and others, 1977; Williams, 1978a, 1978b; 1979a.

Geologic Setting. The McArthur deposit (Fig. 3) occurs more than 3 km above the base of a thick (>5 km) sedimentary sequence that accumulated in the slowly subsiding Batten Trough (Fig. 4). This sequence is dominated by shallow-water dolomitic strata containing stromatolites, evaporite mineral pseudomorphs, and shallow-water structures (Fig. 5), but the mineralization is within the locally developed, carbonaceous and dolomitic H.Y.C. Pyritic Shale Member.

Minor deformation has resulted in some broad basinal folds and block faulting. There are seven "orebodies" separated by "inter-ore beds" (Fig. 5), the latter comprising mainly intraformational dolomitic breccia, graded dolarenites, and dololutite. The average thickness of the mineralization is 55 m, with a maximum intersection of 130 m. Synsedimentary faulting is implied by the abundant slump structures and breccia beds in the "ore" zone and the wedge of probable talus breccia at the eastern edge of the stratiform mineralization (Cooley Dolomite, Fig. 3). Distant igneous activity during accumulation of the mineralized sequence is indicated by the presence of tuffaceous siltstones and thin, fine-grained, K-feldspar-rich tuffite bands, some of which contain relict vitroclastic textures. Zircons from the tuff horizons have been dated at 1,665 to 1,719 m.y. (Page, 1981).

Mineralization. The typical mineralization comprises conformable sulfide laminae, up to several millimetres thick, which are intercalated with carbonaceous siltstone dololutite and dolarenite. In the absence of metamorphic recrystallization, the sulfides are finely intergrown and have an average grain size of only a few microns. This causes metal recovery problems that remain to be resolved before mining commences, but it means that many original features of the mineralization are preserved, including various types of microfossils (Oehler and Logan, 1977).

TABLE 1. SIZES, METAL GRADES, MINERALOGIES, METAMORPHIC GRADES, AND AGES OF MAJOR PROTEROZOIC PB-ZN DEPOSITS

Deposit	Total size (million tons)	Metal grades				Mineralogy major/minor*	Metamorphism	Age (b.y.)
		Pb%	Zn%	Cu%	Ag(g/t)			
McArthur (or H.Y.C)	>190	4.1	9.5	<0.2	44	py, sp, gn / cp, asp, tet	Sub-green-schist	1.67 to 1.72
Mount Isa†	> 89	7.1	6.1	<0.2	160	py, gn, po, sp / cp, tet, asp, mar	Lower greenshcist	1.65 to 1.69
Hilton	>36	7.7	9.6	∼0.2	180	py, gn, sp, po / cp, asp, tet	Lower greenschist	1.65 to 1.69
Sullivan	155	6.6	5.7	$\lesssim$0.1	68	py, po, gn, sp / cp, asp, cas, tet	Upper green-schist	>1.25 to <1.6
Gamsberg	143	0.6	7.4	0.03	3	py, po, mar, sp, gn / cp, alab	Middle amphibolite	>2.0 to <2.5 or ca. 1.3(?)
Broken Hill	180	14.0	11.1	0.14	200	gn, sp / po, cp, tet, asp, lo, etc.	Granulite	>1.7 to <2.4

Note: References: McArthur-Murray (1975); Mount Isa-Mathias and Clark (1975); Hilton-Mathias and others (1973); Sullivan-Ethier and others (1976); Gamsberg-Rozendaal (1980); Broken Hill-Johnson and Klinger (1975).

*Py = pyrite; po = pyrrhotite; sp = sphalerite; gn = galena; mar = marcasite; cp = chalcopyrite; asp = arsenopyrite; tet = tetrahedrite group; alab = alabandite (Mns); lo = lollingite; cas = cassiterite.

†At Mount Isa there are major Cu lodes immediately adjacent to the Pb-Zn deposit; these total 183 million tons at 3% Cu, mainly in chalcopyrite, and have insignificant Pb and Zn contents.

The deposit contains abundant pyrite and low-Fe sphalerite, and there are two cycles of decreasing Zn/Pb ratio upwards from the bottom to the top "orebody" (Fig. 5). At the northern end of the deposit there is a zone of partly brecciated mineralization that contains only minor sphalerite and is relatively rich in chalcopyrite, galena, and freibergite (Logan and Dennis, 1981). This probably formed in the vicinity of a major point of influx of metalliferous fluids.

Roughly half of the pyrite in the stratiform mineralization occurs as euhedral to spheroidal crystals, which are generally between 2 and 5 microns across. About one-third of the pyrite occurs as larger grains (commonly <20 microns), many of which comprise a rim of later-formed pyrite (Py_2). Pyrite is also abundant at several levels in the hanging-wall strata and moderately abundant laterally away from the mineralization.

Minor discordant mineralization occurs through the fault block to the east of the McArthur deposit (Murray, 1975; Williams, 1978a; Fig. 3). It grades from Pb-Zn rich near the stratiform ore to Cu-rich in the vicinity of the Emu fault zone, several kilometres to the east, and it probably formed from the same, or similar, fluids as the stratiform mineralization (e.g., Lambert, 1976; Rye and Williams 1978, 1981).

Mineral Dispersions Around Deposit. Fe- and Mn-enriched dolomite occurs for considerable distances laterally and vertically from the McArthur deposit (Lambert and Scott, 1973). Authigenic K-feldspar occurs to the virtual exclusion of albite throughout the mineralized zone, and the albite/microcline ratio increases in a general manner with distance from the deposit, as does the calcite/dolomite ratio (Scott and Lambert, unpub. data). There are anomalously high concentrations of Zn (sphalerite), As (mainly in arsenopyrite), and Hg (mainly in pyrite) at widespread localities in the basal H.Y.C. Pyritic Shale (Lambert and Scott, 1973).

Isotope Data. The sulfur isotope trends in the single reported profile through the McArthur deposit are interesting, with $\delta^{34}S$ values for pyrite (Py_1 plus Py_2) cutting across the trends for galena and sphalerite (Smith and Croxford, 1973; Fig. 6). Therefore, while the latter minerals appear to have approached isotopic equilibrium as they precipitated, pyrite could not have incorporated sulfur

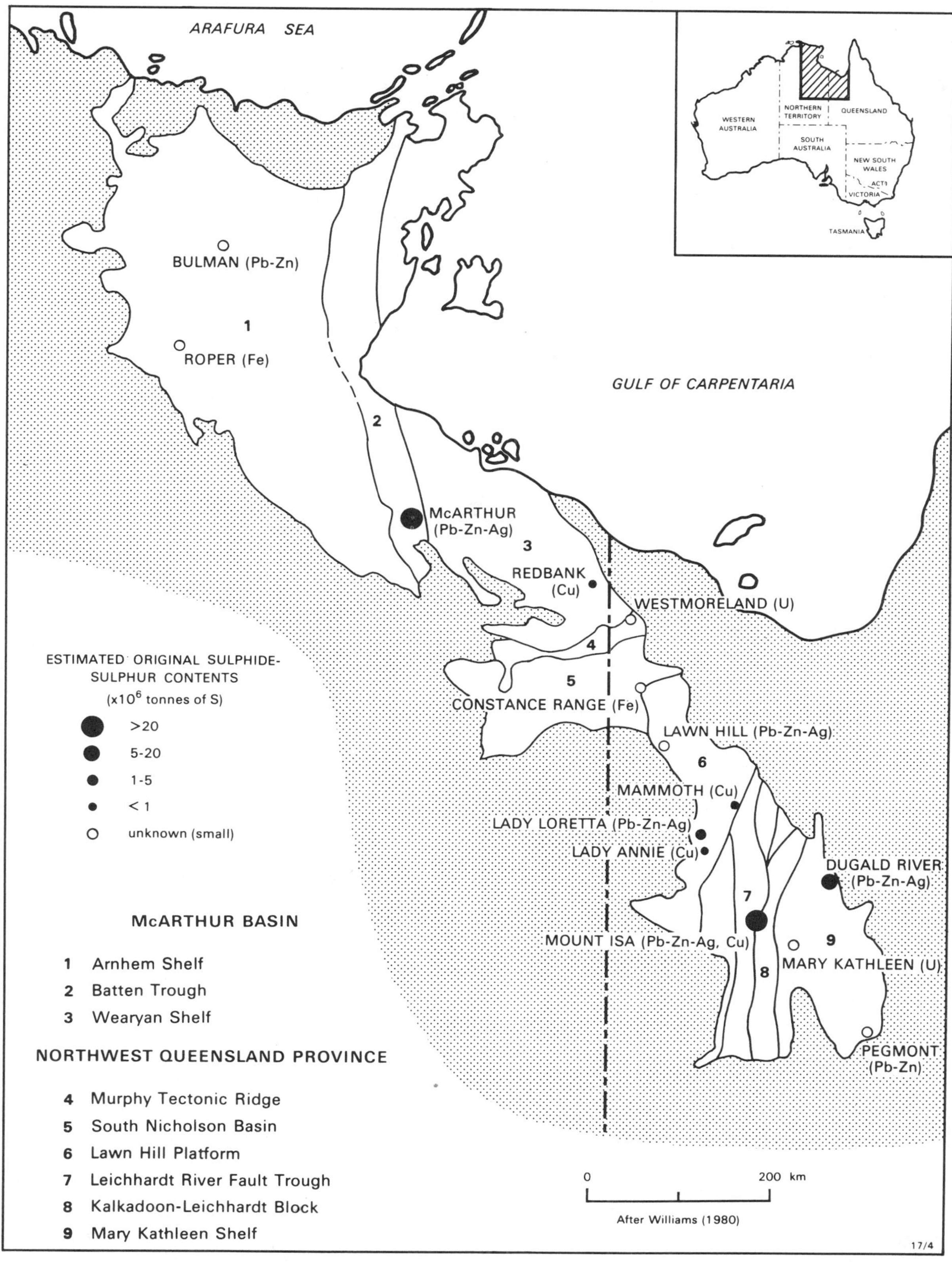

Figure 4. Geological sketch map of the Precambrian of the McArthur-Cloncurry region of northern Australia showing main mineral deposits and geological domains (after Williams, 1980).

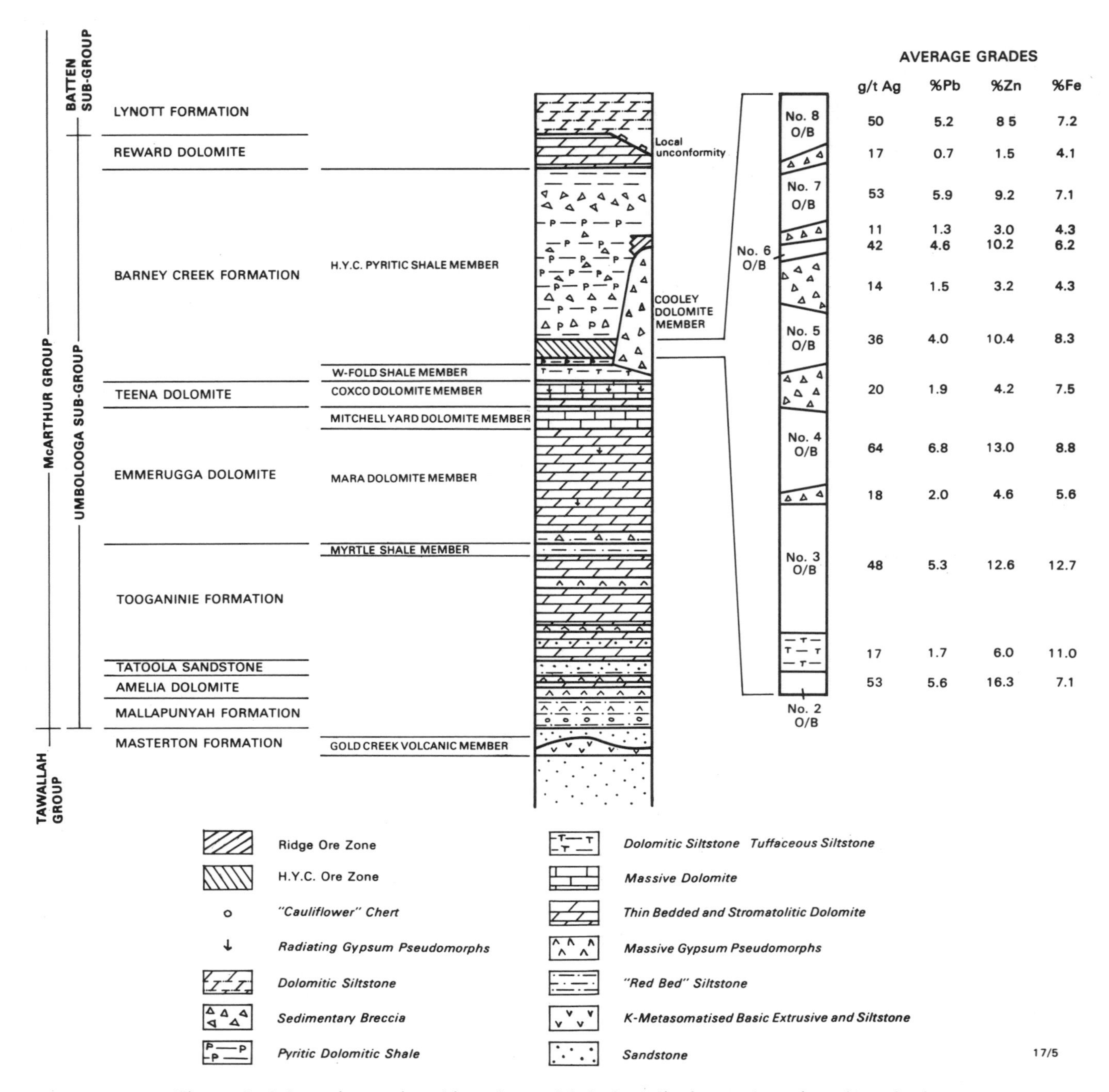

Figure 5. Schematic stratigraphic column, McArthur district, and section through the McArthur deposit. O/B = "orebody" (from Walker and others, 1978; Murray, 1975).

wholly from the same hydrothermal fluid, and it probably includes a biogenic component. Furthermore, there are marked changes in the isotopic compositions of pyritic sulfur at the top and bottom of the McArthur deposit (Smith and Croxford, 1975; Fig. 6).

C- and O-isotope compositions have been determined on dolomite from the discordant deposits in the Western Fault Block (Fig. 3), from the stratiform mineralization, and from rocks away from mineralization (Smith and Croxford, 1975; Rye and Williams, 1978, 1981). In contrast with the unmineralized dolomites, ($\delta^{13}C_{PDB}$ from -5.1‰ to +0.3‰, $\delta^{18}O_{SMOW}$ + 16.5‰ to +26.1‰), those from discordant and stratiform mineralization fall on a linear trend on a $\delta^{13}C$ versus $\delta^{18}O$ plot with $\delta^{13}C$ values varying from -3.8‰ to -1.4‰, and $\delta^{18}O$ from +18.6‰ to +25.5‰. The results suggest equilibrium between these carbonates

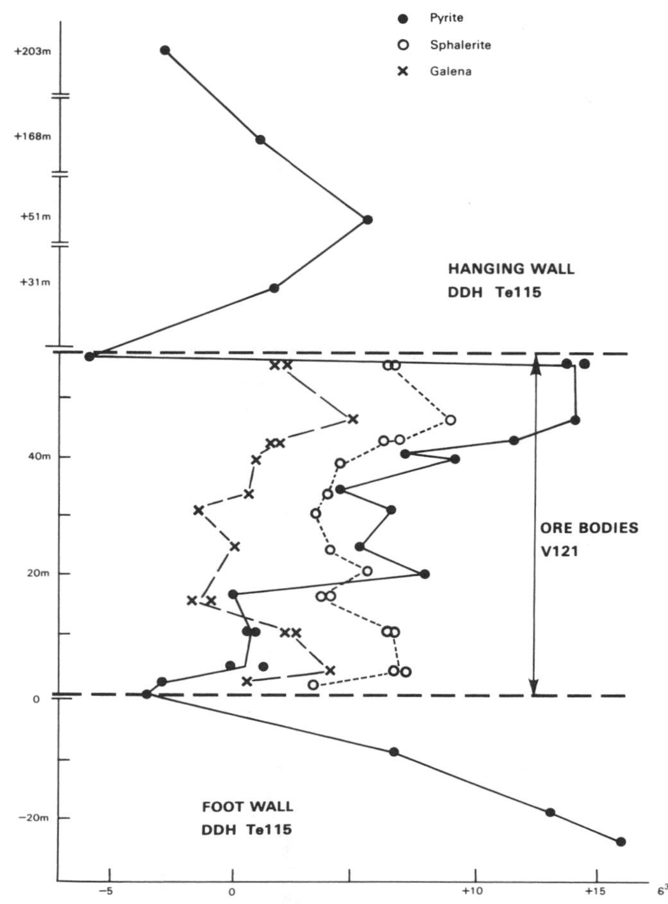

Figure 6. Sulphur isotope data from McArthur deposit and adjacent rocks (after Smith and Croxford, 1973, 1975).

and cooling mineralizing fluids (Rye and Williams, 1981). If the $\delta^{13}C$ and $\delta^{18}O$ values of these fluids remained constant, the model temperatures calculated by Rye and Williams (1981) are as high as 325°C in the Emu Fault zone and decrease to about 175°C in the concordant mineralization; if minor amounts of isotopically light bicarbonate were incorporated in the fluids so that the $\delta^{13}C$ value of the latter decreased by $2^0/_{00}$, the model temperature range is from around 200°C down to less than 100°C. The significance of these results will be discussed further in the section on timing of mineralization.

Kerogen from the H.Y.C. Pyritic Shale has $\delta^{13}C$ values from $-26.5^0/_{00}$ to $-31^0/_{00}$, consistent with derivation from microorganisms (Smith and Croxford, 1975).

The Pb from McArthur galena and sphalerite is isotopically homogenous, averaging $^{208}Pb/^{204}Pb = 35.83$, $^{207}Pb/^{204}Pb = 15.46$, and $^{206}Pb/^{204}Pb = 16.15$ (Gulson, 1975; Richards, 1975; Fig. 7). It is isotopically "conformable" and indicates crustal derivation of the base metals. In terms of the plumbotectonic concepts of Doe and Zartman (1979), it falls close to the average or orogene Pb-growth curve, yielding a model age close to its geological age of ca. 1.69 b.y. (Fig. 7).

In an attempt to obtain more specific information on the source of metals in the McArthur deposit, Lambert and Höhndorf (in prep.) determined the isotopic compositions of Pb in the underlying sedimentary strata. The measured (present-day) isotopic compositions of the sedimentary Pb define a linear array which extrapolates to pass through the ore Pb (Fig. 7). They are in accord with derivation of the ore metals from such strata, but could equally well reflect

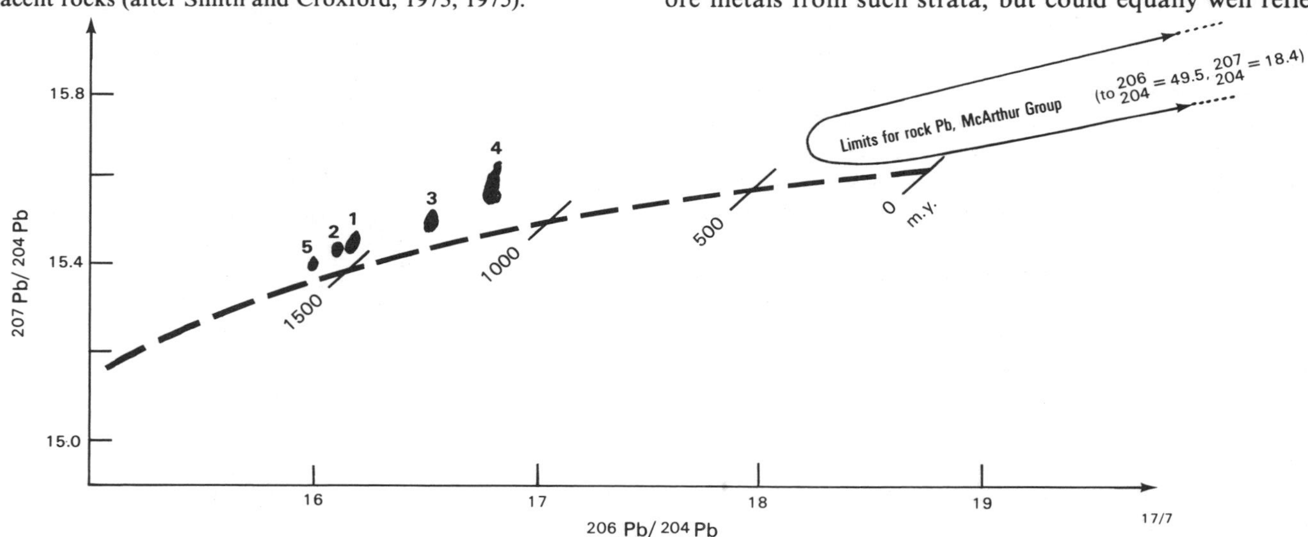

Figure 7. Lead-isotope compositions of major Proterozoic Pb-Zn deposits. 1 = McArthur (Richards, 1975); 2 = Mount Isa (Richards, 1975); 3 = Sullivan (LeCouteur, 1973); 4 = Gamsberg-Aggeneys (Köppel, 1980); 5 = Broken Hill (Cooper and others, 1969). Limits indicated for Pb from unmineralized McArthur Group strata (uncorrected for radiogenic Pb from U decay) are based on unpublished data by Lambert and A. Höhndorf. Upper and lower lines are Pb-isotope growth curves of Doe and Zartman (1979) for upper crust and orogene (average curve), respectively.

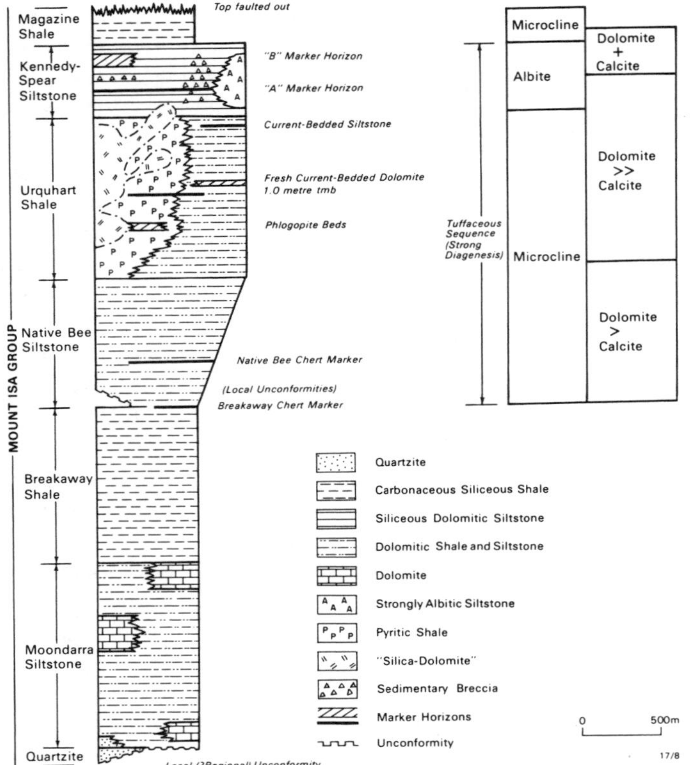

Figure 8. Schematic stratigraphic column, Mount Isa district (after Mathias and Clark, 1975).

addition of ore Pb to the strata. Distinction between these possibilities requires assessment of the initial Pb isotopic compositions of the sediments, which have to be calculated from the measured values by subtraction of Pb generated by decay of U and Th since sedimentation. However, it was found that these calculations cannot be made with sufficient accuracy for the McArthur strata (and presumably many other ancient sedimentary sequences) because of unfavourably low Pb contents and Pb/U ratios, coupled with uncertainties concerning postdepositional mobility of U and Pb in the strata.

Other Pb-Zn Mineralizations in Region. There are several other Pb-Zn deposits of lower grades and tonnages within the H.Y.C. Pyritic Shale and numerous minor discordant Pb-Zn deposits in various carbonate units.

Mount Isa

General References. Bennett, 1965, 1970; Stanton 1963, 1972; Mathias and Clark, 1975.

Geologic Setting. The sedimentary sequence in the Mount Isa region, though more metamorphosed and deformed, is of broadly similar character and age to that at McArthur (Plumb and Derrick, 1975; Plumb and others, 1980; Page, 1981). The ~5-km-thick Mount Isa Group, which accumulated in the Leichardt River Fault Trough (Fig. 4), comprises mainly dolomitic and siliceous shales and siltstones (Fig. 8). Fine-grained tuffite bands are widespread, and some are distinctive enough to be used as regional marker horizons. Pseudomorphs after gypsum and anhydrite were tentatively proposed by van den Heuvel (1969) and later confirmed by McClay and Carlile (1978) and Neudert and Russell (1981); the latter workers also recognized widespread stromatolites and shallow-water sedimentary structures.

The stratiform Pb-Zn ore bodies occur more than 3 km above the base of the sequence, within the 1,500-m-thick Urquhart Shale, which comprises mainly tuffaceous, carbonaceous, dolomitic shale and siltstone (Figs. 9, 10). Whilst there has probably been local thickening by faulting and folding, the original thickness of the mineralized interval was clearly many times greater than at McArthur. The inter-ore beds are mainly dolomitic siltstones and shales and contain negligible to significant sulfide. There are no talus or intraformational breccias in the mine, but thickness and facies changes suggest there was syndepositional fault-

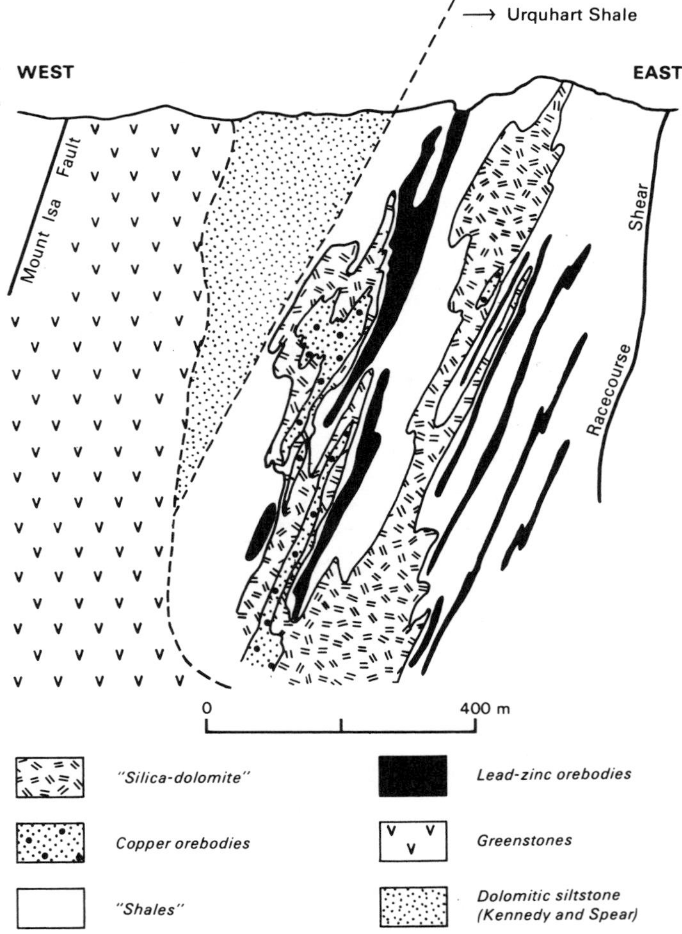

Figure 9. Generalized section through the Mount Isa Pb-Zn and Cu deposits (after Bennett, 1965).

ing and graben subsidence in the Mount Isa region (Smith, 1969; Bennett, 1970; Plumb and others, 1980).

Mineralization. Mount Isa ore is slightly coarser grained than the McArthur mineralization, reflecting mild recrystallization. It contains abundant pyrrhotite, which is probably partly a primary constituent reflecting a deficiency of sulfur in the depositional environment (Plimer and Finlow-Bates, 1978), although some is clearly secondary and may have formed during the lower greenschist facies metamorphism (Lambert, 1973). Pyrite, argentiferous galena, and sphalerite (average Fe content of ~6 wt%) are the other major minerals in the Pb-Zn mineralization, freibergite being the most important of the minor constituents.

In contrast with the other giant Proterozoic Pb-Zn deposits, Mount Isa also has major, non-stratiform Cu mineralization, comprising mainly chalcopyrite, pyrrhotite, and cobaltite. It occurs within the brecciated "silica-dolomite" facies of the Urquhart Shale adjacent to its contact with an upfaulted block of altered basic volcanics (Fig. 9). Although lobes of cupriferous silica dolomite interfinger with the Pb-Zn deposits, there is always sharp demarcation between Cu and Pb-Zn, and a variety of features imply that the bulk of the Cu was introduced epigenetically. There is a general lateral zonation Pb (Ag) → Zn → Fe (pyrite) away from the "silica dolomite" (Finlow-Bates, 1979).

Mineral Dispersions Around Deposit. As at McArthur, there are general decreases in microcline/albite ratios, dolomite/calcite ratios, and Fe and Mn contents of dolomites away from the mineralization (van den Heuvel, 1969; Fig. 8).

Isotope Data. The Mount Isa Pb-Zn ore is more enriched overall in ^{34}S than the McArthur deposit. Solomon (1965) recorded the following $\delta^{34}S$ ranges for samples taken throughout the mine: pyrite +7‰ to +31‰, pyrrhotite +8‰ to +29‰, sphalerite +10‰ to +23‰, and galena +3‰ to +15‰. Smith and others (1978) found similar but slightly more restricted $\delta^{34}S$ ranges in their more systematic sampling of selected parts of the mine, and noted an approach to isotopic equilibrium between all the sulfides. These results imply that thermochemical reduction of sulfate was an important source of sulfide. While the isotopic equilibration could be reflecting precipitation of all the sulfide minerals from the same hydrothermal solution, Smith and others (1978) favoured metamorphic equilibration between biogenic pyrite and hydrothermal galena and sphalerite. They also concluded that a lack of isotopic equilibrium between chalcopyrite and pyrrhotite in the Cu ore is consistent with postmetamorphic introduction of this mineralization.

Smith and others (1978) found narrow ranges of isotopic compositions for kerogen ($\delta^{13}C_{PDB}$ = -21‰ to -26‰) and carbonate ($\delta^{13}C_{PDB}$ = -5.7 to -2.9‰, $\delta^{18}O_{SMOW}$ = +11‰ to +13‰) in the Pb-Zn mineralization. These differ from the McArthur compositions in a manner consistent with isotopic exchange during regional metamorphism at Mount Isa.

Mount Isa galena is isotopically homogeneous and similar to that at McArthur, averaging $^{208}Pb/^{204}Pb$ = 35.84, $^{207}Pb/^{204}Pb$ = 15.45, and $^{206}Pb/^{204}Pb$ = 16.12 (Richards, 1975; Fig. 7).

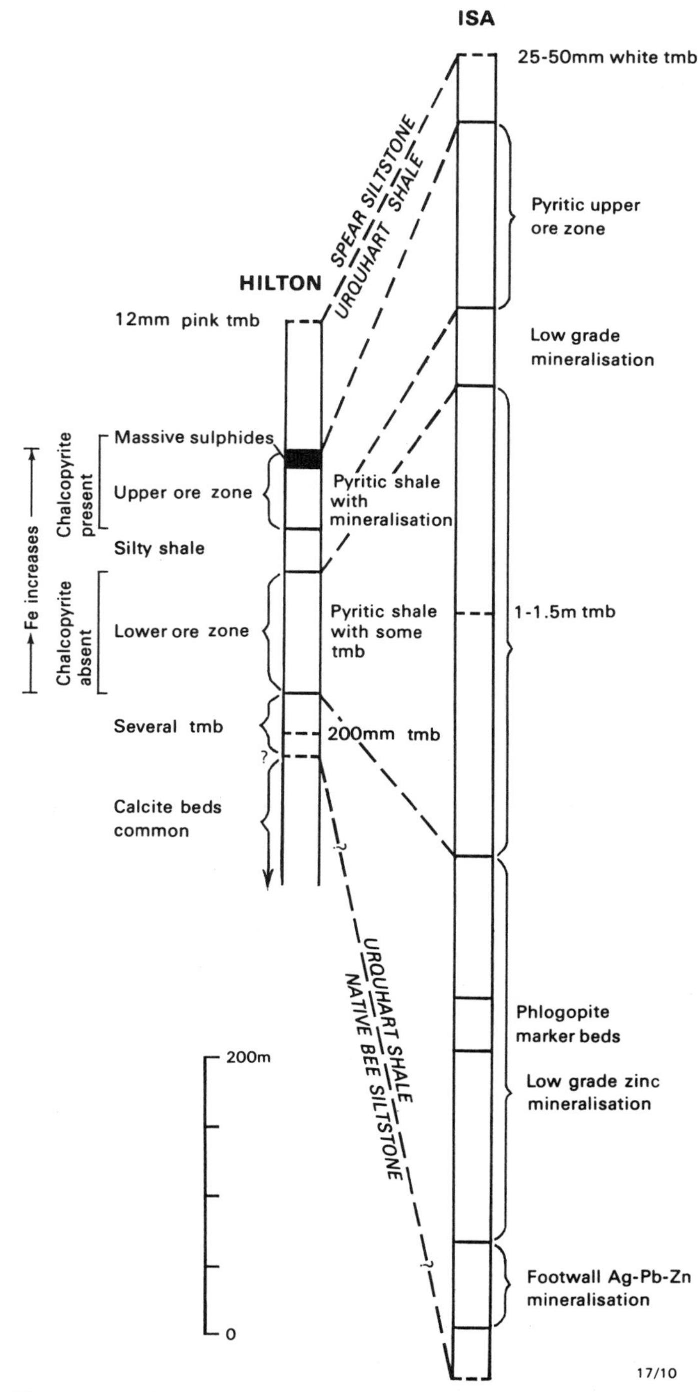

Figure 10. Comparison of simplified stratigraphic columns, Mount Isa and Hilton deposits (from Mathias and Clark, 1975).

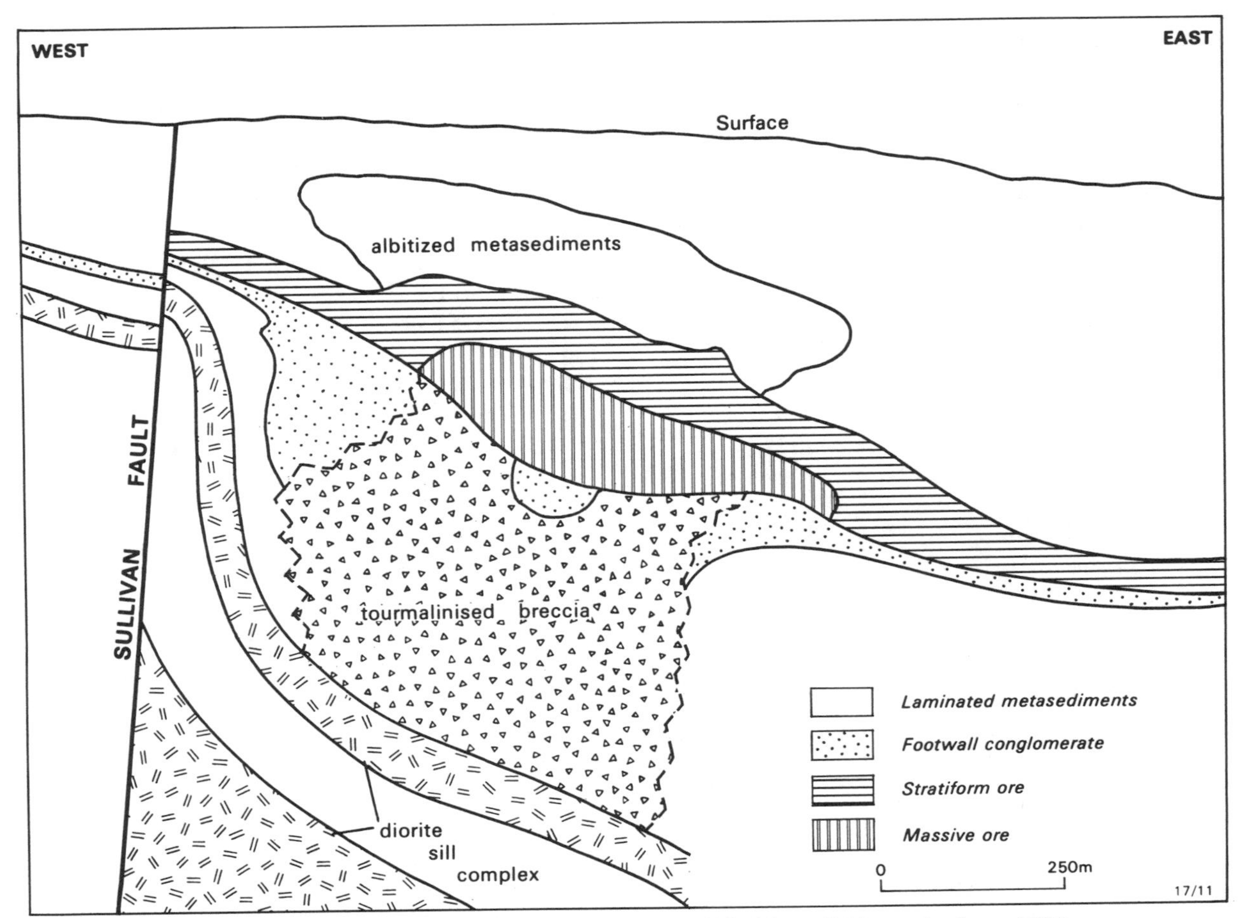

Figure 11. Schematic section, Sullivan deposit (simplified from Ethier and others, 1976).

Other Pb-Zn Mineralization in Region. The Hilton deposit (Mathias and others, 1973; Mathias and Clark, 1975) is also within the Urquhart Shale, some 20 km to the north of Mount Isa. The two deposits are essentially similar, but Hilton has a thinner mineralized sequence (~250 m; Fig. 10), smaller ore tonnage, higher bedded chalcopyrite content (averaging 0.5%) in the upper Pb-Zn ore bodies, but no "silica-dolomite" or separate Cu deposit.

Other significant stratiform Pb-Zn deposits in the Mount Isa–Cloncurry province of northwestern Queensland include Dugald River, Lady Loretta, and Pegmont (Fig. 4; Williams, 1980).

Sullivan

General References. Freeze, 1966; Ethier and others, 1976.

Geologic Setting. The Sullivan deposit is 30 to 90 m thick (Fig. 11) and occurs within a sequence of laminated carbonaceous shales and siltstones at the boundary between the Lower and Middle Aldridge Formations of the Belt-Purcell Supergroup (Fig. 12). In the Sullivan area, the Lower Aldridge is ~2,300 m thick and comprises mainly thin bedded, pyrrhotitic siltstones and quartzites, while the Middle Aldridge is of similar thickness and contains, in addition, abundant turbidites. Immediately beneath the ore, there is an intraformational conglomerate that appears to have formed in a steep-sided depression as a result of syndepositional faulting. Superimposed on parts of this, and apparently developed to depths of at least 450 m below the ore, is a breccia that may reflect cycles of hydraulic fracturing as well as fault movements. On a regional scale, there is widespread evidence of penecontemporaneous block faulting and Kanasewich (1968) postulated from gravity data that a basement rift zone exists beneath Sullivan. Metamorphosed basic to intermediate sills, and felsic stocks, are widespread in the Aldridge Formation.

Mineralization. The Sullivan deposit has been extensively recrystallized by metamorphism. It contains a massive core of pyrite and chlorite and an adjacent massive pyrrhotite lens, both of which have only sporadic sphalerite and galena concentrations. Overlying and surrounding the massive ore is the laminated Pb-Zn-rich ore. Zn/Pb ratios and pyrite/pyrrhotite ratios increase in the laminated mineralization with increasing distance from the massive sul-

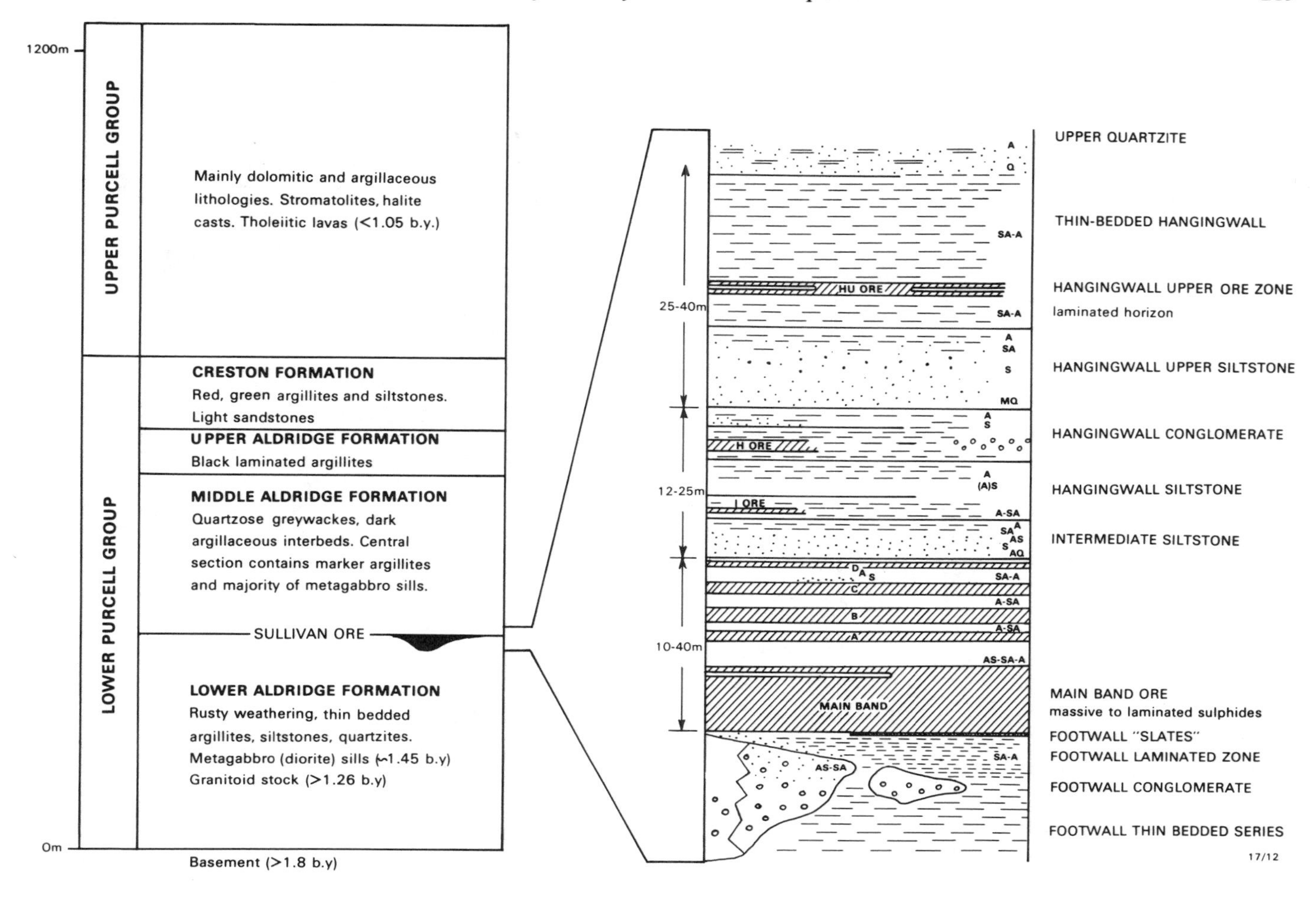

Figure 12. Generalized stratigraphic column, Sullivan area, and section through Sullivan deposit (after Cominco Limited).

fides, and sporadic Zn-enrichment is found in the carbonaceous sediments for several kilometres laterally beyond the limit of the laminated ore. In the footwall, there are considerable amounts of pyrrhotite as blebs, laminations and veins, and minor chalcopyrite. Ag occurs in tetrahedrite and galena and is most abundant in the upper ore bodies near the central massive zone. Unlike the other major Proterozoic Pb-Zn deposits, Sullivan contains recoverable quantities of Sn, mainly as cassiterite, which occur in mineralized fracture systems in the footwall and decrease in concentration upwards and outwards in the ore.

Mineral Dispersions Around Deposit. There is abundant stratiform and discordant tourmaline in the footwall to the massive ore, pervasive albite-chlorite alteration in the central hanging wall, and Fe-Mn garnets in silty beds within the laminated ore. Tourmaline alteration is not found around any of the other major Pb-Zn deposits.

Isotope Data. Sulfides from Sullivan have been studied by Campbell and others (1978) who found the following $\delta^{34}S$ ranges: pyrrhotite -8.4‰ to +4.6‰, pyrite -7.4‰ to +4.7‰, sphalerite -5.8‰ to +3.0‰, galena -10.4‰ to +1.3‰. There is a general approach to equilibrium between sulfide pairs, consistent with their hydrothermal precipitation, or with metamorphic equilibration. Campbell and others (1978) concluded that Proterozoic seawater was the S source, and this could have been reduced chemically and/or biologically.

The Pb in galena is again isotopically homogeneous and plots close to the orogene curve (Fig. 7). Its average values are $^{208}Pb/^{204}Pb$ = 36.18, $^{207}Pb/^{204}Pb$ = 15.48, $^{206}Pb/^{204}Pb$ =16.52 (Leech and Wanless, 1962; LeCouteur, 1973).

Other Pb-Zn Mineralization in Region. There are numerous examples of relatively minor, stratiform and discordant Pb-Zn mineralization in the East Kootenay province of British Columbia (e.g., Leech and Wanless, 1962). On Pb isotope grounds these fall into two groups: a uniform group with middle Proterozoic model ages (isotopically similar to Sullivan) and a more radiogenic group of apparent Mesozoic-Cenozoic age.

Gamsberg

General References. Rozendaal, 1975, 1980.

Geologic Setting. The Zn-rich Gamsberg deposit is situated within the Namaqua Mobile Belt. The host Bushmanland Sequence comprises sedimentary and igneous rocks that have been subjected to polyphase deformation and medium to high grade metamorphism. The unit containing the deposit is the mineralogically complex Fe-(Mn-) rich Gams Iron-Formation, which changes from fine-grained, pyrite-rich, quartz-muscovite-sillimanite-graphite schist at the base, through pyrrhotite-rich cordierite hornfels, to pyrrhotite-rich banded quartz-garnet-grunerite rocks with or without clinopyroxene at the top (Fig. 13). Laterally, this iron-formation passes into sillimanite quartzite.

The features of the Bushmanland Sequence are consistent with accumulation under shallow-water conditions in a graben, within which the mineralized facies formed in a local restricted basin of chemical and fine-detrital (tuffaceous?) sedimentation.

Mineralization. The ore sulfides are medium grained as a result of metamorphic recrystallization. There is an upward trend from pyrite to pyrrhotite, accompanied by increasing sphalerite/galena ratios. The sphalerite is mainly marmatitic and manganiferous, although there is some light-coloured, Fe-Mn-poor sphalerite. Banded massive barite is mined from Gamsberg and shows an inverse thickness relationship with the sulfide mineralization.

Mineral Dispersions Around Deposit. Magnetite, hematite, and Fe-calcite are abundant both above and below the mineralization, while pyrite is present in the footwall rocks. Mn-rich garnet and muscovite are features of the country rocks.

Isotope Data. I am not aware of any S, C, or O isotope data for this deposit.

The Pb-isotopic compositions of galena (Köppel, 1980) are slightly less homogeneous than for the other Pb-Zn deposits considered herein (Fig. 7). Also, they require a component of Pb from rocks with relatively high U/Pb and Th/Pb ratios, possibly Archean craton. Köppel (1980) called on additional components of Pb from granulite facies rocks (U- and Th-depleted) and from a "volcanogenic" source of the type involved in formation of the penecontemporaneous Preiska Cu deposit (in the Copperton Volcanics, some 350 km to the east). The Pb isotope model age, supported by recent Rb-Sr data (Cornell, 1977), led Köppel to conclude that the Bushmanland sequence in the Gamsberg region must have been deposited between 1.6 and 1.2 b.y. ago, not pre-1.8 b.y. as proposed earlier from stratigraphic correlations (e.g., Joubert, 1976).

Other Pb-Zn Mineralization in Region. The Aggeneys stratiform deposits occur 15 to 20 km to the west of Gamsberg at a similar stratigraphic position. From west to east, these deposits are Black Mountain, Broken Hill, and Big Syn. They have very large tonnages of low average-grade mineralization. The stratiform deposits exhibit a general regional zonation of decreasing Cu and Pb (Ag) and increasing Zn from Black Mountain to Gamsberg. The Pb isotope compositions of the Aggeneys galenas are indistinguishable from those at Gamsberg (Köppel, 1980).

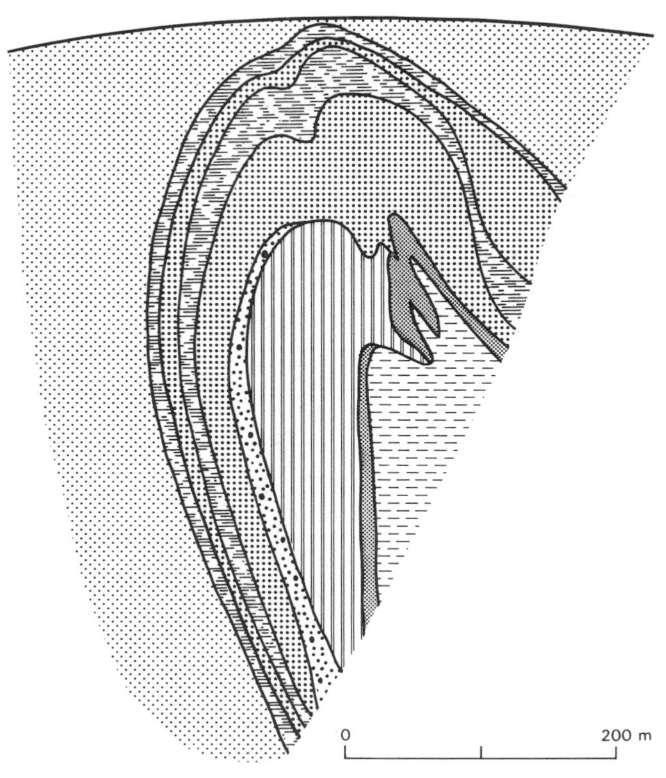

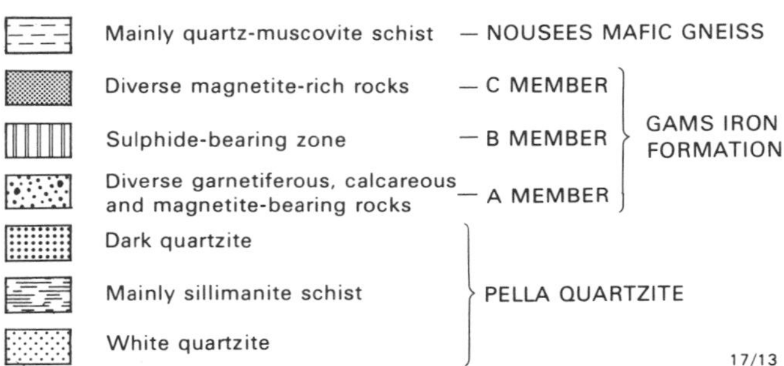

Figure 13. Cross-section through the Gamsberg deposit (after Rozendaal, 1980).

Broken Hill

General References. Carruthers and Pratten, 1961; Lewis and others, 1965; Johnson and Klingner, 1975; Both and Rutland, 1976; Stanton, 1976a, 1976b; Laing and others, 1978; Stevens, 1980.

Geologic Setting. The Broken Hill deposit is situated in the high-grade metamorphic Willyama Complex, within

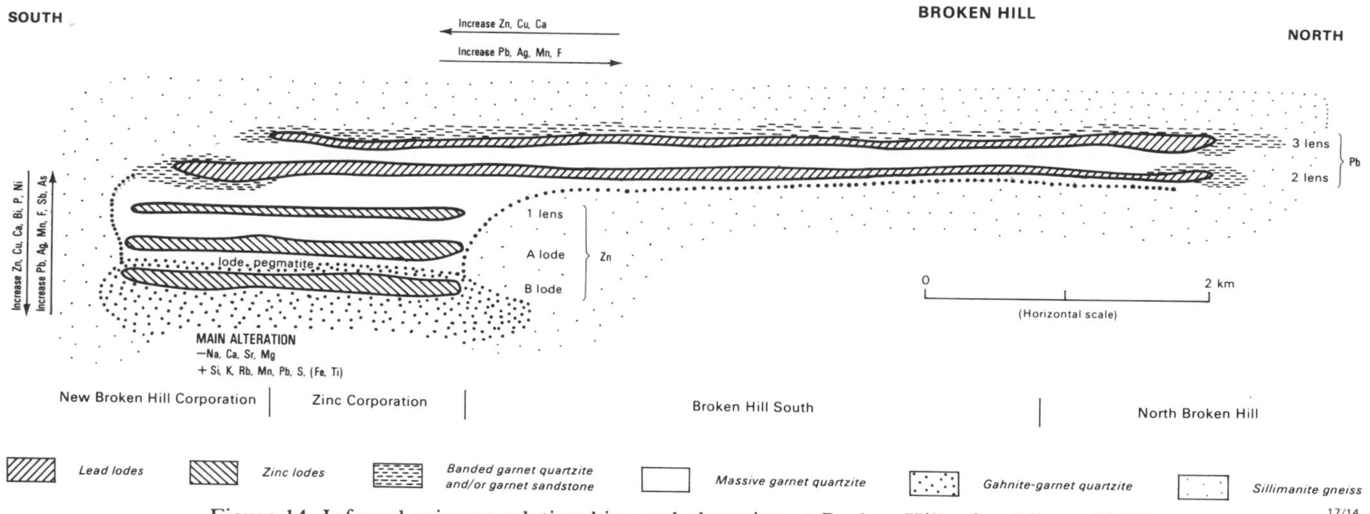

Figure 14. Inferred primary relationships and alteration at Broken Hill, after Plimer (1979), Spry and Both (1980), Rutland and Both (1983).

a lode horizon comprising sillimanite gneiss, blue gahnite quartzite, garnet quartzite, garnet "sandstone," and conformable and irregular pegmatites (Figs. 14, 15). Overall, the main rock types in the more than 5-km-thick sequence of the Willyama Complex are quartzofeldspathic gneiss with or without garnet, sillimanite-garnet-biotite gneiss, quartzite, mica schist, amphibolite, and banded iron-formation (BIF).

The high-grade metamorphism and deformation mean that it is difficult to reconstruct original stratigraphic and tectonic features. Stanton (1976b) considered the main folding was produced by soft-sediment slumping, which was followed by static metamorphism. However, recent mapping by Laing and others (1978) suggested a complex deformation and metamorphic history; they concluded that the mine sequence has been moved many kilometres from its original location; that the orebodies are in an antiformal zone between two major synforms, and that the sequence was inverted before the main macroscopic folding.

The above complexities render it difficult to evaluate the premetamorphic nature of the rocks, synsedimentary faulting, and other features of the depositional environment. However, it appears that the orebodies formed in a local elongated basin, some 3 km or more above the base of a thick trough sequence of argillaceous to quartzose clastics, felsic and mafic volcanics and/or intrusives, and exhalative BIF and chert. Although there is essentially no graphite in the mine sequence, carbon could have been extensively consumed by diagenetic and metamorphic reactions.

Mineralization. The five orebodies are coarse grained and have been significantly remobilized within the lode horizon. They contain abundant marmatitic, manganiferous sphalerite and galena, and have a low overall pyrrhotite content. There are minor amounts of numerous other sul-

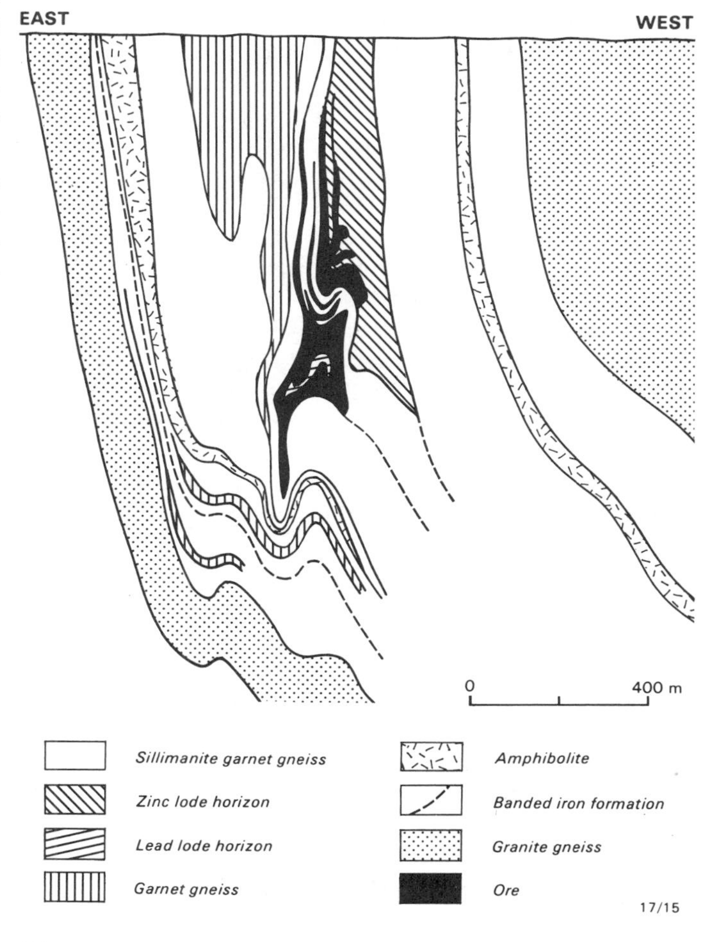

Figure 15. Composite section (looking south) of the southern part of the Broken Hill deposit (after The Zinc Corporation).

fide minerals, and the main gangue minerals are quartz, calcite, various Ca-Fe-Mn silicates, feldspars, fluorite, gahnite, and apatite. The stratigraphically lowermost three orebodies, which are economic only in the southern portion of the field, have the highest Zn/Pb ratios, and Cu is highest (0.2%) in the basal lode. The stratigraphically higher orebodies are much more Pb and Ag rich, but still have high Zn contents and Cu contents of ~0.14%; from south to north, the Pb orebodies increase in Pb and Ag. These metal distribution patterns imply that there was a general increase in the Pb contents of the ore fluids with time, with some superimposed differential metal precipitation.

Mineral Dispersions Around Deposit. As at Gamsberg, the Broken Hill country rocks contain Mn-rich garnets and gahnite, and many of them are siliceous (Fig. 15).

Isotope Data. The S-isotope compositions of Broken Hill sulfides have been studied by Stanton and Rafter (1966) and Both and Smith (1975). The ranges of $\delta^{34}S$ values for individual minerals are galena -2.1‰ to +1.6‰, sphalerite -0.3 to +2.4‰, and pyrrhotite +1.2‰ to +2.2‰. These compositions are similar to those of most Archean and earliest Proterozoic deposits. They are compatible with sulfur of direct or indirect magmatic derivation, but could equally well be the result of metamorphic modification of originally more variable sulfur isotope compositions of volcanogenic and/or biogenic origin (Both and Smith, 1975).

Pb in Broken Hill galena is isotopically homogeneous, averaging $^{208}Pb/^{204}Pb$ = 35.66, $^{207}Pb/^{204}Pb$ = 15.39, and $^{206}Pb/^{204}Pb$ = 16.00 (Cooper and others, 1969; Fig. 7). It falls on the orogene Pb isotope evolution curve of Doe and Zartman (1979) and has a slightly older model age than McArthur and Mount Isa.

Other Pb-Zn Mineralization in Region. There are numerous minor stratiform Pb-Zn deposits in the Willyama Complex, some of them apparently at the same stratigraphic level as Broken Hill. Discordant "Thackeringa-type" Pb mineralization is also widespread and appears to have formed during an early Paleozoic retrograde metamorphic event.

TIMING OF MINERALIZATION: THE McARTHUR EXAMPLE

Since the 1950s the consensus of geological thought on the genesis of the major stratiform Pb-Zn deposits has moved from intricate replacement of favourable beds to sedimentary-exhalative accumulation. However, the latter concept has been questioned in recent years, particularly with reference to the McArthur deposit (Williams and Rye, 1974; Williams, 1978a, 1978b, 1979a, 1979b; Rye and Williams, 1978). The preferred model of Williams, which he termed "epigenetic," calls on lateral influx of Zn- and Pb-bearing hydrothermal brines. It differs from classic epigenetic concepts in that he acknowledged that these brines would have to have been introduced at depths of less than 100 m below the sediment surface. This constraint comes mainly from the presence of clasts of mineralized shale in "inter-ore" breccia above "orebody" 5 (Fig. 5). In addition, these clasts indicate that all of the "orebodies" could not possibly have formed in a single epigenetic event.

Genetic considerations in this paper complement the discussion of Lambert (1981). They are restricted to aspects of pyrite textures, S/C ratios, isotope patterns, and soft-sediment deformation of sulfide laminae in the McArthur deposit, which are central to the syngenetic versus epigenetic debate. It is maintained that these features can be readily explained by sedimentary exhalative mineralization with predictable postdepositional modifications.

Pyrite Textures

There is no disputing the textural evidence for at least two stages of pyrite formation in the McArthur deposit, but the outstanding point of contention concerns the timing of the later pyrite (Py_2) and the Pb-Zn mineralization. Williams (1978a, 1978b; 1979a, 1979b) argued for biogenic formation of Py_1, followed by introduction of hydrothermal fluids which formed Py_2, and finally sphalerite and galena. To form the entire deposit, this would require cycles of lateral migration of hydrothermal fluids for distances of up to 1 km into the H.Y.C. Pyritic Shale, each cycle comprising an Fe-bearing fluid evolving to a Pb-Zn brine.

The alternative interpretation of the textural features, which I find more plausible, is that sphalerite, galena, and pyrite (Py_1) laminae formed from exhalations, and further pyrite was generated within the mineralized muds. This later pyrite (Py_2), which was presumably reflecting the continuing availability of reactive Fe and biogenic sulfide within the sediments, tended to nucleate on the exhalative pyrite.

Sulfide-S/Organic-C Ratios

Poorly mineralized samples from the McArthur deposit (Pb + Zn <0.2 moles/kg) have a near-symmetrical, unimodal S/C frequency distribution like that of much of the H.Y.C. Pyritic Shale outside the deposit and unmineralized carbonaceous sedimentary rocks from other localities. The well-mineralized samples, in contrast, have generally higher and widely varying S/C ratios. Williams (1978b) carried out calculations of S/C ratios expected for several potential mineralizing processes. On the basis of these, and his interpretation of the textural features (above), he concluded that ore formation involved introduction of metalliferous, sulfate-bearing hydrothermal fluids into pyritic (Py_1) sediments, where the sulfate was reduced by organic matter. Such chemical reduction of sulfate has not yet been proven to occur at significant rates at temperatures below about 250°C (e.g., Trudinger, 1981).

In assessing the S/C ratio calculations, it must be borne in mind that any mathematical model is only as good as the assumptions on which it is based. The main assumptions made by Williams (1978b) are (1) Py_I is biogenic throughout, and both poorly and well-mineralized samples contain "similar and trace amounts of Py_2"; (2) the S/C ratios in the mineralized rocks formed by modification of the unimodal S/C distribution by the process that generated the abundant sphalerite and galena; and (3) the dominant process of oxidation of organic matter was one that reduced sulfate, and all of the resultant sulfide was fixed as sphalerite and galena.

The results of the S/C ratio calculations should not be used as *primary* evidence for extensive epigenetic sulfate reduction because the above assumptions have not been shown to be substantially correct. Firstly, there is no certainty that Py_I in the mineralization is biogenic; it is more likely that some iron sulfide precipitated from the mineralizing fluids, as is accepted for most exhalative deposits. Secondly, Py_2 commonly constitutes more than one-third of the pyrite in mineralized samples, certainly more than a trace component. Thirdly, the S/C ratios in the hanging-wall pyritic shales are similar to those in the mineralization, indicating that sphalerite and galena formation are not necessary to generate such ratios; in an attempt to account for this, Williams (1979b) proposed that pyrite in these hanging-wall strata formed mainly as a result of in situ chemical sulfate reduction (Py_2), in contrast with his assumption of biogenic pyrite in the "orebodies" and the rest of the H.Y.C. Pyritic Shale. Fourthly, there is no evidence that the mineralized strata had much higher initial concentrations of organic matter than interbedded and surrounding unmineralized strata, as required by (3) above.

A syngenetic sulfide-exhalative origin for the mineralization would have produced the observed S/C ratio distribution, provided something like half of the pyrite-S was from exhalations.

Stable Isotope Data

Sulfides. The S-isotope compositions for the McArthur deposit (Fig. 6) do not constrain the timing of Pb-Zn mineralization. They have been interpreted in terms of biogenic pyrite plus exhalative sphalerite and galena (Smith and Croxford, 1973) and biogenic pyrite plus epigenetic sphalerite and galena (Williams, 1978b, 1979a). However, these data do not rule out a significant proportion of exhalative pyrite, particularly in the upper two-thirds of the deposit. The exhalations could have precipitated FeS_2 directly and/or an intermediate "FeS" phase that was converted to pyrite as a result of biological sulfate reduction in the sediments. The exhalative sulfide was most likely formed largely by chemical reduction of sulfate, at the elevated temperatures pertaining at depth and/or near centres of igneous activity.

Carbonates. The isotopic compositions of carbonates in the McArthur deposit can be used to assess the in situ sulfate-reduction model. Williams (1978b) considered this model in terms of two reactions:

$$2C^\circ + SO_4^{2-} + M^{2+} + 2H_2O \rightarrow MS + 2HCO_3^- + 2H^+ \quad (1)$$

(2 moles of organic C oxidized to form 1 mole of sulfide and 2 moles of bicarbonate);

$$CH_4 + SO_4^{2-} + M^{2+} \rightarrow MS + HCO_3^- + H^+ + H_2O \quad (2)$$

(1 mole of organic C oxidized to form 1 mole of sulfide and 1 mole of bicarbonate).

The overall average S content of sphalerite and galena in the McArthur "orebodies" is at least 6%, and to produce this by reactions (1) and (2) would utilize an average of ~4.5 wt% C° and ~2.5 wt% CH_4, respectively. The bicarbonate from such reactions would have $\delta^{13}C$ values more negative than -15‰, and the amounts produced, expressed as CO_2, would have been ~16 wt% and 7 wt%, respectively. These are significant amounts when compared with the average carbonate content of the "orebodies," again expressed as CO_2, of ~10 wt% (Corbett and others, 1975). If one accepts the conclusion of Rye and Williams (1978, 1981) concerning equilibration between the hydrothermal fluids and the carbonate in the deposit, and that there must have been high overall fluid to rock ratios, then it follows that in situ epigenetic sulfate reduction is unlikely to have played a major role in the generation of the McArthur mineralization. Had it done so, the high proportion of isotopically light bicarbonate thus generated should have resulted in considerably more negative $\delta^{13}C$ values for dolomite in the deposit than the minimum observed value of -3.8‰.

The C- and O-isotope data are compatible with minor to major interaction of sedimentary carbonates with exhalative fluids and/or precipitation of some carbonate from these exhalations.

Sulfide Laminae and Soft Sediment Structures

At scales of a few centimetres or more, there are intervals of irregularly folded, conformable sulfide laminae that are most reasonably interpreted in terms of precipitation and slumping of these sulfides prior to deposition of immediately overlying, undisturbed laminae.

The epigenetic model requires lateral flow of Zn, Pb, and sulfate-bearing fluids along relatively permeable arenite and breccia interbeds, and their diffusion into adjacent, fine-grained, organic-rich sediments. There is no basis for concluding this would have produced conformable sulfides in both slumped and undisturbed sediments. The recent experiments of Bubela (1981) do not support the epigenetic mineralizing process at McArthur, despite that author's contentions. He formed sulfide bands along a curved interface between metal- and sulfide-bearing fluids flowing side by side in a permeable medium (glass beads).

SUMMARY

The major Proterozoic Pb-Zn deposits formed close to contemporaneous continental margins, in large intracratonic troughs (e.g., McArthur), or epicratonic embayments (e.g., Sullivan). Thick sequences of sediments accumulated in these subsiding basins, but their nature varies: in some places shallow-water carbonates are abundant (e.g., McArthur, Mount Isa), whereas in other places siliceous and argillaceous sediments are dominant (e.g., Sullivan).

The main deposits formed a few kilometres above the bases of their host trough sequences, within thin-bedded, fine-grained, Fe- and Mn-enriched detrital and chemical sedimentary facies. The restricted occurrences and marked thickness variations of these mineralized facies reflect accumulation in local basins that apparently developed mainly as a result of subsidence controlled by synsedimentary faults. Along strike from the deposits there can be sporadic enrichments of Hg, As, and Tl, in addition to Zn and Pb. The deposits can be subdivided on the basis of metamorphic grade and host lithologies: the highly metamorphosed and relatively S- and C-poor country rocks at Broken Hill and Gamsberg imply more tectonically active (rift-mobile belt) environments than at McArthur, Mount Isa–Hilton, and Sullivan.

Minor stratiform and disseminated Pb-Zn mineralization occurs at widespread localities around the major deposits and in some regions it is established that stratiform Pb-Zn is concentrated about a particular stratigraphic level. Igneous activity in the Pb-Zn provinces is expressed as tuffaceous sediments, lavas, and/or intrusives. It was typically bimodal and not centred close to the mineralization.

The Pb isotope data for all the major Pb-Zn deposits indicate that the ore metals are of crustal derivation, probably mainly from the underlying sedimentary piles and/or distant centres of igneous activity.

The features of the relatively pristine McArthur deposit are in accord with sulfide-exhalative mineralization, as is widely accepted for the more metamorphosed deposits, the banded nature of the mineralization implying multiple pulses of ore fluids. At McArthur, and probably also to varying degrees in the other deposits, there was some slumping of sulfide laminae and growth of authigenic minerals during the period of mineralization.

The exhalative sulfide in the Pb-Zn deposits was most likely derived from sulfate that was reduced chemically at elevated temperatures pertaining at depth and/or near igneous centres. However, contributions of magmatic sulfide cannot be ruled out and could have been dominant at Broken Hill. Biogenic sulfide was responsible for formation of some of the pyrite in and around the deposits.

ACKNOWLEDGMENTS

The paper presents my interpretation of views of many people who know the deposits concerned in much more detail than I ever will. It has benefited considerably from comments by Lewis B. Gustafson, Malcolm R. Walter, and an anonymous reviewer. Jock Smith and Joe Janecek of Carpentaria Exploration Company provided some of the samples for the Pb-isotope tracer study at McArthur. The Baas Becking Laboratory is supported by the Australian Mineral Industries Research Association Limited, the Bureau of Mineral Resources, and the Commonwealth Scientific and Industrial Research Organisation.

REFERENCES CITED

Bennett, E. M., 1965, Lead-zinc-silver and copper deposits of Mount Isa, *in* McAndrew, J., ed., Geology of Australian ore deposits, Volume 1: Melbourne, Australia, Institute of Mining Metallurgy, p. 233–246.

—— 1970, History, geology and planned expansion of Mount Isa properties: Paper presented to World Symposium on the Mining and Metallurgy of Lead and Zinc, American Institute of Mining Engineers, St. Louis.

Both, R. A., and Rutland, R.W.R., 1976, The problem of identifying and interpreting stratiform ore bodies in highly metamorphosed terrains: The Broken Hill example, *in* Wolf, K. H., ed., Handbook of strata-bound and stratiform ore deposits, Volume 4: Amsterdam, Elsevier, p. 261–325.

Both, R. A., and Smith, J. W., 1975, A sulphur isotope study of base metal mineralization in the Willyama Complex, western New South Wales, Australia: Economic Geology, v. 70, p. 308–318.

Bubela, B., 1981, Banded sulfide ores: The experimental formation of sulfide bands in sediments from flowing liquids: Economic Geology, v. 76, p. 171–172.

Campbell, F. A., Ethier, V. G., Krouse, H. R., and Both, R. A., 1978, Isotopic composition of sulfur in the Sullivan orebody, British Columbia: Economic Geology, v. 73, p. 246–268.

Carruthers, D. S., and Pratten, R. D., 1961, The stratigraphic section and structure in The Zinc Corporation Limited and Broken Hill Consolidated Limited, Broken Hill, N.S.W.: Economic Geology, v. 56, p. 1088–1102.

Cooper, J. A., Reynolds, P. H., and Richards, J. R., 1969, Double spike calibration of the Broken Hill standard lead: Earth and Planetary Science Letters, v. 6, p. 467–478.

Corbett, J. A., Lambert, I. B., and Scott, K. M., 1975, Results of analyses of rocks from the McArthur area, Northern Territory. CSIRO Minerals Research Laboratories, Technical Communication 57.

Cornell, D. H., 1975, Age and metamorphism of the Copperton Formation, Prieska district: Geological Society of South Africa, Special Publication 4.

Croxford, N.J.W., and Jephcott, S., 1972, The McArthur lead-zinc-silver deposit, N.T.: Proceedings of Australasian Institute of Mining and Metallurgy, v. 243, p. 1–26.

Croxford, N.J.W., Gulson, B. L., and Smith, J. W., 1975, The McArthur deposit: A review of the current situation: Mineralium Deposita, v. 10, p. 302–304.

Doe, B. R., and Zartman, R. E., 1979, Plumbotectonics I. The Phanerozoic, *in* Barnes, H. L., ed., Geochemistry of hydrothermal ore deposits (2nd edition): New York, Wiley, p. 22–70.

Ethier, V. G., Campbell, F. A., Both, R. A., and Krouse, H. R., 1976, Geological setting of the Sullivan orebody and estimates of temperatures and pressures of metamorphism: Economic Geology, v. 71, p. 1570–1588.

Finlow-Bates, T., 1979, Cyclicity in the lead-zinc-silver bearing sediments at Mount Isa mine, Queensland, Australia, and rates of sulfide accumulation: Economic Geology, v. 74, p. 1408–1419.

Freeze, A. C., 1966, On the origin of the Sullivan orebody, Kimberley, B. C., *in* Tectonic history and mineral deposits of the Western Cordillera: Canadian Institute of Mining and Metallurgy, Special Volume 8, p. 263–294.

Gulson, B. L., 1975, Differences in lead isotope composition in the stratiform McArthur zinc-lead-silver deposit: Mineralium Deposita, v. 10, p. 277–286.

Hurley, P. M., and Rand, J. R., 1969, Pre-drift continental nuclei: Science, v. 164, p. 1229–1242.

Johnson, I. R., and Klingner, G. C., 1975, The Broken Hill ore deposit and its environment, *in* Knight, C. L., ed., Economic Geology of Austrlia and Papua New Guinea, Melbourne, Australasian Institute of Mining and Metallurgy, v. 1: Metals, p. 476–491.

Joubert, P., 1976, The relationship between the Namaqualand Metamorphic Complex and the Kheis Group: South African Journal of Science, v. 72/10, p. 312–314.

Kanasewich, E. R., 1968, Precambrian rift: Genesis of stratabound ore deposits: Science, v. 161, p. 1002–1005.

Köppel, V., 1980, Lead isotope studies of stratiform ore deposits of the Namaqualand, NW Cape Province, South Africa, and their implications on the age of the Bushmanland Sequence: Proceedings of Fifth IAGOD Symposium, Stuttgart, E., Schweizerbart'sche Verlagsbuchhandlung, p. 195–207.

Laing, W. P., Marjoribanks, R. W., and Rutland, R.W.R., 1978, Structure of the Broken Hill Mine area and its significance for the genesis of the ore bodies: Economic Geology, v. 73, p. 1112–1136.

Lambert, I. B., 1973, Post-depositional availability of sulphur and metals, and formation of secondary textures and structures in stratiform sedimentary sulphide deposits: Geological Society of Australia Journal, v. 20, p. 205–215.

——1976, The McArthur zinc-lead-silver deposit: Features, metallogenesis and comparisons with some other stratiform ores, *in* Wolf, K. H., ed., Handbook of stratabound and stratiform ore deposits: Amsterdam, Elsevier, v. 6, p. 535–585.

——1981, Constraints on the genesis of Australian lead-zinc-silver deposits: from Ramdohr to recent, *in* Kluth, C., Zimmermann, R. A., and Amstutz, G. C., eds., Ore genesis, 1980, p. 625–636.

Lambert, I. B., and Groves, D. I., 1981, Early earth evolution and metallogeny, *in* Wolf, K. H., ed., Handbook of stratabound and stratiform ore deposits, Volume 8: Amsterdam, Elsevier, p. 339–447.

Lambert, I. B., and Scott, K. M., 1973, Implications of geochemical investigations of sedimentary rocks within and around the McArthur zinc-lead-silver deposit, Northern Territory: Journal of Geochemical Exploration, v. 2, p. 307–330.

Lambert, I. B., Donnelly, T. H., Dunlop, J.S.R., and Groves, D. I., 1978, Stable isotopic compositions of early Archaean sulphate deposits of probably evaporitic and volcanogenic origins: Nature, v. 276, p. 808–811.

Large, D., 1980, Geological parameters associated with sediment-hosted, submarine exhalative Pb-Zn deposits: An empirical model for mineral exploration: Geologisches Jahrbuch, v. D40, p. 59–129.

LeCouteur, P. C., 1973, A study of lead isotopes from mineral deposits in southeastern British Columbia and in the Anvil Range, Yukon Territory [Ph.D. thesis]: University of British Columbia, Vancouver, 142 p.

Leech, G. B., and Wanless, R. K., 1962, Lead isotope and potassium-argon studies in the East Kootenay district of British Columbis, *in* Engel, A.E.J., James, H. L., and Leonard, B. F., eds., Petrologic studies [Buddington volume]: Geological Society of America, p. 241–79.

Lewis, B. R., Forward, P. S., and Roberts, J. B., 1965, Geology of the Broken Hill lode, reinterpreted, *in* McAndrew, J., ed., Geology of Austrlian ore deposits, Volume 1: Melbourne, Australasian Institute of Mining and Metallurgy, p. 319–332.

Logan, R. G., and Dennis, R. W., 1981, Pb-Cu-Ag mineralisation in the H.Y.C. deposit, McArthur River, Northern Territory: Fifth Australian Geological Convention, Perth, Abstract Volume, p. 8–9.

Mathias, B. V., and Clark, G. J., 1975, Mount Isa copper and silver-lead-zinc orebodies—Isa and Hilton mines, *in* Knight, C. L., ed., Economic Geology of Australia, Volume 1: Melbourne, Australasian Institute of Mining and Metallurgy, p. 351–376.

Mathias, B. V., Clark, G. J., Morris, D., and Russell, R. E., 1973, The Hilton deposit—stratiform silver-lead-zinc mineralisation of the Mount Isa type, *in* Fisher, N. H., ed., Metallogenic provinces and mineral deposits in the southwest Pacific: Bureau of Mineral Resources, Australia, Bulletin 141, p. 33–58.

McClay, K. R., and Carlile, D. G., 1978, Mid-Proterozoic sulphate evaporites at Mount Isa mine, Queensland, Australia: Nature, v. 274, p. 240–241.

Murray, W. J., 1975, McArthur River H.Y.C. lead-zinc and related deposits, *in* Knight, C. L., ed., Economic geology of Australia and Papua New Guinea, Volume 1: Melbourne, Australasian Institute of Mining and Metallurgy, p. 329–339.

Neudert, M. K., and Russell, R. E., 1981, Shallow water and hypersaline evaporites from the Middle Proterozoic Mount Isa sequence, Queensland, Australia: Nature, v. 293, p. 284–286.

Oehler, J. H., and Logan, R. G., 1977, Microfossils, cherts and associated mineralization in the Proterozoic McArthur (H.Y.C.) lead-zinc-silver deposit: Economic Geology, v. 72, p. 1393–1409.

Page, R. W., 1981, Depositional ages of the stratiform base metal deposits at Mount Isa and McArthur River, Australia, based on U-Pb zircon dating of concordant tuff horizons: Economic Geology, v. 76, p. 648–658.

Plimer, I. R., 1979, Sulphide rock zonation and hydrothermal alteration at Broken Hill, Australia: Transactions of Institute of Mining and Metallurgy, Section B, v. 88, p. B161–B176.

Plimer, I. R., and Finlow-Bates, T., 1978, Relationship between primary iron sulphide species, sulphur source, depth of formation and age of submarine exhalative deposits: Mineralium Deposita, v. 13, p. 399–410.

Plumb, K. A., and Derrick, G. M., 1975, Geology of the Proterozoic rocks of the Kimberley to Mount Isa region, *in* Knight, C. L., ed., Economic geology of Australia and Papua New Guinea, Volume 1: Melbourne, Australian Institute of Mining and Metallurgy, p. 217–252.

Plumb, K. A., Derrick, G. M., and Wilson, I. H., 1980, Precambrian geology of the McArthur-Mount Isa region, northern Australia, *in* Stephenson, P. J., and Henderson, R. A., eds., Geology and geophysics of Northeastern Australia: Brisbane Geological Society of Australia, Queensland Division, p. 71–88.

Reynolds, D. G., Brook, W. A., Marshall, A. E., and Allchurch, P. D., 1975, Volcanogenic copper-zinc deposits in the Pilbara and Yilgarn Archaean Blocks, *in* Knight, C. L., ed., Economic geology of Austra-

lia and Papua New Guinea, Volume 1: Melbourne, Australasian Institute of Mining and Metallurgy, p. 185–194.
Richards, J. R., 1975, Lead isotope data on three north Australian galena localities: Mineralium Deposita, v. 10, p. 287–301.
Rozendaal, A., 1975, The Gamsberg zinc deposit, Namaqualand, *in* Verwoerd, W. J., ed., Mineralization in metamorphic terranes: Geological Society of South Africa, Special Publication 4, p. 235–264.
—— 1980, The Gamsberg zinc deposit, South Africa: A banded stratiform base-metal sulfide ore deposit: Proceedings of Fifth IAGOD Symposium, Stuttgart, E., Schweizerbart'sche Verlagsbuchandlung, p. 619–633.
Rutland, R.W.R., and Both, R. A., 1983, Major stratiform base metal deposits of the Australian Proterozoic: Contribution to United Nations Inter-regional Seminar on Development Potential of Precambrian Mineral Deposits, Moscow (1979) (in press).
Rye, D. M., and Williams, N., 1978, Stable isotope geochemistry of the McArthur River ore deposits: An epigenetic sedimentary type Pb-Zn deposit [abs.]: Society of Economic Geologists, fall meeting, Toronto, 1978, Economic Geology, v. 73, p. 1397.
—— 1981, Studies of the base metal sulfide deposits at McArthur River, Northern Territory, Australia: III. The stable isotope geochemistry of the H.Y.C., Ridge and Cooley deposits: Economic Geology, v. 76, p. 1–26.
Sangster, D. F., and Brook, W. A., 1977, Primitive lead in an Australian Zn-Pb-Ba deposit: Nature, v. 270, p. 423.
Smith, J. W., and Croxford, N.J.W., 1973, Sulphur-isotope ratios in the McArthur lead-zinc-silver deposit: Nature Physical Sciences, v. 245, p. 10–12.
Smith, J. W., and Croxford, N.J.W., 1975, An isotopic investigation of the environment of deposition of the McArthur mineralisation: Mineralium Deposit, v. 10, p. 269–276.
Smith, J. W., Burns, M. S., and Croxford, N.J.W., 1978, Stable isotope studies of the origins of mineralisation at Mount Isa: Mineralium Deposita, v. 13, p. 369–381.
Smith, W. D., 1969, Penecontemporaneous faulting and its likely significance in relation to Mount Isa ore deposition: Geological Society of Australia, Special Publication 2, p. 225–235.
Solomon, P. J., 1965, Investigation into sulphide mineralisation at Mount Isa, Queensland: Economic Geology, v. 60, p. 737–765.
Spry, P. G., and Both, R. A., 1980, The origin of garnet-rich rocks associated with the Broken Hill orebody: Fourth Australian Geological Convention, Programmes and Abstracts, p. 47.
Stanton, R. L., 1963, Constitutional features of the Mount Isa sulphide ores and their interpretation: Proceedings Australian Institute of Mining and Metallurgy, v. 205, p. 131–153.
—— 1972, Ore petrology: New York, McGraw-Hill, 713 p.
—— 1976a, Petrological studies of the ore environment at Broken Hill, New South Wales: 3—Banded ore formations and sulphide orebodies: Constitutional and genetic ties: Transactions of Institute of Mining and Metallurgy, Section B., v. 85, p. B132–B141.
—— 1976b, Petrochemical studies of the ore environment at Broken Hill, New South Wales: 4—Environmental synthesis: Transactions of Institute of Mining and Metallurgy, Section B, v. 85, p. B221–B233.
Stanton, R. L., and Rafter, T. A., 1966, The isotopic composition of sulphur in some stratiform lead-zinc ores: Mineralium Deposita, v. 1, p. 16–29.
Stevens, B.P.J., editor, 1980, A guide to the stratigraphy and mineralisation of the Broken Hill Block, New South Wales, v. 20, part 1, 153 p.
Trudinger, P. A., 1981, Origin of sulfide in sediments: Bureau of Mineral Resources Journal of Geology and Geophysics, v. 6, p. 279–285.
Van den Huevel, H. B., 1969, Sedimentation, stratigraphy and post-depositional changes in the sediments of the upper formations of the Mount Isa Group, northwest Queensland [Ph.D. thesis]: University of Queensland, 217 p.
Walker, R. N., Logan, R. G., and Binnekamp, J. G., 1977, Recent geological advances concerning the H.Y.C. and associated deposits, McArthur River, N. T.: Geological Society of Australia Journal, v. 24, p. 365–380.
Williams, N., 1978a, Studies of base metal sulfide deposits at McArthur River, Northern Territory, Australia: I. The Cooley and Ridge deposits: Economic Geology, v. 73, p. 1005–1035.
—— 1978b, Studies of base metal sulfide deposits at McArthur River, Northern Territory, Australia: II. The sulfide-S and organic-C relationships of the concordant deposits and their significance: Economic Geology, v. 73, p. 1036–1056.
—— 1979a, The timing and mechanisms of formation of the Proterozoic stratiform Pb-Zn and related Mississippi Valley–type deposits at McArthur River, N. T., Australia: Society of Economic Geologists–American Institute of Mining Engineers, Joint Meeting, New Orleans, Preprint 79–51, 15 p.
—— 1979b, Reply *to* comment *on* 'Studies of the base metal sulfide deposits at McArthur River, Northern Territory, Australia, II. The sulfide-S and organic-C relationships of the concordant deposits and their significance: Economic Geology, v. 74, p. 1695–1697.
—— 1980, Precambrian mineralization in the McArthur-Cloncurry region, with special reference to stratiform lead-zinc deposits, *in* Stephenson, P. J., and Henderson, R. A., eds., Geology and geophysics of Northeastern Australia: Geological Society of Australia, Queensland Division, p. 89–107.
Williams, N., and Rye, D. M., 1974, Alternative interpretation of sulfur isotope ratios in the McArthur lead-zinc-silver deposit: Nature v. 247, p. 535–537.
Windley, B. F., 1977, The evolving continents: London, Wiley, 385 p.

Manuscript Accepted by the Society April 14, 1983

Printed in U.S.A.

Geological Society of America
Memoir 161
1983

Constraints on genetic modeling of Proterozoic iron formations

Michael M. Kimberley
Department of Marine, Earth, and Atmospheric Sciences
North Carolina State University
Raleigh, North Carolina 27650

ABSTRACT

The wide variety of genetic models for Proterozoic iron formations indicates a lack of agreement about constraints on models. Constraints are reviewed in this paper to help focus the evidence for modeling. Useful constraints are found in modern processes of iron concentration and in variation among iron formations through earth history, as well as in characteristics of Proterozoic iron formations.

INTRODUCTION

Iron formations are considered to be mappable rock bodies dominantly composed of ironstone, chemical sedimentary rock that contains over 15 percent Fe. Two environments have produced most ironstone. Fully marine environments have produced cherty ironstone whereas clastic-dominated, inland-sea environments have generated chert-poor ironstone (Kimberley, 1978, 1979b). Fully marine environments include continental-shelf, volcanic-platform, and deep-water environments. These three are not differentiable in all cases (Gole and Klein, 1981), but general trends are apparent; e.g., individual beds of cherty ironstone typically accumulate to greater thicknesses on shallow shelves than in deep water (Shegelski, 1978; Larue, 1981). Clastic-dominated, inland-sea environments include both landlocked seas and shallow extensions of the ocean into continental interiors. Oolitic texture is characteristic of chert-poor, inland-sea iron formations and also occurs in shallow-water facies of cherty iron formations. Chert-rich, fully marine and chert-poor, inland-sea iron formations have formed contemporaneously since at least the Early Proterozoic and have maintained both their textural similarities and compositional differences throughout this time span (Kimberley, 1978, 1979b).

Highly voluminous iron formations are cherty and mostly formed on Proterozoic continental shelves and nonvolcanic platforms like the modern Bahaman platforms (Kimberley, 1978). These iron formations may extend over 1100 km and display an aggregate thickness of over 1 km. The prime constraint on the origin of voluminous iron formations is that iron is highly insoluble in both oxidizing and reducing, sulfide-rich seawater. Moreover, the high degree of segregation of Fe, Mn, and Si from other elements is unexpected because the geochemical behavior of Si does not resemble that of Fe or Mn, whereas some depleted elements behave more like Fe and Mn. Several models have been presented to resolve these problems. The prime candidates for the sources of dissolved iron and silica to form voluminous cherty iron formations are (1) mixed volcanogenic-seawater solutions (Mel'nik and others, 1973; Gross, 1980); (2) river water and/or groundwater draining a weathered continent laterally into a shallow sea (Lepp and Goldich, 1964; Button, 1976); (3) lake water in a lake affected by annual climatic variation (Govett, 1966; Eugster and Chou, 1973); and (4) seawater upwelling from an anoxic zone of submarine weathering (Holland, 1973; Drever 1974). The prime candidates for the source of chert-poor, inland-sea iron formations, including Proterozoic examples, are (1) dissolved iron in river water entering the sea; (2) fluvial colloidal suspension; (3) ferric oxides and hydroxides adsorbed on fluvial clays; and (4) upwelling marine water (Table 1 in Kimberley, 1979a).

The extent of variation among genetic models for iron formations indicates either a lack of constraints on models or a lack of application of constraints. Typically, constraints have been discussed in the context of a favored model, and thus an uneven view of constraints has been presented, e.g., Kimberley (1979a). The present paper examines constraints for their own sake without marshalling them in support of any particular model. Five types of constraints are discussed, i.e., cyclicity within specific iron formations, stratigraphic relationships, ironstone lithology, changes in iron formations through earth history, and modern concentrations of iron.

EXAMPLES OF IRON FORMATIONS: THE GUNFLINT

The Gunflint iron formation crops out along the northwestern shore of Lake Superior and is one of the best preserved and most thoroughly studied Proterozoic iron formations. The basal transgressive unit of the Gunflint is an algal biostrome with intercolumnar ooids. Microbiota are excellently preserved locally in this unit and have been well documented (e.g., Awramik and Barghoorn, 1977). The algal biostrome resembles silicified calcareous sediment mmorphologically. Debate continues over the issues of primary versus diagenetic silicification and of ooid cracking by subaerial desiccation versus submarine syneresis (Markun and Randazzo, 1980). Nonetheless, most investigators interpret the algal unit to represent a high-energy, shallow-water facies of ferriferous silica sedimentation.

The basal algal biostrome averages about 0.6 m in thickness and is overlain by tuffaceous, carbonaceous shale that ranges up to 6 m in thickness (Goodwin, 1956). Overlying the tuffaceous shale is a unit of cherty banded ironstone up to 45 m thick. Water depth apparently increased between the time of initial transgressive sedimentation and the time of ironstone sedimentation. The ironstone occurs in beds of 5 to 15 cm in thickness, separated by 2 to 5 cm of shale. Greenalite, hematite, magnetite, and siderite occur intermixed in the ironstone. Superimposed on this ironstone-shale cyclicity is an increase in brecciation and diagenetic oxidation toward the top of the unit, apparently due to a decrease in water depth (Goodwin, 1956). The diagenetic oxidation associated with this increased influence of the atmosphere indicates that the Proterozoic atmosphere was more oxidizing than the seawater that transported dissolved iron.

A key feature of the Gunflint iron formation is that it repeated the foregoing stratigraphic sequence of algal chert, tuffaceous shale, and then ironstone. The second unit of algal chert transgressed over partially oxidized banded ironstone and accumulated initially as algal stromatolite, granule-bearing chert, and chert breccia before grading up to lensoidal chert through a total thickness of 15 to 26 m (Goodwin, 1956). The overlying tuffaceous shale in this second sequence extends more than 160 km parallel to the northwestern shore of Lake Superior and averages 12 m in thickness. Characteristic features include pyrite nodules, calcareous concretions, and tuff beds with accretionary lapilli. The carbon content is generally high, and veins contain an asphaltite, anthraxolite. The overlying banded ironstone unit contains abundant ellipsoidal grains that traditionally have been called granules but which are mostly sand-sized. Granules in the Gunflint iron formation range widely in shape. They are either intraclasts that have been altered diagenetically, or else they formed entirely by diagenetic chemical segregation. Oxidation increased upward through the upper banded ironstone unit as through the lower banded unit, and overlying the second cyclothem is a few metres of slightly ferriferous limestone that contains pyroclastic fragments and calcareous ooids (Kimberley, 1979a, Fig. 3E). This grades upward to the Rove Formation which consists of up to 980 m of argillite and sandstone (Morey, 1967).

Repetition of the algal chert-shale-ironstone sequence offers a major constraint on modeling the Gunflint iron formation because it indicates that ironstone sedimentation was controlled by some type of cyclicity that also affected relative sealevel. One of several possibilities would be an interrelated increase in marine volcanism, sealevel rise, and increase in iron-silica supply by seafloor alteration.

A key petrographic constraint in modeling the Gunflint iron formation is the occurrence of ferrous iron silicates in the thinnest oolitic layers, hence the conclusion that ferrous minerals were among the initial precipitates (Floran and Papike, 1975). These minerals were clearly out of equilibrium with the contemporaneous atmosphere, given other evidence of early diagenetic oxidation (Goodwin, 1956), and yet are found in the shallow-water, high-energy oolitic facies. Ferrous silicates are also abundant in ooids of Phanerozoic inland-sea iron formations, including several Tertiary examples (Kimberley 1979a, 1980). In both environments, oolitic layers have been added only onto an exterior surface, including exterior surfaces of broken ooids. There is no evidence of oolitic layering having developed secondarily within previously formed ooids, as occurs in bauxite spherules and other "oolitic" spherules formed during subaerial weathering. Nahon and others (1980) have recently argued for a weathering origin of ironstone ooids but do not illustrate any secondary development of concentric layering within and cross-cutting primary layering in ironstone ooids. Gygi (1981) has suggested that layers of ferrous silicates form during intermittent burial of ooids and that these layers are only surficially oxidized during subsequent exposure to oxygenated seawater.

The Sokoman Iron Formation

The Proterozoic Sokoman iron formation is one of the most extensive in the world, with a strike length in excess of 1100 km north-south through eastern Quebec and Labrador, Canada (Gross, 1968). The underlying Ruth Slate grades upward to the Sokoman through an interbedded sequence of carbonaceous mudrock and cherty ironstone. Thickness of the Sokoman is typically less than 300 m and the overlying Menihek Slate is also carbonaceous. Gross (1968, p. 33) suggests that "much of the fine clastic material may have originated as tuff."

The Sokoman resembles the Gunflint in its wide variety of high-energy (oolitic, intraclastic) and low-energy (thinly laminated) facies and similar transgressive-regressive cycles (Dimroth, 1976; Dimroth and Chauvel, 1972). The majority of other Proterozoic iron formations are not as texturally diverse as the Sokoman and Gunflint. The Sokoman is typical of most Proterozoic iron formations in being richer in iron oxides than the greenalite-rich Gunflint iron formation. The mineralogy of these and other Proterozoic iron formations is reviewed in Table 1.

The Hamersley and Frere Iron Formations

Stratigraphic relationships are listed in Table 1 for the three iron formations in the Hamersley Basin of Western Australia. These iron formations display great continuity in laminae of both ironstone and associated carbonaceous shale over an area of 25,000 km^2. This continuity constrains genetic models to processes capable of widespread uniform dissemination, e.g., aeolian supply of volcanic ash that weathered to carbonaceous shale and evaporite-varving or storm-layering of chemical sediment. The ironstone displays regular cyclicity in sedimentary structures and in proportion of iron minerals over stratigraphic thicknesses of 5 to 20 cm; total thickness of ironstone exceeds 1 km (Trendall and Blockley, 1970). Stilpnomelane-rich laminae tend to cap Hamersley cyclothems; this stilpnomelane may be weathered ash (Trendall and Blockley, 1970, p. 59, p. 290). Facies variation and high-energy sedimentary structures are minimal in the Hamersley compared to the Gunflint and Sokoman iron formations; no oolitic texture has been found. The Gunflint and Sokoman are younger than the Hamersley and this conforms to a global trend toward more high-energy structures in ironstone from the Archean to the Tertiary (Kimberley, 1978).

Trendall (1973) notes that regular cyclicity of the Hamersley cyclothems constrains models to explain the periodicity, e.g., through astronomical control on climate. Climate could have affected polar ice caps and eustatic sealevel change. Periodicity of this sealevel change would have been on the order of tens of thousands of years if due to Milankovitch variation in solar radiation (Weertman, 1976). Microbanding cyclicity would not have been as uniformly periodic, however, if due to storm-layering, as in modern carbonate sediment on the Andros platform (Hardie and Ginsburg, 1977).

The Hamersley iron formations have been correlated with the shallow-water Frere iron formation to the south (Hall and Goode, 1978). The Frere and associated units display algal stromatolite and oolitic-peloidal texture in ironstone, chert, limestone, dolostone, and rocks gradational among these end members (Hall and Goode, 1978). By contrast, evidence for shallow-water brecciation is rare in the Hamersley (Trendall and Blockley, 1970, p. 168). The Frere grades upward through peloidal chert, banded calcareous chert, banded marble, oolitic chert, and vadose pisoliths to chamositic ironstone. The chamositic ironstone is also peloidal and resembles typical inland-sea ironstone with a high content of Al, P, Cu, and Zn (Hall and Goode, 1978). Some other Lower Proterozoic cherty iron formations are similarly overlain by inland-sea iron formations (Kimberley, 1978).

STRATIGRAPHIC AND FACIES CONSTRAINTS

Facies relationships are now well known for several Proterozoic iron formations. Most sedimentation occurred on extensive platforms with sufficiently deep or well-protected environments that finely laminated ironstone could accumulate. Some platforms extended to shallow areas characterized by luxuriant algal growth and oolite sedimentation (Button, 1976). The textures, sedimentary structures, and facies relationships of voluminous Proterozoic iron formations are sufficiently similar to those of carbonate platforms that analogous environments may be assumed as a first approximation (Dimroth, 1976).

The key stratigraphic relationship of Proterozoic iron formations is gradation to other rock types. Where apparent, most gradations are to some type of carbonaceous mudrock or to dolostone. For example, the Malmani Dolomite under the Penge iron formation of South Africa cyclically increased in iron content prior to ironstone sedimentation (Button, 1976). The primary sediment in the Malmani Dolomite was calcareous, as revealed by remnant limestone (Button, 1976). Iron-poor dolostone displays abundant oolitic-intraclastic-algal structures indicative of a high-energy environment. In the transition to ironstone, there is cross-cutting silicification of dolostone, an increase in argillaceous sediment, and a decrease in high-energy structures. Button (1976) concluded that ironstone sedimentation occurred when a barrier of carbonate sediment restricted seawater from a continental shelf and the shelf became evaporitic. Burton (1976) hypothesized both ferruginization of calcareous sediment and direct precipitation of ironstone by the concentrated seawater.

The carbonaceous nature of shale associated with Proterozoic iron formations also is characteristic of shale associated with iron formations of other ages and constrains genetic models to explain the proliferation of microorganisms near iron-silica precipitation (Goodwin and others, 1976). For example, Moore (1977) reported that argillite interbedded with the Outerring iron formation on an Archean volcanic platform averages 5 percent C_{org}, whereas argillite that accumulated contemporaneously in deeper water off the volcanic platform contains only 0.2

TABLE 1: STRATIGRAPHY AND MINERALOGY OF PROTEROZOIC IRON FORMATIONS

IRON FORMATION NAME	LOCATION	THICKNESS IN METERS	ROCKS BELOW,ABOVE	MINERALOGY
Uda	USSR	300	Chert, Chert	Cht: Hm,Mg/Sd,Ch,Go,Py
Rapitan	Canada	150	Mixtite, Mixtite	Cht: Hm
Hsuanhua	China	6.2	Sandstone, Slate	Cht: Hm
Lower Hakos-Damara	S. Africa	16	Schist, Schist	Cht: Hm,Ma,Mg
Roper River	Australia	51	Shale, Shale	Qtz: Hm,Sd,Mg/Ch,Gn,Py
Constance Range	Australia	21	Shale, Shale	Qtz: Hm,Sd,Ch/Py
Der Geijer-Kiruna	Sweden	250	Keratophyre, Sandst	Apa: Mg,Hm/Ma
Kiirunavaara-Kiruna	Sweden	75	Conglom, Keratophyre	Apa: Mg,Hm/Am,Bi
Serra dos Carajas	Brazil	7200	Phyllite, Phyllite	Cht: Mg,Ma/Hm,Sd
Caue	Brazil	300	Phyllite, Dolostone	Cht: Hm/Mg,Ma,Cl,Am
Broken Hill	Australia	0.9	Chert, Chert	Cht: Mg,Ga/Bi,Hm,Il,Py
Zhuantobe	USSR	50	Porphyry, Slate	Cht: Hm/Mg,Ma,St
Okouma + Bafoula	Gabon	10	Mudrock, Mudrock	Cht: Sd,Gn,Py/Cl,St
Sokoman	Canada	244	Slate, Slate	Cht: Hm,Mg,Mn,Sd/Ma,St,Gn
Temiscamie	Canada	160	Mudrock, Graywacke	Cht: Sd,An,Mg,St/Hm,Mn,Py
Gunflint	Canada	165	Conglom, Limestone	Cht: Gn,Hm,Sd/Mg,Py
Biwabik	USA	230	Conglom, Limestone	Cht: Mn,Gn,St,Mg,Sd,Hm/Py
Trommold	USA	153	Mudrock, Mudrock	Cht: Sd,Mn,St,Hm/Mg,Cl,Gr
Mansfield	USA	46	Slate, Slate	Cht: Mg,St,Sd,Gr
Vulcan	USA	198	Schist, Unconform	Cht: Mg,Ma,Hm/Gr,Ga,An
Ironwood	USA	274	Quartzite, Slate	Cht: Sd,Mg,Hm,Mn,St/Cl,Py
Iron River	USA	91	Slate, Graywacke	Cht: Sd/Cl,Py
Negaunee	USA	1067	Graywacke, Conglom	Cht: Sd,Mg,Hm,Ma/Mn,St,Cl
Goose Lake	USA	30	Slate, Slate	Cht: Sd,Mg,Cl,St
Daspoort	S. Africa	2.4	Shale, Mudrock	Qtz: Hm,Mg,Go,Ch/An,Py
Clayband-Timeball	S. Africa	1.2	Shale, Shale	Apa: Mg,Ch,Sd
Pisolitic-Timeball	S. Africa	1.8	Shale, Sandstone	Qtz: Hm,Go,Ch,An
Magnetic-Timeball	S. Africa	8.2	Shale, Shale	Qtz: Mg,Go,Hm,Ch
Kuruman + Penge	S. Africa	700	Limestone, Jasper	Cht: Mg,Sd,Mn,Gr/Hm,Re,St
Hotazel	S. Africa	85	Andesite, Unconform	Cht: Ma,Mg,Hm
Boolgeeda-Hamersley	Australia	213	Tuff, Shale	Cht: Hm,Mg,Sd,An/St,Re,Py
Brockman-Hamersley	Australia	610	Shale, Shale	Cht: Hm,Mg,Sd,An/Gn,St,Py
Marra Mamba-Hamersley	Australia	183	Shale, Dolostone	Cht: Hm,Mg,Sd,An/St,Re,Py
Kipalu	Canada	125	Quartzite, Slate	Cht: Hm,Mg,Gn,Sd
Kursk	USSR	477	Slate, Slate	Cht: Mg,Hm,Fs/Sd,Py
Krivoy Rog	USSR	2000	Volcanics, Schist	Cht: Ma,Hm,Mg,Sd/Cl,Am,St
Bihar + Orissa	India	1000	Phyllite, Phyllite	Cht: Hm,Ma/Mg,Sd
Nimba	Liberia	450	Phyllite, Phyllite	Cht: Mg,Ma,Hm/Am,Sd,Py,Cl
Anshan	China	250	Quartzite, Slate	Cht: Mg,Hm/Gr,Cu,Cl,Sd
Contorted Bed	S. Africa	22	Chert, Mudrock	Cht: Mg,Ma
Subganian	USSR	200	Gneiss, Gneiss	Cht: Mg/Am,Ma,Ga,Bi
Belinga	Gabon	200	Schist, Schist	Cht: Ma,Hm/Mg,Am
West Melville	Canada	400	Schist, Schist	Cht: Mg,Hm/Am,Cl,Bi,Po,Py
Main-Atlantic City	USA	49	Schist, Schist	Cht: Mg,Am/Bi,Cl,Hy,Ga

Note: A "+" sign connects names of correlative iron formations. The latitude and longitude at which the given thickness was measured is listed in NAPS document 3161, available from Microfiche Pubs., P.O. Box 3513, Grand Central Station, New York, NY 10017. If the rocks above an iron formation overlie it unconformably, these are labeled "Unconform." The last column lists the prime nonferriferous mineral, i.e. chert (Cht), detrital quartz (Qtz), or apatite (Apa), followed by the iron-rich minerals in approximate order of decreasing abundance. Minerals to the right of a slash, /, are distinctly subordinate. The abbreviations are Am=undifferentiated ferriferous amphiboles, An=ankerite, Bi=biotite, Ch=chamosite, Cl=iron-rich chlorite, Cr=crocidolite, Cu=cummingtonite, Fs=undifferentiated ferriferous silicates, Ga=iron-rich garnet, Gn=greenalite, Go=goethite, Gr-grunerite, Hb=iron-rich hornblende, Hm=hematite, Hy=hypersthene, Il=ilmenite, Ma-martite, Mg=magnetite, Mn=minnesotaite, Po=pyrrhotite, Py=pyrite, Re=riebeckite, Sd=siderite, and St=stilpnomelane.

percent C_{org}. This organic carbon could simply represent thermophytic bacteria near a former vent and provide no evidence about water depth during sedimentation. However, intraclastic and oolitic textures provide independent evidence for shallow-water sedimentation of the Outerring iron formation (Lambert, 1978; Kimberley 1978, 1979a, Fig. 3F).

LITHOLOGIC AND COMPOSITIONAL CONSTRAINTS: BANDING

Fine lamination (microbanding) in cherty ironstone has been interpreted to indicate seasonal sedimentation below wave base (e.g., Trendall and Blockley, 1970). However, Hardie and Ginsburg (1977, p. 111) have shown that algal binding is producing a similar effect in extremely shallow-water carbonate sediment on the Bahaman Andros platform. Algal laminae extend several tens of kilometres on Andros and are not cracked by desiccation. Evidence for some mud cracking in the Hamersley iron formations may be found in intraclastic interbeds of microlaminated ironstone (Trendall and Blockley, 1970, p. 168). Prior to metazoans, algal binding in the Proterozoic would have been far more widespread than it is presently.

Isotopic Ratios

Carbon isotopic ratios in Proterozoic cherty ironstone consistently record organic concentration of ^{12}C in carbonate minerals whereas contemporaneous limestone and dolostone display no such concentration (Becker and Clayton, 1972; Perry and others, 1973; Perry and Tan, 1973). Phanerozoic chert-poor ironstone displays a similar concentration of ^{12}C in siderite (Hangari and others, 1980). These values constrain genetic models to include organic processes; e.g., values of $\delta\ ^{13}C$ in the range of -10 to -15 $^{0}/_{00}$ may record a sequence of microbial oxidation and sulfate reduction (-25 to -28 $^{0}/_{00}$) followed by microbial fermentation (+10 to +15 $^{0}/_{00}$) (Coleman and Raiswell, 1981). Carbonaceous matter is locally preserved in Proterozoic ironstone and $\delta\ ^{13}C$ values vary with sedimentary facies (Barghoorn and others, 1977).

Oxygen-isotope ratios in Proterozoic iron formations are difficult to interpret sedimentologically because of partial exchange among various minerals during burial metamorphism (Becker and Clayton, 1976; Perry and others, 1973). Moreover, the isotopic ratio of oxygen in marine precipitates has changed with time, either due to variation of the ratio in seawater (Perry and Tan, 1973), or to variation in oceanic temperature (Knauth and Epstein, 1976). To identify ^{16}O-rich nonmarine water in cherty ironstone, it would be necessary to compare $\delta\ ^{18}O$ in ironstone to $\delta\ ^{18}O$ in contemporaneous marine precipitates. In Western Australia, both the Wittenoom Dolomite and the Hamersley iron formations have similar values of $\delta\ ^{18}O$. Both may have precipitated from warm seawater. However, an upper Devonian inland-sea iron formation in Libya displays enrichment in ^{16}O that is safely attributable to nonmarine precipitation rather than an oceanic paleotemperature of 50° C (Hangari and others, 1980).

A few initial ratios of $^{87}Sr/^{86}Sr$ greater than 0.715 have been reported for the Hamersley iron formations and have been interpreted to indicate a concentration of radiogenic ^{87}Sr that is incompatible with precipitation from normal seawater or from seawater that had reacted with seafloor basalt (Vander Wood, 1977). More strontium isotopic work is needed to verify this unexpected observation.

Elemental Abundances

The consistent purity of Proterozoic cherty ironstone is unlike the metal enrichment of most modern hydrothermal precipitates. Virtually the only elements concentrated in ironstone above crustal-average values are Fe (x7) and Mn (x4); Si, Ca, and Mg are typically over half crustal abundance (Gross and McLeod, 1980). Carbonate content varies considerably; total carbon commonly is far greater than the crustal average. Elements depleted with respect to the crustal average include Na, K, Sr, Ba, Al, Ti, V, Cr, Co, Ni, and Cu (Fryer, 1977; Gross and McLeod, 1980). Sodium is the most depleted of these elements whereas the alkaline-lake genetic model of Eugster and Chou (1973) would predict some enrichment. Significant enrichment in trace metals occurs only in oxidized ironstone (Fryer, 1977).

Cherty ironstone is slightly enriched in heavy rare-earth elements (REE) relative to light REE, compared to average shale (Fryer, 1977). This may reflect the greater mobility of heavy REE as carbonate complexes during silicate weathering (Guichard and others, 1979). Modern seawater is similarly enriched in heavy REE, compared with average shale (Elderfield and Greaves, 1982).

EVOLUTION OF IRON FORMATIONS THROUGH EARTH HISTORY

Some genetic models are constrained by the concept that the period between about 2100 and 2000 m. yr. B.P. was a unique time in the evolution of iron formations (Cloud, 1973). Other models emphasize continuity of cherty ironstone sedimentation through the Archean and Early Proterozoic to about 1800 m. yr. B.P. (Gole and Klein, 1981) whereas others trace patterns from the Archean through the Phanerozoic (Kimberley, 1978). One long-term trend is illustrated in Figure 1, i.e., the consistent increase in relative abundance of chert-poor iron formations from the Archean to the Tertiary. The concurrence of Proterozoic iron formations with this trend supports the

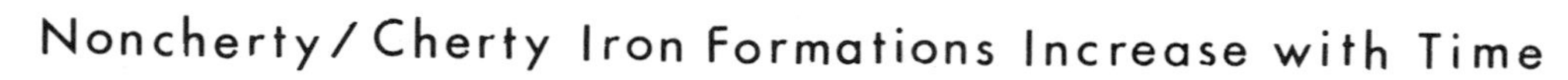

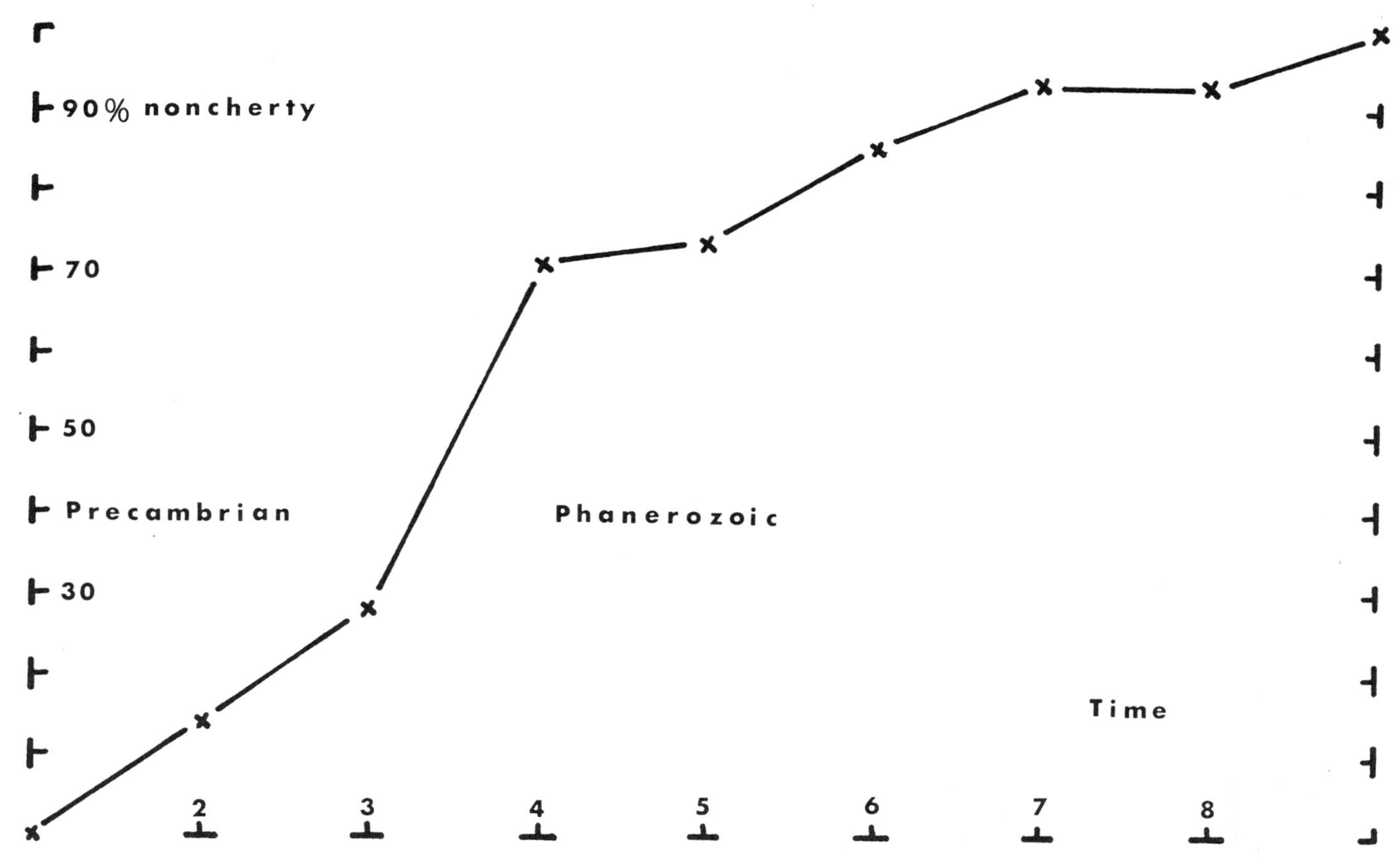

Figure 1. Proportion of noncherty/cherty iron formations as a function of earth history. Noncherty deposits contain less than about 5% chert. The time divisions are 1 = Precambrian W, 2 = Precambrian X, 3 = Precambrian Y+Z, 4 = Cambrian + Ordovician, 5 = Silurian + Devonian, 6 = Mississippian + Pennsylvanian + Permian, 7 = Triassic + Jurassic, 8 = Cretaceous, and 9 = Tertiary. The percentage of noncherty deposits at any given time has been calculated from the number of noncherty and cherty deposits listed in Table 2 of Kimberley (1978). Kimberley (1978) lists 155 deposits altogether. Where the age of a deposit is uncertain, the middle of the possible range, or slightly older age, has been chosen. Noncherty deposits are all of these classified by Kimberley (1978) as SCOS, COSP, and SOPS types. Many of these contain 1% to 5% chert. Cherty deposits are all those classified as MECS, SVOP, and DWAT types, except for one DWAT deposit which contains only a small proportion of chert, i.e., the Cretaceous Mackenzie Delta deposit.

concept that genetic models for Proterozoic iron formations should be constrained by genetic models for older and younger iron formations. In particular, a few Proterozoic iron formations are very similar to chert-poor, inland-sea iron formations as young as 5 m. yr. old, and the better constraints on genetic modeling for such young deposits may offer insight into Proterozoic processes.

MODERN CONCENTRATION OF IRON

As noted by James (1966, p. 1), "The origin of the iron-rich sedimentary rocks remains a matter of speculation, as no modern-day examples exist." Much has been learned about marine iron concentrations in the past 15 years and some examples partially resemble Proterozoic cherty ironstone, e.g., slabs and pavements up to 10 cm thick in the Gulf of Bothnia between Finland and Sweden (Winterhalter, 1966). Unlike marine manganese nodules, these laminar accumulations have ratios of Fe/Mn greater than 10 and low trace-element contents; iron exceeds 25 percent Fe_2O_3. Iron pavements are abundant over an area 200 km by 300 km. Mobility of iron has been substantial in this partially barred gulf because Pleistocene fluctuation of sealevel transformed it into an organic-rich, sulfate-poor lake. Water lacking oxygen and sulfur would have dissolved abundant iron during the Pleistocene. Subsequent oxidation of aqueous iron to ferric hydroxide is the probable source of observed pavements. The concept of a partially barred gulf like Bothnia is essential to several genetic models for Proterozoic iron formations, as reviewed by Eichler (1976, p. 191). The Bothnian iron concentrations deserve further study by those who advocate a barred basin.

Hydrothermal supply of iron to modern seawater is an indication of the potential supply to Proterozoic seawater. Modern alteration of basaltic crust is estimated to be supplying 50×10^{12}g Fe and $O.8 \times 10^{12}$g Mn annually to seawater (Elderfield, 1977). This is twice the estimate of annual supply of iron and manganese that formed the voluminous Hamersley iron formations in Western Australia (Trendall and Blockley, 1970, p. 282). However, ferromanganese nodules and crusts that precipitate from modern seawater are distinctly different from cherty ironstone. Ferromanganese precipitates are typically enriched in some metals by more than five times crustal average (V, Co, Ni, Cu, Zn, Pb, REE), and others (B, As) over fifty times (Elderfield, 1977). Ferriferous sediment more like cherty ironstone is accumulating near hot springs along active centers of seafloor spreading. Toth (1980, p. 49) notes that these "marine hydrothermal deposits are characterized by extreme Fe/Mn values, Fe and Si contents which co-vary, and generally very low concentrations of trace metals and REE." These crusts are composed of iron-rich nontronite, amorphous hydrated iron oxides, and silica. The only abundant trace element is arsenic, an element also concentrated in some Precambrian iron formations (Goodwin, 1961). The occurrence of this modern cherty ironstone and the calculation of abundant hydrothermal supply of iron should constrain genetic modelers of Proterozoic iron formations to consider observed marine processes rather than purely hypothetical processes. An important factor may be the rate of sedimentation. Given that trace-element depletion in modern ironstone occurs where there is rapid accumulation (Toth, 1980), a similar constraint may apply to Proterozoic ironstone. If so, trace elements should have been enriched along disconformities within iron formations, i.e., surfaces of prolonged exposure to seawater. Chemical analysis of disconformable surfaces would evaluate this constraint.

The most significant geochemical constraint on modeling Proterozoic iron supply is the insolubility of iron in both oxygen-rich and sulfide-rich (reducing) seawater. The solubility products of iron sulfides limit aqueous iron content in the presence of high aqueous sulfide. In recognition of this constraint, Holland (1973) hypothesized the former existence of a large sulfide-poor oceanic zone at an intermediate state of oxidation. This state of intermediate oxidation is exemplified within the Black Sea where iron reaches 50 ppb versus 10 ppb in underlying sulfide-rich seawater (Brewer and Spencer, 1974). Typical oxidized seawater contains only about 3 ppb Fe. The solutions which formed voluminous Proterozoic iron formations must have contained at least 3 ppm Fe (Holland, 1973; Drever, 1974). Intermediate oxidation produces iron contents of up to 2 ppm Fe through thicknesses of a few centimetres to a few decimetres within modern marine sediment, with sharp decreases in overlying and underlying sediment. This abundance clearly indicates the potential for intermediate oxidation in Proterozoic models. An alternative concept is that the entire Proterozoic ocean was depleted in both sulfide and sulfate sulfur (Drever, 1974). This concept is constrained, however, by the occurrence of gypsum casts in the Proterozoic Gunflint iron formation (Barghoorn and others, 1977). Moreover, Archean sulfate-rich evaporites occur in Western Australia (Barley and others, 1979).

Experimentation with seawater-basalt reactions helps constrain models of iron supply by seafloor alteration. Reaction of sulfate-bearing seawater with basalt causes anhydrite precipitation, and additional sulfate reacts to form sulfides (Mottl et al., 1979). Further reaction of this sulfur-depleted seawater with basalt under a stratified ocean could cause substantial dissolution of iron, given the much more abundant ferrous iron than sulfur in basalt. Upwelling of this water could lead to precipitation of a sulfide-poor iron formation in shallow water, as envisioned by Drever (1974) and others. Sulfides are indeed scarce in most Proterozoic iron formations, although abundant in some associated argillaceous formations (James, 1966). One exception is the iron-poor Gunflint iron formation northwest of Lake Superior (Gross and McLeod, 1980).

Constraints on modeling the origin of thick iron formations are similar to constraints on modeling thick dolomite sequences. Neither ironstone nor dolostone is accumulating significantly in modern oceans. Most genetic models for dolomite sequences invoke evaporation or dilution of seawater that had a composition like modern seawater (Friedman, 1980; Land, 1980). However, Mottl and Holland (1975) have shown that the content of magnesium in seawater may change due to interaction of seawater with seafloor basalt.

The only apparent alternative to compositional variation of seawater with time is some type of early diagenetic dissolution-reprecipitation of iron. Early diagenetic mobility of iron is invoked in many models for chert-poor, inland-sea iron formations, including Proterozoic examples. Gygi (1981) envisions concentration of iron that dissolved from submarine mud, precipitated at the sediment-water interface, moved in suspension downslope from the mud bank, and aggregated to form ooids. Kimberley (1979a) envisioned early diagenetic replacement of calcareous oolite by solutions draining weathering mud. In both models, precipitation occurs near an argillaceous source and the precipitate is aluminous. Neither type of model applies well to nonaluminous cherty iron formations. The lateral extent and purity of Proterozoic cherty iron formations is difficult to reconcile with the concept of a proximal argillaceous source of iron. Moreover, diagenetic models do not readily explain variation in abundance of cherty iron formations through earth history. These constraints have convinced most genetic modelers that iron was dissolved and transported large distances in Proterozoic oceans.

Modern mobility of iron within fresh water helps to constrain models of lacustrine sedimentation of Proterozoic iron formations (e.g., Govett, 1966). The most significant constraint is that iron supply to lakes is primarily fluvial rather than due to seafloor alteration. Rivers also carry detritus that could readily dilute chemical sediment. Sulfide insolubility is not a significant constraint because of low dissolved sulfur content, and so dissolved iron is locally abundant, exceeding 20 ppm Fe within anoxic lacustrine sediment (Emerson, 1976). Production of methane in the upper few centimetres of sediment drastically lowers oxidation potential, and fresh water does not contain sufficient sulfur to precipitate much of the ferrous iron that becomes dissolved.

Modern bacterial precipitation of iron may be used to evaluate proposals of a microbiotic origin of Proterozoic iron formations. Bacteria apparently cause very selective precipitation of iron in bogs. Groundwater in New Jersey has an Fe/Mn ratio typical of cherty ironstone, 37/1, but surficial precipitates from the groundwater have an Fe/Mn ratio of 7900/1 (Crerar and others, 1979). This degree of segregation of Fe from Mn is unknown in ironstone and the persistence of low Fe/Mn ratios, close to the crustal average, constrains genetic models that invoke direct organic mediation of precipitation.

CONCLUSION

A consensus has yet to be achieved on the origin of Proterozoic iron formations, largely because modeling is poorly constrained. More discussion is needed on the constraints rather than the models, and this paper has reviewed some of these constraints to enhance discussion.

REFERENCES CITED

Awramik, S. M., and Barghoorn, E. S., 1977, The Gunflint microbiota: Precambrian Research, v. 5, p. 121–142.

Barghoorn, E. S., Knoll, A. H., Dembicki, H., Jr., and Meinschein, W. G., 1977, Variation in stable carbon isotopes in organic matter from the Gunflint iron formation: Geochimica et Cosmochimica Acta, v. 41, p. 425–430.

Barley, M. E., Dunlop, J.S.R., Glover, J. E., and Groves, D. I., 1979, Sedimentary evidence for an Archean shallow-water volcanic-sedimentary facies, eastern Pilbara block, Western Australia: Earth and Planetary Science Letters, v. 43, p. 74–84.

Becker, R. H., and Clayton, R. N., 1972, Carbon isotopic evidence for the origin of a banded iron-formation in Western Australia: Geochimica et Cosmochimica Acta, v. 36, p. 577–595.

—— 1976, Oxygen isotope study of a Precambrian banded iron-formation. Hamersley Range. Western Australia: Geochimica et Cosmochimica Acta, v. 40, p. 1153–1165.

Brewer, P. G., and Spencer, D. W., 1974, Distribution of some trace elements in Black Sea and their flux between dissolved and particulate load, *in* Degens, E. T., and Ross, D. A., eds., The Black Sea—geology, chemistry and biology: Tulsa, Oklahoma, American Association of Petroleum Geologists, p. 137–143.

Button, A., 1976, Iron-formation as an end member in carbonate sedimentary cycles in the Transvaal Supergroup, South Africa: Economic Geology, v. 71, p. 193–201.

Cloud, P. E., 1973, Paleoecological significance of the banded iron-formations: Economic Geology, v. 68, p. 1135–1143.

Coleman, M. L., and Raiswell, R., 1981, Carbon, oxygen and sulphur isotope variations in concentrations from the Upper Lias of N.E. England: Geochimica et Cosmochimica Acta, v. 45, p. 329–340.

Crerar, D. A., Knox, G. W., and Means, J. L., 1979, Biogeochemistry of bog iron in the New Jersey Pine Barrens: Chemical Geology, v. 24, p. 111–135.

Dimroth, E., 1976, Aspects of the sedimentary petrology of cherty iron-formation, *in* Wolf, K. H., ed., Handbook of strata-bound and stratiform ore deposits, v. 7, Amsterdam, Elsevier, p. 203–254.

Dimroth, E., and Chauvel, J.-J., 1972, Petrographie des minerais de fer de la Fosse de Labrador: Geologische Rundschau, v. 61, p. 97–115.

Drever, J. I., 1974, Geochemical model for the origin of Precambrian banded iron formations: Geological Society of America Bulletin, v. 85, p. 1099–1106.

Eichler, J., 1976, Origin of the Precambrian banded iron-formations, *in* Wolf, K. H., ed., Handbook of strata-bound and stratiform ore deposits, v. 7, p. 157–201.

Elderfield, H., 1977, The form of manganese and iron in marine sediments, *in* Glasby, G. P., ed., Marine manganese deposits: Amsterdam, Elsevier, p. 269–289.

Elderfield, H., and Greaves, M. J., 1982, The rare earths in seawater: Nature, v. 296, p. 214–219.

Emerson, S., 1976, Early diagenesis in anaerobic lake sediments: chemical equilibria in interstitial waters: Geochimica et Cosmochimica Acta, v. 40, p. 925–934.

Eugster, H. P., and Chou, I.-M., 1973, The depositional environments of Precambrian banded iron-formations: Economic Geology, v. 68, p. 1144–1168.

Floran, R. J., and Papike, J. J., 1975, Petrology of the Gunflint Iron Formation, Ontario-Minnesota: the low grade rocks: Geological Society of America Bulletin, v. 86, p. 1169–1190.

Friedman, G., 1980, Dolomite is an evaporite mineral: evidence from the rock record and from sea-marginal ponds of the Red Sea, *in* Zenger, D. H., Dunham, J. B., and Ethington, R. C., eds., Concepts and models of dolomitization, Society of Economic Paleontologists and Mineralogists, Special Publication 28, p. 69–80.

Fryer, B. J., 1977, Trace element geochemistry of the Sokoman iron formation: Canadian Journal of Earth Sciences, v. 14, p. 1598–1610.

Gole, M. J., and Klein, C., 1981, Banded iron-formations through much of Precambrian time: Journal of Geology, v. 89, p. 169–193.

Goodwin, A. M., 1956, Facies relations in the Gunflint iron formation: Economic Geology, v. 51, p. 565–595.

——1961, Genetic aspects of Michipicoten iron formation: Trans. Canadian Institute Mining Metallurgy, v. 64, p. 32–36.

Goodwin, A. M., Monster, J., and Thode, H. G., 1976, Carbon and sulfur isotope abundances in Archean iron-formations and early Precambrian life: Economic Geology, v. 71, p. 870–891.

Govett, G. S., 1966, Origin of banded iron-formations: Geological Society of America Bulletin, v. 77, p. 1191–1212.

Gross, G. A., 1968, Iron ranges of the Labrador geosyncline, vol. 3 of Geology of iron deposits of Canada: Geological Survey of Canada, Economic Geology Report 22, 179 p.

——1980, A classification of iron formations based on depositional environments: Canadian Mineralogist, v. 18, p. 215–222.

Gross, G. A., and McLeod, C. R., 1980, A preliminary assessment of the chemical composition of iron formation in Canada: Canadian Mineralogist, v. 18, p. 223–229.

Guichard, F., Church, T. M., Treuil, M., and Jaffrezic, H., 1979, Rare earths in barites: distribution and effects on aqueous partitioning: Geochimica et Cosmochimica Acta, v. 43, p. 983–997.

Gygi, R. A., 1981, Oolitic iron formations: marine or not marine?: Eclogae Geologicae Helvetiae, v. 74, p. 233–254.

Hall, W.D.M., and Goode, A.D.T., 1978, The early Proterozoic Nabberu Basin and associated iron formations of Western Australia: Precambrian Research, v. 7, p. 139–184.

Hangari, K. M., Ahmad, S. N., and Perry, E. C., Jr., 1980, Carbon and oxygen isotope ratios in diagenetic siderite and magnetite from Upper Devonian ironstone, Wadi Shatti district, Libya: Economic Geology, v. 75, p. 538–545.

Hardie, L. A., and Ginsburg, R. N., 1977, Layering: the origin and environmental significance of lamination and thin bedding, *in* Hardie, L. A., ed., Sedimentation on the modern carbonate tidal flats of northwest Andros island, Bahamas: Baltimore, Johns Hopkins University Press, p. 50–123.

Holland, H. D., 1973, The oceans: a possible source of iron in iron-formations: Economic Geology, v. 68, p. 1169–1172.

James, H. L., 1966, Chemistry of the iron-rich sedimentary rocks, *in* Fleischer, M., ed., Data of Geochemistry, sixth ed., p. W1–W61.

Kimberley, M. M., 1978, Paleoenvironmental classification of iron formations: Economic Geology, v. 73, p. 215–229.

——1979a, Origin of oolitic iron formations: Journal of Sedimentary Petrology, v. 49, p. 111–131.

——1979b, Geochemical distinctions among environmental types of iron formations: Chemical Geology, v. 25, p. 185–212.

——1980, The Paz de Rio oolitic inland-sea iron formation: Economic Geology, v. 75, p. 97–106.

Knauth, L. P., and Epstein, S., 1976, Hydrogen and oxygen isotope ratios in nodular and bedded cherts: Geochimica et Cosmochimica Acta, v. 40, p. 1095–1108.

Lambert, M. B., 1978, The Back River volcanic complex—a cauldron subsidence structure of Archean age: Geological Survey of Canada, Paper 78-1A, p. 153–157.

Land, L. S., 1980, The isotopic and trace element geochemistry of dolomite: the state of the art, *in* Zenger, D. H., Dunham, J. B., and Ethington, R. L., eds., Concepts and models of dolomitization, Society of Economic Paleontologists and Mineralogists, Special Publication 28, p. 87–110.

Larue, D. K., 1981, The Early Proterozoic pre-iron-formation Menominee Group siliclastic sediments of the southern Lake Superior region: evidence for sedimentation in platform and basinal settings: Journal of Sedimentary Petrology, v. 51, p. 397–414.

Lepp, H., and Goldich, S., 1964, Origin of Precambrian iron-formations: Economic Geology, v. 59, p. 1025–1060.

Markun, C. D., and Randazzo, A. F., 1980, Sedimentary structures in the Gunflint iron formation, Schreiber Beach, Ontario: Precambrian Research, v. 12, p. 287–310.

Mel'nik, Yu, P., Drozdovskaya, A. A., and Vorob'yeva, K. A., 1973, New experimental and computational information about the conditions of Precambrian iron-silica deposition (in Russian): Geologicheskiy Zhurnal, v. 33, no. 2, p. 12–23.

Moore, D. W., 1977, Geology and geochemistry of gold-bearing iron formation and associated rocks, Back River, Northwest Territories [M.S. dissert.]: Toronto, Canada, University of Toronto, 177 p.

Morey, G. B., 1967, Stratigraphy and sedimentology of the Middle Precambrian Rove Formation in northeastern Minnesota: Journal of Sedimentary Petrology, v. 37, p. 1154–1162.

Mottl, M., and Holland, H. D., 1975, Basalt-sea water interaction, seafloor spreading, and the dolomite problem [abs.]: American Geophysical Union Transactions, v. 56, p. 1074.

Mottl, M., Holland, H. D., and Corr, R. F., 1979, Chemical exchange during hydrothermal alteration of basalt by seawater-II. Experimental results for Fe, Mn, and sulfur species: Geochimica et Cosmochimica Acta, v. 43, p. 869–884.

Murray, J. W., Grundmanis, V., and Smethie, W. M., Jr., 1978, Interstitial water chemistry in the sediments of Saanich Inlet: Geochimica et Cosmochimica Acta, v. 42, p. 1011–1026.

Nahon, D., Carozzi, A. V., and Parron, C., 1980, Lateritic weathering as a mechanism for the generation of ferruginous ooids: Journal of Sedimentary Petrology, v. 50, p. 1287–1298.

Perry, E. C., Jr., and Tan, F. C., 1972, Significance of oxygen and carbon isotope determinations in early Precambrian cherts and carbonate rocks of southern Africa: Geological Society of America Bulletin, v. 83, p. 647–664.

——1973, Significance of carbon isotope variations in carbonates from the Biwabik iron formation, Minnesota, *in* Kiev Symposium on Genesis of Precambrian iron and manganese deposits, Proceedings, New York, UNESCO, p. 299–305.

Perry, E. C., Jr., Tan, F. C., and Morey, G. B., 1973, Geology and stable isotope geochemistry of the Biwabik iron formation, northern Minnesota: Economic Geology, v. 68, p. 1110–1125.

Shegelski, R. J., 1978, Stratigraphy and geochemistry of Archean iron formations in the Sturgeon Lake-Savant Lake greenstone terrain, northwestern Ontario [Ph.D. dissert.]: Toronto, Canada, University of Toronto, 251 p.

Toth, J. R., 1980, Deposition of submarine crusts rich in manganese and iron: Geological Society of America Bulletin, v. 91, p. 44–54.

Trendall, A. F., 1973, Varve cycles in the Weeli Wolli Formation of the Precambrian Hamersley Group, Western Australia: Economic Geology, v. 68, p. 1089–1097.

Trendall, A. F., and Blockley, J. G., 1970, The iron formations of the Precambrian Hamersley Group, Western Australia: Geological Survey of Western Australia, Bulletin 119, 366 p.

Vander Wood, T. V., 1977, Strontium isotope systematics in the Hamersley Range; theories of origin of banded iron formations and their significance to atmospheric history [M.S. dissert.]: Tallahassee, Florida, Florida State University, 105 p.

Weertman, J., 1976, Milankovitch solar radiation variations and ice age ice sheet sizes: Nature, v. 261, p. 17–20.

Winterhalter, B., 1966, Iron-manganese concretions from the Gulf of Bothnia and the Gulf of Finland: Geoteknillisia julkaisuja, no. 69, 77 p.

Manuscript Accepted by the Society April 14, 1983

Printed in U.S.A.

Geological Society of America
Memoir 161
1983

Proterozoic uranium deposits and the Precambrian atmosphere

F. F. Langford
Department of Geological Sciences
University of Saskatchewan
Saskatoon, Saskatchewan S7N OWO
Canada

ABSTRACT

The Proterozoic System contains many of the world's major uranium deposits. The earliest are of the quartz pebble conglomerate-type and are typified by the deposits at Elliot Lake, which belong to the uranium-thorium association. They have uraninite with both uranium and thorium, and represent paleoplacers. Except for some very small occurrences, this type of deposit developed only before 2,000 Ma ago. The principal economic deposits that first appeared during the Middle Proterozoic contain uranium without thorium, and all three types (sandstone, vein, and unconformity) were formed in conjunction with fluvial sandstone. It appears that prior to 2,000 Ma ago the low level of oxygen in the atmosphere permitted thorium-bearing uraninite to be weathered from igneous rocks, transported, and then deposited as detrital minerals. With the increase of oxygen in the atmosphere, about 2,000 Ma ago, meteoric waters could oxidize and thus dissolve uranium during weathering, separating it from the thorium which remained as an insoluble residue. The uranium was carried in solution and deposited in reducing zones within fluvial environments. This also explains the geochemical association of uranium with Ni, Co, Mo, Cu, Zn, Mn, Fe, V, Ag, Si, Se, and As, which is a characteristic of these deposits.

INTRODUCTION

The Proterozoic System is the host for several of the major uranium deposits of the world and represents one of the principal uranium-depositing periods of geological time. It is particularly noted for the unconformity-type deposits in the Alligator Rivers region of the Northern Territory of Australia and the Athabasca area of Saskatchewan, Canada, as well as the quartz-pebble conglomerate-type deposits in the Elliot Lake area of Ontario, Canada. Despite their Archean age, the uranium- and gold-bearing quartz-pebble conglomerates in the Witwatersrand region of South Africa can be included with the Elliot Lake deposits, because their geological character and setting are almost identical to the Elliot Lake deposits and unlike those of typical Archean terrains.

During the Proterozoic, the nature of sedimentary uranium deposits underwent a significant change from deposits such as Elliot Lake in which the uranium minerals were detrital to deposits such as the unconformity, sandstone, and vein-types in which uranium was precipitated from meteoric groundwater. The reason for this profound change is usually ascribed to the development of an oxygenic atmosphere. Cloud (1972) and Roscoe (1973) pointed out that the first appearance of red beds in rocks 2,100 Ma to 1,700 Ma old was probably related to the development of an oxygenic atmosphere at that time. Roscoe (1969), having established the detrital nature of pyrite and uraninite at Elliot Lake, used this concept to suggest that exploration for quartz-pebble conglomerate types of uranium deposits should concentrate on rocks older than 2,000 Ma, since this was about the time free oxygen appeared in the atmosphere.

In magmas, uranium and thorium belong to the group of elements that are concentrated in the final products of differentiation. Thus they form uranium- and thorium-bearing minerals in the granitic rocks, and there are a few economic deposits of uranium in granites and pegmatites. Uraninite from magmatic rocks can be recognized because it contains more than 1% of thorium (Simpson and Bowles, 1977, 1978).

Both uranium and thorium in the reduced (tetravalent) state are virtually insoluble in normal meteoric waters. However, uranium in the oxidized (hexavalent) state is soluble in these same meteoric waters. Thus, if a granite is weathered in a reducing atmosphere, the uraninite is insoluble and it can be eroded and deposited as detrital grains, which retain the same ratio of uranium to thorium as resulted from the initial crystallization. If the granite weathers in an oxidizing environment, the uranium can be oxidized and removed in solution, but thorium having no oxidized state will remain behind as an insoluble resistate. The uranium can be transported in solution until it encounters a reducing environment, where it may precipitate.

The changed behaviour of uranium after the appearance of oxygen in the atmosphere is shown by the change in the ratio of uranium to thorium in marine shales and by the appearance of uranium deposits with thorium-free uranium minerals. The simple classification in Table 1 is based on this difference, and all deposits of the thorium-free group are types that only appeared after the "oxyatmoversion" (Roscoe, 1973)

TABLE 1. CLASSIFICATION OF MAJOR PROTEROZOIC DEPOSITS

A. Uranium and thorium occur together
   1. Magmatic, granite and pegmatite: Bancroft, Ontario
   2. Quartz-pebble conglomerate: Elliott Lake, Ontario; Witwatersrand, South Africa

B. Uranium occurs without thorium
   1. Sandstone-type: Oklo and Mouana, Gabon
   2. Vein type (simple): Beaverlodge, Saskatchewan (complex); Great Bear Lake, Canada
   3. Unconformity-type (simple): Rabbit Lake, Saskatchewan; Jabiluka, Northern Territory, Australia (complex): Key Lake, Midwest, Saskatchewan.

THE QUARTZ-PEBBLE CONGLOMERATE-TYPE URANIUM DEPOSITS

The oldest known uranium deposits in sedimentary rocks are the quartz-pebble conglomerate-type. They differ from later uranium deposits in that the uranium ore minerals contain considerable thorium even though they, like later sedimentary deposits, were restricted to detrital sediments formed in fluvial, lacustrine, and possibly very near-shore marine environments.

The Elliot Lake deposits of Canada and the Witwatersrand deposits of South Africa are the major economic deposits of this type. The former deposits are 2,450 to 2,250 Ma old (Roscoe, 1973) and the latter 2,800 to 2,500 Ma old (Whiteside, 1970). The South African deposits are, strictly speaking, Archean according to North American usage. However, because they occur in virtually unmetamorphosed sediments lying unconformably on a basement complex of Archean granite and greenstone, they have the petrographic, stratigraphic, and structural attributes of other Proterozoic sequences, especially those at Elliot Lake. They are thus included with other quartz-pebble conglomerates of Proterozoic age.

The uranium occurs in thick sequences of fluvial sandstone and conglomerate. The ore is limited to a few mineralized, pyritic conglomerate beds that contain some mineralized, pyritic sandstone and a few thin carbonaceous layers. In the conglomerate, almost all the pebbles are quartz, and the sandstone matrix consists principally of quartz accompanied by sericite, feldspar, rock fragments, and some chlorite. The heavy minerals are typical of sandstones elsewhere in the sequence. Except for the increased uranium, pyrite, carbonaceous material, and (in the Witwatersrand) gold, the ore-bearing beds are like the barren beds above and below. At the Witwatersrand, gold averages about 10 ppm and uranium 200 ppm. At Elliot Lake, gold is virtually absent, but uranium averages about 1,000 ppm. Some enrichment in copper and molybdenum has been noted. The ratio of uranium to thorium (UO_2/ThO_2) in the uranium minerals ranges from 5 to 12 at Elliot Lake and 6 to 18 at Witwatersrand (Kimberley, 1978).

Genetic concepts initially were dominated by magmatic hydrothermal hypotheses (Davidson, 1965), but at present it is widely accepted that the deposits were ancient placers later modified by diagenetic processes (Whiteside, 1970; Robertson, 1978). The placer concept is partly based on the restriction of these deposits to fluvial sedimentary rocks and on the marked stratigraphic control of the distribution of the deposits within the sequences. The placer aspect is further supported by observations on the detrital shapes of the uraninite grains, on the variation of the ratios of uranium to thorium in ore particles, and on the correspondence of the composition of the uraninite in the ore with that of uraninite in the granitic rocks in the Archean source areas (Grandstaff, 1980; Roscoe, 1973; Simpson and Bowles, 1977).

Features such as replacement textures between ore minerals and silicates, as well as pyrite overgrowths, were originally considered to indicate an epigenetic hydrothermal origin. Now these are thought to result from diagenetic recrystallization. However, Hattori and others (1981), on the basis of the uniform distribution of sulfur isotopes in the pyrite at Elliot Lake, proposed that the sulfur may have been introduced in solution. Thus the exact mechanisms of deposition and diagenesis are not yet fully agreed upon.

The occurrence of detrital uraninite has been cited as evidence that oxygen was absent or only present at very low levels in the Precambrian atmosphere. Grandstaff (1980), using thermodynamic methods, determined that 10^{-2} of the present levels of oxygen could have been present in the atmosphere at that time. Dimroth and Kimberley (1978) have presented contrary views arguing that the presence of hematite in Archean weathering profiles indicates that oxygen levels rose to almost their present values early in the Precambrian. Recent uranium placers in British Columbia (Steacy, 1953) and Pakistan (Simpson and Bowles, 1977) show that detrital uraninite and pyrite can occur under present-day levels of oxygen in the atmosphere, where conditions of rapid erosion and low temperatures curtail chemical reaction. Thus local conditions may be at variance with those generally prevailing. The formation and preservation of uranium placer deposits was on a much larger scale in Archean and early Proterozoic times than later. Besides Elliot Lake and the Witwatersrand, there are in the order of a dozen substantial, although as yet uneconomic, deposits of similar pre-2,000-Ma age, among which are the deposits in the Padlei, Cambrian Lake, and Lake Mistassini regions in Canada; the Serra Jacobina and Belo Horizonte areas of Brazil; and the Nullagine area of Australia (Robertson, 1974).

SANDSTONE-TYPE DEPOSITS

The sandstone-type deposits are typified by those of the western United States where uranium in Mesozoic and Tertiary fluvial sandstones constitutes the bulk of that nation's very large resources of that metal. Examples of this type are not common in Proterozoic rocks, but the deposits in the Oklo area of Gabon are a notable exception. Besides being sites of natural nuclear fission, they are also the oldest, unequivocal examples of the low thorium type of uranium deposit (Gancarz, 1978; Simpson and Bowles, 1978).

The sandstone-type of uranium deposit occurs in argillaceous sandstone, commonly intercalated with argillitic beds. Organic matter is generally abundant and occurs in Phanerozoic deposits both as an asphaltic-looking, interstitial material and as coalified woody trash (Squyres, 1980). It is generally believed that the organic matter has acted as the main reducing agent that created conditions favourable for precipitation of much of the uranium.

The sandstone-type deposits are divided into two subtypes. In the peneconformable type, the primary ore bodies occur as generally conformable pods in grey and green sandstone containing pyrite and organic material (Finch, 1967). In the roll-front type, the sandstone host has been invaded by oxidizing solutions, the organic material destroyed, the pyrite converted to hematite, and the uranium remobilized and commonly concentrated at the boundary between the oxidized and the original, reduced pyrite-bearing sandstone. In the Grants district of New Mexico, both the peneconformable and the roll-front types derived from them are present and are referred to as trend and stack orebodies, respectively. The remobilized ore bodies (stack ore) are more complex than elsewhere in their geometry and in their relation to the oxidizing fronts (Smith and Peterson, 1980). In Wyoming and Texas, the roll-front orebodies are considered primary by most authors. Langford (1977) disagreed principally because conventional theories ignore the fact that the sandstone-type deposits occur only in terrestrial sediments (Finch, 1967), although Rich and others (1977) have made reference to the problem.

The Proterozoic sandstone-type deposits at Oklo and Mounana in Gabon have a great many features in common with the Mesozoic deposits of the western United States (Brookins, 1980a). The orebodies formed about 2,000 Ma ago and occur in the Francevillian series, a Proterozoic detrital sequence that occupies a basin underlain by a 2,600-Ma-old granitic basement complex (Gancarz, 1978). The Francevillian from bottom to top consists of a lower unit of about 350 m of dark grey, black and green, fluvial cross-bedded sandstones and conglomerate that is overlain by about 300 m of dark grey argillites, which becomes sandy towards the top. This is overlain in turn by 50 m of black shale, chert, and dolomite, and topped by 250 m of pyroclastics and welded tuffs (Gauthier-LaFaye and others, 1980; Gangloff, 1970). In the vicinity of the deposits, the whole sequence dips 30° to 40° to the east, and near the outcrop of the basement, the beds are sharply folded and cut by faults (Gauthier-Lafaye and others, 1978).

The uranium deposits are confined to four fluvial, upward-fining, conglomerate to fine sand beds which make up the upper 7 or 8 m of the lower unit over a strike length of about 3 km. Most of the uranium occurs in small pods in silicic, black sandstone that contains pyrite and organic material, including fossil algae. Grades run from 0.2% to 0.5% uranium (Gauthier-Lafaye and others, 1978, 1980). The high-grade orebodies, with tens of percent uranium, are remobilized from the podiform ones and form a series of veinlike orebodies in fractures and thin (0.5 m), tabular bodies a few metres long enclosed in clay. Brookins (1980a) did not believe that true roll-front deposits are present. High-grade orebodies that have undergone nuclear reactions have a well-defined aureole of illite, magnesian chlorite, and a quartz-free inner zone of illite, chlorite, vermiculite, and hematite. Beyond 2 m from the reaction zone, the clay is disordered illite (Gauthier-LaFaye and others, 1980), which argues for low-temperature diagenesis despite the heat produced in the reactor zones. As pointed out by Brookins (1980a), except for the nuclear reactions, the Oklo deposits seem to have resulted directly from fluvial sedimentation accompanied by, or very quickly followed by, deposition of uranium. The abundance of magnesian chlorite in the reactor aureole has been attributed to the nuclear fission, but this hardly explains the magnesium metasomatism.

VEIN-TYPE DEPOSITS

Uranium was first mined from veins in the Erzgebirge district of Czechoslovakia and later at Shinkolobwe in the then Belgian Congo. At present, mining is occurring in Carboniferous-Permian veins in the Massif Central and Amorican Massif in France, and in Tertiary veins at the Schwartzwalder and Midnite mines in the United States. The major Proterozoic vein deposits occur in the Beaverlodge and Great Slave Lake areas of Canada. The deposits characteristically have low-thorium uraninite, and the other mineral compositions of simple veins are not unlike the sandstone-type deposits. The oldest known veins are those in the Beaverlodge area, dated at 1,760 Ma (Koeppel, 1968).

The Proterozoic uraniferous veins occur as fracture fillings in basement rocks. In areas such as Beaverlodge where they are unconformably overlain by fluvial sandstones, the ages of the veins are substantially younger than the enclosing basement rocks and, where good dates are available, about the same age as the sandstone.

In the Beaverlodge area, the basement consists of the Tazin gneisses and granites that were formed during the Hudsonian orogeny (about 1,800 Ma ago). This basement is unconformably overlain by the Martin Formation, an unmetamorphosed fluvial sandstone and conglomerate. With well over 1,000 uranium occurrences in the area, it is easily demonstrated that the number and size of the occurrences decrease with distance from the unconformity (Tremblay, 1972). The major mines consisted of mineralized fractures and breccia cones below the unconformity with the Martin Formation, and there is a small amount of mineralization in the overlying sandstone.

In most veins the basic mineral assemblage is simple. It consists of pitchblende, some coffinite, generally less than 5% pyrite and marcasite, together with minor amounts of galena, chalcopyrite, and sphalerite. The uraninite commonly occurs as a lustrous, botryoidal, early variety that was fractured and then partially replaced by a sooty variety that may be coeval with coffinite. The principal gangue minerals are hematite, carbonate, chlorite, and small amounts of graphite. Cherty quartz is abundant in some veins. Iron-rich chlorite is related to the regional metamorphism, but the chlorite associated with uranium mineralization is magnesian (Tortosa, 1983) like that in the sandstone and unconformity deposits.

The veins in the Great Bear Lake area of Canada have a complex suite of minerals. Besides uraninite, coffinite, and pyrite, the mineral suite includes an abundance of arsenides and sulf-arsenides of nickel, cobalt, silver, and bismuth (Ruzicka, 1971). In the Great Bear Lake area, the veins are currently being worked for silver, not uranium. In the Beaverlodge area, some of the deposits have this complex mineral assemblage.

UNCONFORMITY-TYPE DEPOSITS

During the past decade, the discovery of several of the world's largest orebodies at the unconformity between granitic basement and overlying Proterozoic fluvial sediments has made the Middle Proterozoic period recognized as one of major uranium deposition. This type of deposit was defined by Derry (1973). Hoeve and others (1980) suggested it might be unique to the Proterozoic.

These deposits occur in the Athabasca area of Saskatchewan and in the Pine Creek geosyncline of the Alligator Rivers region of the Northern Territories of Australia. In both areas, the deposits are remarkably similar, differing principally in the absence of arsenide mineralization in the Australian deposits.

In Saskatchewan, the Athabasca basin is floored with an extensive layer of coarse fluvial sandstone and conglomerate lying on a thick kaolinitic regolith developed on the granitic gneisses of the 1,800-Ma-old basement (Sibbald and others, 1981). The unconformity deposits are mostly long (up to 1,800 m), pencil-shaped bodies lying in the regolith with veinlike apophyses extending as much as 200 m up into the sandstone and down into the basement. At Cluff Lake, the D-ore body is entirely in the sandstone; at Rabbit Lake the ore body appears to have been entirely in the basement; and at McClean Lake the northeast end of the pencil-like body is within the basement and rises gently to the other end, which is entirely in the sandstone (Brummer and others, 1981).

Deposits appear to be space-filling within breccia and fracture zones, postulated to be within major faults in some deposits. They also occur on graphitic biotite schist and gneiss units in the basement. A few deposits, such as Dawn Lake and McClean Lake, occur in calc-silicates intercalated with these gneisses: some of the breccia may represent a karst, developed on the unconformity surface.

The orebodies occur within zones of altered basement and sandstone country rock, up to a few hundred metres thick. The alteration minerals, which are predominantly illite, sericite, chlorite, and tourmaline, differ from those of the regolith, which is a paleolaterite dominated by kaolin. The abundance of magnesian chlorite in the alteration zones suggests the introduction of considerable magnesia, a situation similar to that at Oklo. Deposits show great variation in the kinds of ore minerals present and elements concentrated. Some deposits, such as Rabbit Lake, have uranium and only traces of other elements. The D zone at Cluff Lake has uranium and considerable selenium and gold; Key Lake and Midwest Lake have abundant uranium, nickel, cobalt, molybdenum, and arsenic. Overall, these uranium deposits represent enrichments in U, Ni, Co, As, V, Mo, Se, Ag, and Au. Hydrocarbons are common, as is carbon in the form of graphite (Sibbald and others, 1981).

The unconformity deposits in the Pine Creek geosyncline of the Northern Territories of Australia are very similar to the Athabasca deposits. The basement consists of Lower Proterozoic sediments metamorphosed to schist and gneisses about 1,800 Ma ago. It is unconformably overlain by the Kombolgie fluvial sandstone, which is about 1,688 Ma old (Page and others, 1980). The orebodies lie just below the unconformity, although the Jabiluka II and Ranger 25 are the only ones still covered. Uranium mineralization occurs exclusively in the basement rocks and is associated with intense sericite and magnesian-chlorite alteration halos. At Jabiluka II, chlorite alteration extends well up into the sandstone, but uranium mineralization is confined to the basement (Binns and others, 1980). Within the basement, the orebodies lie in the brecciated Cahill Formation, consisting of metamorphosed, carbonaceous argillites, siltstones, and carbonates that are rather similar to the host rocks in the Athabasca area. The mineralization is of the simple type accompanied by some gold at Jabiluka II.

South of the area of the unconformity-type deposits, in the South Alligator River Valley, uranium veins occur in Lower Proterozoic slightly metamorphosed sediments correlative with those that enclose the unconformity deposits. The veins are located at the same unconformity, although the overlying rocks are the terrestrial sandstones and volcanics of the Edith River Formation, which are in turn overlain by the Kombolgie Sandstone (Crick and others, 1980). One of the mines contains some cobalt and nickel arsenides; otherwise the type of wall rock alteration and the mineralization are the same as the unconformity-type deposits.

At Rum Jungle, the uranium deposits occur in slightly metamorphosed correlatives of the Cahill Formation, (Needham and others, 1980), and there is some evidence that they may lie just below an unconformity, although well-defined Middle Proterozoic sandstones do not occur nearby. The deposits here are associated with base metal deposits, and their origin is customarily related to a single ore-forming event. However, the distribution of the deposits may be merely overlapping, since some are base metal deposits without uranium, and some, such as the Rum Jungle Creek South mine, have only uranium. This latter mine has a mineral assemblage very similar to the unconformity-type deposits, although wall-rock alteration is not so extensive.

THORIUM-FREE DEPOSITS AND THE ATMOSPHERE

The appearance of oxygen in the atmosphere about 2,000 Ma ago coincided with the appearance of the sandstone-, unconformity-, and vein-types of uranium deposits, characterized by having uranium minerals that are devoid of thorium and enriched in vanadium. The importance of oxidizing and reducing conditions to the mobility of uranium has been discussed in connection with the quartz-pebble conglomerate deposits. Thus it remains to establish whether or not these thorium-free deposits have origins connected to the atmosphere.

TABLE 2. PARTIAL SUITES OF TRACE ELEMENTS

	A	B	C	D	E	F	G	H
			(Parts per Million)					
U	1	3	1.3	5.9	3800	6000	2600	17670
Mo	1.5	1.5	14	4.5	30	14	4	5300
Pb	6	19	80	22	41	680	48	9600
Ag	0.11	0.05	0.11	0.41		0.3		29
Zn	105	39	165	114	16	58	5	2600
Co	48	1	74	22	1	41	3	60
V	250	44	120	188		108	84	280
Mn	1500	390	6700			1200		2200
Ni	130	4.5	225	57	13	99	16	120
Th	4	17	7			21	5	
Cu	87	10	250	75	40		5	770
As	2	1.5	13	23	39	5	34	
Se	0.05	0.005	0.17		27			
S	300	300	1300	650		10000		

Note: Data available permits only the most general comparison.
A - Basaltic rocks (Turekian and Wedepohl, 1961).
B - Low calcium granites (turekian and Wedepohl, 1961).
C - Deep-sea clay (Turekian and Wedepohl, 1961).
D - Middle Proterozoic shales (Cameron and Garrels, 1980).
E - Sandstone-type uranium deposit (average of 6 samples from Place and others, 1980).
F - Unconformity-type uranium deposit, Australia, Jabiluka II, (Binns and others, 1980).
G - Unconformity-type uranium deposit, Canada, Fond-du-Lac, (Homeniuk and others, 1982).
H - Vein-type uranium deposit (Young, 1980)

The heavy metal content of black shale results from syngenetic reactions that remove these metals from seawater. The reactions are both inorganic and biological and bring together in dark shales a suite of elements that are characteristic of the surficial reducing environment (Table 2, columns C and D).

Sandstone-type uranium deposits have a trace-element suite much like that of the dark shales, which strongly suggests deposition in surficial reducing environments (Table 2, column E). There is some dispute whether the uranium orebodies were precipitated very shortly after deposition of the host sandstone—by the shallow groundwater connected to the streams that deposited the sands (Langford, 1977)—or whether they were deposited by more deeply circulating groundwater after substantial burial had occurred (Finch, 1967; Fischer, 1970). More refined radiometric dating shows that the ages of the ores are close to if not the same as those of the host rocks (Brookins, 1980b), which limits the probable depth of burial. Thus, most concepts favour a close relationship to surficial processes.

The elemental compositions of unconformity-type orebodies are similar to those of sandstone-types so far as data are available (Table 2, columns F and G). In addition, the close association of these deposits with terrestrial sandstones has led to proposals of origins similar to those of the sandstone-type (Sibbald and others, 1981). However, some authors have proposed that the unconformity-type ores originated from hydrothermal solutions issuing from faults in the basement rocks, having leached the ore elements from the rocks through which they passed, particularly highly metamorphosed shales (Binns and others, 1981).

It seems unlikely that such solutions could have produced deposits with trace element assemblages so similar to the surficial reducing suite, particularly given the diverse behaviour of some of these elements under deep-seated conditions. Vanadium is a good example. In the surficial environment, it has a geochemical behaviour similar to uranium. During igneous differentiation, vanadium is concentrated in gabbroic rocks but not granitic, whereas the opposite is true for uranium and thorium. During metamorphism, vanadium remains locked in the mafic minerals long after uranium and thorium have been released (Martin, 1979). Nickel and cobalt behave more like vanadium than uranium. Thus an origin of these unconformity-type deposits by igneous or metamorphic processes should separate these elements from uranium, not bring them together as they are in deposits such as Key Lake. As well, deep-seated thermal processes should bring uranium, thorium, and rare-earths together, not separate them as appears to have occurred.

The similarity of vein-type deposits and unconformity-type deposits is evident in the South Alligator River Valley in Australia and the Beaverlodge area of Canada where the veins occupy a similar stratigraphic and structural position as the major nearby unconformity-type deposits. So far as the data are available, the deposits have a rather similar elemental and mineral composition. As with the unconformity deposits, there are two fundamentally different concepts of origin. The older one favours deposition by hydrothermal solutions ascending from a hot source (Ruzicka, 1971; Sassano, 1972), whereas the later concepts favour formation from meteoric solutions descending from surface (Langford, 1974).

For the Proterozoic vein-type deposits, the association with fluvial sediments is fairly well established. For the more recent deposits such as the Schwartzwalder and Midnite mines, the association is much less well established, but even here recent publications favour origins by descending solutions. At the Midnite mine, early investigations (Barrington and Kerr, 1961) postulated deep-seated origins for ore-forming solutions, but with better data, the low temperature direct meteoric source has gained favour (Ludwig and others, 1981). Young (1979) has argued for a meteoric source for the Schwartzwalder deposits, and the trace element composition is what would be expected (Table 2, column N). He also points out characteristics in the pitchblende that tend to support this source.

Thus the appearance of oxygen in the atmosphere about 2,000 Ma ago resulted in the development of a new type of uranium deposit—one characterized by the surficial-reducing suite of elements and an association with terrestrial sandstones. The sudden appearance of these deposits without any types transitional with the quartz-pebble conglomerate types seems to indicate that the increase of oxygen to near present-day levels was fairly fast, possibly less than 400 Ma.

ACKNOWLEDGMENT

The author wishes to acknowledge his appreciation of the comments made by H. C. Granger.

REFERENCES CITED

Barrington, J., and Kerr, P. F., 1961, Uranium mineralization at the Midnite mine, Spokane, Washington: Economic Geology, v. 56, p. 241–258.

Binns, R. A., McAndrew, J., and Sun, S. S., 1980, Origin of mineralization at Jabiluka, *in* Feguson, J., and Goleby, A., eds., Uranium in the Pine Creek Geosyncline: Proceedings of a symposium, Sydney, 1979: International Atomic Energy Agency, Vienna, p. 543–562.

Brookins, D. G., 1980a, Syngenetic model for some early Proterozoic uranium deposits: Evidence from Oklo, *in* Ferguson, J., and Goleby, A. B., eds., Uranium in the Pine Creek Geosyncline: Proceedings of a symposium, Sydney, 1979: International Atomic Energy Agency, Vienna, p. 709–720.

—— 1980b, Geochronological studies in the Grants Mineral Belt, *in* Rautman, C. A., ed., Geology and mineralogy of the Grants uranium region, 1979: New Mexico Bureau of Mines and Mineral Resources Memoir 38, p. 52–58.

Brummer, J. J., Saracoglu, N., Wallis, R. H., and Golightly, J. P., 1981, McClean uranium deposits of Part 2, Geology: CIM Geology Division, Uranium Field Excursion Guide, Saskatoon, Saskatchewan, p. 51–64.

Cameron, E. M., and Garrels, R. M., 1980, Geochemical compositions of some Precambrian shales from the Canadian Shield: Chemical Geology, v. 28, p. 181–197.

Cloud, P., 1972, A working model of the primitive Earth: American Journal of Science, v. 272, p. 537–548.

Crick, I. H., Muir, M. D., Needham, R. S., and Roarty, M. J., 1980, Geology and mineralogy of the South Alligator Uranium Field, *in* Ferguson, J., and Goleby, A. B., eds., Uranium in the Pine Creek Geosynclne: Proceedings of a symposium, Sydney, 1979: International Atomic Energy Agency, Vienna, p. 273–276.

Davidson, C. F., 1965, The mode of origin of blanket orebodies: Transactions of the Institute of Mining and Metallurgy, London, v. 74, p. 319–337.

Derry, D. R., 1973, Ore deposition and contemporaneous surfaces: Economic Geology, v. 68, p. 1374–1380.

Dimroth, E., and Kimberley, M. M., 1976, Precambrian atmospheric oxygen; evidence in the sedimentary distributions of carbon, sulfur, uranium, and iron: Canadian Journal of Earth Sciences, v. 13, p. 1161–1185.

Finch, W. I., 1967, Geology of epigenetic uranium deposits in sandstone in the United States: U.S. Geological Survey Professional Paper 538.

Fischer, R. P., 1970, Similarities, differences and some genetic problems of the Wyoming and Colorado Plateau types of uranium deposits in sandstone: Economic Geology, v. 65, p. 778–784.

Gancarz, A., 1978, U-Pb age (2.05×10^9 years) of the Okla uranium deposit, *in* Natural fission reactors (les reacteurs de fission naturels): Proceedings of a technical committee meeting, Paris, International Atomic Energy Agency, Vienna, p. 513–520.

Gangloff, A., 1970, Notes sommaires sur la geologie des principaux districts uraniferes études par le CEA, *in* Uranium exploration geology:

Proceedings of a pannel, Vienna: International Atomic Energy Agency, Vienna, p. 77–104.

Gauthier-Lafaye, F., Besnue, Y., and Weber, F., 1978, Donnees nouvelles sur l'environment geologique des reacteurs naturels, *in* Natural fission reactors: International Atomic Energy Agency Pannel Proceedings Series, Paris, p. 35–71.

Gauthier-LaFaye, F., and others, 1980, Le gisement d'Okla et ses reacteurs de fission naturels, *in* Ferguson, J., and Goleby, A. B., eds., Uranium in the Pine Creek Geosyncline: Proceedings of a symposium, Sydney, 1979: International Atomic Energy Agency, Vienna, p. 663–674.

Grandstaff, D. E., 1980, Origin of uraniferous conglomerates at Elliot Lake, Canada, and Witwatersrand, South Africa: implications for oxygen in the Precambrian atmosphere: Precambrian Research, v. 13, p. 1–26.

Hattori, K., Campbell, F. A., and Krouse, H. R., 1981, Stable isotope study on uraniferous conglomerate in Elliot Lake: Geological Association of Canada, Abstracts, v. 6, p. A27.

Hoeve, J., and others, 1980, Athabasca basin unconformity-type uranium deposits: A special class of sandstone-type deposits?, *in* Ferguson, J., and Goleby, A. B., eds., Uranium in the Pine Creek Geosyncline: Proceedings of a symposium, Sydney, 1979: International Atomic Energy Agency, Vienna, p. 575–594.

Kimberley, M. M., 1978, Origin of stratiform uranium deposits in sandstone, conglomerate and pyroclastic rock, *in* Kimberley, M. M., ed., Uranium deposits; their mineralogy and origin: Mineralogical Association, Canada, p. 339–382.

Koeppel, V., 1968, Age and history of uranium mineralization of the Beaverlodge area, Saskatchewan: Geological Survey of Canada Paper 67-31.

Langford, F. F., 1974, A supergene origin for vein-type uranium ores in the light of the Western Australian calcrete-carnotite deposits: Economic Geology, v. 69, p. 516–526.

——1977, Surficial origin of North American pitchblende and related uranium deposits: American Association of Petroleum Geologists Bulletin, v. 61, p. 28–42.

Ludwig, K. R., Nash, J. T., and Naeser, C. W., 1981, U-Pb isotope systematics and age of uranium mineralization, Midnite mine Washington: Economic Geology, v. 76, p. 89–110.

Martin, H., 1979, Geochemical behaviour of major and trace elements during incongruent melting of bictite in the St. Malo massif migmatites: Neues Jahrbuch für Mineralogie, p. 509–524.

Needham, R. S., Crick, I. H., and Stuart-Smith, P. G., 1980, Regional geology of the Pine Creek Geosyncline, *in* Ferguson, J., and Goleby, A. B., eds., Uranium in the Pine Creek Geosyncline: Proceedings of a symposium, Sydney, 1979: International Atomic Energy Agency, Vienna, p. 1–22.

Page, R. W., Compston, W., Needham, R. S., 1980, Chronology and evolution of the Late-Archean basement and Proterozoic rocks in the Alligator Rivers Uranium Field, Northern Territory, Australia, *in* Ferguson, J., and Goleby, A. B., eds., Uranium in the Pine Creek Geosyncline: Proceedings of a symposium, Sydney, 1979: International Atomic Energy Agency, Vienna, p. 39–68.

Place, J., Della Valle, R. S., and Brookin, D. G., 1980, Mineralogy and geochemistry of Mariano Lake uranium deposit, Smith Lake district, *in* Rautmann, C. A., ed., Geology and mineral technology of the Grants uranium region 1979: New Mexico Bureau of Mines and Minerals Memoir 38, p. 172–184.

Rich, R. A., Holland, H. D., and Peterson, U., 1977, Hydrothermal uranium deposits: Elsevier, Amsterdam.

Robertson, D. S., 1974, Basal Proterozoic units as fossil time markes, and their use in uranium prospection, *in* Formation of uranium ore deposits: Athens symposium: International Atomic Energy Agency, Vienna, p. 495–512.

Robertson, J. A., 1978, Uranium deposits in Ontario, *in* Kimberley, M. M., ed., Uranium deposits; their mineralogy and origin: Mineralogical Association of Canada, p. 224–280.

Roscoe, S. M., 1969, Huronian rocks and uraniferous conglomerates in the Canadian Shield: Geological Survey of Canada Paper 68-40.

——1973, The Huronian Supergroup, a Palaeoaphebian succession showing evidence of atmospheric evolution, *in* Young, G. M., ed., Huronian stratigraphy and sedimentation: Geological Association of Canada Special Paper 12, p. 31–48.

Ruzicka, V., 1971, Geological comparison between east European and Canadian uranium deposits: Geological Survey of Canada Paper 70-48.

Sassano, G. P., Fritz, P., and Morton, R. D., 1972, Paragenesis and isotopic composition of some gangue minerals from the uranium deposits of Eldorado, Saskatchewan: Canadian Journal of Earth Sciences, v. 9, p. 141–157.

Sibbald, T.I.I., and others, 1981, Saskatchewan uranium field trip guide, *in* Thompson, R. I., and Cook, D. G., eds., Field guides to geology and mineral deposits: Calgary meeting, GAC-MAC-CGU: Geological Association Canada, p. 121–142.

Simpson, P. R., and Bowles, J.F.W., 1977, Uranium mineralization of the Witwatersrand and Dominion Reef systems: Philosophical Transactions of the Royal Society of London, ser. A, v. 286, p. 527–548.

——1978, Mineralogical evidence for the mode of deposition and metamorphism of reaction zone samples from Oklo, *in* Natural fission reactors: International Atomic Energy Agency Pannel Proceedings Series, Paris, p. 297–303.

Smith, D. A., and Peterson, R. J., 1980, Geology and recognition of a relict uranium deposit in sec, 28, T. 14N, R, 10W., Southwest Ambrosia Lake area, McKinley County, *in* Rautman, C. A., ed., Geology and mineral technology of the Grants uranium region: New Mexico Bureau of Mines and Mineral Resources Memoir 38, p. 215–225.

Squyres, J. B., 1980, Origin and significance of organic matter in uranium deposits of Morrison Formation, San Juan Basin, New Mexico, *in* Rautman, C. A., ed., Geology and mineral technology of the Grants uranium region, 1979: New Mexico Bureau of Mines and Mineral Resources Memoir 38, p. 86–96.

Steacy, J. R., 1953, An occurrence of uraninite in a blacksand: American Mineralogist, v. 38, p. 549–550.

Tortosa, D.J.J., 1983, Geology of the Cenex Mine [M.Sc. thesis]: University of Saskatchewan.

Tremblay, L. P., 1972, Geology of the Beaverlodge mining area, Saskatchewan: Geological Survey of Canada Memoir 367.

Turekian, K. K., and Wedepohl, K. H., 1961, Distribution of the elements in some major units of the Earth's crust: Geological Society of America Bulletin, v. 72, p. 175–192.

Whiteside, H.C.M., 1970, Uraniferous Precambrian conglomerates of South Africa, *in* Uranium exploration geology: Proceedings of a pannel, Vienna: International Atomic Energy Agency, Vienna, p. 49–73.

Young, E. J., 1979, Genesis of the Schwartzwalder uranium deposit, Jefferson County, Colorado: University of Wyoming Contributions to Geology, v. 17, p. 179–186.

MANUSCRIPT ACCEPTED BY THE SOCIETY APRIL 14, 1983

Printed in U.S.A.

Geological Society of America
Memoir 161
1983

Aspects of Proterozoic biogeology

Preston Cloud
Baas Becking Geobiological Laboratory
Canberra, A.C.T. 2601, Australia

and

Department of Geological Sciences
University of California
Santa Barbara, California 93106

ABSTRACT

The sialic plutonism that transformed prevailing petrographic, sedimentary, and paleogeographic styles from Archean to Proterozoic aspects lasted for 600 million years. It created the first extensive cratonal surfaces, with all their potential for interaction among a diversity of microbiotas and their physical surroundings. Earth, in fact, was essentially completed during the Proterozoic. Continental and oceanic crusts and waters achieved their approximate present dimensions and chemistries. O_2-releasing photosynthesis became established. Life at the cellular level differentiated, culminating in eucaryotic heredity and leading to Metazoa at the Proterozoic-Phanerozoic transition. A kinetic lag between sources and sinks of O_2 eventually created an oxygenous atmosphere, its development being reflected by such sedimentary peculiarities as detrital uraninite, banded-iron-formation, distinctive soil profiles, red beds, and perhaps sedimentary phosphorites and metal sulfides. Combined with biological evidence, the temporal distribution of such materials suggests an O_2 growth curve connecting these *provisional* points: (1) near zero O_2 until $\sim 2.3 \times 10^9$ years ago, (2) 1 percent present atmospheric level (PAL) O_2 2-2.3 $\times 10^9$ years ago, (3) ~ 7 percent PAL 670×10^6 years ago, (4) ~ 10 percent PAL 550×10^6 years ago, and (5) present atmospheric levels beginning $\sim 400 \times 10^6$ years ago.

INTRODUCTION

In the beginning, some 4.57 Gyr (4.57×10^9 years) ago, there was no hydrosphere, nor soil, nor solid surface on which soil might form, nor any place where life might have survived had it been present. A fierce, early solar wind, blowing at thousands of kilometers a second, kept Earth stripped of any gases that might have formed a permanent atmosphere, and from which water might have condensed on cooling.

Iron settled through the hot primordial silicate mush—a product of gravitational and early radiogenic heating—giving rise to a fluid core, a magnetic field, and a shielding magnetosphere that brought the early solar wind to bay. An atmosphere could then be retained as it was outgassed from the heaving Hadean Earth (Fig. 1), and from this a hydrosphere could eventually condense to deposit the first Archean sediments. Thus originated, within the limiting range of surface temperatures, the conditions under which the atmosphere, the oceans and fresh waters, and life could arise to begin the interactions we address here.

The later, profoundly diachronous transition from Archean to Proterozoic conditions (Fig. 1) altered the *prevailing* chemistry, tectonic style, sites of sedimentation, and potential sites of life on Earth. It generated an unprecedented diversity and extent of shallow-water epicontinental and coastal habitats. It exerted new pressures on biologic, atmospheric, and hydrospheric evolution.

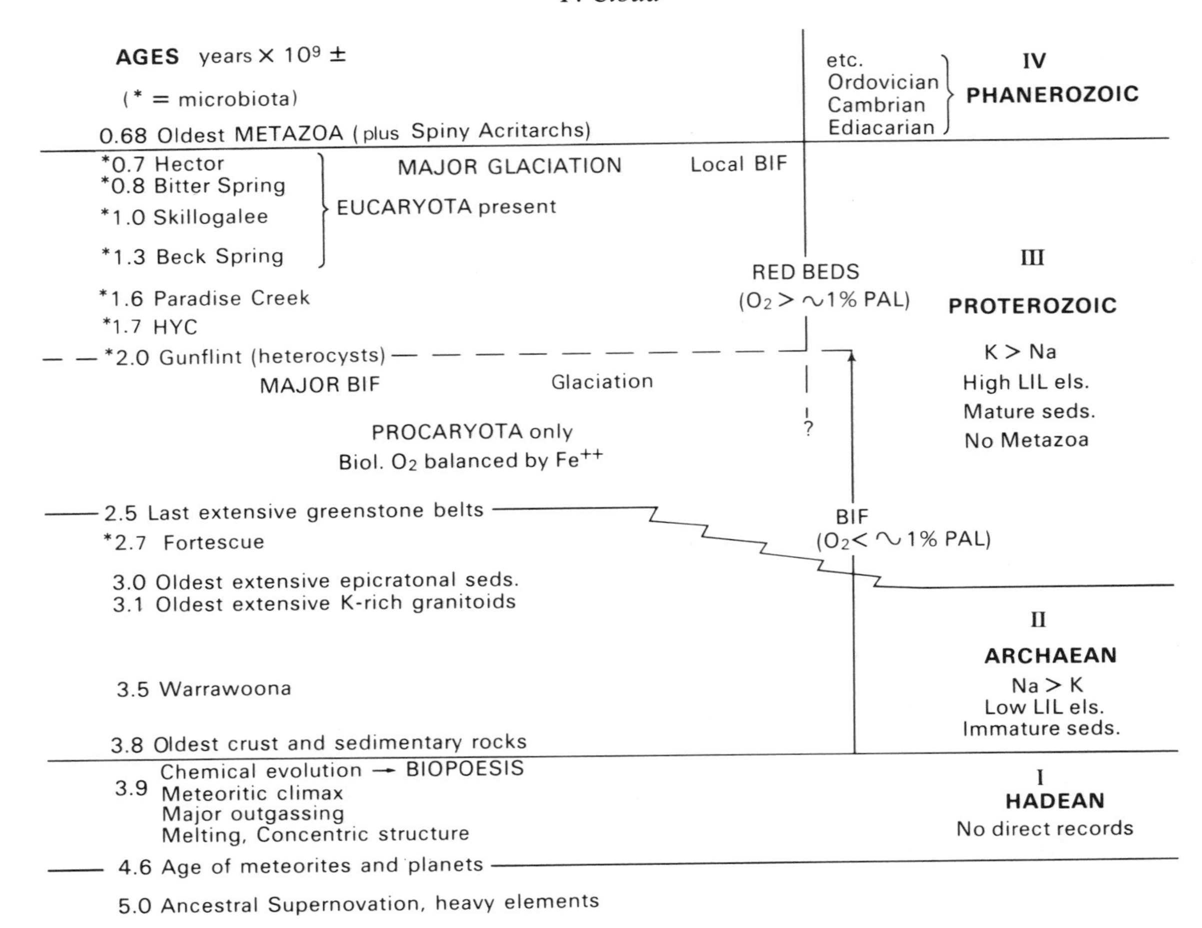

Fig. 1 Abbreviated outline of pre-Phanerozoic history

Considered broadly, Earth was essentially completed during the Proterozoic. The continental and oceanic crusts of the planet achieved their approximate present dimensions and thicknesses then. Plate tectonics in the modern sense began. Life at the cellular level evolved a differentiation of functions and characteristics, culminating in mitotic cell division and eventually the complete eucaryotic hereditary apparatus. This led, when other conditions were appropriate, to multicellular animal life and the beginning of Phanerozoic history about 670 Myr (670×10^6 years) ago. Meanwhile, oxidative phosphorylation had evolved, while a kinetic lag between sources and sinks of O_2 gave rise to an oxygenous atmosphere that eventually reached levels supportive of metazoan evolution. The history of hydrospheric and atmospheric O_2 is reflected in the sedimentary record by oxidized sediments such as sulfates and red beds, by sediments that are not oxidized but would be under a fully oxygenous atmosphere, by distinctive weathering profiles, and by the development of certain strata-bound mineral deposits and stages in the evolution of life.

PROTEROZOIC LIFE, AIR, WATER, AND SEDIMENTS AS AN INTERACTING BIOGEOLOGIC SYSTEM

The net sedimentary result of the transition from Archean to Proterozoic was a large increase in the sedimentary mass and a change in its prevailing character from immature volcanogenic and ensimatic to mature epicratonal and ensialic. This transition was marked by a shift toward more felsic composition, higher K/Na ratios, a higher ratio of ferric to ferrous iron, an increase in multicycle clastic sediments, the first appearance of sedimentary phosphorites, a conspicuous increase in the volume of carbonate rocks, and a great expansion of epicratonal habitats. Veizer and Jansen (1979) have estimated that the global sedimentary mass attained its present volume by ~2 Gyr ago, and that the ensuing sedimentary budget has been about two-thirds recycled and thus relatively invariant in its main characteristics. Some large Proterozoic sedimentary piles are wedge-like, similar to those of passive continental margins. Others are thick basin fills, more or less deformed, implying subsurface transfer of mass. Some are thin veneers reminiscent of pre-breakup or platform sedimentation. Few are truly eugeosynclinal.

The waning heat flux from initial and radiogenic sources combined with the growth of Proterozoic continental area to reduce the chemical effects of mantle sources on the hydrosphere and to increase the volume of fresh waters and their influence in the flux of sediments and dissolved matter from land to sea. Interactions with atmosphere and biosphere resulted in other changes. The origin of chlorophyll-*a*-based photosynthesis, with oxidative phosphorylation, led to changes in the buffer capacity of sea water, lessening and finally eliminating the capability of normal sea water to carry iron in solution and increasing its capacity for Ca^{++}, Mg^{++}, and HCO_3^- ions and the precipitation of dolomite and limestone. The evolution of the eucaryotic cell eventually resulted in sea water becoming undersaturated in silica because of its removal by silica secreting microorganisms (but probably not until after the Proterozoic).

The chemistry of sea water has presumably changed to some extent as a result of such variables, although we cannot as yet say in detail how. We can say, however, that the present buffering system of the sea, controlled as it is by the joint kinetics of mantle and continental fluxes (Holland, 1978), and by large-scale biological processes, was probably both a product of and a factor in the evolution of the Proterozoic biosphere and atmosphere.

Clearly these and other aspects of Proterozoic history cannot be explained as the consequences of a narrow methodological uniformitarianism. On the other hand, our only hope of understanding them invokes a different aspect of uniformitarianism—the well-warranted assumption that natural laws have not changed over geologic time, or that, if they have changed, they have changed in lawful ways.

Consider Proterozoic history from this viewpoint. Despite gaps in the record, it is manifest from the evidence of rock weathering and aquatic sediment transport given by the Isua and younger Archean metasediments that both hydrosphere and atmosphere had already long been in existence, and in copious volume, when the Proterozoic began. Life, too, had been in existence at least since 3.56 Gyr ago, if we accept the presumptive evidence for it of stromatolites from the Warrawoona Group of Western Australia (Lowe, 1980; Walter and others, 1980) and if we accept the age of those rocks to be the Sm-Nd age determined by O'Nions and others (1980).

But if we accept the constancy of natural laws, we must conclude that the atmosphere under which life arose lacked or contained only trivial and evanescent free O_2. I have gone through the ample evidence to this effect on several prior occasions (e.g., Cloud 1976b, 1980) and will not repeat it here.

Although evidence for a source of O_2 is given by sedimentary barite in the Swaziland sediments (Perry and others, 1971) and by barite after gypsum in the Warrawoona beds (Walter and others, 1980), that O_2 need never have been a free component of the atmosphere. Bacteria that oxidize sulfides and sulfite to sulfate release no free O_2 in the process. In fact, the slight sulfur isotope fractionation observed in these ancient sediments would be consistent either with such a bacterial origin, or with physical processes that may or may not have involved evanescent O_2 from the photolysis of H_2O or CO_2.

A few very early Proterozoic nannofossil and stromatolite records described by Schopf and Walter (1980) present similar equivocal evidence as to contemporary biology and biochemistry. The stromatolites, however, do imply that CO_2 assimilation and therefore some form of photosynthesis, perhaps O_2-releasing, could have been going on as far back as Warrawoona time. And Schidlowski and others (1979) have proposed that carbon isotope ratios indicate a continuity of biological processes from Isua time (~3.8 Gyr ago) until now.

There is, in any case, no question that biological activity was important throughout Proterozoic history. The question is, by what and in what ways? The most important events were probably (1) the origin of O_2-producing photosynthesis, (2) the origin of bacterial sulfate reduction, and (3) the origin of the eucaryotic cell. These events were important because (1) O_2-releasing photosynthesis, followed by carbon burial, eventually led to an oxidizing hydrosphere and atmosphere, with feedbacks to sedimentation and ore-forming processes; (2) bacterial sulfate reduction produced much of the sulfides in the succeeding sedimentary record, probably including some that form or are associated with ore deposits; and (3) the origin of the eucaryotic cell opened the way for eucaryotic diversification in later Proterozoic history, leading eventually to multicellular plants and animals, with all the influences they were to impose on the following Phanerozoic world.

The appearance and levels of O_2 in the Proterozoic hydrosphere and atmosphere are both important to all of the interactions with which we are here concerned and an aspect of Proterozoic history about which some evidence is available. That evidence comes not only from the sedimentary and paleontological record but also from modern microbial ecology and the existing oxygen cycle.

The evolution and persistence of an aerobic atmosphere was a highly improbable event. The products of either photosynthetic or photolytic O_2 production are thermodynamically unstable, promptly recombining unless segregated. O_2 could not have accumulated in either hydrosphere or atmosphere except as the result of a kinetic lag between sinks and sources. The result of that lag was temporarily to suspend thermodynamic balances which, even today, would eliminate all resident O_2 in the atmosphere in ~3 million years (Holland, 1978).

The principal current O_2 sinks are the exposure by erosion of once buried reduced carbon, sulfides, and ferrous iron and the oxidation of volcanic gases. According to Holland, they account for about three-fourths and one-fourth, respectively, of the approximately 400 million metric tons of 0_2 that are added yearly to the atmosphere as a result of photosynthesis, followed by burial of organic matter.

The O_2 sinks of early Proterozoic and Archean time were vast by comparison. They comprised all of the reduced atmospheric components inherited from Earth's initial aggregation, including any residual H_2 from the early solar wind, the reduced products of the copious volcanic outgassing of Hadean and Archean time, and a high rate of flux of reduced matter in solution, both from weathering and from volcanic exhalation—e.g., ferrous iron, carbon monoxide, sulfite, and various sulfides.

Although it is certain that photolytic dissociation of H_2O was actively producing O_2 from earliest times onward, the amount of accumulatable free O_2 so produced has probably always been small (summarized by Cloud, 1980). It is very unlikely that such O_2 could have effectively overfilled early O_2 sinks to become more than a trivial and evanescent atmospheric component—enough, perhaps, to account for local hematitic films that have been reported on iron-rich rocks under an atmosphere that might be described as weakly oxygenous, but not aerobic.

With the appearance of chlorophyll-*a*, however, O_2-producing microbial photosynthesis became potentially important. Just how it happened that a powerful biological poison like O_2 came to be tolerated and eventually essential to biological processes is a mystery on which the geological record is mute. We must turn to modern microbiology and microbial ecology for clues. There we observe two distinct phases in the photosynthetic mechanism of the myxophytes or blue-green algae (a current and nomenclaturally invalid fad-word is Cyanobacteria, which should appear any day now as Kyanobacteria). The nutrient-manufacturing activities of these procaryotes include two photosystems, just as among the eucaryotic algae and higher plants. Photosystem I drives a bacterial-type anaerobic photosynthesis, with H_2S as the electron donor and sulfur as a by-product. Photosystem II, using water as the electron donor, yields free O_2. A number of living aquatic blue-green algae (BGA), unlike most eucaryotic algae and all higher plants, are able to switch from aerobic to anaerobic photosynthesis, using only photosystem I (e.g., *Oscillatoria limnetica* and others, Oren and others, 1977). Even when engaged in O_2-producing photosynthesis, these microbes prefer environments having low P_{O_2}.

I have elsewhere suggested that the first O_2-producing photosynthesizers may have been something like this (Cloud, 1976b, 1980, 1982). I have also suggested that ferrous iron in their ambient hydrosphere may have exercised an O_2-depressing effect comparable to that of H_2S during the operation of photosystem II. That suggestion is reinforced by the prevalence of iron in the radiation-shielding scytonemine pigments that envelop so many modern BGA, as well as by the part played by ferrous iron in the construction of the cytochromes and other vital macrocyclic pigments. It takes only a little imagination to link these conclusions in a response to the riddle of the banded-iron-formation (BIF): i.e., how to explain the appearance, in the same setting, of ferrous iron in solution, its precipitation in the ferric or ferro-ferric state, and the alternating thin laminae of iron-rich and iron-poor silica that are locally traceable for hundreds of kilometers. A mutual interaction between fluctuating populations of oxygen-sensitive BGA or their progenitors and fluctuating sources of ferrous iron in an oxygen-deprived environment is visualized (Cloud, 1973, 1976b, 1980).

Microorganisms found in association with the 2 Gyr-old Gunflint BIF are consistent with such an interpretation (Barghoorn and Tyler, 1965; Cloud, 1965). Some of them, in fact, show a cellular differentiation so similar to that of modern heterocyst-bearing myxophycean algae (Cloud, 1978, Fig. 17) as to imply both systematic affinity and functional equivalence. The heterocysts of modern BGA are devices for shielding sites of nitrogen fixation from ambient O_2. Similar structures in Gunflint time imply that enough O_2 was present 2 Gyr ago to call for such shielding.

Important historical changes in O_2 levels are implied by the widespread occurrence of easily oxidized detrital uraninite and pyrite in continental sediments older than ~2.3 Gyr, the BIF that is so prominent before 2 Gyr ago and so unusual afterwards, and the wide extent of oxidized sedimentary rocks younger than ~2 Gyr.

Although traces of detrital uraninite are reported from unusual local modern settings, Grandstaff (1980) concludes that the Proterozoic uraninites imply fluctuating low levels of O_2 between $\sim 10^{-4}$ and 1 percent PAL until their last abundant record in the $\sim 2.3 \times 10^9$ year-old lower Huronian fluviatile sediments. The thin upper Huronian red beds and those beneath the iron formation of the Labrador geosyncline (Dimroth, 1970) may have formed diagenetically at or near the top of this range—near the Pasteur Level of ~1 percent PAL O_2 that denotes the transition from anaerobic to microaerophilic and aerobic modes of life.

I have long considered 2 Gyr ago to mark the approximate time at which atmospheric O_2 first permanently attained levels above about 1 percent PAL and began to accumulate—based on the presence of abundant BIF until then and red beds after, in combination with the foregoing evidence. I have also recognized that there had to have been some evanescent free O_2 earlier: that there was necessarily a long lag and probably times of fluctuating disequilibrium between the beginning of O_2-producing photosynthesis and the filling of all the major O_2 sinks. Now that geochemistry is giving us better numbers, and keen field observers are fleshing out the observational data base, my earlier number for the beginning of O_2 buildup might best be changed from 2 to somewhere between 2 and 2.3 Gyr ago, perhaps closer to the latter, as Roscoe suggested in 1969, and as the work of Dimroth (1970), Button (1979), and others increasingly suggests.

What biogeological effects might be recorded in Proterozoic history other than a relation to O_2 levels in hydrosphere and atmosphere, with feedback in the form of BIF, detrital uraninite, and red beds? A possible effect is the widespread stratabound metal-sulfide mineralization and local sedimentary (perhaps diagenetic) phosphorites first known in rocks about 2 Gyr old. The phosphorites may denote the beginning of upwelling to shallow platforms, and the sulfides may be related to biological SO_4^{2-} reduction. G. W. Skyring and T. H. Donnelly (personal communication), however, have observed that bacteria assimilate *sulfite* preferentially over sulfate when both are available—implying that bacterial sulfate reduction may be a later evolutionary event. They first observe the conspicuous S-isotope fractionation indicative of bacterial sulfate respiration in sediments ~1.8 to 2 Gyr old—coincident with the onset of extensive massive sulfide deposition reported by A. J. Baer (this volume).

Although I have had to modify particular dates and other details of my earlier model of the primitive Earth (Cloud, 1965, 1973, 1976a-b) and will continue to do so as called for by convincingly documented evidence, the preponderance of new data has, in my opinion, been more supportive than otherwise. Anaerobic BGA photosynthesis was not widely known and was unknown to me when I first proposed the need for minimal O_2 levels for ancestral forms. Distinctive sediment types have stayed close to age-levels predicted—except for sulfates, which remain minor among older sediments and which tell us little about O_2 metabolism before ~2 Gyr ago. Studies of weathering profiles older than 2 Gyr are consistent with very low levels of atmospheric O_2 before that time. No undoubted Metazoa or metazoan traces of coeval origin have yet been found in rocks demonstrably older than 670 million years. And so on. I conclude, then, that the broad outlines of the model remain consistent with known evidence.

But the discussion so far has dealt primarily with the record before 2 Gyr ago. What about younger Proterozoic history? Here we enter the domain of stromatolite ascendancy, about which others will have more to say in this symposium. Suffice it to note that the long argument over whether stromatolite morphology is a result of ecology or biology has been resolved in favor of both. Studies so far support a broad stratigraphic utility that has found global if somewhat generalized applications as well as more detailed local use. Analyses of modern stromatolite analogs are casting light both on morphogenesis and on a kind of functional morphology that carries paleoecological implications.

The flood of publication on pre-Phanerozoic paleontology since the midsixties also reveals among younger Proterozoic rocks a growing diversity and abundance of nannofossils that begin to foreshadow a microbial stratigraphy, along with a distressing abundance of pseudofossils and contaminants. An abrupt microbial size increase at about 1.3 to 1.4 Gyr ago suggests both the appearance of the eucaryotic cell and a microbial marker level that is close to the lower-to-middle Riphean stromatolite transition. A diversity of spore-like objects of uncertain affinity (acritarchs) and other microbial forms in uppermost Proterozoic and lower Phanerozoic strata offers promise of a locally detailed biostratigraphy (e.g., Vidal, 1979 and Vidal and Knoll, this volume). It also reveals some distinctive forms that bracket the transition from older rocks that lack metazoan fossils to younger ones that have them, thus supplementing the metazoan record in identifying the onset of Phanerozoic history. The *Sphaerocongregus* (cf. *Bavlinella*) group of multicomponent spheroids, for instance, seems to range only from uppermost Riphean to Cambrian. The spiny acritarch *Micrhystridium* is unknown to me below Ediacarian equivalents. The spiral filaments of *Obruchevella* range from strata of Ediacarian age to Ordovician, but with apparently distinctive species at several levels, including a small form that seems to be distinctive of an Ediacarian age.

Why the Proterozoic-Phanerozoic transition also seems to be approximately marked by the near disappearance of previously extensive diamictites remains a puzzle. Perhaps the breakup of a Proterozoic supercontinent (or supercontinents) had something to do with it—simultaneously reducing continentality and glaciation while providing the stresses and niche variety that stimulated metazoan emergence as Harland (1964) once suggested.

It seems more likely, however, both that metazoan emergence was linked with some more essential requirement and that the beginnings of breakup predated the diamictites. Reflection reminds one that two essential preconditions had to be satisfied before a metazoan level of biologic evolution could be reached. First, cellular evolution had to have attained the eucaryotic level, whether by serial endosymbiosis as Margulis (1971) so persuasively argues or by other modes. Second, a sufficient level of free O_2 was also necessary. As I interpret it, the marked increase in cell size and the branching of filamentous forms observed at 1.3 to 1.4 Gyr ago are probably as good a biogeological manifestation of the attainment of a eucaryotic level of organization as we are likely to see before the first Metazoa themselves. If, then, eucaryotes were already present, a level of free O_2 sufficient for epithelial diffusion to metazoan interiors may have been the trigger that set off the initial metazoan radiation, ushering in the Phanerozoic.

Others prefer to think of the attainment of the eucaryotic state itself as the initiating event for Metazoa. To support that position, however, they must argue for the prior attainment of the P_{O_2} required, while deferring the beginning of eucaryotic evolution until just before the first appearance of Metazoa ~670 million years ago. In favor of O_2 as the trigger, I would add to the evidence I find compelling for an earlier time of eucaryotic origin (Cloud, 1976b) the prevalence of medusae and the flimsy and unprotected nature of others among the oldest known metazoans—the Ediacarian fauna. Although some of these are remarkably large in two dimensions, the third dimension (or body wall) remains either thin and unprotected, or, as in the medusae, but one cell thick. Their attenuation and lack of exoskeletons suggest that they may have acquired their respiratory O_2 by simple epithelial diffusion at relatively low ambient O_2 levels. The acquisition of diffusion-blocking exoskeletons near the beginning of conventional Cambrian time implies the evolution of special breathing organs and a rise toward higher levels of free atmospheric O_2. Thus commenced a burst of diversification that led, by the end of Early Cambrian history, to a majority of the classes and most of the phyla of Metazoa ever to be known from the fossil record.

If the preceding observations are valid, they provide grounds for an approximate O_2 growth curve (Cloud, 1978, Fig. 20). One might draw such a curve through the following inferred levels of oxygen: (1) near zero until ~2.3 Gyr ago; (2) ~1 percent PAL beginning between ~2.3 and ~2 Gyr ago; (3) ~7 percent PAL at the first appearance of Metazoa ~670 Myr ago, the best number I have found for the lower limit of O_2 diffusion to a naked metazoan <1 mm thick; (4) ~10 percent PAL 550 Myr ago, being about the lowest level of O_2 tolerated by Metazoa with conventional O_2 transfer systems; and (5) the attainment of roughly steady-state O_2 levels comparable to the present, signalled by the emergence of a land biota and large predatory fish ~400 Myr ago.

These numbers are not immutable. The trend might better be suggested by a broad swath. But drawing a line rather than a swath provides a clear target for the bright new cohort of geochemists to improve upon. I await their results with much interest.

In seeking to advance our knowledge and refine our understanding of matter discussed, three main needs stand out in addition to a continuing flow of good radiometric ages. (1) We need a great deal more good pre-Phanerozoic sedimentology and geologic mapping. (2) We need continuing search in Proterozoic and older rocks for new, authentic, and well-dated microbial records and geochemical clues to early Earth history. (3) And we need quantitative assessments of phenomena that may be related to the history of atmospheric O_2.

The history of free O_2 is a particularly attractive problem because there are several cross-checking ways to get at it and because we already have made some progress toward resolving it. Further to advance our understanding of this problem we must ask:

1. How can we write more believable, better quantified geochemical budgets for oxygen and its coproducts, whether carbon, hydrogen, or something else?

2. Have we identified all of the early oxygen sinks that delayed the buildup of O_2 in the hydrosphere and atmosphere? Besides ferrous iron, volcanic sulfides and sulfites, and reducing atmospheric gases such as hydrogen, ammonia, methane, and carbon monoxide, were there other important oxygen sinks on the primitive Earth? What might some yet unidentified ones be? And what are the best estimates we can make of quantities involved at all levels, including quantities recycled over geologic history?

3. What kinds of evidence other than that suggested might tell us when O_2 first appeared in the hydrosphere and atmosphere as more than a trivial and transient gas and at what levels?

4. When and why did O_2 start to build up in the atmosphere, and what evidence might there be for earlier episodes of low-level atmospheric oxygenation that were overwhelmed by new oxygen sinks, turning the trend back toward anoxic states?

5. Once O_2 began to accumulate in the atmosphere on a sustained scale, how rapidly did it build up? And what clues might we find to O_2 levels at various times in Earth history? What, for instance, might the ratios of carbon and sulfur isotopes, ferro-ferric ratios, the characteristics of sedimentary uranium and copper ores, and weathering profiles tell us of O_2 levels and possible swings in abundance with time?

6. What likely interactions may have taken place between events and processes suggested and living systems, known or yet unknown? The biogeologic evidence of cell diameter, filament branching, and oxidation suggests an age of perhaps 1.4 and a possible age range of 1.3 to 2×10^9 Gyr ago for the origin of the eucaryotes. Can we narrow that down? Similarly, a variety of evidence suggests the first appearance of Metazoa perhaps 670 Myr ago. Will that date bear up, or will authentic older Metazoa be found? What other points or ranges dare we hypothesize or can we establish or bracket on a provisional curve of oxygen growth?

REFERENCES CITED

Barghoorn, E. S., and Tyler, S. A., 1965, Microorganisms from the Gunflint chert: Science, v. 147, p. 563–577.

Button, A., 1979, Early Proterozoic weathering profile on the 2200 m.y. old Hekpoort Basalt, Pretoria Group, South Africa: Preliminary Results: University of Witwatersrand, Economic Geology Research Unit, Information Circular, No. 133, 21 p.

Cloud, P., 1965, Significance of the Gunflint (Precambrian) microflora: Science, v. 148, p. 27–45.

—— 1973, Paleoecological significance of the banded iron-formation: Economic Geology, v. 68, p. 1135–1143.

—— 1976a, Major features of crustal evolution: Geological Society of South Africa Bulletin, v. 79 (Annexure), 33 p.

—— 1976b, Beginnings of biosphere evolution and their biogeochemical consequences: Paleobiology, v. 2, no. 4, p. 351–387.

—— 1978, Cosmos, earth, and man: New Haven, Yale University Press, 372 p.

—— 1980, Early biogeochemical systems, *in* Trudinger, P. A., and others, eds., Biogeochemistry of ancient and modern environments: Berlin, Springer-Verlag, p. 7–27.

—— 1983, Early biogeologic history: the emergence of a paradigm, *in* Schopf, J. W., ed., Origin and evolution of earth's earliest biosphere: an interdisciplinary study: Princeton, Princeton University Press, (in press).

Dimroth, E., 1970, Evolution of the Labrador geosyncline: Geological Society of America Bulletin, v. 81, p. 2717–2742.

Grandstaff, D. E., 1980, Origin of uraniferous conglomerates at Elliot Lake, Canada and Witwatersrand, South Africa: implications for oxygen in the Precambrian atmosphere: Precambrian Research, v. 13, no. 1, p. 1–26.

Harland, W. B., 1964, Evidence of late Precambrian glaciation and its significance, *in* Nairn, A.E.M., ed., Problems in paleoclimatology: New York, Wiley (Interscience), p. 119–149.

Holland, H. D., 1978, The chemistry of the atmosphere and oceans: New York, John Wiley and Sons, 351 p.

Lowe, D. R., 1980, Stromatolites 3,400-Myr old from the Archaean of Western Australia: Nature, v. 284, p. 441–443.

O'Nions, R. K., Hamilton, P. J., and Evensen, N. M., 1980, The chemical evolution of the earth's mantle: Scientific American, v. 242, no. 5, p. 91–101.

Oren, A., Padan, A., and Avron, M., 1977, Quantum yields for oxygenic and anoxygenic photosynthesis in the cyanobacterium *Oscillatoria limnetica*: Proceedings of the National Academy of Science, v. 74, no. 5, p. 2152–2156.

Perry, E. C., Monster, J., and Reimer, T. O., 1971, Sulfur isotopes in Swaziland System barites and the evolution of Earth's atmosphere: Science, v. 171, p. 1015–1016.

Roscoe, S. M., 1969, Huronian rocks and uraniferous conglomerates in the Canadian Shield: Geological Survey of Canada Paper 68–40, 205 p.

Schidlowski, M., and others, 1979, Carbon isotope geochemistry of the 4.7 $\times 10^9$-yr-old Isua sediments, West Greenland: implications for the Archean carbon and oxygen cycles: Geochimica et Cosmochimica Acta, v. 43, p. 189–199.

Schopf, J. W., and Walter, M. R., 1980, Archaean microfossils and "microfossil-like" objects—a critical appraisal: Geological Society of Australia, 2nd International Archaean Symposium, Perth, p. 23–24.

Veizer, J., and Jansen, S., 1979, Basement and sedimentary recycling and continental evolution: Journal of Geology, v. 87, p. 341–370.

Vidal, G., 1979, Acritarchs and the correlation of the upper Proterozoic: University of Lund, Institutes of Mineralogy, Paleontology, and Quaternary Geology Publications, No. 219, 21 p.

Walter, M. R., Buick, R., and Dunlop, J.S.R., 1980, Stromatolites 3,400-3,500 Myr old from the North Pole area, Western Australia: Nature, v. 284, p. 443–445.

MANUSCRIPT SUBMITTED MAY 1981; ACCEPTED BY THE SOCIETY APRIL 14, 1983

Printed in U.S.A.

Geological Society of America
Memoir 161
1983

Oxygen isotope geochemistry of Proterozoic chemical sediments

E. C. Perry, Jr.
S. N. Ahmad
Department of Geology
Northern Illinois University
De Kalb, Illinois 60115

ABSTRACT

Proterozoic chemical sediments are depleted in ^{18}O with respect to Phanerozoic analogs. The suggestion that this results entirely from weathering and low temperature exchange with groundwater is not tenable. Metamorphism also fails to explain observed low ^{18}O values. Two hypotheses that fit the isotopic data are: 1) precipitation of chert and carbonate from a hot Proterozoic ocean (60° C for Precambrian X), or (2) precipitation of chert and carbonate from a Proterozoic ocean depleted in ^{18}O. Both of these hypotheses have important implications.

Close association of diamictite with the Kuruman Iron Formation (Precambrian X) suggests that hypothesis 2 is more likely. A detailed study of this diamictite and its stratigraphic relation to the iron formation, however, is required to confirm this observation. A Late Archean (Precambrian W) iron formation (Weld Range, Western Australia) is strongly depleted in ^{18}O. If this depletion results from deposition in a brackish water environment, it implies that the hydrologic regime during the Archean/Proterozoic transition was similar to the modern hydrologic regime.

INTRODUCTION

Average and maximum values of $\delta^{18}O$ (^{18}O variation with respect to Standard Mean Ocean Water (SMOW) as defined by Craig (1957) and Gonfiantini (1978)) of Proterozoic chemical sediments are lower than corresponding values for modern marine carbonates and cherts. In the case of Holocene sediments, values of $\delta^{18}O$ near the maximum frequently result from precipitation in equilibrium, or near-equilibrium with sea water. Much of the ocean has a relatively uniform oxygen isotope composition, and the distribution of oxygen isotopes between carbonates and water varies measurably as a function of equilibration temperature. This relationship between mineral $\delta^{18}O$, water $\delta^{18}O$, and temperature is so well established that determination of $\delta^{18}O$ in the tests of selected organisms has been used extensively to estimate past ocean temperatures from fossils as old as the Cretaceous (Savin, 1977). Low ^{18}O values in Holocene carbonates and cherts often are demonstrably related to recrystallization occurring in the presence of groundwater. Such recrystallization is accompanied by isotopic exchange with waters that, as part of the meteoric water cycle, are distinctively depleted in ^{18}O compared to ocean water.

The oxygen isotope composition of metamorphosed Proterozoic chemical sediments is more difficult to interpret than that of Holocene sediments. $\delta^{18}O$ of a mineral in a Proterozoic marine chemical sediment is modified from the $\delta^{18}O$ of the original sea water precipitate by an uncertain number of poorly defined hydrospheric and metamorphic processes operating over 600 to 2500 m.y. Most of these processes produce unidirectional downward shifts in the original ^{18}O content of the mineral; consequently, it has been common to assume that *all* low $\delta^{18}O$ values in ancient sediments result from secondary processes. Yet, Paleozoic micritic carbonate (Choquette, 1968) and recrystallized, metamorphosed chert (Jones and Knauth, 1979) have been shown to preserve primary ^{18}O values. This demonstrates the possibility that primary oxygen isotope information is preserved in Proterozoic rocks. With one exception (Tucker, 1982), neither recently elaborated petrographic criteria like those of Choquette (1968) nor additional geochemical criteria (Brand and Veizer, 1980) have been applied in any published study of Proterozoic chemical sediments. Nevertheless, the isotopic data of Tables 1 and 2 contain evidence suggesting that the primary oxygen composition of some rocks has been preserved.

Two hypotheses have been advanced to explain the ^{18}O depletion observed in Proterozoic chemical sediments. 1) The oxygen isotope composition in these rocks crudely preserves a temperature record of the ancient ocean (Knauth and Epstein, 1976; Knauth and Lowe, 1979). This hypothesis assumes that the oxygen isotopic composition of the oceans has remained fixed in the past, presumably by hydrothermal exchange reactions like those now occurring near midocean ridges (Muehlenbachs and Clayton, 1976; Gregory and Taylor, 1981). A consequence of this hypothesis is that the climate of the Earth during the Proterozoic was significantly warmer than the modern climate. 2) Another hypothesis is that lower ^{18}O content in precipitated minerals resulted from a lower ^{18}O content of the Proterozoic ocean (Perry, 1967; Perry and Tan, 1972; Perry, Ahmad, Swulius, 1978). This hypothesis requires no drastic difference in Proterozoic and modern climates (consistent with periods of glaciation in both). Instead, it interprets the oxygen isotope record as one of changing chemical interaction of the crust, mantle, and hydrosphere resulting primarily from a decrease toward the present in Earth's radioactive heat generation (Perry, Ahmad and Swulius, 1978; Veizer, in press). It is, of course, not impossible that both climate and ocean isotopic composition are significantly different now than in the Proterozoic.

SYSTEMATICS

Experimentally determined curves showing temperature dependence of the relative ^{18}O enrichment of one substance with respect to another are shown in Figure 1. Relative ^{18}O enrichment is plotted as a fractionation factor defined by the relation:

$$\Delta_{AB} = 1000 \ln \alpha_{AB} = 1000 \ln \frac{(\delta_A - \delta_B)}{(\delta_A - \delta_B)} \simeq \delta_A - \delta_B \qquad 1)$$

Note that since

$$\Delta_{AC} - \Delta_{BC} \equiv \Delta_{AB}, \qquad 2)$$

these fractionation factors may be combined algebraically. $\Delta_{quartz\text{-}water}$, at low temperature, is the largest fractionation factor measured between common and abundant geologic substances (O'Neil, 1977). Two estimates of quartz-water fractionation are shown in Figure 1. The Knauth and Epstein (1976) estimate, which has been fitted to low temperature occurrences, is expressed by the equation:

$$\Delta_{QW} = 3.09 \times 10^6 / T^2\ (^0K) - 3.29. \qquad 3)$$

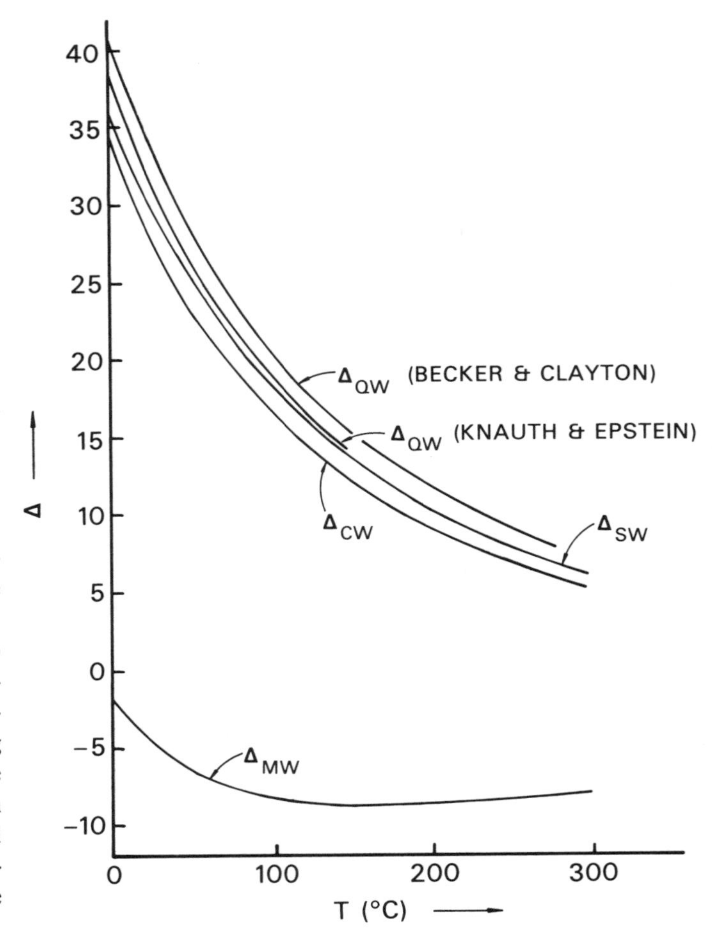

Figure 1. Isotope fractionation versus temperature curves. Quartz-water fractionation estimate of Becker and Clayton (1976) is based on experimental data. The quartz-water fractionation curve of Knauth and Epstein (1976) (equation 3)) is based on measurement of natural cherts. The difference between these curves suggests the range of uncertainty in Δ_{QW}. Δ_{CW} is plotted from equation 4). Δ_{SW} and Δ_{MW} are estimates by Becker and Clayton (1976).

The calcite-water fractionation factor (Δ_{CW}) at 25°C is 27.9. This comes from the equation (O'Neil and others, 1969):

$$\Delta_{CW} = 2.78 \times 10^6 / T^2\ (^0K) - 3.40 \qquad 4)$$

Except that different comparison standards are used, this equation is nearly identical to the paleotemperature equations of Epstein and others (1953) and Craig (1965). At equilibrium, calcite is depleted in ^{18}O with respect to coexisting quartz (chert). The fractionation factor (Δ_{QC}) can be calculated from equations 3) and 4):

$$\Delta_{QC} = 0.31 \times 10^6 / T^2\ (^0K) + 0.11 \qquad 5)$$

In addition, calcite is prone to exchange with ^{18}O-depleted groundwater (Hudson, 1977). Brand and Veizer (1980) have described a geochemical technique useful in evaluating whether or not calcite has exchanged with groundwater. This test involves measurement of the Sr/Ca ratio, which decreases as a result of groundwater interaction, as well as the Mn content of the mineral, which increases during groundwater exchange. Although this technique offers a useful way of distinguishing unaltered calcite, analyses of both Mn and Sr are not available for the Proterozoic calcite samples that are listed in Table 2.

Low temperature dolomite-water fractionation was estimated by O'Neil and Epstein (1966) to be comparable to Δ_{QW} from data obtained at high temperature. Matthews and Katz (1977) have performed hydrothermal experiments in which $CaCO_3$ was transformed to dolomite in $CaCl_2$/ $MgCl_2$ solutions at 252° to 295°C. For protodolomite formed by replacement of $CaCO_3$, they give the following dolomite-water (Δ_{DW}) fractionation:

$$\Delta_{DW}=3.06\times 10^6/T^2\ (^0K)-3.74 \qquad 6)$$
(using α_{CO_2-W} = 1.0407, cf. Matthews and Katz, 1977).

This can be combined with equation 4) to give an equation for equilibrium fractionaton between calcite and dolomite:

$$\Delta_{DC}=0.28\times 10^6/T^2(^\circ K)-0.18. \qquad 7)$$

Note that crystallinity and precise chemical composition can modify these equations somewhat.

Direct precipitation of dolomite at 25°C is a rare process in nature, at least in modern sedimentary environments (Land, 1980). McKenzie (1980) has investigated a more common phenomenon, the diagenetic alteration of calcite and aragonite to dolomite, in a modern sabkha of Abu Dhabi. In this environment, apparent Δ_{DC} ranges from –2.2 to +3.2 with an average value of +0.3. Variations in the oxygen isotopic composition of dolomite samples from this locality mimic variations in the isotopic composition of pore water. McKenzie concludes that the dolomite is formed in isotopic equilibrium with pore water and that the variability of apparent Δ_{DC} results from partial exchange between calcium carbonate and pore water. The largest apparent Δ_{DC} value found by McKenzie was +3.2. This can be compared with a calculated value from equation 7) of 2.8 for a temperature of 35°C. Since the sabkha water is enriched in ^{18}O by evaporation ($\delta^{18}O_{water}$ ranges from +2.7 to +5.60$^0/_{00}$), $\delta^{18}O_D$ is greater than would be predicted from substitution of a $\delta^{18}O$ value of seawater in equation 6). The actual range of $\delta^{18}O$ values for samples of Abu Dhabi sabkha dolomite is 30.0 to 34.4$^0/_{00}$ with an average value of 32.5$^0/_{00}$ (McKenzie, 1980). To state this another way, suppose these dolomite samples had been found in an ancient rock. Their maximum and minimum temperatures of formation calculated from equation 6), using the $\delta^{18}O$ of SMOW (0$^0/_{00}$) to represent seawater, would be about 28°C and 10°C respectively. The temperatures corrected for pore water δ's of +3.1 and +5.1$^0/_{00}$ are 45°C and 34°C. Thus, the temperature of an ancient evaporite environment would be underestimated if $\delta^{18}O$ of normal sea water were used in the estimate.

Other important fractionation factors are plotted in Figure 1. Siderite-water fractionation (Δ_{SW}) (Becker and Clayton, 1976) is intermediate between Δ_{CW} and Δ_{QW}. Magnetite-water fractionation (Δ_{MW}) is small (Becker and Clayton, 1976); thus, magnetite is depleted in ^{18}O compared to most other minerals and contributes to the low bulk $\delta^{18}O$ of whole rock samples in which it is an abundant constituent.

The oxygen isotope record for Proterozoic sedimentary rocks can be divided conveniently into two categories: 1) Calcium and magnesium carbonate rocks, and 2) cherts and iron formations. Problems are associated with the interpretation of each. Tables 1 and 2 list data for each.

One problem in interpreting the oxygen isotopic composition of Precambrian carbonates arises from uncertainty over the mode of deposition of these rocks. Most Phanerozoic dolomite apparently has formed by diagenetic replacement reactions acting on calcium carbonate (see, for example, "Concepts and Models of Dolomitization," Zenger and others, eds., 1980). Dolomite is, relative to limestone, considerably more abundant in the Precambrian than in the Phanerozoic. Tucker (1982) reports the results of a petrographic study of Beck Springs Dolomite (Precambrian Y) of Arizona. The detailed preservation of sedimentary fabric and structure in this rock leads him to the conclusion that dolomite is primary and not a replacement mineral. Generalizing, he concludes that: "The results suggest that in the Precambrian, dolomite was the principal carbonate mineral precipitated and that it behaved in a manner identical to calcium carbonate in the formation of limestones during the Phanerozoic" (Tucker, 1982).

Tucker also found (1982) that the oxygen (and carbon) isotopic composition of different textural components varies in a manner analogous to variations reported in corresponding components of Phanerozoic limestone. Thus (Tucker, 1982), algal laminates, micrite, and pisolites of the Beck Springs Dolomite are enriched in ^{18}O encompassing a $\delta^{18}O$ range of about +27 to +30.5$^0/_{00}$ wheras sparry dolomite (of secondary origin) is depleted in $\delta^{18}O$ with a range of variation from +17$^0/_{00}$ to about +25$^0/_{00}$.

Cherts and cherty iron formations pose a different set of problems. No good modern analog exists for the cherty iron formations of the Proterozoic. Depositional environments suggested range from glacial (Beukes, 1973; Visser, 1971; Young, 1976) to evaporitic (Trendall and Blockley, 1970; Dimroth and Chauvel, 1973). A glacial environment could result in mixing of ^{18}O-depleted glacial melt-water with sea water to produce an ^{18}O-depleted water of low salinity (Epstein and Mayeda, 1953). Silica precipitated from such water would be depleted in ^{18}O, but a compensating effect is that each 4°C cooling produced by the cold fresh water and melting ice would produce an increase in

Δ_{QW} of about 1 (Fig. 1, Eq. 3). Conversely, precipitation in a warm climate would lower Δ_{QW}. If, however, the climate were both warm and dry, evaporation would occur; this might increase $\delta^{18}O$ of the local water to a value greater than sea water as in sabkha environments. A consequence of this evaporation would be enrichment in $\delta^{18}O$ of precipitated chert and, as in the case of dolomite, an underestimation of depositional temperature or an overestimation of $\delta^{18}O$ of seawater from equation 3).

The oxygen isotope composition of minerals in iron formation is affected by exchange during metamorphism. Inasmuch as virtually all Precambrian rocks have undergone at least mild metamorphism, that is an important factor in interpreting Proterozoic isotope geochemistry. Exchange is facilitated by an oxygen-bearing fluid (water at low temperature, perhaps CO_2–water at high temperature). Also, at low metamorphic temperature, isotope exchange occurs most readily when it accompanies recrystallization or mineralogical reaction (Shen, Perry, and Ueng, in preparation).

Iron formation contains quartz and siderite that concentrate ^{18}O. It also contains magnetite, a mineral notably depleted in ^{18}O. It is not clear whether magnetite can be a primary mineral or whether it always forms from some precursor. It has, however, been identified in Paleozoic iron-rich sediments that have not been metamorphosed (Hangari and others, 1980). When quartz and magnetite equilibrate as part of a closed system exposed to increasing temperature during diagenesis or low-grade metamorphism, isotope exchange tends to increase $\delta^{18}O$ of magnetite and, correspondingly, to decrease $\delta^{18}O$ of quartz (Fig. 1). Similar but less dramatic exchange can be expected between quartz and iron silicates (O'Neil, 1977). A consequence of this exchange is that some ^{18}O decrease in quartz of most Proterozoic iron formations may be expected as a result of diagenesis and metamorphism.

DATA AND INTERPRETATION

Published oxygen isotope data on Proterozoic chemical sediments, summarized in Tables 1 and 2 and plotted in Figure 2, show that in all cases Proterozoic carbonates as well as chert and iron formation have lower $\delta^{18}O$ values than the maximum values reported for modern analogs. We shall first examine the oxygen isotope record in Proterozoic chert and iron formation. Since much of the data on carbonate rocks is a by-product of research on the isotopic composition of carbon, the oxygen isotope record in these is perhaps less systematic than the iron formation record, although in the rocks of the Griquatown Series (South Africa) and in the Hamersley Group (Western Australia), the two rock types are closely associated (Beukes, 1973); Trendall and Blockley, 1970).

At one time, age estimates of the Middle Proterozoic

TABLE 1. $\delta^{18}O_{SMOW}$ OF MINERALS IN PROTEROZOIC IRON FORMATION

Mineral	Maximum $\delta^{18}O$, ‰	Minimum $\delta^{18}O$(oxides), ‰	Average $\delta^{18}O$, ‰
Brockman Iron Formation (Dales George Member) (Hamersley Basin, Precambrian X, Becker and Clayton, 1976)			
Ankerite	20.0	-	19.5
Hematite	-	-2.2	-2.0
Magnetite	-	0.3	3.4
Quartz	21.7	-	21.2
Riebeckite	16.9	-	15.1
Siderite	21.2	-	20.7
Talc	17.9	-	16.8
Marra Mamba Iron Formation (Hamersley Basin, Precambrian X, Becker and Clayton, 1976)			
Quartz	24.0		
Gunflint Iron Formation (Canada, Precambrian X, Perry and others, 1973)			
Quartz	23.5 (cherty horizon)		
Gunflint Iron Formation (Canada, Precambrian X, Knauth and Epstein, 1976)			
Quartz	23.6 (cherty horizon)		
Kuruman Iron Formation (South Africa, Precambrian X, Perry and Ahmad, 1980)			
Quartz	24.1		

iron formations were similar enough that, given the associated errors, they could all be considered roughly contemporaneous. Further geochronological research has changed that simple picture. Current age determination range from about 1900 m.y. for the Biwabik/Gunflint (Goldich, 1973) to about 2500 m.y. for the Brockman Iron Formation (Compston and others, 1981). Considering both the measured ages and the uncertainty of the geochronologic measurements yields a possible depositional interval that could be as long as the entire Phanerozoic.

Oxygen isotope analyses are available for three carefully studied Proterozoic iron formations. Maximum $\delta^{18}O$ of quartz from the Biwabik/Gunflint Iron Formation (United States/Canada), the Kuruman Iron Formation

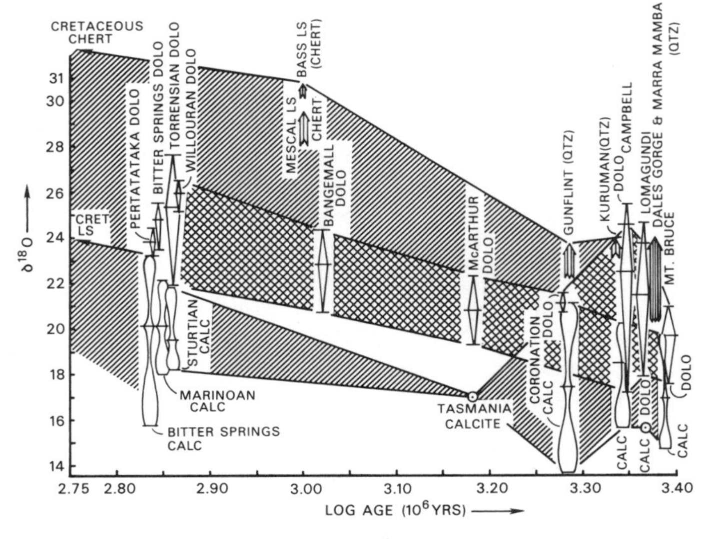

Figure 2. Isotopic composition of Proterozoic chert, dolomite, and calcite (Beck Springs Dolomite (Table 2) is not plotted).

TABLE 2. $\delta^{18}O$ (LIMESTONE, DOLOMITE, AND ASSOCIATED CHERT)

Mineral	Maximum $\delta^{18}O$, ‰	Average $\delta^{18}O$, ‰	Comment
Mt. Bruce Supergroup (Hamersley Basin, Precambrian X) (Veizer and Hoefs, 1976)			
Calcite	16.2	-	only 2 values
Dolomite	20.9	19.7	
Wittenoom Dolomite (a formation in the Mt. Bruce Supergroup, Hamersley Basin, Precambrian X) (Becker and Clayton, 1976)			
Calcite	19.7	16.9	
Dolomite	16.4	-	only 1 value
Quartz	24.1	20.4	
Campbell Rand Dolomite (Transvaal Supergroup, South Africa, Precambrian X) (Schidlowski and others, 1975)			
Calcite	20.2	18.5	(Stalagmite 28.7)
Dolomite	25.4	22.5	α_{CO_2-D} not given (Note 3)
Lomagundi/Umkondo Group (Precambrian X, Zimbabwe, Rhodesia) (Schidlowski and others, 1975)			
Calcite	15.6	-	1 sample
Dolomite	24.6	22.4	(1 "obviously recrystallized" sample 26.9, Note 3)
Coronation Geosyncline (Northwest Canadian Shield, Precambrian X) (Veizer and Hoefs, 1976)			
Calcite	21.1	17.4	2 samples
Dolomite	21.5	21.1	2 samples
Mc Arthur Group (Georgina Basin, Precambrian Y) (Veizer and Hoefs, 1976)			
Calcite	22.3	20.8	
Tasmania (Precambrian Y) (Veizer and Hoefs, 1976)			
Calcite	17.0	-	1 sample
Bangemall Group (Hamersley Basin, 1000-1100 m.y.) (Veizer and Hoefs, 1976)			
Dolomite	24.3	22.8	
Beck Spring Dolomite (Death Valley, California, Precambrian Y) (Tucker, 1982)			
Dolomite	30.5	29	(read from graph)
Bass Limestone (Grand Canyon, Arizona, Precambrian Y) (Knauth and Epstein, 1976)			
Quartz	30.8	-	1 sample
Mescal Limestone (Roosevelt Dam, Arizona, Precambrian Y) (Knauth and Epstein, 1976)			
Quartz	29.5	28.8	2 samples
Marinoan Fm (Adelaide Geosyncline, Precambrian Z) (Veizer and Hoefs, 1976)			
Calcite	22.1	20.1	
Dolomite	21.8	-	1 sample
Sturtian Formation (Adelaide Geosyncline, Precambrian Z) (Veizer and Hoefs, 1976)			
Calcite	21.8	19.5	
Dolomite	24.7	-	1 sample
Torresian Formation (Adelaide Geosyncline, Precambrian Z) (Veizer and Hoefs, 1976)			
Dolomite	27.6	25.3	
Willouran (Adelaide Geosyncline, Precambrian Z) (Veizer and Hoefs, 1976)			
Dolomite	26.4	25.9	
Pertatataka Formation (Amadeus Basin, Precambrian Z) (Veizer and Hoefs, 1976)			
Dolomite	24.4	23.8	2 samples
Bitter Springs Formation (Amadeus Basin, Precambrian Z) (Veizer and Hoefs, 1976)			
Calcite	23.2	20.1	
Dolomite	25.5	24.8	

Notes: (1) $\delta^{18}O$ vs. SMOW (Gonfiantini, 1977). (2) Conversion used for $\alpha^{CO_2}_{H_2O_1}$ = 1.0407 (cf. Friedman and O'Neil, 1977). (3) For Veizer and Hoefs (1976) $\alpha_{CO_2 - calcite}$ = 1.01025. For data of Schidlowski et al. (1975) α's are not explicitly stated. The conversion for $\delta^{18}O_{calcite}$ measured vs. PDB CO_2 for these factors is: $\delta^{18}O_{SMOW} = 1.03068\ \delta^{18}O_{PDB} + 30.37$. For data of Veizer and Hoefs (1976), $\alpha_{CO_2 - DOLOMITE}$ = 1.01109; for data of Schidlowski et al. (1975), α's are not explicitly given.

(Cape Province, South Africa), and the Brockman Iron Formation (Western Australia) is about 24‰ (Perry, Tan, and Morey, 1973; Perry and Ahmad, 1980; Becker and Clayton, 1976). We shall subsequently deal with the question of whether this is the primary isotopic composition of these rocks or whether it has been altered by metamorphism. For the moment, we assume it to be an unaltered sedimentary value. If the temperature of formation of these rocks were known independently, it would be possible to enter temperature and $\delta^{18}O_Q$ in equation 3) and thus to calculate $\delta^{18}O$ of the water from which these sediments precipitated. Alternatively, if $\delta^{18}O_{water}$ were known independently, temperature could be calculated.

Some environmental information can be obtained from physical characteristics of the units studied. On the question of marine/nonmarine origin, Trendall and Blockley (1970) opt for an evaporite basin with limited access to the ocean for the Dales Gorge Member of the Brockman Iron Formation. For the quite similar Kuruman Iron Formation, and for associated carbonate units, Beukes (1973, 1978) has reported evidence for a variety of depositional environments ranging from marine platforms to intertidal and lagunal. Whether directly connected to the ocean or not, the Gunflint/Biwabik, Kuruman, and Brockman Iron Formations are part of depositional sequences of impressively large basins. The Kuruman Iron Formation, for example, helps define a sedimentary basin more than 950 km across (Beukes, 1973).

Dimroth and Chauvel (1973) report length-slow chalcedony in iron formation of the Labrador Trough and attribute this to replacement of gypsum. This occurrence and the suggestion by Trendall and Blockley (1970) that the Dales Gorge Member of the Brockman Iron Formation is an evaporitic deposit raise the possibility that some iron formation is deposited in hot, dry climates. In contrast (Beukes, 1973), the Kuruman Iron Formation and the overlying Griquatown Iron Formation are associated with diamictite of probable glacial origin, as are younger South African iron formations of the Damara Supergroup. Elsewhere, glacial origin has been postulated for sediments associated with iron formation of the Rapitan Group (Canada) (Young, 1976). The high sodium content (presence of riebeckite in abundance), microbanding, and contemporaneous ages of the Brockman and Kuruman Iron Formations (Trendall and Blockley, 1970; Beukes, 1973) suggest similar conditions of deposition for these two iron formations. Thus, it may be worthwhile to reexamine the evidence for the very different environments of deposition (glacial versus evaporitic) proposed for these two rock units.

Markedly different interpretations of environment (temperature) of deposition do not necessarily lead to equally large divergence in estimates of $\delta^{18}O$ of contemporary ocean water. In the case of marine platform deposition in cool water, temperature (perhaps 10°C) and $\delta^{18}O_Q$ (+24‰) should be substituted directly into equation 3) to yield a $\delta^{18}O$ for sea water of about −11‰. If, on the other hand, precipitation of iron formation took place in the evaporitic environment of a restricted basin in which evaporation is as important as it is in the sabkha deposit discussed by McKenzie (1980), the local water might be enriched in ^{18}O by 3 to 5‰ with respect to normal sea water. Substitution of $\delta^{18}O_Q$ = 24‰ and T = 35°C leads to an estimate of $\delta^{18}O_W \cong -5$‰. If local water is enriched in ^{18}O by 3 to 5‰ with respect to contemporary sea water, this implies a value of −8 to −10‰ for the composition of sea water.

One approach to the question of whether primary isotope ratios are preserved in slightly metamorphosed iron formations is to examine the effect of progressive metamorphism on iron formation of uniform composition. This examination can be done by investigating contact metamorphism of an iron formation, for example, the metamorphism of the Biwabik Iron Formation by the Duluth Complex in Minnesota (Perry and others, 1973). Also, within a given iron formation metamorphosed under uniform conditions, metamorphism involving isotope exchange can cease at one temperature in one subunit while it persists to a higher temperature in another subunit. In the Dales Gorge Member of the Brockman Iron Formation (Becker and Clayton, 1976), closely spaced samples have different quartz-magnetite oxygen isotope fractionations (Δ_{QM}'s), indicating different apparent temperatures of reaction. These variable Δ_{QM}s are most readily explained (Becker and Clayton, 1976) by local variations in porosity and permeability that isolated different parts of the system at different stages of metamorphism.

Perry and others (1978) showed that in both the Dales Gorge Member and in the Biwabik Iron Formation in the contact aureole of the Duluth Complex, oxygen isotope exchange between quartz and magnetite occurred as if each unit had been metamorphosed to varying temperatures as chemically closed subsystems of uniform bulk composition. The Kuruman Iron Formation behaved similarly. This regular behavior can be seen in Figure 3, a plot of Δ_{QM} (=f(T)) versus $\delta^{18}O_{mineral}$. During metamorphism, Δ_{QM} becomes progressively smaller. In a closed equilibrium system of quartz and magnetite, quartz becomes progressively depleted in ^{18}O and magnetite becomes progressively enriched. An approximate linear relationship of $\delta^{18}O_{quartz}$ versus Δ_{QM} exists in a closed system even if other phases such as siderite are present (Perry and others, 1978). The intercept at Δ_{QM} = 0, infinite temperature, would be proportional to the bulk porportions of quartz and magnetite in the rock if only these two minerals were present. In the case of an iron formation that is a homogeneous mixture of several minerals, this intercept is still a rough indicator of the bulk ^{18}O content of the rock and is probably most

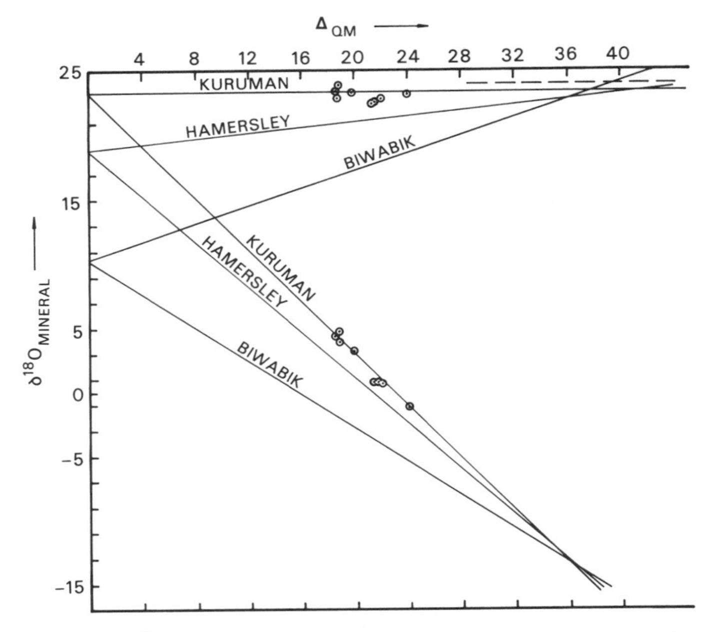

Figure 3. $\delta^{18}O_{MINERAL}$ versus Δ_{QM} plots for quartz and magnetite in the Biwabik, Brockman, and Kuruman Iron Formations. These show a common intersection at $\delta^{18}O_{QUARTZ}$ of about +24‰, a value approximating that found in pure chert layers associated with the Biwabik and Brockman Iron Formations.

sensitive to the presence of quartz and siderite (high intercept value) and of magnetite (low intercept value). Projections of the quartz line for each of the three Proterozoic iron formations plotted in Figure 3 intersect at a $\delta^{18}O$ of about +24‰. The Kuruman Iron Formation is a chert-siderite-rich rock mined for asbestos (Riebeckite/crocidilite). It has been metamorphosed only to low temperature (less than 200°C, Perry and Ahmad (1980), and the quartz isotope composition is not sensitive to metamorphism because of the preponderance of ^{18}O-rich minerals. The Dales Gorge Member of the Brockman Iron Formation has been metamorphosed to an estimated 270° to 310°C (Becker and Clayton, 1976). Quartz isotope composition in this unit is moderately sensitive to metamorphic grade. In associated rocks, Wittenoom Dolomite and the Marra Mamba Member of the Brockman Iron Formation, the maximum $\delta^{18}O$ of chert is +24‰, Tables 1 and 2. This is a value that Becker and Clayton (1976) consider to approximate the original composition of chert in the three rock units. Isotopic composition of quartz in the Biwabik Iron Formation, which has a magnetite content high enough so that it is mined for its magnetite, is much more affected by local metamorphic conditions than the other two iron formations. This iron formation, however, has been metamorphosed at very low temperature ($\Delta_{QM} \simeq 25$, giving an estimated temperature of about 150°C (Perry and others, 1973)). The values of 23.5‰ for quartz, used to estimate the primary isotope composition, was obtained from a cherty unit of the correlative Gunflint

Iron Formation; because of its low magnetite content, the cherty unit is less subject to ^{18}O lowering in quartz during metamorphism.

We consider that the linear trends in Figure 3 strongly suggest that the three iron formations represented have behaved as closed systems during diagenesis and metamorphism. Furthermore, the isotopic relationships established during metamorphism have persisted since without alteration by weathering or other processes. Contact metamorphism of the Biwabik Iron Formation occurred about 1100 m.y. ago. No major metamorphic event is associated with the Brockman Iron Formation (Trendall and Blockley, 1970). The maximum temperature attained is likely to have resulted from burial. The fact that these rocks have been protected from alteration for 1000 to 2000 m.y. is important to the discussion of the effect of weathering on isotopic composition. These results support the $+24^0/_{00}$ as a reasonable estimate of the isotopic composition of chert precipitated from sea water.

Jones and Knauth (1979) offer further evidence about the effect of metamorphism on oxygen isotope composition. They were able to monitor the effects of metamorphism in a chert of Devonian-Mississippian age. Metamorphic recrystallization in this chert (the Arkansas Novaculite) resulted in isotopic decreases in $\delta^{18}O$ of 0 to $7^0/_{00}$. The large isotopic shifts were produced by contact metamorphism. Jones and Knauth (1979) concluded that the low $\delta^{18}O$ values in weakly metamorphosed Precambrian cherts probably cannot be explained as a metamorphic effect. Furthermore, they report that the presence of carbonate in the cherts of the Arkansas Novaculite appears to have promoted early diagenetic recrystallization of silica to crystalline quartz that was subsequently resistant to exchange. It should be noted that chert in iron formation generally is associated with carbonate minerals.

Most mechanisms that might alter $\delta^{18}O$ of metamorphosed chemical precipitates proceed in the direction of lowering $\delta^{18}O$ of chert and carbonate. Knauth and Lowe (1979) considered a case in which proximity to a contact aureole might actually increase ^{18}O of metachert. We add here a Proterozoic example from the Negaunee Iron Formation of Michigan (Ueng, unpublished MS thesis, NIU). Figure 4 shows a core profile in this iron formation within the biotite zone of metamorphism ($\Delta_{QM} \sim 14.2$, T = 320C). This core is taken from near the town of Negaunee and is adjacent to a large metamorphic aureole. Siderite with a $\delta^{18}O_S > \delta\ ^{18}O_Q$ is a certain sign of isotopic disequilibrium. Thus, assuming, as is probable, that carbonate exchanges more readily than quartz, the carbonate in the lower part of the core has been enriched in ^{18}O by some postdepositional process by as much as $7^0/_{00}$. Judging from the uniformity of $\delta^{18}O_Q$ in other cores from the area, quartz has also been enriched in ^{18}O in one sample of this core from just below 700 m. Other data obtained in the study indicate that this

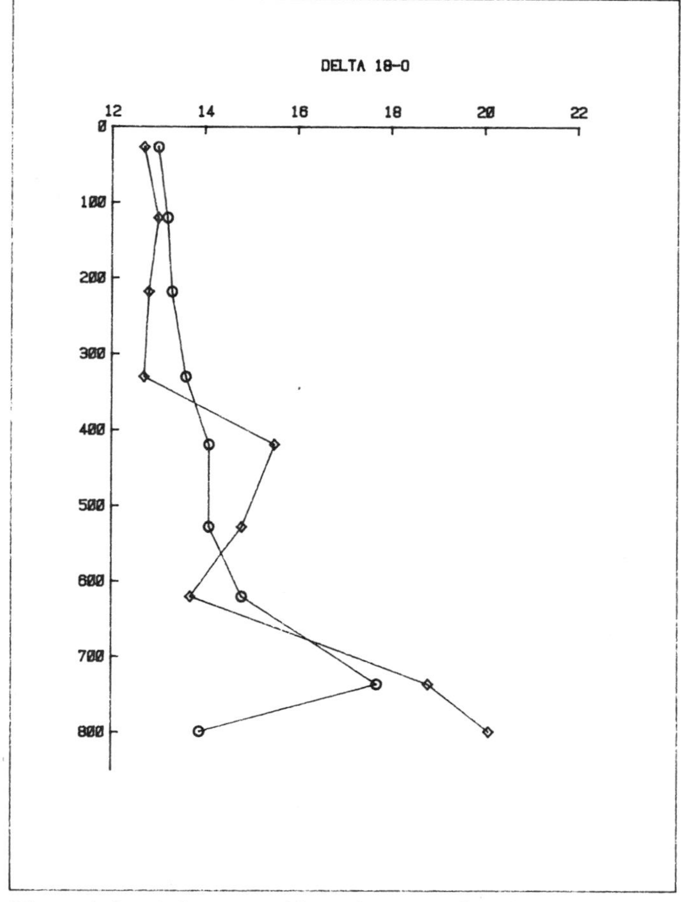

Figure 4. Isotopic composition of quartz (circles) and carbonate (diamonds) from a metamorphosed, hydrothermally altered core in the Proterozoic Negaunee Iron Formation, Michigan. Vertical axis in meters. (Ueng, 1981).

^{18}O enrichment results from exchange with hydrothermal waters circulating during metamorphism. Meteoric water with a low ^{18}O content reacting with ^{18}O-rich sediments at high temperatures (above about 300°C) becomes enriched in ^{18}O (see fractionation factors, Fig. 1). Subsequently, this high ^{18}O water can react with rocks at low temperature (~200°C or less) to cause ^{18}O enrichment of any minerals that are subject to exchange. Hydrothermal activity in rocks of the area is well established (Gair, 1975). Although ^{18}O enrichment during metamorphism is not common, it is clear from this study that high ^{18}O values in metasediments much be examined critically just as low values are.

CALCITE AND DOLOMITE

Data for Proterozoic limestones are consistent in their general pattern with data from Proterozoic iron formations (Table 2, Fig. 2). Highest measured ^{18}O for the Bitter Springs Formation (800 m.y., Australia) is $23.2^0/_{00}$. For the

Coronation Geosyncline (~1800 m.y., Canada), maximum measured $\delta^{18}O$ = 21.1‰. For eight samples of limestone from the Campbell Rand Dolomite, Transvaal Supergroup (2500 m.y., South Africa), the highest measured $\delta^{18}O_{calcite}$ = 20.2‰, except for a stalagmite ($\delta^{18}O$ = 28.7‰); this anomaly, produced by weathering in a dry climate, emphasizes the need to examine each sample carefully. The Transvaal Supergroup includes not only the Campbell Rand Dolomite but also the Kuruman Iron Formation. Calcite from the Wittenoom Dolomite (~2500 m.y., Western Australia) is temporally and spatially associated with the Brockman Iron Formation. Maximum measured $\delta^{18}O$ of calcite from these rocks is 19.7‰.

There are two places where the isotopic composition of quartz in Proterozoic chert bands or iron formation can be compared directly with the isotopic composition of calcite in thick carbonate units of the same stratigraphic succession. Since calcite and quartz can exchange isotopically during metamorphism, it is perhaps best to compare the highest value for each mineral presumably taken from mineralogically homogeneous bands protected from exchange. These can be considered "fractionations," Δ_{QC}, even though equilibrium in a strict sense is not proved and is, in fact, improbable. (In neither of the stratigraphic sequences of interest is there evidence of hydrothermal activity like that found in the Negaunee Iron Formation.) For the Wittenoom Dolomite/Brockman Iron Formation pair, Δ_{QC} = 4.3. For the Campbell Rand/Kuruman Iron Formation pair, Δ_{QC} = 3.8. From equation 5), the average value of Δ_{QC} corresponds to a temperature of about 7° C. This is not a credible estimate of temperature of deposition, but it suggests that both $\delta^{18}O_{quartz}$ and $\delta^{18}O_{calcite}$ values are preserved in these rocks.

Some problems in the interpretation of oxygen isotope data from dolomite have already been mentioned. In evaluating the relationship between $\delta^{18}O$ of Proterozoic dolomite and the isotopic composition of contemporary ocean water, the following points should be considered:

1) Dolomite is much more common in Triassic and older rocks than in more recent rocks. Since about 60% of the present annual river flux of magnesium (Holland, 1978) appears to be removed by conversion to montmorillonite at midocean ridge hydrothermal systems, Holland suggests that dolomite abundance may record (inversely) the intensity of hydrothermal cycling at ridges. The Precambrian, in particular, contains abundant dolomite, including dolomite of probable primary origin (Tucker, 1981). If this dolomite is an indicator of plate tectonic style, the conditions under which ocean water reacted with igneous rock of the oceanic crust may have been quite different in the Precambrian than they are today.

2) Dolomite may be expected to be enriched by 1 to 6‰ in ^{18}O compared to associated calcite (Land, 1980). Experiments by Matthews and Katz (1977) and a field study by McKenzie (1980) suggest that the equilibrium value is about 3‰ at surface temperatures (equation 7).

3) Variable but significant exchange has occurred between platform-type dolomites and formation waters. This exchange is, in fact, by dissolution-redeposition rather than by solid state diffusion. Inhomogenieties in isotopic composition that have been preserved in dolomitized rocks indicate that early chemistry has not been completely erased (Land, 1980).

4) With one exception, available isotopic analyses of Proterozoic dolomites presented here are from broad survey studies with little or no supporting petrographic information. The exception is the combined petrographic/isotopic study of the Beck Springs Dolomite (Tucker, 1982) that should serve as a model for other studies.

5) Given the nature of the Proterozoic sample suite, it is perhaps most valid to compare maximum $\delta^{18}O$ of dolomite with maximum $\delta^{18}O$ of calcite in a given rock unit, taking care to eliminate any obviously anomalous samples. The resulting Δ_{DC}, although not an equilibrium value, is useful because it can be compared with similar differences in Phanerozoic rocks. Since calcite is more readily altered than dolomite, this value can indicate serious exchange.

In carbonate rocks of Precambrian Z, the highest $\delta^{18}O_{dolomite}$ = 27.6‰ in Torresian dolomite (about 700 m.y.). No calcite values are available for comparison (Table 2, Fig. 4). In Sturtian rocks (also about 700 m.y.), $\delta^{18}O_D$ = 24.7‰, $\delta^{18}O_C$ = 21.8‰, and Δ_{DC} = 3.9. Bitter Springs Formation (Australia) dolomite has a maximum $\delta^{18}O_D$ value of 25.5‰ and a maximum $\delta^{18}O_C$ value of 23.3‰ for a Δ_{DC} of 2.3.

In rocks of Precambrian Y, the maximum $\delta^{18}O_D$ (of only two samples) from the Coronation geosyncline is 21.5‰ compared to a value of 21.1‰ for calcite (Δ_{DC} = 0.4). Maximum $\delta^{18}O_D$ for the Bangemall Group (Hamersley Basin) is 24.3‰. No coexisting calcite value is reported. The most probable unaltered value for primary $\delta^{18}O_D$ in rocks of Precambrian Y is the 10^9-year-old Beck Springs Dolomite (Tucker, 1982), which contains algal laminates, micrites, and pisolites with a $\delta^{18}O_D$ range of +27 to +30.5‰. No calcite values are available for this rock, but dolomite isotopic composition can be compared to the $\delta^{18}O_Q$ of 30.8‰ (Table 2) for chert from the Bass Limestone, a rock that is roughly comparable in age. Equations 3) and 6) indicate that at 25° C, quartz and dolomite equilibrated together would have a Δ_{QD} value of about 0.8. The actual $\Delta_{QD} \simeq 30.8-30.5 = 0.3$ agrees, perhaps more closely than we should expect for rocks collected in adjacent geographic states.

Highest ^{18}O concentration (Table 2) in dolomites of Precambrian X is that for the Campbell Rand Dolomite, Transvaal Supergroup with a $\delta^{18}O_D$ of 25.4‰. Maximum Δ_{DC} in this unit is 5. For the Umcondo Group of Zimbabwe (Rhodesia) the highest $\delta^{18}O_D$ is 26.9‰ in a sample described as "obviously recrystallized." If this sample is excluded, the highest $\delta^{18}O_D$ for the Lomagundi/Umcondo Group is 24.6‰ (Table 2). Maximum $\delta^{18}O$ values reported for dolomite of Precambrian X thus are slightly more than 1‰ greater than for associated quartz. Note that if Schidlowski and others (1975) used the same fractionation factor (α_{CO_2-C}) for dolomite and calcite (note 3, Table 2), their dolomite values are about 0.8‰ higher than other values cited (see Land, 1980).

DISCUSSION

Several investigators have accepted the oxygen isotopic data from Precambrian cherts older than Precambrian Y, part of which we have summarized here, as indicative that ^{18}O depletion in these rocks is a primary or early diagenetic characteristic (Jones and Knauth, 1979; Knauth and Lowe, 1979; Gregory and Taylor 1981; Perry and Tan, 1972; Perry and others, 1978). Beaty (1980) interprets evidence from contemporary Archean hydrothermally altered volcanic rocks to indicate that the oxygen isotopic composition of the ocean in the Late Archean was similar to that of the modern ocean. Knauth and Lowe (1979) have explained all of the isotopically depleted Precambrian cherts as a response to higher surface temperatures in the Precambrian. For example, the temperature from equation 3), calculated for deposition of the cherts associated with the Biwabik/Gunflint, Kuruman, and Brockman Iron Formation, is about 60°C, assuming contemporary sea water of $\delta^{18}O$ = 0‰.

The main objection to high surface temperature in the Proterozoic as an explanation of the oxygen isotopic data in chemical sediments was raised originally by Perry and Tan (1972); widespread glaciations have been documented during the same general time interval. Since all known cherts and carbonates of Precambrian W and X are depleted in ^{18}O, this is an important argument whether or not the glacial deposits are strictly contemporaneous. Work by Visser (1970) and DeVilliers and Visser (1977) has established the presence of diamictite of presumed glacial origin within the Ghaap Group, which includes the Kuruman and Griqualand Iron Formations of Cape Province, South Africa (Perry and Ahmad, 1980). Furthermore, these diamictite layers are interbedded with sediments containing cherty iron carbonate and chamosite (DeVilliers and Visser, 1977), suggesting that the change from iron formation deposition to diamictite deposition was a gradational phenomenon occurring within a limited time interval rather than an accidental association of rocks from different depositional environments. If the diamictite layers are an independent thermometer measuring local Earth surface temperature during iron formation deposition, then we can evaluate $\delta^{18}O_D$ of the contemporary ocean from the relation in Figure 1 and $\delta^{18}O_Q$. For T = 15°C, $\delta^{18}O_Q$ = 24‰, $\delta^{18}O_W$ would be about −16‰.

The presence of glacial deposits, if they do indeed bear a close temporal relation with the Kuruman Iron Formation, suggests the possibility that the ^{18}O content of precipitating water (sea water) was lowered locally by mixing with glacial melt-water. The association with diamictite units is too restricted, and the stratigraphic range of ^{18}O-depleted rocks (including the Campbell Rand Dolomite) is too great to make this explanation viable.

Additional data that may bear on the climate of the Early Proterozoic comes from an isotopic study of Late Archean (2600 m.y.) iron formation from the Weld Range, Western Australia (Gole, Perry, and Ahmad, in preparation). The iron formation units of the Weld Range are thick lensoid bodies metamorphosed to various temperatures, in one case as low as 230°C (based on a Δ_{QM} of 18.6). All of these rocks have a remarkably low bulk ^{18}O composition (Fig. 5). No evidence suggests isotopic interaction of the thick iron formation units with associated basalts, nor does it appear that magnetite is unusually abundant (this could depress $\delta^{18}O$). A reasonable, although perhaps not unique, explanation of these data is that these iron formation units are brackish water deposits depleted in ^{18}O, perhaps similar in their depositional environment to the Devonian ironstones discussed by Hangari and others (1980). If this is so, an important implication is that the Late Archean, and therefore, presumably the Early Preoterozoic, climate was characterized by a hydrologic regime much like the present one. Only if a significant temperature difference existed between equator and poles would one expect Raleigh fractionation of meteoric water and, thus, ^{18}O-depleted rain. A major rise in surface temperature would increase the water

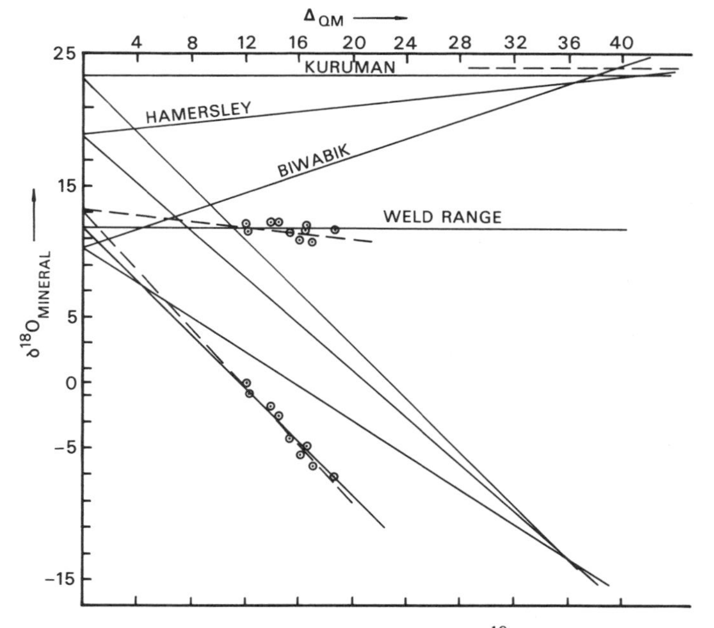

Figure 5. Weld Range Iron Fromation. A $\delta^{18}O_{MINERAL}$ versus Δ_{QM} plot for quartz and magnetite shows the striking ^{18}O depletion of this iron formation.

content of the atmosphere, improve atmospheric heat transfer, and reduce equator-to-pole thermal gradients (Manabe and Stouffer, 1979). Thus, Weld Range iron formations suggest, but do not prove, an atmospheric circulation pattern and a surface temperature regime similar to that which exists today and an ocean buffered in ^{18}O at a value different than the modern value.

For the modern ocean, there is good circumstantial evidence to suggest that the ocean is buffered with respect to ^{18}O by reaction with basalt at about 300°C in midocean ridge hydrothermal systems (Muehlenbachs and Clayton, 1976; Gregory and Taylor, 1980). Perry and others (1978) suggested that during Precambrian W, at a time of higher radiogenic heat flow, volcanogenic products would be particularly abundant and that isotopic interaction of basalts and pyroclastic rocks with sea water at lower temperature would be common. To explain the apparent ^{18}O depletion of the ocean, they postulated that higher heat flow from the mantle might, actually, result in lower average temperature of oxygen isotope exchange than at present. Lower temperature exchange results in larger isotope fractionation between rock and water (Fig. 1). If the system is dominated by the isotopic composition of basalt (~$6^0/_{00}$), then the equilibrium water value is about $0^0/_{00}$ at 300°C and is appreciably less than $0^0/_{00}$ at lower temperatures. Fryer and others (1979) have discussed other aspects of low temperature rock-water interaction during Precambrian W. Veizer (in press) has demonstrated that the chemistry of the ocean was dominated by the mantle during Precambrian W (cf. $^{87}Sr/^{86}Sr$ of .7002 reported for 3400-m.y.-old barites by Perry and others, 1971; and Perry and others, 1975). Studies indicating that magnesium in the ocean is controlled by hydrothermal reactions at midocean ridges, summarized by Holland (1978), suggest that the dolomite content of the sedimentary column may record changes in the midocean ridge hydrothermal regime. Thus, the abundance of dolomite in the stratigraphic sequence of the Proterozoic may indicate that the hydrothermal circulation model of Gregory and Taylor (1980) is not a realistic representation of conditions in that era. During the Proterozoic, Veizer (in press) reports that continental weathering becomes important and begins to dominate ocean chemistry. It is during this transitional interval that $\delta^{18}O$ of chemically precipitated sediments begins to increase systematically toward modern values (Fig. 2).

ACKNOWLEDGMENTS

Support for this research came from National Science Foundation grant EAR 7911334 and from the Northern Illinois University Graduate School. I thank the organizers for the opportunity to participate in the Proterozoic Symposium. This paper was transcribed from left-handed scrawl into a manuscript by Sue Stewart.

REFERENCES CITED

Beaty, D. W., 1980, The oxygen isotope geochemistry of the Abitibi Greenstone Belt [Part II of a thesis]: Pasadena, Calif. Inst. Tech., 463 p.

Becker, R. H., and Clayton, R. N., 1976, Oxygen isotope study of a Precambrian banded iron-formation, Hamersley Range, Western Australia: Geochim. et Cosmochim. Acta 40, 1153–1165.

Beuckes, N. J., 1973, Precambrian iron-formation of southern Africa: Econ. Geol. 68, 960–1004.

——1978, The carbonate rocks and iron-formations of the Ghaap Group of the Transvaal Supergroup in the northern Cape Province [Unpubl, Ph.D. thesis]: Johannesburg, Dept. of Geology, Rand Afrikaans University, 580 p. (in Africaans, English abstr.).

Brand, U., and Viezer, J., 1980, Chemical diagenesis of multicomponent carbonate system-1: Trace elements: J. Sed. Pet. 50, 1219–1236.

Choquette, P. W., 1968, Marine diagenesis of shallow marine lime-mud sediments—insights from δ ^{18}O and δ ^{13}C data: Science 161, 1130–1132.

Compston, W., Williams, I. S., McCulloch, M. T., Foster, J. J., Arriens, P. A., and Trendall, A. F., 1981, A revised age for the Hamersley Group [abs.]: *in* Geol. Soc. Australia Abstracts 3, p. 40.

Craig, H., 1957, Isotopic standards for carbon and oxygen and correction factors for mass spectrometric analysis of carbon dioxide: Geochim. et Cosmochim. Acta 12, 133–149.

De Villiers, P. R., and Visser, J. N. J., 1977, The glacial beds of the Griqualand West Supergroup as revealed by four deep boreholes between Postmasburg and Sishen: Trans. Geol. Soc. S. Afr. 80, 1–8.

Dimroth, E., and Chauvel, J. J., 1973, Petrography of the Sokoman Iron Formation in part of the central Labrador Trough, Quebec, Canada: G.S.A. Bull. 84, 111–134.

Fryer, B. J., Fyfe, W. S., and Kerrich, A., 1979, Archean volcanogenic oceans: Chem. Geol. 24, 25–33.

Epstein, S., Buchsbaum, R., Lowenstam, H. A., and Urey, H. C., 1953, Revised carbonate-water isotopic temperature scale: Bull. Geol. Soc. Am. 64, 1315–1326.

Epstein, S., and Mayeda, T. K., 1953, Variation of ^{18}O content of waters from natural sources: Geochim. et Cosmochim. Acta 4, 213–224.

Gair, J. E., 1975, Bedrock geology and the deposition of the Palmer quadrangle, Marquette County, Michigan: USGS Prof. Paper 764.

Goldich, S. S. 1973, Ages of Precambrian banded iron-formations: Econ. Geol. 68, 1126–1134.

Gole, M. J., Perry, E. C., Jr., and Ahmad, S. N., Stable isotope study of medium- and low-metamorphic grade Archean Iron Formation, Western Australia (in preparation).

Gonfiantini, R., 1978, Standards for stable isotope measurements in natural compounds: Nature 271, 534–536.

Gregory, R. T., and Taylor, H. P., Jr., 1981, An oxygen isotope profile in a section of Cretaceous oceanic crust, Samail Ophiolite, Oman: Evidence for δ ^{18}O-buffering of the oceans by deep (>5 km) seawater-hydrothermal circulation at mid-ocean ridges: J. Geophys, Res. 86, 2737–2755.

Hangari, R. M., Ahmad, S. N., and Perry, E. C., Jr., 1980, Carbon and oxygen isotope ratios in diagenetic siderite and magnetite from Upper Devonian Ironstone, Wadi Shatti District, Libya: Econ. Geol. 75, 538–545.

Holland, H. D., 1978, The chemistry of the atmosphere and oceans: New York, John Wiley and Sons, 351 p.

Hudson, J. D., 1977, Stable isotopes and limestone lithification: J. Geol. Soc. Lond. 133, 637–660.

Jones, D. L., and Knauth, L. P., 1979, Oxygen isotopic and petrographic evidence relevant to the origin of the Arkansas Novaculite: J. Sed. Pet. 49, 581–598.

Knauth, L. P., and Epstein, S., 1976, Hydrogen and oxygen isotope ratios in nodular and bedded cherts: Geochim. et Cosmochim. Acta 40, 1095–1108.

Knauth, L. P., and Lowe, D. R., 1978, Oxygen isotopic geochemistry of cherts from the Onverwacht Group (3.4 billion years), Transvaal, South Africa with implications for secular variations in the isotopic composition of cherts: E.P.S.L. 41, 209–222.

Land, L. S., 1980, The isotopic and trace element geochemistry of dolomite: the state of the art: SEPM Special Publication 28, 87–110.

Manabe, S., and Stouffer, R. J., 1979, A CO_2-climate sensitivity study with a mathematical model of the global climate. Nature 282, 491–493.

Matthews, A., and Katz, A., 1977, Oxygen isotope fractionation during the dolomitization of calcium carbonate: Geochim. et Cosmochim. Acta 41, 1431–1438.

McKenzie, J. A., 1981, Holocene dolomitization of calcium carbonate sediments from the coastal sabkhas of Abu Dhabi, U.A.E.: a stable isotope study: J. Geol. 89, 185–198.

Mottl, M. J., and Holland H. D., 1978, Chemical exchange during hydrothermal alteration of basalt by seawater-I. Experimental results for major elements: Geochim. et Cosmochim. Acta 42. 1103–1115.

Muehlenbachs, K., and Clayton, R. N., 1976, Oxygen isotope composition of the oceanic crust and its bearing on sea water: J. Geophys, Res. 81, 4365–4369.

O'Neil, J. R., 1977, Stable isotopes in Mineralogy: Phys. Chem. Minerals 2, 105–123.

O'Neil, J. R., and Epstein, S., 1966, Oxygen isotope fractionation in the system dolomite-calcite-carbon dioxide: Science 152, 198–201.

Perry, E. C., Jr., 1967, The oxygen isotope chemistry of ancient cherts: EPSL 3, 62–66.

——, The oxygen isotope geochemistry of iron formation, *in* A. F. Trendall and R. C. Morris, eds., IGCP Project Iron Formation: Amsterdam, Elsevier Press (in press).

Perry, E. C., Jr., and Ahmad, S. N., 1980, Oxygen isotope study of the Transvaal Ssytem Iron Formation from the vicinity of Kuruman, Cape Province, South Africa: G.S.A. Abstracts with Programs 23, 497 p.

Perry, E. C., Jr., Ahmad, S. N., and Swulius, T., 1978, The oxygen isotope composition of 3800 m.y. old metamorphosed chert and iron formation from Isukasia, West Greenland: J. Geol. 86, 223–239.

Perry, E. C., Jr., Hickman, A. A., and Barnes, I. L., 1975, Archean Sedimentary barite, Pilbara Goldfield, Western Australia [abs.]: G.S.A. Abstracts with Programs 7, 1226.

Perry, E. C., Jr., Monster, J., and Reimer, T., 1971, Sulfur isotopes in Swaziland System barites and the evolution of the Earth's atmosphere: Science 171, 1015–1016.

Perry, E. C., Jr., and Tan, F. C., 1972, Significance of oxygen and carbon isotope variations in early Precambrian cherts and carbonate rocks of southern Africa: G.S.A. Bull. 83, 647–664.

Perry, E. C., Jr., Tan, F. C., and Morey, G. B., 1973, Geology and stable isotope geochemistry of the Biwabik Iron Formation, northern Minnesota: Econ. Geol. 68, 1110–1125.

Savin, S. M., 1977, The history of the Earth's surface temperature during the past 100 million years: Ann. Rev. Earth and Planet. Sci. 5, 319–355.

Schidlowski, M., Eichmann, R., and Junge, C. E., 1975, Precambrian sedimentary carbonates: carbon and oxygen isotope geochemistry and implications for the terrestrial oxygen budget: Precamb. Res. 2, 1–69.

Trendall, A. F., and Blockley, J. G., 1970, The iron formations of the Precambrian Hamersley Group Western Australia: Geological Survey of Western Australia Bull. 119, 336 p.

Tucker, M. E., 1982, Precambrian dolomites: Petrographic and isotopic evidence that they differ from Phanerozoic dolomites: Geology 10, p. 7–12.

Ueng, C. E., 1981, The fractionation of carbon and oxygen isotopes in a banded iron formation, Marquette District, Northern Michigan [M.S. thesis]: Dekalb, Northern Illinois Univ., 78 p.

Young, G. M., 1976, Iron formation and glaciogenic rocks of the Rapitan Group, Northwest Territories, Canada: Precamb. Res. 3, 137–158.

Veizer, J. Geologic evolution of the Archean-Early Proterozoic Earth, *in* J. W. Schopf, ed., Origin and evolution of Earth's earliest biosphere: an interdisciplinary study: Princeton Press (in press).

Viezer, J., and Hoefs, J., 1976, The nature of O^{18}/O^{16} and C^{13}/C^{12} secular trends in sedimentary carbonate rocks: Geochim. et Cosmochim. Acta 40, 1387–1395.

Visser, J. N. J., 1971, The deposition of the Griquatown Glacial Member in the Transvaal Supergroup: Geol. Soc. South Africa Trans. 74, 187–199.

Zenger, D. H., Dunham, J. B., and Ethington, R. L., eds. 1980, Concepts and Models of Dolomitization: SEPM Spec. Pub. 28, 320 p.

Manuscript Accepted by the Society April 14. 1983

Printed in U.S.A.

Geological Society of America
Memoir 161
1983

Proterozoic plankton

Gonzalo Vidal
Kemicentrum Micropalaeontological Laboratory
Box 740
S-220 07 LUND 7, Sweden

Andrew H. Knoll
Biological Laboratories
Harvard University
Cambridge, Massachusetts 02138

ABSTRACT

Planktonic microfossils in Proterozoic sedimentary rocks can be recognized on the basis of their facies distribution, morphology, independence of the distributions of benthic microbial associations, and, where observable, spatial distribution within a rock sample as seen in thin section. Like their Phanerozoic counterparts, late Precambrian plankters exhibit discernible inshore-offshore patterns of distribution. Inshore and, especially, lagoonal biotas are characteristically low diversity assemblages dominated by one or a few taxa, while contemporaneous plankton assemblages from open shelf environment contain a diverse heterogeneous array of morphologically complex forms. As the paleoecological ranges of Proterozoic plankters are discernible, so are their stratigraphic ranges, and this permits the establishment of a series of microfossil assemblage zones that have proven to be of considerable value in correlating Upper Riphean and Vendian sequences and establishing the position of the Precambrian/Cambrian boundary within sedimentary successions. Because it is possible to observe diversity distributions within a single time plane and biostratigraphic distributions in successive time intervals, it is possible to examine diversity trends through time. The plankton record documents the initial observable radiation of cyst-forming eukaryotic microorganisms during the late Proterozoic and indicates, as well, that the plankton biota suffered major extinctions near the end of the eon. A second radiation of baltisphaerid and other morphologically complex taxa restored high plankton diversity levels, but not until well into the early Cambrian.

INTRODUCTION

The paleontological importance of Phanerozoic microplankton is well established; organic and mineralized remains of both algae and protozoans have proven immensely valuable in studies of biostratigraphy, paleoecology, and evolutionary biology. In this paper, we review the evidence for planktonic life in the Precambrian and argue that, as in their younger counterparts, Proterozoic plankters have environmental and stratigraphic distributions that are both delimitable and useful. Equally important, planktonic microfossils found in Precambrian sequences document important evolutionary events whose record is either severely dampened or not observable in the restricted carbonate facies where silicification of stomatolitic microbiotas was most common.

THE NATURE AND RECOGNITION OF PROTEROZOIC PLANKTON

The presence of acid-resistant, organic-walled microfossils in Upper Proterozoic detrital and carbonate rocks was established through the pioneering work of Timofeev (1959, 1966, 1969, 1973; Timofeev and others, 1976). Microfossils released during the maceration of Proterozoic siltstones and shales and in general morphologically simple, vesicular remains 10 to 500 (or more) μm in diameter exhibiting some limited variation in shape and ornamentation. The planktonic nature of these fossils can be inferred on two separate grounds: morphological and functional analysis and facies distributional data.

Most Late Proterozoic acid-resistant fossils are morphologically and ecologically comparable to Paleozoic microfossils included in the group Acritarcha (Evitt, 1963), a nomenclaturally informal category established to serve as an umbrella for organic-walled microfossils of problematic biological affinities (divisible into 16 subgroups and a number of form genera, Downie and others, 1963). Gross morphological features, as well as their problematic nature, make it practical to place the spheroidal remains from Proterozoic clastic (and some carbonate) facies among the acritarchs; however, this by no means implies clear phylogenetic lines of connection between Precambrian and Paleozoic acritarch taxa.

Some common Late Proterozoic sphaeromorphs have been regarded as possible relatives of the Phanerozoic Tasmanaceae (Muir and Sarjeant, 1971), a group that, in turn, has been identified as the abandoned zoosporangia of prasinophycean green algae. This could be true of a number of Late Proterozoic taxa (e.g., *Chuaria, Leiosphaeridia, Kildinosphaera* and some species of *Trachysphaeridium*); however, it is hazardous to ascribe Proterozoic acritarchs to younger taxa on the basis of gross morphological similarities alone, particularly when the critical mechanism of excystment is not known with certainty. Morphological similarity could result from the evolutionary convergence of unrelated or only distantly related algal clades. Similar morphological solutions to recurring environmental problems could have been evolved by algae widely separated in time, a feasible possibility for the explanation of the considerable time gap separating some gross-morphologically comparable Proterozoic and Paleozoic acritarch taxa.

The type species of the form-genus *Kildinella* Timofeev (*Kildinella hyperboreica* Timofeev) was transferred by Lindgren (1982) to the form-genus *Leiosphaeridia* Eisenack. The new taxonomic combination is *L. asperata* (Naumova) Lindgren 1982. The remaining form-species of the form-genus *Kildinella* were transferred by Vidal (in Vidal and Siedlecka, 1983) to the new form-genus *Kildiosphaera;* the type-species being *K. chagrinata* (= *Kildinella sinica* Timofeev). The new genus *Kildinosphaera* also includes *Kildinosphaera granulata* Vidal 1983 (in Vidal and Siedlecka, 1983); previously *Kildinella* sp. A, *Kildinosphaera verrucata* Vidal 1983 (in Vidal and Siedlecka, 1983); previously *Kildinella* sp. B, and *Kildinosphaera Lophostriata* (Jankauskas) Vidal 1983 (in Vidal and Siedlecka, 1983). Additionally, the binomial combination *Podolina angulata* Herman, mentioned above, refers to *Podolina minuta* (Herman) Vidal 1983 (in Vidal and Siedlecka, 1983).

Some sturdily built and strongly ornamented Late Proterozoic acritarch taxa are occasionally found enclosed within thin, transparent organic sheaths (e.g., *Trachysphaeridium laminaritum* (Timofeev) and *T. laufeldi* Vidal; Vidal, 1976a, 1979a). When found isolated, these acritarchs often display clear openings. Openings have also been recorded in other contemporaneous acritarch taxa (e.g., *Trachysphaeridium apertum* Vidal, *Protosphaeridium* cf *flexuosum* Timofeev *sensu* Vidal, 1976a, and *Leiosphaeridia kulgunica* Jankauskas, 1980). The nature of such openings is, of course, problematic, but their regularity and commonness in the taxa concerned suggest that they can safely be interpreted as excystment structures, or pylomes (Vidal, 1976a, 1979a). One of the above mentioned taxa, *T. laufeldi,* often displays bud-shaped spiny protuberances with raised rims tentatively interpreted as operculate excystment mechanisms (Vidal, 1976a, 1979a; Fig. 1G). Certainly this peculiar structure is characteristic of the species and is found in numerous specimens, not only in the type population from the Visingsö Beds of southern Sweden (Vidal, 1976a), but also in assemblages from the probably contemporaneous Upper Chuar Group in Arizona (Vidal, unpublished data; Elston and McKee, 1982). Vase-shaped acritarch taxa reported by Bloeser (1980) from the Upper Chuar Group display round or polygonal excystment openings that are commonly bordered by a neck or collar and plugged with an operculum. The morphology of these excystment openings is regarded by Bloesser as diagnostic at the specific level.

Some Paleozoic acritarchs, particularly the morphologically simple leiosphaerids, apparently effected excystment by a "median split" mechanism—a linear rupture in the equatorial plane of the cyst (Downie, 1973). Median splits have occasionally been observed in Late Proterozoic species of *Kildinosphaera* (particularly *K. chagrinata* Vidal; in Vidal and Siedlecka, 1983) and in other Proterozoic acritarchs (cf. Timofeev, 1969; Peat and others, 1978; Knoll, 1983).

The conditions of occurrence and environmental distribution of Proterozoic acritarchs also appear to be very similar to what has been reported for their Phanerozoic counterparts. Relative abundances of Middle and Late Ordovician acritarch associations appear to mirror facies differences (Jacobson, 1979), and the same is true of Late Proterozoic acritarch assemblages. The taxonomically most diverse Late Proterozoic acritarch assemblages are generally those found in fine-grained rocks (siltstones, shales, and calcareous siltstones) formed under moderately shallow to shallow marine shelf conditions (Vidal, 1976a, 1979a, 1979b, 1981a). Taxonomically uniform acritarch assemblages consisting of morphologically simple taxa with

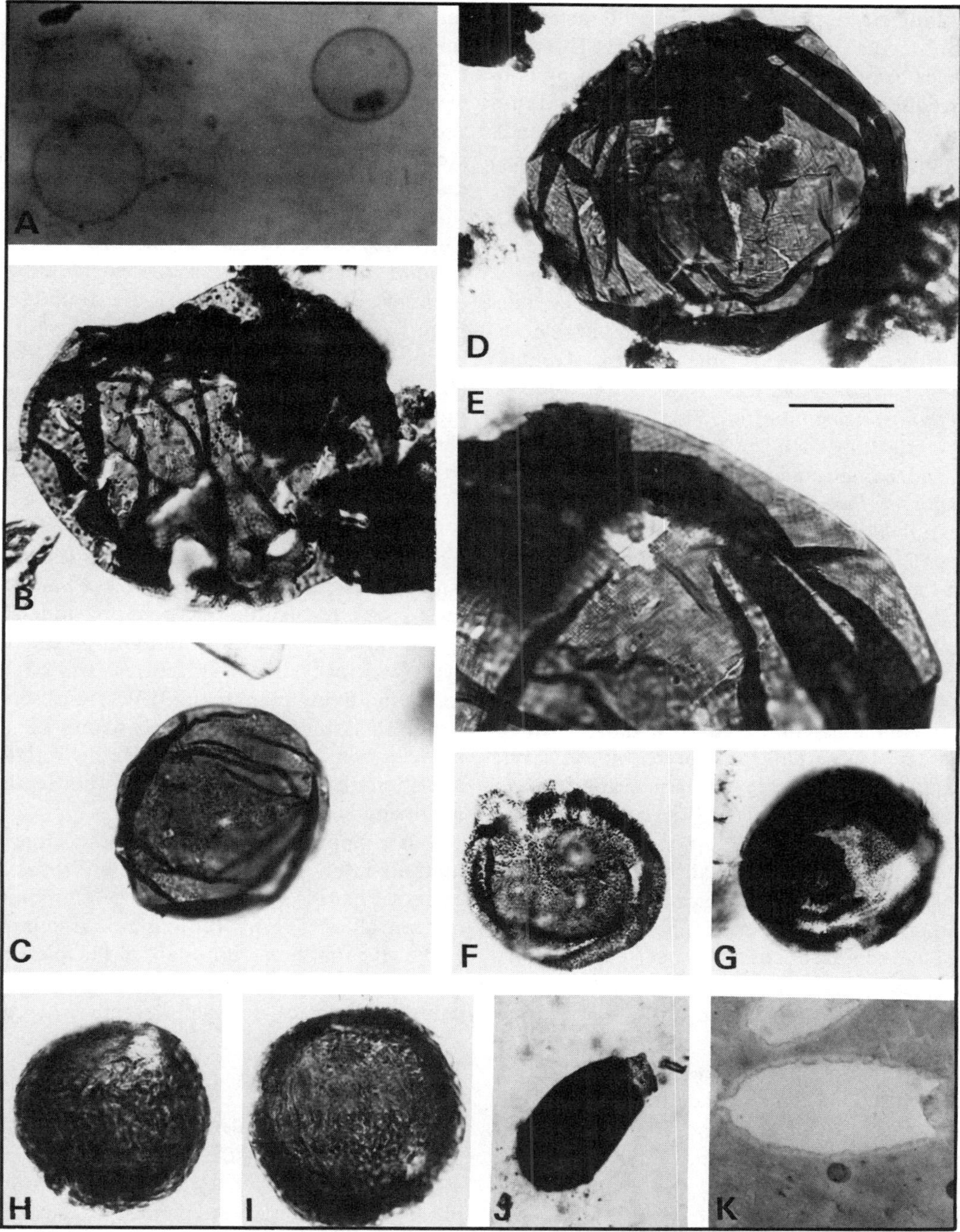

Figure 1. Scale bar in E is as follows: 15 μm for A; 30 μm for B; 20 μm for C, D, and E; 25 μm for F, G, H, and I; and 50 μm for J and K. A, *Leptoteichos golubicii* Knoll, Barghoorn, and Awramik from nonstromatolitic cherts of the 2,000-m.y.-old Gunflint Iron-Formation, Ontario; B, *Kildinosphaera verrucata* Vidal 1983 from the Lower Vendian Ekkerøy Formation, East Finnmark, Norway; C, *Kildinosphaera granulata* Vidal 1983 from the Upper Riphean Andersby Formation, East Finnmark, Norway; D and E, *Kildinosphaera lophostriata* (Jankauskas) Vidal 1983 from the Upper Riphean Kwagunt Formation, Chuar Group, Arizona; F and G, *Trachysphaeridium laufeldi* Vidal from Upper Riphean units of the Visingsö Beds, Sweden; the budlike spiny protuberance visible in G is interpreted as an operculate excystment mechanism; H and I, *Trachysphaeridium laminaritum* (Timofeev) Vidal, also from the Visingsö Beds; J and K, vase-shaped heterotrophic protists, J organically preserved from the Backlundtoppen Formation, Svalbard, and K preserved as a silica-infilled mold lined with apatite in a silicified phosphorite nodule from the Visingsö Beds, Sweden.

extraordinarily long stratigraphic ranges are characteristic of inshore environments (Vidal, 1979b; Knoll, 1983). These latter assemblages are usually dominated by one or two taxa showing frequency fluctuations that are relatable to lithofacies changes (Vidal, 1976a). A similar distributional pattern was reported by Wall (1965) for Lower Jurassic palynomorphs from Great Britain. Jacobson (1979) indicated that in Ordovician sequences acritarch associations dominated by peteinosphaerid acritarchs and Dicommopala reflect a shoal environment. Although none of those acritarch taxa are found in Upper Proterozoic rocks, two Late Proterozoic taxa morphologically comparable to some Ordovician peteinosphaerids (one of them, *Vandalosphaeridium reticulatum* Vidal, was originally regarded as a species of *Peteinosphaeridium;* cf. Vidal 1979b, 1981a) occur in strata reflecting such environmental conditions (Vidal, 1981a). Indeed, specimens of the Late Proterozoic genus *Vandalosphaeridium* are usually found poorly preserved with generally disrupted and worn-out processes and outer membranes (Vidal, 1976a, 1981a), a feature in strong agreement with the high energy environment suggested for the formation of the rocks in which this taxon is found.

Jacobson (1979) also suggested that a baltisphaerid-veryhachid-*Polygonium*-micrhystrid Ordovician acritarch assemblage should represent an offshore open-marine environment. Again, obvious counterparts of those Ordovician acritarchs are absent in the Late Proterozoic; however, the polyhedral Late Proterozoic species *Octoedryxium truncatum* (Rudavskaya) Vidal (1976a) and *Podolina minuta* (Hermann *in* Timofee and others, 1976) can be considered broadly comparable to the above-mentioned veryhachids and *Polygonium. Octoedryxium* and *Podolina* usually occur in small numbers in shallow marine shales and siltstones, but their frequency has been noted to increase to extraordinary levels at certain horizons (e.g., in the upper Visingsö Beds; Vidal, 1976a, in the Biri Formation of southern Norway, and in the lower part of the Båtsfjord Formation of the Barents Sea Group in northern Norway; Vidal, 1981a). One can speculate that these abrupt frequency peaks are ascribable to temporary bloom conditions (Vidal, 1976a) in nearshore waters. Certainly, Proterozoic plankton diversity was highest in offshore shelf or platform environments.

Plankton are often too sparsely distributed in Proterozoic rocks for effective observation in petrographic thin sections, but when this is possible, additional criteria for habitat recognition become available. In silicified stromatolitic carbonates, benthic mat building and mat dwelling populations can be beautifully preserved (Schopf, 1968; Knoll, 1981). Mat builders occur as densely interwoven populations of filaments (Schopf and others, 1977; Knoll, 1981, 1982a) or as dense billowy clouds of entophysalidacean unicells (Hofmann, 1976) that are distributed along bedding. Mat dwelling microbes are sometimes specifically related to a single builder taxon (Knoll, 1982) and although they can be patchily distributed, they also tend to be distributed parallel to bedding. In contrast, allochthonous elements that fell into and were preserved among the benthos tend to be more or less randomly distributed in thin sections. Solitary individuals and clusters of up to several hundred cells are scattered indiscriminately. In the Bitter Springs Formation, Australia, the large populations of 10 μm spheroids belonging to the *Myxococcoides/Glenobotrydion* complex appear to be planktonic "drop-ins" (Schopf, 1972); these unicells are abundantly scattered in both *Eomycetopsis* and *Tenuofilum* built subtidal mats, but are absent from intertidal *Eoentophysalis* associations (Knoll, 1981). In the approximately coeval Draken Conglomerate, Svalbard, presumed plankters are found among *three* distinct benthic communities that are almost non-overlapping in builder and dweller taxa and occur, as well, in interbedded nonstromatolitic muds (Knoll, 1982).

In summary, Proterozoic plankton are potentially recognizable on the basis of at least four criteria: (1) They have wide facies distribution, but like Phanerozoic plankters tend to be resolvable into inshore and offshore associations. (2) They are morphologically and functionally (in cysts with excystment structures) similar to Phanerozoic fossil and living plankters. (3) Where observable, their distribution is independent of preserved benthic microfossil associations. (4) Unlike most benthic microbial taxa, they are often distributed randomly in thin sections rather than mirroring bedding planes.

It is apparent that these are the same general criteria used to infer the nektonic or planktonic nature of such extinct Phanerozoic organisms as ammonites, conodonts, or graptolites. There is room for error in interpretation, but we believe that most, if not all, of the microorganisms identified as Proterozoic plankters did indeed inhabit the water column of coastal and shelf Precambrian oceans.

PALEOECOLOGY

The potential paleoenvironmental value of Late Proterozoic plankton assemblages is implicit in the preceding discussion. Low-diversity assemblages dominated by morphologically simple taxa appear to be diagnostic for inshore coastal environments, while higher diversity microfloras containing a heterogeneous array of morphologically sophisticated forms indicate more open-shelf conditions (Vidal, 1981a). Quantitative comparison of plankton diversities is possible for several silicified carbonate formations. Supratidal to intertidal dolomites of the latest Riphean to Vendian Narssârssuk Formation, northwestern Greenland, contain well-preserved stromatolitic microfossils, but no robust walled acritarchs. Except for some *Microcystis*-like colonial cyanobacterian populations, which possibly lived as plankton or periphyton, fossils likely to represent plankters are extremely rare (Strother and others, 1983). Intertidal stromatolites from the slightly older Bitter Springs Formation likewise contain few if any planktonic taxa (Knoll and Golubic, 1979), but subtidal Bitter Springs mats are rich in presumed planktonic cells (Schopf, 1972). Although individuals are abundant (and, in fact, are the most abundant fossils in the microbiota), species diversity is low. Species richness, defined here by the simple formula S = Number of species/1,000 individuals, is low—ranging from 3.8 to 6.9. Calculation of Simpson's Index of Dominance Concentration ($C = \Sigma (n_i/N)^2$, where n_i is the relative importance value for each species and N is the summed importance for all species) yields values of C = 0.45 to 0.73, indicating that one or two taxa strongly dominate the assemblage (Knoll, 1981). Similarly, lagoonal carbonates from the approximately coeval Hunnberg Formation, Svalbard, have low S values (7 to 8) and high C values (0.65 to 0.69).

In contrast to these assemblages, plankton assemblages in open coastal rocks of the Hunnberg Formation have species richness values of 24 to 26 and dominance concentration values as low as 0.21 to 0.27. The lagoonal and open coastal facies of the Hunnberg were separated by conspicuous columnar stromatolitic bioherms that must have functioned at least indirectly as partial ecological barriers (Knoll, 1983).

It is apparent that species diversity indices can be useful in determining paleoenvironments of deposition in Upper Riphean and Vendian carbonate units, and that inshore-offshore differences approximate those qualitatively determined for contemporaneous detrital deposits. At least in carbonate sequences, this inshore-offshore diversity gradient is paralleled by size differences among preserved acritarchs.

In Bitter Springs assemblages, most presumed plankters have diameters falling between 8 and 20 μm; individuals >30 μm are rare, and specimens exceeding 100 μm are, to our knowledge, unknown. Hunnberg lagoonal rocks similarly contain relatively small numbers of large acritarchs, about 3% of all cells are >30 μm and 1% are >100 μm. In open coastal shelf deposits of the Hunnberg Formation, cells >30 μm and >100 μm make up more than 15% and 4% of the total population, respectively. The observed inshore-offshore size differences correspond in a single time plane to a stratigraphic increase in cell size documented by Schopf (1977) for spheroidal unicells in a series of stromatolitic microbiotas representing most of Proterozoic time.

Megascopic acritarchs have been reported from a variety of Proterozoic rock units around the world (Ford and Breed, 1973; Vidal, 1974, 1976; Hofmann, 1977; Vidal, 1979a; Hofmann and Aitken, 1979; Vidal, 1981a). The majority of these fossils have been attributed to *Chuaria circularis* Walcott; however, the only established criterion for this attribution is a rather arbitrarily chosen lower size limit of 0.5 mm for these fossils (Ford and Breed, 1973; cf. Vidal, 1974, 1976a; Hofmann, 1977; Vidal, 1979a, 1981a). Most objects attributed to *C. circularis* are simple, disc-shaped bodies preserved as carbonaceous films on bedding surfaces. Some of them are apparently carbonaceous intraclasts and fragments of algal mats whose resemblance to *C. circularis* is only superficial (cf. Horodyski, 1980). Furthermore, in a number of instances the presence of *Chuaria* has been reported on the basis of circular imprints on bedding surfaces without any trace of organic wall. Material isolated by palynological extraction methods shows *C. circularis* to be a completely smooth and extremely thick-walled acritarch that varies in size from about 80 μm to about 3 mm (Vidal, 1976a, 1981a). In most respects, it is morphologically comparable to other Upper Proterozoic acritarch taxa. In fact, *Chuaria* is but one of several megascopic Proterozoic acritarchs; a few species of *Kildinosphaera, Protosphaeridium, Tasmanites* (Lower Cambrian), and other as yet undescribed taxa are visible to the unaided eye. The megascopic condition of Upper Proterozoic plankton appears to be closely related to special environments, particularly coastal waters rich in nutrients, which may have offered unusually suitable growth conditions for algae (Vidal, 1979a, 1981a).

It is evident that more paleoecological studies of Precambrian plankton will be necessary to test and refine the observations discussed here. Diver's (1980) ongoing paleoecological analysis of apparently nonmarine microfossils from the 817-m.y.-old Torridon Group, Scotland, is especially worth noting as an example of careful sedimentologically controlled investigation that is extending our knowledge of Proterozoic microfossil distributions. The evolutionary and biostratigraphic dividends on such investment of effort are of demonstrated worth.

BIOSTRATIGRAPHY

Over the past two decades, vigorous research on the dating and correlation of ancient rocks has transformed the Precambrian from a *terra incognita* to an increasingly coherent system of geological knowledge of the early earth. Two biostratigraphic systems have arisen during the period, one based on columnar stromatolites (cf. Walter, 1976) and a second, discussed here, based on acritarchs.

Upper Proterozoic and Lower Paleozoic acritarchs are relatively well known; however, this is true only for a few areas in the Soviet Union (cf. Timofeev, 1966, 1969,1973; Timofeev and others, 1976; Jankauskas, 1978, 1979a, 1979b, 1980a, 1980b), Scandinavia (Vidal, 1974, 1976a, 1979a, 1979b, 1981a), Poland (cf. Volkova and others, 1979; Moczydlowska, 1980), and Greenland (Vidal, 1976a, 1979b; Vidal and Dawes, 1980). Thus, the biostratigraphic system discussed here depends heavily on an understanding of acritarch distribution in the peri-North Atlantic region.

Absolute age dates of ca. 810 m.y. to 600 m.y. bracket the Late Proterozoic acritarch-bearing strata of this region, but radiometric dates for sedimentary horizons within these sequences are rather scarce and of variable reliability. The above-mentioned time interval includes the upper part of the Riphean (Shatsky, 1945, Kozlov, 1978) and the Vendian (Sokolov, 1952, 1972; see also Vidal, 1979a, 1981a). Problems regarding the correlation of Upper Proterozoic sequences with the type Riphean of the southern Urals in the Soviet Union were reviewed by Vidal, 1979a, 1981c); however, recent work of Jankauskas (1978, 1979a) on the type Riphean sequence does permit correlation of those strata with sequences from the peri-North Atlantic region (cf. Vidal, 1981a). We emphasize that in this paper the terms "Riphean" and "Vendian" are used *sensu lato* as proposed by Vidal (1979a).

In all investigated areas of the North Atlantic region, several distinctive acritarch assemblages are found. The stratigraphically lowest assemblage is found in the lower, middle, and lower upper Visingsö Beds in Sweden (Vidal, 1974, 1976a, 1979b), as well as in the upper Eleonore Bay Group, East Greenland (Vidal, 1976b, 1979a) and the bulk of the Vadsö Group, East Finnmark (Vidal, 1981a; see also Figs. 1 and 3). Similar assemblages have also been recognized in the middle part of the Barents Sea Group (Båsnaering and Båtsfjord Formations) around the Barents Sea coast of the Varanger Peninsula in northern Norway (Vidal, 1981a), in the lower part of the Thule Group, northwestern Greenland (Wolstenholme Formation; Vidal and Dawes, 1980), and in the Realdtoppen Group of Nordaustlandet, Svalbard (Knoll, 1983). The assemblage, indicative of the Upper Riphean, consists exclusively of sphaeromorphic acritarch taxa; among them *Chuaria circularis* Walcott, *Kildinosphaera chagrinata,* Vidal 1983, *K. granulata,* Vidal 1983, *K. verrucata,* Vidal 1983 (in Vidal and Siedlecka, 1983), *Leiosphaeridia asperata* (Naumova) Lindren 1982, *K. Lophostriata* (Jankauskas), *Pterospermopsimorpha ?densicoronata* Vidal, cf. *Stictosphaeridium* sp., *Synsphaeridium* sp., *Trachysphaeridium laminaritum* (Timofeev) Vidal, *T. laufeldi* Vidal, *T. levis* (Lopukhin) Vidal, *Tasmanites rifejicus* Jankauskas, and, in the upper part of the sequence, vase-shaped microfossils (Vidal, 1979a; Fig. 1B–K). It deserves mention that this assemblage of taxa has also been recovered from rocks of the Chuar Group (Kwagunt Formation) of the Grand Canyon, Arizona (Vidal, unpublished data); it was in these beds that the evolutionarily important vase-shaped microfossils were first discovered (Bloeser and others, 1977; Bloeser, 1980).

Microfossiliferous Lower Vendian strata are well represented in southern Sweden (upper Visingsö Beds; Vidal, 1976a, 1979b), southern Norway (in particular, the Ring and Biri Formations of the Hedmark Group; Vidal, unpublished data), and northern Norway (the topmost formation of the Vadsö Group and the entire succeeding Tanafjord Group; the lower Båtsfjord Formation of the Barents Sea Group; Vidal, 1981a). The absolute age of the Lower Vendian is bracketed by as yet unpublished (cf. Vidal, 1979b, 1981a) Rb/Sr whole-rock dating on shales of the upper Visingö Beds (707 ± 37 m.y.) and of the Ekre Shale (612 ± 18 m.y.). The latter overlies and consequently postdates the Moelv Tillite of the above-mentioned Hedmark Group in southern Norway. The Båtsfjord Formation is younger than the 810 ± 60 m.y. Rb/Sr whole-rock age obtained for shales of the stratigraphically underlying Kongsfjord Formation of the lower Barents Sea Group (Siedlecki, 1980).

Most of the above-mentioned Upper Riphean acritarch taxa persist in Lower Vendian acritarch assemblages. Vendian innovations (Fig. 2) include the appearance of purported endosporulating planktonic cyanobacteria [*Bavlinella faveolata* (Shepeleva) Vidal = *Sphaerocongregus variabilis* Moorman], polygonomorphic acritarchs (*Octoedryxium truncatum, Podolina minuta*), and acritarchs with double walls (*Pterospermopsimorpha mogilevica* Timofeev, *P. ?densicoronata* Vidal), some of them displaying tiny perforations [*P. concentrica* (Sin & Liu) Vidal]. Of particular interest is the appearance in Lower Vendian rocks of acritarchs provided with processes supporting a surrounding thin membrane [*Vandalosphaeridium reticulatum* (Vidal) Vidal, 1981a, and *V. varangeri* Vidal, 1981a]. Furthermore, the Lower Vendian assemblage has yielded strongly ornamented sphaeromorphs of large dimensions (*Favososphaeridium favosum* Timofeev) and abundant vase-shaped microfossils (Knoll and Vidal, 1980).

The Varangerian sequence, which in places immediately succeeds the Lower Vendian sequence (see Fig. 1), encompasses the Varangerian glacial episode of Scandinavia and Greenland (see Vidal, 1979b and 1981a concerning putative glacial deposits in adjacent regions). The absolute age of the Varangerian sequence has been established by Rb/Sr whole-rock dating of shales of the intertillitic Nyborg Formation in northern Norway (Fig. 1) which has yielded an age of 653 ± 7 m.y. Rocks of Ekre Shale (unfortunately unfossiliferous; Vidal, unpublished data) in southern Norway, which overlie the Moelv Tillite, have yielded an unpublished Rb/Sr whole-rock age of 612 ± 18 m.y.

Varangerian acritarchs are poorly documented because the Varangerian glacial episode resulted in the deposition of nonmarine sediments in many places; however, acritarchs have been recovered from parts of the sequence in East Greenland (Vidal, 1976b, 1979a) and in northern Norway (Vidal, 1981a). The recovered assemblages are taxonomically depauperate, consisting of a few preexisting taxa that trespass the boundary marked by the base of the Varangerian glaciogenic strata (cf. Vidal, 1979b, 1981a). Varangerian rocks that on sound grounds are regarded as having formed under marine depositional conditions have yielded assemblages consisting of *B. faveolata, C. circularis, Kildinosphaera* sp., *Leiosphaeridia* sp., *L. asperata, O.*

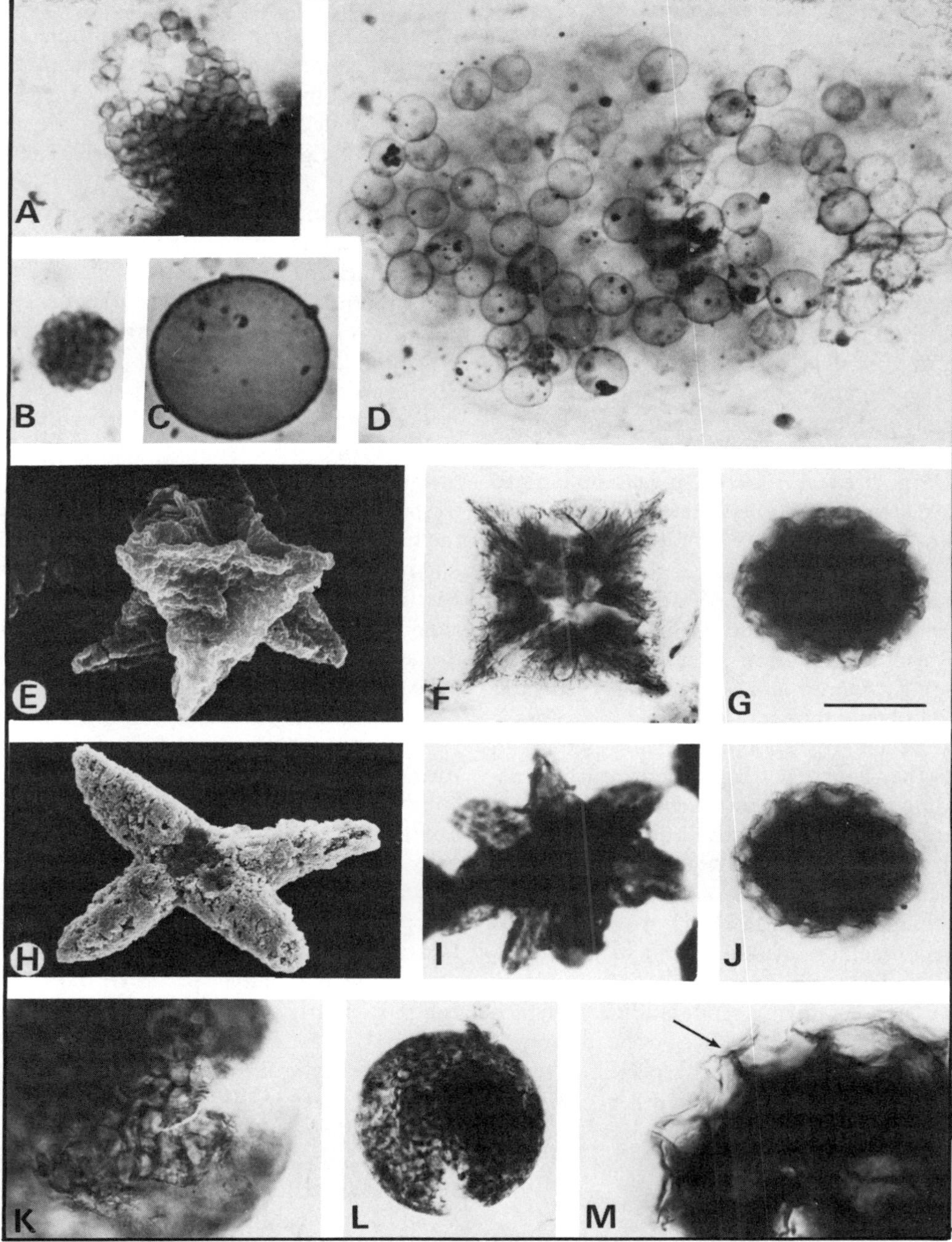

Figure 2. Scale bar in G is as follows: 12 μm for A, B, and C; 25 μm for D, F, G, I, J, and K; 20 μm for E and H; 50 μm for L; and 15 μm for M. A and B, *Bavlinella faveolata* (Shepeleva) Vidal—A from the Mineral Fork Formation, Utah, and B from the Shields Formation, Tennessee; C and D, thin-walled, presumable plankters preserved as allochthonous elements within silicified microbial mats of the Draken Formation, Svalbard—C is an isolated individual, D a cluster of cells at lower magnification; E and F, *Octoedryxium truncatum* (Rudavskaja) Vidal, from the Upper Visingsö Beds, Sweden—E is a scanning electron micrograph; G, J, and M, *Vandalosphaeridium reticulatum* (Vidal) Vidal from the Upper Visingsö Beds, Sweden—G and J are different optical sections through a single specimen; M shows the pillar-supported nature of the outer wall (arrow) at higher magnification; H and I, *Podolina minuta* (Hermann) Vidal 1983 from the Lower Båtsfjord Formation, Barents Sea Group, Finnmark, Norway—H is an SEM micrograph; K and L, *Favososphaeridium favosum* Timofeev from the Upper Visingsö Beds, Sweden—K is an enlarged detail of the specimen illustrated in L, showing the reticulate nature of the wall sculpture.

truncatum, P. laccatum, cf. *Stictosphaeridium* sp., *Trachysphaeridium* sp., *T. levis* and *T. timofeevi.* Thus, the only innovation noted in the Varangerian assemblage is the appearance of thin, smooth, and rather undiagnostic sphaeromorphs attributed to *Leiosphaeridia* sp., together with an explosive dominance of *B. faveolata* (see below).

Rocks of latest Proterozoic (Late Vendian) Valdai age are widely represented in the East European Platform, in northern Scandinavia, and in areas bordering the eastern margins of the Scandinavian Caledonian fold belt (cf. Føyn and Glaessner, 1979; Vidal, 1981a). No reliable radiometric dates are available from the Valdai sequence (except for the above-mentioned unpublished dating of the Ekre Shale in southern Norway; cf. Vidal, 1979b, for a review). Northern European Valdaian sequences are transgressive (Vidal, 1981a) and therefore tend to be of considerably variable thickness over a large area. Acritarchs, megascopic algae (i.e., vendotaenids), and soft-bodied metazoans (cf. Volkova, 1968; Volkova and others, 1979, Føyn and Glaessner, 1979; Vidal, 1976b, 1981a) have been reported from Valdai rocks and their correlatives. Valdaian acritarchs consist of simple, thin-walled, and rather undiagnostic leiosphaerids of variable dimensions, a few persisting taxa from older strata (e.g., *B. faveolata, P. ? densicoronata* and *P. mogilevica*), and filamentous cyanophycean microfossils (cf. Volkova and others, 1979). Paradoxically, although consisting of taxa that have few diagnostic characters, assemblages (including the characteristic vendotaenids) from Valdaian rocks are completely different from any other assemblages known from either older or younger rocks. The most diagnostic components of the Valdaian assemblage are the above-mentioned megascopic ribbon-shaped membranes of vendotaenids, usually found in great profusion among acid-resistant residues. In addition, Valdaian rocks from the Russian Platform and Poland have yielded scattered specimens of micrhystrid acritarchs belonging to a single stratigraphically long-lived species, *Micrhystridium tornatum* Volkova (Volkova and others, 1979).

Acritarchs and the Precambrian/Cambrian Boundary

Various groups of invertebrates, including trilobites, archaeocyathids, calcareous worm tubes, and other problematic shelly remains, have been proposed as paleontological indicators of the Precambrian/Cambrian boundary (or transition). A persistent problem with all such taxa is that their occurrence is in part facies dependent and tends to be patchy. Also, the stratigraphic ranges of such "Tommotian" shelly invertebrates appear rather uncertain (Landing and others, 1980; Bergström, 1981; Vidal, 1981a). Because planktonic microfossils are of almost ubiquitous distribution in unmetamorphosed marine sedimentary rocks, they constitute a particularly valuable means of dating and correlating boundary sections. In most parts of Scandinavia, the Lower Cambrian sequence rests with profound disconformable contact on either Precambrian crystalline complexes or Upper Proterozoic sedimentary rocks. So far, investigated Lower Cambrian sections have yielded acritarchs of distinctive *Holmia* age (Vidal, 1981b). Older Cambrian rocks (i.e., sub-*Holmia*) may succeed Late Vendian strata in East Finnmark (Vidal, 1981a, 1981c); however, data confirming this assumption are lacking at the moment. Thus, there are no Scandinavian sequences containing acritarchs that may indicate the existence of rocks equivalent to the oldest Cambrian beds recognized in the East European Platform. Available data from the latter area indicate that earliest Cambrian acritarchs differ substantially from their Upper Proterozoic counterparts. A small number of taxa (most of them left under open nomenclature) are known to trespass the Proterozoic/Cambrian boundary (see Fig. 1) in the East European Platform (cf. Volkova and others, 1979) and in Scandinavia (cf. Vidal, 1979b). In the East European Platform these include very generalized types of *Leiosphaeridia* spp. and the above mentioned *Micrhystridium tornatum*; in Scandinavia rocks referred to the *Holmia* "stage" (cf. Vidal, 1981b) have occasionally yielded specimens of *T. timofeevi* and *B. faveolata.*

The lowermost Cambrian of the East European Platform (klimontov Stage, sometimes called the sub-*Holmia* "horizon" or, alternatively, "zone") comprises the Rovno and Lontova Beds and embraces the *Sabellidites, Platysolenites,* and *Mobergella* zones. These beds have yielded two distinctive, but taxonomically low-diversity, assemblages of morphologically simple acritarchs (and other microproblematica; *cf.* Volkova and others, 1979). The first appearance of the distinctive species *Granomarginata squamacea* is a particularly good datum marking the lowermost Cambrian. A drastic change follows at the disconformable boundary between the sub-*Holmia* and *Holmia* "stages" (as informally used by Vidal, 1981b). The *Holmia* "stage" (Lukati Beds = *Holmia* A, and the Vergale Beds = *Holmia* B; cf Volkova and others, 1979; Vidal, 1981b) has yielded the first known trilobite faunas and with them extremely diverse assemblages of morphologically complex acritarchs. These microfloras are also recognized in beds ascribed to the *Holmia* (A and B) "stage" in Scandinavia (Vidal, 1981a, 1981b) and East Greenland (Vidal, 1979a). Taxonomically, these assemblages include species referrable to a large percentage of the known Lower Cambrian genera (*e.g., Baltisphaeridium, Granomarginata, Cymatiosphaera, Micrhystridium, Archaeodiscina, Tasmanites, Lophosphaeridium,* and others). An increasing number of taxa are reported for the succeeding Rausve Beds (*Protolenus* Zone) and Kibartai Beds (Middle Cambrian; *cf.* Volkova and others, 1979).

Figure 3 summarizes the stratigraphic ranges of morphologically distinctive late Proterozoic microfossils as de-

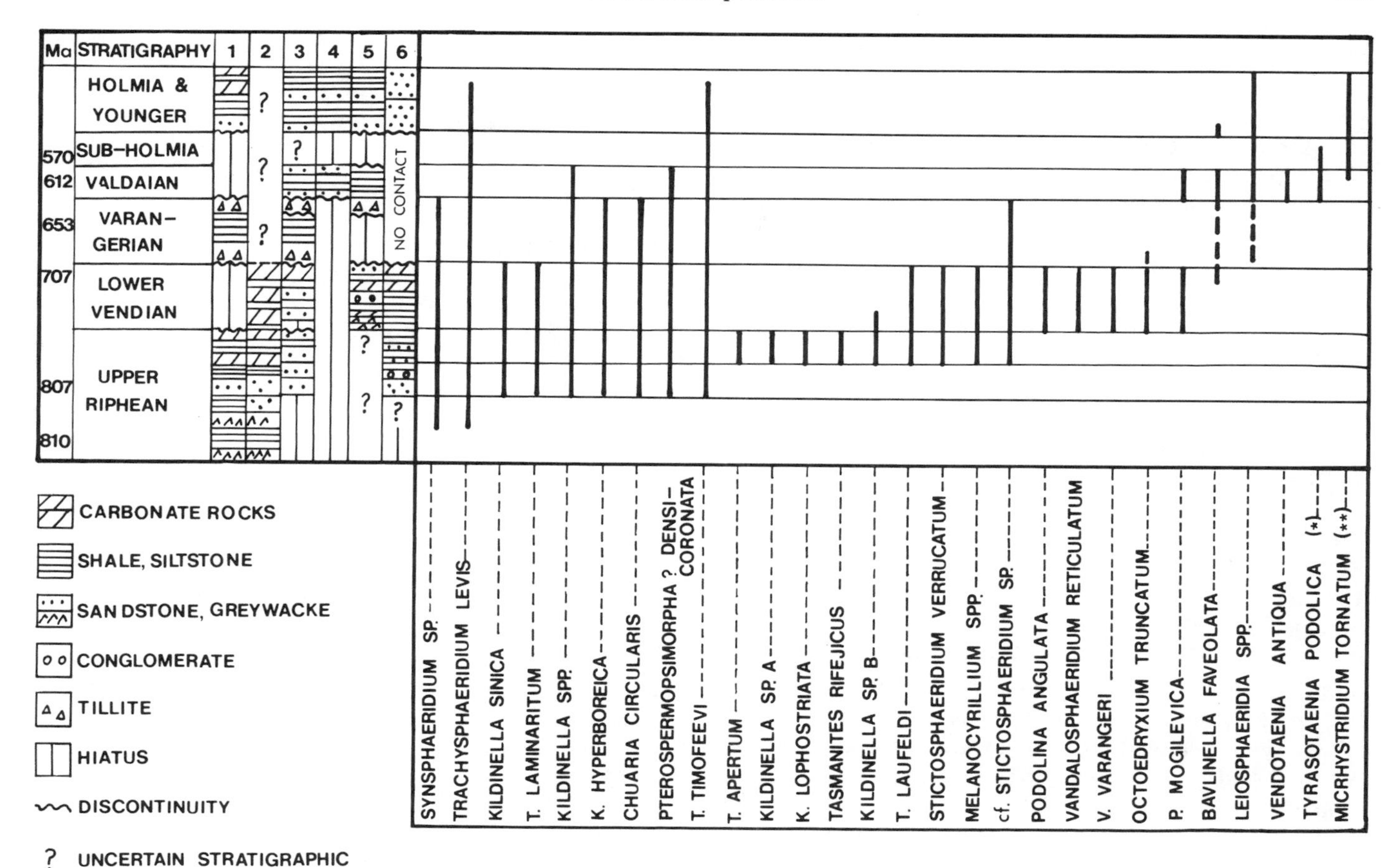

Figure 3. Stratigraphic ranges of selected Upper Riphean, Vendian, and lowermost Cambrian microfossil taxa. The sections from which the chart was compiled are from 1, East Greenland; 2, Barents Sea; 3, East Finnmark, Norway; 4, Lappland, Sweden; 5, Southern Norway; and 6, Southern Sweden. See p. 266 concerning recently revised taxonomic combinations.

termined from their vertical distribution in Scandinavia and East Greenland. Well-studied sequences from the Soviet Union corroborate the ranges shown here and clearly indicate the realization of a workable Upper Riphean and Vendian acritarch biostratigraphy.

EVOLUTIONARY CONSIDERATIONS

The oldest microfossils that can reasonably be interpreted as planktonic are populations of relatively large (5 to 31 μm) unicells scattered throughout distal, nonstromatolitic chert facies of the 200-m.y.-old Gunflint Iron-Formation, Ontario (Knoll and others, 1978; Fig. 1-A). It is likely, however, that the planktonic realm was invaded much earlier, probably in Archean times. Circumstantial evidence supporting this hypothesis comes from the abundance and distribution of organic matter in Archean sedimentary rocks. Basic similarities to Phanerozoic sedimentary rocks suggest similarities in sites of organic production and mechanisms of transport; that is, the implication is that at least some of the organic matter in distal facies of Archean sequences came from the sedimented remains of early planktonic prokaryotes. The modern microplankton biota includes both coccoidal and filamentous cyanobacteria (Waterbury and others, 1979) as well as various other bacteria. Staley (1980) has, in fact, suggested that the gas vacuoles found in many cyanobacteria and photosynthetic bacteria, as well as in some anaerobic heterotrophs and methanogens, represent a very early evolutionary solution to the problem of vertical motility in the water column.

Various factors may have limited the total productivity of Archean plankters. Walker (1978) has suggested that in the absence of an effective ozone shield, Archean primary producers would have been scarce in the top few meters of the ocean. With the advent of an oxygen-rich atmosphere in the Early Proterozoic, this problem would have been ameliorated. A second and, we believe, important environmental limitation on Archean plankton would have been availability of nutrients, particularly phosphates. In the absence of large continents, the erosional supply of nutrients, as well as the circulational recovery of nutrients from deep waters, must have been relatively low. The extensive cratonization that marks the Archean/Proterozoic transition must have contributed to increased plankton productivity (Knoll, 1979).

While it is of interest to speculate on the early history of the planktonic microbiota, it is more enlightening to examine the documentable record of late Proterozoic plankton evolution. Figure 4 summarizes the late Precambrian–early Cambrian history of the marine phytoplankton.

Reports of acritarchs older than 900 m.y. are extremely rare, and a crucial problem common to many of these reports is the inadequacy of radiometric age determinations. Jankauskas (1978 and following) described acritarchs from units of the type Riphean sequence in the southern Urals that have yielded radiometric ages interpreted as Early and Middle Riphean; however, these ages must be regarded as extremely unreliable (Vidal, 1981a). Similarly, acritarchs have been reported from the Roper Group in the Northern Territory of Australia (Peat and others, 1978) in rocks radiometrically dated at about 1,300 m.y. The Roper fossils, however, are surprisingly similar to Upper Riphean forms, and the above-mentioned absolute age of the group is regarded as extremely questionable (Peat, 1980, personal communication). Horodyski (1980) has reported a somewhat different assemblage from the approximately 1,400-m.y.-old Lower Belt Supergroup, Montana. In addition to filamentous cyanobacterial sheaths and thin-walled spheroidal vesicles (possibly sheaths), this microbiota includes what may be the oldest reliably dated robust-walled acritarchs. A low-diversity acritarch assemblage has also been recovered from the 1,100-m.y.-old Nonesuch Shale, Michigan (Strother, 1980).

As is evident from Figures 3 and 4, the Upper Riphean is characterized by the widespread expansion of sphaeromorphic acritarchs displaying a variety of sculptural patterns and excystment mechanisms. The succeeding Lower Vendian biota is even more diverse.

The importance of this expansion can best be understood by analogy to the well-known Lower Cretaceous diversification of angiosperm pollen taxa documented by Doyle (1969; Doyle and Hickey, 1976). For decades, arguments over the antiquity of the flowering plants centered on sterile debate concerning the affinities of scattered and often poorly preserved individual plant fossils. Doyle's singular contribution was to demonstrate that no matter when the angiosperms first evolved, the early Cretaceous marked the evolutionary ratiation and ecological rise to dominance of the group. We contend that the late Riphean diversification of marine acritarchs tells a similar story about eukaryote evolution. Much of the debate concerning the antiquity of nucleated cells has involved the interpretation of morphologically bland fossils, some of which contain regularly shaped internal bodies. The interpretation of most, if not all, of these fossils remains ambiguous; however, there is no question that the acritarch expansion in the Late Riphean represents the initial observable diversification and rise to ecological dominance of cyst-forming eukaryotic plankton. Eukaryotes radiated in the late Precambrian and, insofar as the fossil record permits us to compare different environments, first established dominance in the open-shelf planktonic realm. By the end of the Riphean, the preservable plankton biota included vase-shaped heterotrophic protists as well as algae (Bloeser and others, 1977; Knoll and Vidal, 1980).

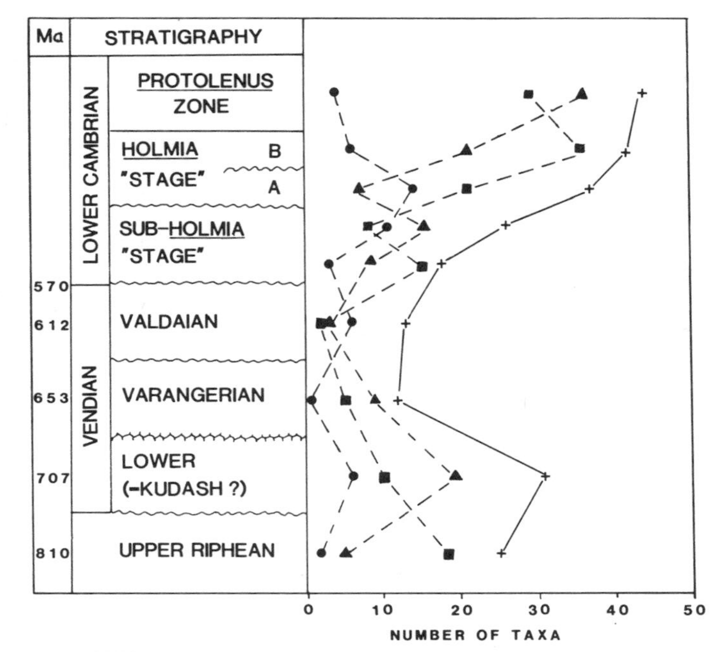

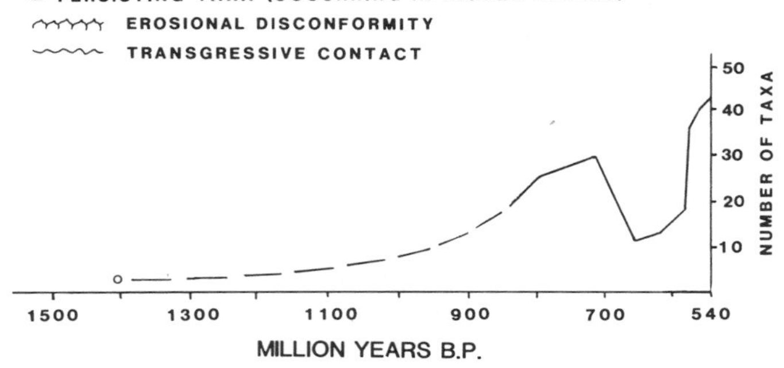

Figure 4. Diversity changes in the late Precambrian and Early Cambrian plankton record. Upper chart shows details of diversity changes near the Precambrian/Cambrian (wavy lines between stratigraphic intervals indicate transgressive contacts in Scandinavia; saw-tooth lines indicate erosional disconformities). The lower chart illustrates diversity changes within a broader framework of time. The dotted line is an estimate of the course of eukaryotic plankton diversity from 1,400 m.y. B.P., the date marking the oldest known probable eukaryotic plankters, to the Upper Riphean (where data become quantitatively reliable).

A drastic change in the planktonic biota coincided with the Varangerian glaciations. Most of the distinctive Lower Vendian taxa disappeared (Fig. 1), leaving a depauperate biota of simple sphaeromorphs and multi-sphere microfossils interpreted as endosporulating cyanobacteria (*Bavlinella faveolata*). *B. faveolata* is known to have dominated glacially influenced marine environments, probably proliferating under ecologically stressed conditions (Vidal, 1976b; Knoll and others, 1981).

Although the Varangerian acritarch record leaves much to be desired because of associated erosional contacts and hiatuses, the severity of the extinction episode is real and can be supported on several grounds.

1. Marine Varangerian sedimentary rocks do exist and contain low-diversity plankton assemblages. The diversity data plotted in Figure 2 is "total," or gamma (*sensu* Whittaker, 1975), diversity information; that is, the tabulated diversity for each level includes all taxa that we accept as valid. The cosmopolitan nature of almost all forms examined suggests that the graph is equally representative of "within flora," or alpha (Whittaker, 1975), diversity trends. Comparisons of alpha diversity do not depend on equal outcrop representation in the way that most gamma diversity tabulations do (Bambach, 1977), so long as similar environments are being considered.

2. One can reasonably argue that observed low Varangerian plankton diversities result from a biased sampling of environments; that is, we are looking predominantly at glacially influenced sequences. This is true for the most part; however, immediately superjacent Valdaian strata are equally species poor, and these deposits are widespread and well sampled. In fact, the diversity trends observable in Figure 4 are as applicable to sequences like the Nama Supergroup in South West Africa (Namibia) as they are to North Atlantic successions. Taxa that disappeared at the end of the Early Vendian simply did not reappear, even though nonglacially influenced environments appropriate for their growth and preservation returned.

3. The taxa that disappeared apparently went extinct without recognizable issue. That is, not only does a taxon like *Trachysphaeridium laufeldi* disappear at the end of the Early Vendian, but younger acritarch assemblages contain no fossils that seem to belong to the same phylogenetic lineage. When diversity did rebound, and this did not occur until well into the Early Cambrian, the new radiation was predominantly of baltisphaerids and other structurally complex forms. Their relationships to older fossils are unclear to say the least.

Thus, there is little doubt that the latest Proterozoic Era was a time of major extinction in the microplankton realm. It is tempting to relate this biological event to the Varangerian glaciation because of the time coincidence; however, any hypothesis relating the two phenomena necessarily remains speculative and *ad hoc* at this time.

To summarize, Upper Riphean and Lower Vendian microplankton assemblages indicate a dramatic late Proterozoic diversification that represents the first recognizable radiation of eukaryotic algae and documents their rapid rise to dominance in coastal planktonic environments. An equally dramatic diversity drop in the latest Proterozoic is interpreted as the earliest recognizable episode of widespread extinction. The plankton crisis appears to be related to the Varangerian glaciation; however, the problems of going from correlation to causation are considerable. More data are needed to test and extend the arguments set forth in this paper. Particularly pressing is the need for more careful analyses of plankton assemblages of Middle Proterozoic age; however, stratigraphically controlled studies of Upper Proterozoic sequences outside of the North Atlantic and northern Eurasian regions are also much to be desired. Planktonic microfossils are important keys to the understanding of critical Precambrian evolutionary events, and there is a great deal left to learn.

ACKNOWLEDGMENTS

This paper is a contribution to IGCP projects Nos. 29 (Precambrian/Cambrian boundary) and 118 (Upper Precambrian correlations). The Micropalaeontological Laboratory, University of Lund, is supported by grants from the Swedish Natural Science Research Council (NFR) and Knut och Alice Wallenbergs stiftelsen to G. Vidal. A. H. Knoll acknowledges the support of National Science Foundation Grant DEB 8004290.

In memory of the late Boris V. Timofeev, pioneer of Precambrian micropaleontology.

REFERENCES CITED

Bambach, R. K., 1977, Species richness in marine benthic habitats through the Phanerozoic: Paleobiology, v. 3, p. 152–167.

Bergström, J., 1981, Lower Cambrian shelly faunas and biostratigraphy in Scandinavia. Short papers for the second International Symposium on the Cambrian System 1981: U.S. Geological Survey Open-File Report 81-743, p. 22–25.

Bloeser, B., 1980, Structurally complex microfossils from shales of the Late Precambrian Kwagunt Formation (Walcott Member, Chuar Group) of the eastern Grand Canyon, Arizona [M.Sc. thesis]: Los Angeles, University of California, 100 p.

Bloeser, B., Schopf, J. W., Horodyski, R. J., and Breed, W. J., 1977, Chitinozoans from the late Precambrian Chuar Group of the Grand Canyon, Arizona: Science, v. 195, p. 676–679.

Diver, W. L., 1980, Some factors controlling cryptarch distribution in the late Precambrian Torridan Group: Fifth International Palynological Conference, Cambridge, Abstracts, p. 113.

Downie, C., 1973, Observations on the nature of the acritarchs: Palaeontology, v. 16, p. 239–259.

Downie, C., Evitt, W. R., and Sarjeant, W.A.S., 1963, Dinoflagellates, hystrichospheres, and the classification of acritarchs: Stanford University Publications in Geological Sciences, v. 7, p. 3–16.

Doyle, J. A., 1969, Cretaceous angiosperm pollen of the Atlantic coastal plain and its evolutionary significance: Journal of the Arnold Arboretum, v. 50, p. 1–35.

Doyle, J. A., and Hickey, L. J., 1976, Pollen and leaves from the mid-Cretaceous Potomac Group and their bearing on early angiosperm evolution, *in* Beck, C. B., ed., Origin and early evolution of angiosperms: New York, Columbia, p. 139–206.

Elston, D. P., and McKee, E. H., 1982, Age and correlation of the Late Proterozoic Grand Canyon Orogeny, Northern Arizona: Geological Society of America Bulletin, v. 93, p. 681–699.

Evitt, W. R., 1963, A discussion and proposals concerning fossil dinoflagellates, hystrichospheres, and acritarchs, II: Proceedings of the National Academy of Science, U.S.A., v. 49, p. 298–302.

Ford, T. D., and Breed, W. J., 1973, The problematical Precambrian fossil *Chuaria:* Palaeontology, v. 16, p. 535–550.

Føyn, S., and Glaessner, M. F., 1979, *Platysolenites,* other animal fossils, and the Precambrian-Cambrian transition in Norway: Norsk Geologisk Tidsskrift, v. 59, p. 25–46.

Hofmann, H. J., 1976, Precambrian microflora, Belcher Islands, Canada: Significance and systematics: Journal of Paleontology, v. 50, p. 1040–1073.

——1977, The problematic fossil *Chuaria* from the late Precambrian Uinta Mountain Group, Utah: Precambrian Research, v. 4, p. 1–11.

Hofmann, H. J., and Aitken, J. D., 1979, Precambrian biota from the Little Dal Group, Mackenzie Mountains, northwestern Canada: Canadian Journal of Earth Sciences, v. 16, p. 150–166.

Horodyski, R. J., 1980, Middle Proterozoic shale-facies microbiota from the lower Belt Supergroup, Little Belt Mountains, Montana: Journal of Paleontology, v. 54, p. 249–663.

Jacobson, S. R., 1979, Acritarchs as paleonenvironmental indicators in middle and upper Ordovician rocks from Kentucky, Ohio, and New York: Journal of Paleontology, v. 53, p. 1197–1212.

Jankauskas, T. V., 1978, Plant-microfossils from the Riphean of the southern Urals: Doklady of the Academy of Sciences of the U.S.S.R., Earth Science Sections, v. 242, p. 913–915 (in Russian).

——1979a, Middle Riphean microbiota from the southern Urals and the Bashkirian Urals: Doklady of the Academy of Sciences of the U.S.S.R., Earth Science Sections, v. 248, p. 190–193 (in Russian).

——1979b, The Lower Riphean microbiota of the southern Urals: Doklady of the Academy of Sciences of the U.S.S.R., Earth Science Sections, v. 247, p. 1465–1467 (in Russian).

——1980a, The oldest complex of plant microfossils from the Vendian of the adjacent areas of Bashkiria (Sergejevskaya microbiota): Doklady of the Academy of Sciences of the U.S.S.R., Earth Science Sections, v. 250, p. 1434–1436 (in Russian).

——1980b, Shishenyakskaya microbiota from the Upper Riphean of the southern Urals: Doklady of the Academy of Sciences of the U.S.S.R., Earth Science Sections, v. 251, p. 190–192 (in Russian).

Knoll, A. H., 1979, Archean photoautotrophy: Some alternatives and limits: Origins of Life, v. 9, p. 313–327.

——1981, Paleoecology of late Precambrian microbial assemblages, *in* Niklas, K., ed., Paleobotany, paleoecology, and evolution: New York, Praeger, v. 1, p. 17–54.

——1982, Microorganisms from the late Precambrian Draken Conglomerate, Ny Friesland, Spitsbergen: Journal of Paleontology, v. 56, p. 755–790.

——1983, Microbiotas of the late Precambrian Hunnberg Formation, Nordaustlandet, Svalbard: Journal of Paleontology, v. 57.

Knoll, A. H., and Golubic, S., 1979, Anatomy and taphonomy of a Precambrian algal stromatolite: Precambrian Research, v. 10, p. 115–151.

Knoll, A. H., and Vidal, G., 1980, Late Proterozoic vase-shaped microfossils from the Visingsö Beds, Sweden: Geologiska Föreningens i Stockholm Förhandlingar, v. 102, no. 3, p. 207–211.

Knoll, A. H., Barghoorn, E. S., and Awramik, S. M., 1978, New microorganisms from the Aphebian Gunflint Iron Formation, Ontario: Journal of Paleontology, v. 52, p. 576–592.

Knoll, A. H., Blick, N., and Awramik, S. M., 1981, Stratigraphic and ecologic implications of late Precambrian microfossils from Utah: American Journal of Science, v. 281, p. 247–263.

Kozlov, V. I., 1978, The main features of the Upper Precambrian stratigraphy of the Bashkirian Urals, *in* Precambrian sequences of the Bashkirian mega-anticline of the Urals and their metallogenesis: Academy of Sciences of the U.S.S.R., Ural Scientific Center, Institute of Geology and Geochemistry, v. 133, p. 3–15 (in Russian).

Landing, E., Nowlan, G. S., and Fletcher, T. P., 1980, A microfauna associated with Early Cambrian trilobites of the *Callavia* Zone, northern Antigonish Highlands, Nova Scotia: Canadian Journal of Earth Sciences, v. 17, p. 400–418.

Lindgren, S., 1982, Algal coenobia and Leiospheres from the Upper Riphean of the Turukhansk region, eastern Siberia: Stockholm Contributions to Geology, v. 38, p. 35–45.

Moczydlowska, M., 1980, Acritarchs from the Cambrian of the borehole Okuniew IG 1: Kwartalnik Geologicznef, v. 24, no. 3, p. 461–487 (in Polish).

Muir, M. D., and Sarjeant, W.A.S., 1971, An annotated bibliography of the Tasmanaceae and of related living forms (Algae: Prasinophyceae), *in* Jardine, S., Secretaire de Redaction, C.I.M.P. Microfossiles organiques du Paléozoique, 3, Les Acritarches: Paris, France, Editions du Centre National de la Recherche Scientifique.

Peat, C. J., Muir, M. D., Plumb, K. A., McKirdy, D. M., and Norvick, M. S., 1978, Proterozoic microfossils from the Roper Group, Northern Territory, Australia: Bureau of Mineral Resources, Journal of Australian Geology and Geophysics, v. 3, p. 1–17.

Schopf, J. W., 1968, Microflora of the Bitter Springs Formation, late Precambrian, central Australia: Journal of Paleontology, v. 42, p. 651–688.

——1972, Evolutionary significance of the Bitter Springs (late Precambrian) microflora: International Geological Congress, 24th, Montreal, Section 1, p. 68–77.

——1977, Biostratigraphic usefulness of stromatolitic Precambrian microbiotas: A preliminary analysis: Precambrian Research, v. 5, p. 143–173.

Schopf, J. W., Dolnik, T. A., Krylov, I. N., Mendelson, C. V., Nazarov, B. B., Nyberg, A. V., Sovietov, Yu.K., and Yakshin, M. S., 1977, Six new stromatolitic microbiotas from the Proterozoic of the Soviet Union: Precambrian Research, v. 4, p. 269–284.

Shatsky, N. S., 1945, Essays on tectonics of the Volga-Ural oil-bearing region and adjacent part of the western slope of the Lower Ural: Materials on the study of geological structure of the U.S.S.R., new series, v. 2, n. 6 (in Russian).

Siedlecki, S., 1980, Geologist Kart over Norge, berggrundskart VADSO-M: Norges Geologiske Undersøkelse, scale 1:250,000.

Sokolov, B. S., 1952, Age of the most ancient sedimentary cover in the Russian Platform. Doklady of the Academy of Sciences U.S.S.R., Earth Sciences Section, v. 5, p. 21–31 (in Russian).

——1972, Vendian of Eurasia, *in* Pitcher, M. G., ed., Arctic: American Association of Petroleum Geologists Memoir 19, p. 204–218.

Staley, J. T., 1980, The gas vacuole: An early organelle of prokaryote motility? *in* Ponnamperuma, C., and others, eds., Limits of life: Dordrecht, Holland, Riedel, p. 55–60.

Strother, P. K., 1980, Microbial communities from Precambrian strata [Ph. D. thesis]: Harvard University, Cambridge, Massachusetts.

Strother, P. K., Knoll, A. H., and Barghoorn, E. S., 1983, Microorganisms from the late Precambrian Narssârssuk Formation, northwestern Greenland: Palaeontology, v. 26, p. 1–32.

Timofeev, B. V., 1959, Ancient flora of the Baltic area and its stratigraphic significance: Trudy Institute for the All-Union Scientific Investigation and Prospecting of Petroleum, no. 129, 320 p. (in Russian).

—— 1966, Microphytological investigations of ancient formations: Academy of Sciences, U.S.S.R., Laboratory of Precambrian Geology, Leningrad, Nauka, 145 p. (in Russian).

—— 1969, Proterozoic sphaeromorphs: Academy of Sciences, U.S.S.R., Institute for Precambrian Geology and Geochronology, Leningrad, Nauka, 146 p. (in Russian).

—— 1973, Microphytofossils from the Precambrian of the Ukraine: Academy of Sciences, U.S.S.R., Institute Geology and Geochronology of the Precambrian, Nauka, 58 p. (in Russian).

Timofeev, B. V., Herman, T. N., and Mikhajlova, N. S., 1976, Microphytofossils from the Precambrian, Cambrian and Ordovician: Academy of Sciences, U.S.S.R., Institute Geology and Geochronology of the Precambrian, Nauka, p. 1–106 (in Russian).

Vidal, G., 1974, Late Precambrian microfossils from the basal sandstone unit of the Visingsö beds, South Sweden: Geologica et Palaeontologica, v. 8, p. 1–14.

—— 1976a, Late Precambrian microfossils from the Visingsö Beds in southern Sweden: Fossils and Strata, n. 9, 57 p.

—— 1976b, Late Precambrian acritarchs from the Eleonore Bay Group and Tillite Group in East Greenland: Grφnlands Geologiske Undersφgelse Rapport, n. 78, 19 p.

—— 1979a, Acritarchs and the correlation of the Upper Proterozoic: Publications of the Institutes of Mineralogy, Palaeontology and Quaternary Geology, University of Lund, Sweden, n. 219, 22 p.

—— 1979b, Acritarchs from the Upper Proterozoic and Lower Cambrian of East Greenland: Grφnlands Geologiske Undersφgelse Bulletin, n. 134, 55 p.

—— 1981a, Micropalaeontology and biostratigraphy of the Upper Proterozoic and Lower Cambrian sequence in East Finnmark, northern Norway: Norges Geologiske Undersφgelse Bulletin, v. 362, p. 1–53.

—— 1981b, Lower Cambrian acritarch stratigraphy in Scandinavia: Geologiska Föreningens i Stockholm Förhandlingar, v. 103, p. 183–192.

—— 1981c, Micropaleontology and biostratigraphy of the Lower Cambrian sequence in Scandinavia. Short papers for the Second International Symposium on the Cambrian System 1981: U.S. Geological Survey Open-File Report 81-743, p. 232–235.

Vidal, G., and Dawes, P. R., 1980, Acritarchs from the Proterozoic Thule Group, North-west Greenland: Grφnlands Geologiske Undersφgelse Rapport, n. 100, p. 24–29.

Vidal, G., and Siedlecka, A., 1983, Planktonic, acid-resistant microfossils from the Upper Proterozoic strata of the Barents Sea region of Varanger Peninsula, East Finnmark, Northern Norway: Norges Geologiske Undersφgelse Bulletin 382, p. 45–79.

Volkova, N. L., 1968, Acritarcha of Precambrian and Lower Cambrian deposits of Estonia: Academy of Sciences, U.S.S.R., Geological Institute, Nauka, v. 188, p. 8–36 (in Russian).

Volkova, N. L., Gnilovskaya, M. B., Lendzion, K., Kiryanov, V. V., Palij, V. M., Pashchkyavichene, L. T., Piskun, L. V., Posti, E., Rozanov, A. Yu, Urbanek, A., Fedonkin, M. A., and Jankauskas, T. V., 1979, Upper Precambrian and Cambrian paleontology of East-European Platform: Academy of Sciences, U.S.S.R., Geological Institute, Nauka, 210 p.

Walker, J.C.G., 1978, The early history of oxygen and ozone in the atmosphere: Pure and Applied Geophysics, v. 116, p. 222–231.

Wall, D., 1965, Microplankton, pollen, and spores from the Lower Jurassic in Britain: Micropaleontology, v. 11, p. 151–190.

Walter, M. R., editor, 1976, Stromatolites: Amsterdam, Elsevier, 790 p.

Waterbury, J. B., Watson, S. W., Guillard, R.R.L., and Brand, L. E., 1979, Widespread occurrence of a unicellular marine planktonic cyanobacterium: Nature, v. 277, p. 293–294.

Whittaker, R. H., 1975, Communities and ecosystems: New York, Macmillan, 385 p.

MANUSCRIPT ACCEPTED BY THE SOCIETY APRIL 14, 1983

Printed in U.S.A.

Geological Society of America
Memoir 161
1983

The Proterozoic glacial record

W. B. Harland
Department of Earth Sciences
University of Cambridge
Downing Street
Cambridge CB2 3EQ
England

ABSTRACT

This attempt to postulate a pattern in time of Proterozoic glaciations is based on a new international compilation Earth's Pre-Pleistocene Glacial Record, edited by M. J. Hambrey and W. B. Harland. While the compilation is designed so far as possible on objective and comprehensive lines, this paper selects critical records of tillites arranged so as to provide a speculative outline/temporal model for development and testing. The selection is biased towards a limited number of discrete glaciations.

The sequence is arranged regionally under broad headings of glacial eras, periods, and epochs approximately as follows:

Late Archean to Early Proterozoic Glacial Era
- **Witwatersrand glacial period with four or more epochs (about 2.65 Ga)**
- **Huronian glacial period with three or more epochs (about 2.3 Ga)**
  - **possible younger glaciations**

Mid-Proterozoic Interglacial Era (2.0 to 1.0 Ga)
Late Proterozoic Glacial Era
- **Lower Congo glacial period (about 0.9 Ga)**
- **Sturtian glacial period (with two main epochs) (about 0.8 Ga)**
- **Varangian glacial period (with two main epochs) (about 0.65 Ga)**
- **Late Sinian glacial epoch (0.60 Ga)**

INTRODUCTION

Reconstructing glacial history depends almost entirely on the recognition of ancient glacigenic sediments. The criteria by which sediments can be interpreted as having a glacial origin have been studied many times (for example, Schwarzbach, 1961; Crowell, 1964; Harland, Herod, and Krinsley, 1966; Schermerhorn, 1974; Chumakov, 1978; Hambrey and Harland, 1981b; and papers by Schermerhorn, by Dreimanis, and by Crowell in this volume and will not be repeated here. What follows, however, depends on implicit application of these criteria to the sedimentary record.

Because so many alleged tillites require detailed knowledge for such assessment, I led an International Geological Correlation Programme (I.G.C.P.) project to invite experts with local knowledge to describe all such pre-Pleistocene diamictites for publication in a single volume (Hambrey and Harland, eds., 1981b). It contains 212 contributions, some referring to large areas with many alleged tillite formations; about half of these are Proterozoic. The editors of the volume and I did not use any such privileged information before publication in September 1981. The manuscript was, however, submitted then and no changes have been made to take account of scientific developments since. This is therefore a review as of mid-1981.

Only the best-documented and dated records are used

here. If more extensive than local mountain glaciation is in evidence, then the climatic cause is most likely to have a far wider effect than a local mountain glaciation. Such an approach depends on recognition in the stratigraphic record of distinct glaciations or ice ages. If these were frequent and if uncertainty of age were to span more than one such episode, the prospects for interpretation would be poor. Here it is argued that glacial events were widespread and the intervening time spans may have been greater than the errors in age determination.

The term "ice age" has been so loosely used as to imply glacial events of many durations, from one spanning a few score of years to episodes such as the Würm glaciation spanning perhaps several tens of thousands of years, to a combination of such events spanning tens of millions of years in the late Cenozoic ice age that culminated in the Pleistocene/Quaternary ice age, or to eras and even eons if generalizations be made. Instead of "ice age," glacial episodes, epochs, periods, eras, and eons are used informally to give a measure of their relative magnitude.

The word "tillite" is used here to signify a glacigenic rock, based on the evidence presented in Hambrey and Harlands (1981b); tilloid is a tillite-like rock used without genetic intention. Radiometric ages are believed to be consistent with contemporary (1976) agreed constants. Paleolatitudes are based only on geomagnetic and not climatic evidence. *Alleged glacigene stratigraphic units are distinguished by italics at their main entry.* Most references are to the papers in *Earth's Pre-Pleistocene Glacial Record* (Hambrey and Harland, 1981b)[1] where fuller references are to be found.

The Proterozoic eon is defined as beginning precisely 2.5 Ga ago and ending at whatever reference point the International Union of Geological Science (IUGS) shall agree on in a stratotype yet to be decided. Its age in years can never be more than an estimate, currently at about 0.60 Ga so as to include the Ediacaran faunas but to exclude most, if not all, Tommotian faunas.

LATE ARCHEAN TO EARLY PROTEROZOIC GLACIAL ERA

Witwatersrand Glacial Period

Witwatersrand rocks [A32], reviewed by W. B. Harland contain a suite of probable tillites; they are currently estimated as older than Ventersdorp lavas (2,643 ± 80 Ma) and younger than the underlying granites (2,640 ± 55 Ma), or about 2,660 Ma. Prior to 1978, they were generally considered to be of Proterozoic age. At least four distinct tilloid horizons have been established. More are possible if the maximum possible identity in correlation is not assumed. Moreover, if Wiebols' interpretation [in A32] is correct, each widespread conglomerate (or reef) could be a reworked till, allowing a total of up to about 15 glacial horizons.

Other Archean tilloids may be glacial and may be of the same age or older, but I am not aware of other unequivocal Archean tillites.

[1]The author's name, number of the contribution used in *Earth's Pre-Pleistocene Glacial Record* in square brackets, and an indication of the title in the text will replace a full list of these 61 papers in the References Cited.

Huronian Glacial Period

Ontario. The *Huronian* tillites of Ontario described by G. M. Young [F31 and F32] are the best-known glacigenic rocks of Early Proterozoic age, and it now seems that other tillite occurrences in North America, South Africa, Australia, and possibly elsewhere may well be correlatives. There is no doubt about the glacial origins of the three formations concerned.

Resting on Elliot Lake Group or on basement dated at about 2,500 Ma is the Hough Lake Group (3 km) beginning with the *Ramsay Lake Formation* (150 m) diamictite interpreted as formed from a grounded ice shelf with the possibility of ice-wedge structures. The Hough Lake Group is a cycle of formations from the diamictites through siltstones and mudstones (Pecors Formation) to cross-bedded sandstones (Mississagi Formation) at the top.

The succeeding Quirke Lake Group (2 km) has a similar sequence (Bruce, Espanola, and Serpent Formations) and the *Bruce Formation* (diamictite at the base) is also interpreted as forming in part from a grounded ice shelf.

Above this is the Cobalt Group beginning with the *Gowganda Formation.* This has been divided into 14 members. The lower 8 are dominantly glacigenic diamictites interpreted thus: Member 1, grounded ice sheet; Member 2, interglacial; Member 3, grounded and floating ice sheet; Member 4, fluvioglacial or shallow marine; Member 5, glacial readvance; Member 6, subaqueous deposition, regression sequence with dropstones; Member 7, fluvioglacial or shallow marine; Member 8, diamictites formed under grounded and floating ice; Member 9, slumped argillite with dropstones; and Members 10 to 14, dominantly (postglacial) argillites and sandstones.

The succeeding Lorrain Formation contains some aluminous rocks suggesting warm weathering conditions and/or high carbon dioxide concentration in the atmosphere. The remaining two formations in the Cobalt Group are the Gordon Lake and Bar River.

The sequence is cut by Nipissing diabase at 2,100 Ma, so the age of all three groups is between 2,500 and 2,100 Ma. The age of the Gowganda Formation was independently assessed at about 2,300 Ma.

The Huronian sequence is well known for the supposed evidence of a transition from a reducing atmosphere in the Hough Lake and Quirke Lake Groups to an oxidizing one in the Cobalt Lake Group. This is used in correlation, especially the presence of uranium and pyrite associated with quartz pebble conglomerates in the Quirke Lake Group.

In summary: three main glacial cycles or periods are indicated of which the third (Gowganda) is divisible into two episodes, the latter recording at least three glacial maxima. Warm wet conditions followed.

Northwest Territories. [F27] G. M. Young and S. M. McLennan outlined the evidence from the Hurwitz Group whose lowest unit, a diamictite, is the *Padlei Formation,* the lower part of which was probably formed from terrestrial glacial ice; the upper part was deposited in a lacustrine environment with dropstones. The overlying Kinga Formation is dominated by mature quartzites suggestive of an environment similar to the Lorrain Formation, while the underlying Montgomery Lake Group bears uranium and pyrite in quartz pebble conglomerates that have been correlated with those of the Quirke Lake Group. So it is suggested that the Padlei Formation was coeval with the Gowganda Formation. The Montgomery Lake Group rests unconformably on basement at 2,550 Ma. Volcanites in the Hurwitz Group, possibly above an unconformity, give an age of 1,800 Ma. Therefore, the Padlei tillite could be younger.

North Quebec. [F23] D.G.F. Long described the *Chibougamau Formation* with a middle glacigenic member (containing dropstones). Each detailed log of several boreholes shows alternating diamictites and laminites. One logs 11 diamictites and 12 laminates, so it seems that there were many glacial episodes. The age of these glacial events is uncertain. These rocks are probably older than the Mistassini Group, which the Timiscamie Iron-Formation dated at 1,800 Ma.

Southern Wyoming. [F28] R. S. Houston, L. R. Lanthier, K. K. Karlstrom, and G. Sylvester described in the Medicine Bow and the Sierra Madre Ranges a sequence with three tillites (with dropstones) that are correlated with the three main Huronian tillites of Ontario. The sequence rests unconformably on the Phantom Lake metamorphic suite that was intruded by granites at 2,700 Ma and metamorphosed at 1,700 Ma. The rocks are classified in two groups. The (lower) Deep Lake Group has six formations. No. 3 is the *Campbell Lake* Formation (65 m thick), which begins with a 12-m diamictite passing into phyllite and then phyllitic quartzite. No. 5 is the *Vagner Formation* (400 m thick), which begins with a 60-m diamictite followed by 60 m of marble and then phyllite. This sequence is interpreted as resulting from a receding dry-based glacier, the carbonate members having formed in a glacial environment. The overlying Libby Creek Group with eight formations begins with the *Headquarters Formation* (680 m thick) that also has a diamictite member at the base followed by quartzite, phyllite, and diamictite and then laminated phyllites. An aluminum-rich quartz pebble conglomerate in the Deep Lake Group tends to confirm correlation with the Huronian rocks. If substantial sinistral strike-slip faulting were restored, the area might well have been several hundred kilometres nearer to Ontario.

South Dakota. [F29] D. D. Kurtz described diamictites with stones up to 3 m in diameter and with varied lithology. They fall within the U.S. Geological Survey (USGS) grouping "Precambrian X," being cut by the Harvey Peak Granite at 1,600 to 1,700 Ma, and rest unconformably on Little Elk Granite at 2,500 Ma. Scattered outcrops through the Black Hills are not easy to correlate, but up to three potential glacigenic diamictite horizons occur: *Blue Bird Formation* (oldest), *Oveville Formation*(?), and *Bugtown Formation* (youngest).

North Michigan. [F30] J. E. Gair described three tillites in different areas presumed to be of the same age and all occurring at the base of the Marquette Range Supergroup: *Fern Creek Formation* in the Menominee Range; *Enchantment Lake Formation* in the Marquette Synclinorium; and *Reany Creek Formation* in the Dead River Basin. The Marquette Range Supergroup was deformed by the Penokean Orogeny at 1,800 Ma. Gair considered the age of the sedimentary rocks to be 2,000 to 2,100 Ma. The evidence for this is not clear, but if substantiated it would show these rocks to be younger than the Huronian tillites.

Western USSR. Early Proterozoic tilloids have been described, but most of these could be tectonic breccias or olistostromes. No unambiguous glacigenic criteria are reported. T. F. Negrutsa and V. Z. Negrutsa reported: the *Lammos tilloids* of the Kola Peninsula [E33], older than 1,900 ± 50 Ma; the *Yannis-Yarvi tilloids* of S. Karelia [E34], between 2,150 ± 50 and 1,900 ± 50 Ma; and the *Saroli tilloids* of E. Baltic shield [E35] resting on Sumiy Group dated at 2,455 ± 45 Ma and overlain by Yatulain Group dated at 2,180 ± 60 Ma.

Baykal Region (USSR). [C39] N. M. Chumakov reported the Chuya Granite at 1,950 ± 100 Ma, which intruded the Udokan G. containing *Sakukan tilloids.* These are sandstones with scattered (?ice-rafted) pebbles. The group rests on Archean basement at 2,640 ± 100 Ma.

South Africa. The *Griquatown Glacial Member* [A31] described by J.N.J. Visser refers to tillites in two basins identified as one horizon. All occur in the Transvaal Supergroup formed within 20° of the pole. In Griquatown West Basin the *Makganyena Formation* in the Postmasburg Group is overlain by andesite dated at 2,224 ± 21 Ma and rests on the Griquatown Group, which in turn rests on basement at 2,300 ± 100 Ma. The age is well bracketed and probably corresponds to a Huronian (?Gowganda) glaciation. In the Transvaal Basin it is the *Rietfontein Member.*

Western Australia. In the Hamersley Basin, A. F. Trendall [D23] described the *Meteorite Bore Member* (300

m) of the Kungarra Formation of the Turree Creek Group (Mount Bruce Supergroup). Stones are striated and faceted, and the rocks have other glacial characteristics. The age is bracketed roughly between about 2.5 and 2.0 Ga and so might correspond to one of the Huronian glaciations.

Central India. The *Gangau Formation* [C37] was described by S. M. Mathur as the top unit of the Bijawar Group. Its upper member is convincing tillite and shale. The group rests unconformably on the Bundelkhand Granite at 2.6 Ga. It seems that the only younger limit is about 1.8 Ga.

MID PROTEROZOIC INTERGLACIAL ERA

It has already been asserted (Harland and Herod, 1975) and the recent compilation (Hambrey and Harland, 1981b) seems to confirm that the Proterozoic glacial record is in two parts: Early Proterozoic, that is, before 2,000 Ma; and Late Proterozoic, that is, between 1,000 and 600 Ma. This seems to be; I do not assert that there are no well-established and dated tillites of that age that have yet come to our notice.

Middle Siberia. The *Bol'shoy Patom Formation* (and related tilloids) described by N. M. Chumakov [C31] are a possible exception. The formation is of doubtful origin—mudslide of material originating from possible till. This view may be supported by the side extent of the unit (200 × 400 km), which lies 2.5 to 6 km beneath earliest Cambrian strata. Fossil evidence suggests a Middle Riphean age (1,400 ± 50 Ma to 1050 ± 50 Ma) for the Bol'shoy Patom Formation, which is spanned by rather wide radiometric brackets. There are still older tilloids in the same region of the Lena River.

LATE PROTEROZOIC GLACIAL ERA

There is a plethora of diamictites in the time span from about 900 to 600 Ma B.P. Many are very well established tillites according to a wide range of criteria, but only a few are well enough dated to distinguish glacial periods or epochs within the era. The data for this time span are given in about 80 papers in Hambrey and Harland, 1981b. I select first those with more narrowly constrained ages so as to establish some distinct glacial periods which are named: the Lower Congo glacial period about 900, or 950 to 850 Ma; the Sturtian glacial period about 800, or 820 to 770 Ma; the Varangian glacial period about 650, or 700 to 630 Ma; and the Late Sinian glacial epoch about 600 to 590 Ma.

Lower Congo Glacial Period

Lower Zaire. L. Cahen and J. Lepersonne described two diamictites [A26], the *Tillite inférieure du Bas Congo* and the *Tillite supérieure du Bas Congo.* The age of the lower tillite was suggested at 950 ± 50 Ma, and the upper one was bracketed between 1,027 and 733 Ma (interpolated at 820 ± 50 Ma).

Shaba (Katanga) in Zaire and Zambia. L. Cahen and J. Lepersonne described the Katangan sequence [A28] in which the (upper) *Petit Conglomérat* and the (lower) *Grand Conglomérat* occur. The latter comprises two diamictites. Age constraints are wide—between about 950 and 602 Ma.

Sturtian Glacial Period

South Australia. The *Adelaide Geosyncline* is useful for establishing relatively well dated glacial sequences. Sturt is a name familiar since Howchin in 1908 recognized the first pre-Permian tillites in Australia. The earlier glacial period (Sturtian) is separated from the younger one (Marinoan) by 3,000 m of strata. The latter is included with the Varangian glacial period. The Sturtian glacial period is represented by a complex sequence of tillites in the Yudnamutana Group; there may be about 5 distinct glacial episodes, some of which are subdivisible into several phases. This complex sequence has been grouped by R. P. Coats [D21] into Earlier and Later Sturtian, and this twofold division is accepted and followed here.

The chronostratigraphic age is consistent with Late Riphean to possibly Vendian stromatolites. Chronometric ages of Sturtian tillites are constrained between 750 ± 50 Ma and 850 Ma. An interpolated age of about 800 Ma was suggested for the Early Sturtian glacial events. By the same interpolation the Late Sturtian age was suggested at 790 Ma. The constraints on these figures are not very tight.

Early Sturtian Glacial Epoch. [D21] Rocks bearing tillites assigned to this division belong to the lower Yudnamutana Subgroup of the Umberatana Group. Putting the sequences from northern and southern parts of the geosyncline together, we have a granite-bearing tillite member at the base of the *Fitton Formation* followed (after an interglacial member of the Fitton Formation) by the *Bolla Bollana Tillite,* which appears to be coeval with the *Pualco Tillite* farther south. These are followed by the Lyndhurst Formation of the Braemar Ironstone. Several glacial phases within the main Bolla Bollana and Pualco successions might be interpreted from insufficient available data.

Late Sturtian Glacial Epoch. [D21] The later Yudnamutana Subgroup appears to include three main phases.

The *Bibliando Tillite* is followed by the *Hansborough Tillite* and finally by the Sturt tillite, which is equivalent to the *Appila Tillite,* and Calthorinna Tillite, also the Meringina Tillite farther south. This complex sequence of glacial facies interfingers with periglacial facies of the Wilyerpa Formation.

Thus the tillite sequence (Bibliando, Hansborough and Appila) denotes three major phases. "Appila" is used in preference to the prior name "Sturt" to avoid confusion of Sturtian *sensu stricto* with *sensu lato* as applied here.

Western Australia. In the Kimberley-Victoria River

region [D16], K. A. Plumb distinguished two Late Proterozoic glacial periods: an earlier one, the Landrigan Glaciation correlated with the Sturtian, and a later one the Egan Glaciation correlated with the Marinoan of the Adelaide Geosyncline, which will be outlined in the following section.

Tillite formations are the lowest in each stratigraphic group where they occur. The *Landrigan Tillite* is the most convenient representative name occurring in the most complete section of the Mount Ramsay area and is the only tillite now taken to be of Sturtian age because it is about 100 Ma older than the others at about 680 Ma. It is divisible in two parts. The Walsh Tillite, also divisible into two parts, and the pair of tillites, *Fargoo* (older) and *Moonlight Valley* (younger), have been correlated with the Landrigan—but more recently with the Egan Tillite.

Central Australia. In the *Amadeus Basin* [D17] A. T. Wells described lower and upper diamictites, but only the lower ones will be treated here. The lower diamictites, probably tillites, occur within the widespread *Areyonga Formation* as well as in probably coeval *Boord Formation* and *Inindia Beds.* The Areyonga Formation is underlain by the Bitter Springs Formation. Although no direct evidence of age is available, it is generally considered to be of Sturtian age. At least two phases of glaciation are recognized in some units.

In the *Ngalia Basin* [D17] A. T. Wells similarly described lower and upper diamictites. The lower one is the *Naburula Formation.*

In the southwestern *Georgina Basin* [D18] M. R. Walter also described two main diamictite horizons of which the lower is the *Yardida tillite,* and equivalent *Mount Cornish Formation* and *Central Mount Sturt Formation.*

China. There are widespread tillites in Sinian rocks described by Wang Yuelun, Lu Songnian, Gao Zhenjia, Lin Weixing, and Ma Guogan [C33]. Of three main glacial horizons, the earlier two are widespread, the earliest was referred to the Changan Ice Age and was considered Sturtian in age, estimated at about 800 Ma. The *Changan Formation* is separated by 1,000 m of strata from the underlying Banxi Group dated at 837 Ma in southeast Guizhou. It is separated from the Nantuo Formation above by the Fulu Formation. The Guizhou Province Changan tillites are described by Liao Shihfan [C35]. In Xinjiang Province the lowest unit of the 6 km thick Quruq Tagh (Kuruktag) Group is the *Beiyixi (tillite) Formation,* which has been correlated with the Sturtian glaciation. It has 2 to 5 layers of glacial conglomerate.

Utah and Idaho. Diamictites in Utah were first recognized as glacial in 1913 by Hintze and further described by Blackwelder in 1932. Latterly, correlation of the many scattered formations of these rocks has been done by Crittenden whose work and that of others has been summarized by N. Blick [F15], from which this account is made.

Names of formations well established as glacigenic by recent critical work are the *Mineral Fork Formation* and the *Penny Canyon Formation.* Outsize dropstones are ubiquitous; an abraded bedrock surface with grooves and at least one roche moutonnée underlie the Mineral Fork Formation, and elsewhere a diamictite overlies a previously weathered zone.

The diamictite units have not been directly dated, but several thousand metres separate them from overlying beds with Cambrian fossils. Basement is dated at 1,400 to 1,700 Ma. Underlying Big Cottonwood Formation has been estimated at more than 950 Ma. Greenstones overlying possibly correlative diamictites in Washington gave 827 to 918 Ma. Although not rigorously constrained, much critical work has led to an estimate for these glacigenic diamictites at about 800 Ma.

In Idaho to the north [F14] P. K. Link described the probably coeval glacigenic *Scout Mountain Member* of the *Pocatello Formation,* which is the lowest unit exposed in the Late Proterozoic Cordilleran miogeosyncline. There are 2 diamictite members separated by the Bannock Volcanic Member. These rocks are separated by 6 km of detrital rocks from fossiliferous Middle Cambrian strata.

British Columbia, Idaho, and Washington. The *Toby Formation* described by K. R. Aalto [F13] is a tillite unit extending 350 km north-south along the Purcell Mountains. It appears to be post-850 Ma and pre-827 Ma, but the evidence does not warrant so precise a date. It would seem most likely to correlate with an early Sturtian phase similar to those described above.

California. The *Kingston Peak Formation* described by J.M.G. Miller, L. A. Wright, and B. W. Troxel [F16] is of doubtful glacigenic origin and is probably of Sturtian or Varangian age.

Newfoundland. Tillites of the *Gaspers Formation* of the Conception Group described by M. M. Anderson and A. F. King [F20] record a long and complex glacial sequence of age that has been variously assessed but considered by the authors to be late Riphean rather than Vendian at about 800 Ma.

Virginia and Tennessee. A sequence of tillites in the Rogers Formation described by F. L. Schwab [F18] is dated at less than 820 Ma, but probably not much less.

Sierra Leone. Tillites of the *Rokel River* Group described by M. E. Tucker and P. C. Reid [A20] were correlated with the above.

South Africa and Namibia. A. Kröner [A29] described a large number of diamictites, many with good glacial criteria and seemingly grouped into three time divisions. Radiometric constraints are not tight, and the two older ones could well correspond to the Early and Later Sturtian glacial epochs as follows: Early group, 1,000 to 780 Ma, includes *Varianto Formation* in Nosib Group and *Blaubeker Formation* in Damara Supergroup; Later group, 780 to 750

Ma, includes *Chuos Formation* in Swakop Group, and the *Numees Formation* in Gariep Group could be Varangian. Paleolatitudes of 20° have been obtained.

Varangian Glacial Period

North Norway. Reusch Moraine on the coast of Varangerfjord in Finnmark, north Norway, has been used as the eponymous unit for the widespread glaciations that are interpreted as having occurred about this time (for example, Kulling, 1934; Schwarzbach, 1961; Harland, 1964a, 1964b; Harland and Herod, 1975). In addition to widespread application of the name in this sense, there are five reasons for retaining it: (1) Reusch's was only the second pre-Permian glacial record, and he thought it to be Cambrian or Precambrian. (2) The Varangerfjord region exhibits a development of distinct lower and upper tillite horizons separated by the Nyborg Formation, which has yielded one of the more useful radiometric determinations from amongst all Proterozoic tillites. (3) Diamictites in each case pass the usual critical tests for a glacigenic origin. (4) The succession taken as a whole passes upwards into Lower Cambrian rocks and has characteristics that allow widespread correlation. (5) The rocks were probably formed at low latitudes, suggesting an ice age of global extent.

In the North Atlantic region, where analogous tillites are well known, the complex glacial sequence with many episodes is commonly divisible into two distinct units, which are here taken as a basis for distinguishing Early and Late Varangian glacial epochs.

The Finnmark successions have been outlined by M. B. Edwards and S. Føyn with an appendix by G. Vidal and G. Bylund [E21]. Two glacial formations occur in the lower part of the Vestertana Group which rests unconformably on Tanafjord and Vadsø Groups and on older metamorphic rocks. The "lower tillite" is the *Smalfjord Formation* (150 m), and this includes the Reusch Moraine at Bigganjargga. It is overlain by the marine, nonglacial Nyborg Formation with 5 members (up to 400 m), which is unconformably overstepped by the ("upper") *Mortensnes Tillite Formation*) (10 to 60 m) followed by the Stappogiedde (550 m) and Breivik (600 m) Formations.

The Nyborg Formation has been subjected to critical studies. A Rb/Sr determination yielded 668 ± 23 Ma recalculated to 654 ± 23 Ma giving a date that separates the Early and Late Varangian glacial epochs. It gave paleolatitudes of 15° to 40°.

A very early Cambrian fossil *Platysolenites antiquissimus* occurs 650 m above the Mortensnes Formation. Derived late Riphean and Vendian acritarchs are found in both tillite horizons, indicating that the Smalfjord Tillite is not pre-Vendian. The Stappogiedde Formation has yielded Vendian acritarchs, so both glacial epochs are Vendian.

South Norway. K. Bjørlykke and J. P. Nystuen [E16] have reported on the *Moelv* and analogous tillites belonging to the Sparagmite basins. They are widespread in southern Norway. The Koppang Conglomerate, for example, has been suggested as representing a continental margin facies. The occurrence is also important as being the Eocambrian type sequence. In the Moelv succession, Vendian fossils occur beneath the tillite, and about 300 m to 400 m above it, early Cambrian fossils are well known. A radiometric age of 610 ± 18 Ma was obtained from the Ekre shale immediately overlying the tillite. These data are critical also for the Precambrian-Cambrian boundary. The Moelv tillite has been correlated with the upper tillite horizon of Finnmark. Tropical paleolatitudes were obtained.

Central Sweden. The *Långmarkberg Formation* of central Sweden, described by T. Thelander [E14], has been correlated with the Moelv tillite horizon across the international border.

British Isles. The Port Askaig Tillite in Scotland [E18] described by A. M. Spencer is a classic in two respects. His is one of the most detailed accounts of any tillite sequence (Spencer, 1971), and the Garvelloch Islands locality where that description was made is not far removed from, and certainly coeval with, the original Port Askaig locality in Islay (Scotland), first described as glacial by Thompson in 1871 (hence the first recorded Precambrian tillite). Its age was not then known—nor can it be accurately assessed today. Within the Dalradian Supergroup the tillite lies 10 km below rocks with late Early Cambrian trilobites. A paleolatitude of 10° has been determined. The tillite sequence (750 m) is noteworthy for the alternation of mostly grounded and some floating ice facies with 44 glacial episodes. Ice wedges in a dominantly marine sequence show it to have formed at or about sea level.

Correlative boulder beds extend from the coast of western Ireland ([E20] reported on by D. Max) to the east of Scotland. However, the *Kinlochlaggen Boulder Bed* of Central Scotland originally taken as coeval with the Port Askaig Tillite has later been regarded as older [E19] by J. E. Treagus. It has glacial criteria and comes within the Lower or Appin Group of the Dalradian Supergroup, whereas the Port Askaig Tillite lies at the base of the Middle Dalradian Argyll Group. The two horizons might correspond to the Early and Late Varangian glacial epochs in such a rapidly deposited geosyncline. Alternatively, the Kinlochlaggen unit may be Sturtian.

Normandy. The much-debated late Precambrian tilloids of the Armorican Massif have been reviewed by F. Doré [E21]. They are widespread and indicate long-distance transport ending with dropstones. The *Granville Formation* (diamictite) is the lower unit of the Upper Brioverian Group, which is cut by a granodiorite dated at 617 ± 12 Ma.

Central East Greenland. The *Tillite Group* of the Kong

Oscars and Kejser Franz Josefs Fjord region of East Greenland was recorded by A. K. Higgins [F25]. It overlies the Eleonore Bay Group and underlies fossiliferous Early Cambrian strata, the uppermost tillite being separated therefrom by 70 to 425 m. Two distinct tillite formations have long been recognized. The lower tillite is grey to yellow with dominantly limestone and dolostone clasts clearly derived from strata coeval with uppermost Eleonore Bay Group. The upper tillite is generally reddish and contains abundant granite stones. This is a common characteristic of stone composition where two tillite horizons are found in the North Atlantic–Arctic region. Paleolatitudes of 40° or less have been obtained. A similar tillite has been described from Gåseland in Scoresby Sund by W.E.A. Phillips and J. D. Friederichsen [F23].

North Greenland. L. B. Clemmensen described a tillite, the *Moraeneso Formation,* from Peary land of probable Varangian age [F26].

Svalbard. The Vendian tillites and tilloids of Svalbard are extremely numerous and complex, and the literature has been sampled by M. J. Hambrey, W. B. Harland, and P. Waddams [E10]. More data are coming to hand. At least two provinces have been distinguished.

An Eastern Province is characterized by the Hecla Hoek Geosyncline with relatively unmetamorphosed tillites about 250 m thick in successions that are commonly fossiliferous. Tillites occur in Nordaustlandet (the *Sveanor Formation* in the Gotia Group) and in Ny Friesland (the *Wilsonbreen Formation* in the Polarisbreen Group). There are many successions, and whereas most contain only one main tillite formation, some contain two. Tillites as well as associated facies are similar to those of East Greenland.

A Western Province, possibly originating from a position now farther north than the Eastern Province, contains thicker successions with associated volcanic facies that formed in a more mobile environment. These are all more or less tectonized and occur in scattered outcrops. Tillite or a tilloid formation occurs generally in the *Comfortlessbreen, Ferrier,* and *Sofiebogen* Groups. Tilloid units (up to 4 km thick) have been reported elsewhere in the Western Province; in at least two areas, distinct lower and upper tilloid horizons have been described in work not yet published.

Western USSR. In a series of papers [E25 to E32] N. M. Chumakov described the very extensive Vendian tillites that are correlated with the Varangian glacial period. There are generally at least two horizons. A Vendian age is clear from the microfossils. Radiometric ages are mostly from glauconite, at 630 to 650 Ma. N. M. Chumakov has referred to these tillites and their Varangian correlatives elsewhere as Laplandian.

The *Vilchitsy Formation* (upper) [E25] and *Blon Formation* (lower) [E26] are known from extensive boreholes in a large area ranging about 200 to 300 km around Minsk (with paleolatitudes of 3° to 10°). In Podolia and Moldavia [E27] discontinuous tilloids are known as *Grushka* and *Mogilev Formations* in the Ukraine and as the *Soroka* and *Khrustovo Formations* in Moldavia, and while themselves not necessarily of the same age, they are younger than the Vilchitsy and Blon Formations. The *Partsino* (or Toropots) *Formation* [E28] is known from boreholes 200 to 300 km southeast of Moscow; the *Yablonovka Formation* [E29] is known from boreholes in the western shore of Lake Ladoga; the *Churochnaya tillites* [E30] extend along the western Uralian folded zone; the *Tany Formation* [E31], containing two distinct tillites, is known from the middle Urals; and the *Kingashlya tilloids* [E32], also containing two well-marked horizons, are found in the south Urals.

China. [C33] In contrast to the Changan Tillite, probably Sturtian, the most widespread glacigenic rock reported is the *Nantuo Tillite Formation* that has been correlated with the Varangian-Marinoan tillites. At the type Yangtze Gorge locality it was reported by E. Blackwelder and B. Willis as early as 1907. It has abundant characteristics of continental glacial deposits. It occurs far beyond the Yangtze Gorge region in what must have been a very stable shelf area in the provinces of Hubei, Hunan, Sichuan, Yunnan, Guangxi, Guizhou, and Jiangxi. In this region it overlies the Liantuo Formation and is followed by the Doushantuo and Denying Formations, the latter at about the initial Cambrian boundary. A detailed study of the Nantuo tillites of Guizhou Province is by Liao Shihfan [C35].

In Xinjiang in the middle of the Kuruktag (Quruq Tagh) Group occur two formations that have been correlated with the Nantuo tillites. They are the lower or *Altungol (Aletonggou) Formation* and the upper or *Tereeken (Chiruiaiken) Formation.* The *Chiaoen Blak (Qiaoen Bulake) Tillite* is equivalent to the Tereeken Formation because both are overlain by strata with a similar microflora. The Chiaoen Blak Tillite is also correlated by its microflora with the Doushantuo and Denying Formation in central and southern China. Similar deposits are known also in Gansu and Qinghai Provinces.

South Australia. In the Adelaide Geosyncline, R. P. Coats [D21] distinguished the Upper (Marinoan) glacigenic successions. Many formations occur in the Wilpena Group. In the Yerelina Subgroup (near Mount Painter) are the *Mount Curtis Tillite* in the north and *Pepuarta Tillite* in the south; also the *Elatina Formation.* The Marinoan tillites are of Vendian age, and the Pound Sandstone with the Ediacara fauna lies 8 km above them. Radiometric evidence suggests an age of 680 to 690 Ma. On this basis they could be coeval with the Earlier Varangian tillites.

Kimberley Region. K. A. Plumb [D16] distinguished the *Egan Tillite Formation* at the base of the Louisa Down Group, which is overlain by Cambrian strata. The *Walsh* and *Moonlight Valley tillites* may be of the same age (about

680 Ma) but are not well constrained and are correlated with the Marinoan tillites. Low paleolatitudes have been determined.

Central Australia: Amadeus Basin. A. T. Wells [D17] described an upper diamictite named the *Olympic Formation,* and in the Ngalia Basin the upper diamictite is included in the *Mount Doreen Formation.* Both have glacial characteristics but no internal evidence for age. By their position they are correlated with the Marinoan, as also are the *Inindia Beds* and the upper *Central Mount Stuart Formation.* Equatorial paleolatitudes have been obtained.

Queensland. K. A. Plumb reported the *Little Burke Tillite* [D19] to be probably of Marinoan age and formed at 25° latitude.

New South Wales. K. D. Tuckwell [D20] reported the *Torrowahgee Group* to contain lower glacials in the *Yancowinna Subgroup,* then interglacials and upper glacials in the *Teamsters Creek Subgroup.* All are post-700 Ma and so are probably Early and Late Varangian.

Tasmania. J. B. Jago [D22] described three units that postdate 720 Ma and could even be of Cambrian age. The *Cottons Breccia* is probably glacigenic—the others, *Trowutta Breccia* and *Wedge River Beds,* are possibly tillites.

Benin, Niger, Togo, and Upper Volta. R. Trompette described *Tansarga* and *Kadjari* continental tillites in the Volta Basin and several possible equivalents in the Dahomeyides Orogenic Belt [A21]. A number of determinations are consistent with an age of 675 Ma, or Early Varangian.

Northern Yukon–Northwest Territories. G. H. Eisbacher [F11] described diamictites from the lower part of the Rapitan Group (Windermere Supergroup). The *Shezal Formation,* extending 600 km along the northern Canadian Cordillera, has many glacigenic characters. It occurs up to 700 m beneath fossiliferous strata of earliest Cambrian age and immediately overlies a jaspilite-haematite iron-formation member (with dropstones) at the top of the *Sayunei Formation.* This in turn overlies quartzite with basalt sills dated at 760 Ma. Correlation with the Varangian glacial period would be consistent with the evidence.

Kazakstan. T. N. Keraskova described five tilloid units [C22, C23, C24, C25, and C26] whose origin has been claimed as glacial or nonglacial. All are coeval and fall within the Vendian Period from biostratigraphic evidence. If glacial, they would be Varangian. They are: (1) in north Kazakstan *Baykonur Formation* [C24]; (2) in central Kazakstan *Baykonur Formation* [C22], (3) *Satan Formation* [C23], and (4) *Kapal Formation* [C25]; and (5) in south Kazakstan *Shopshoky Formation* [C26].

Late Sinian Glacial Epoch

China. There is, at least in China, a widespread occurrence of latest Precambrian or possibly even earliest Cambrian tillites. Sinian is chosen as a name for this episode because of the immense work done there to describe and to distinguish these from earlier Varangian and Sturtian tillites, both of which fall within the Chinese Early Sinian grouping. Wang Yuelun and others [C33] suggest tentatively that there was a distinct ice age and refer to it as the Third Glaciation. Because there is supporting evidence outside China, it is referred to here as the Late Sinian glacial epoch.

A geosyncline provides the most complete succession in Xinjiang where the top unit of the Quruq Tagh Group is the *Hankalchoug (Hangeerqiaoke) Formation* (434 m). It occurs disconformably but always just beneath the phosphorus-rich and fossiliferous lower Cambrian (e.g., Xitashan Formation). It is separated below from the Tereeken Formation (Varangian) by three formations. The uppermost of these, the Shuiquan Formation, contains microfossils identical to those in the Denying Formation of central and southern China. Elsewhere, *Vendotoenia* and *Sabellitidae* were found in underlying strata. In Gansu the geosyncline reaches a thickness of 842 m. Similar deposits, similarly placed, also occur in Qinghai, southern Shanxi, and western Henan, as well as in the northern slopes of the Qinling and Helan Shab Mountains in Henan and Shanxi provinces and are known as the *Luoquan Formation,* or in some areas the *Zhengmuguan Formation.* This formation and its correlatives have been described in detail by Mu Jongji [C34] who established their stratigraphic position and their glacigenic nature beyond doubt. Paleolatitudes of 47° to 76° have been recorded.

USSR. In describing the Vendian tilloid complex of Tien Shan, USSR [C27], V. G. Korolev, R. A. Maksumova, and K. S. Sagyndykov discussed *inter alia* the *Baykonur Formation,* first thought to be of Middle Cambrian age and commonly referred to as the Upper tillite in the complex. It underlies strata with earliest Cambrian skeletal fossils. Because the whole sequence of two or three distinct horizons is argued from microflora to be Vendian, this uppermost unit is correlated with the Late Sinian glaciations, more positive evidence for which is found not far away in China.

Poland. W. Brochwicz-Lewinski described possible late Precambrian or Cambrian tilloids from boreholes in southern Poland [F23]. A probable latest Proterozoic tillite is suggested.

Sweden. In northern Sweden the *Sito tillite* and its probable correlative *Vakkejokk breccia* have been reviewed by A.G.B. Strömberg [E13]; both are regarded as periglacial. The Vakkejokk breccia (16 m) is separated by only 2 m of sandstone with pebbles in the lower part from overlying shales with Early Cambrian fossils. It is underlain by shales with *Spriggia;* below are sandstones with fossil tracks. The breccia must therefore lie around the Precambrian/Cambrian boundary, though Strömberg correlated it with the Mortensnes tillites of Finnmark.

Alaska. Rocks of the *Upper Tindir Group* of east central Alaska have been described by C. W. Allison, G. M. Young, G. M. Yeo, and G. D. Delaney [F10]. There is no doubt as to their glacigenic nature, but their age is problematic. From paleontological studies in progress, it would appear to be latest Proterozoic or earliest Cambrian.

British Columbia. *Mount Lloyd George Diamictites* of limited extent described by G. H. Eisbacher [F12] are dominantly mass-flow deposits but have a glacial component as from piedmont glaciers. Their age was argued biostratigraphically as latest Proterozoic; they are followed by earliest Cambrian strata.

South Africa and Namibia. A. Kröner in his account of diamictites [A29] lists the youngest of the tillites in the Schwarzrand Subgroup of the Nama Group. There are two glacigenic formations: a lower *Nudaus Formation* that is equivalent to the Schwarzkalk unit and an upper *Nomtsas Formation.* Overlying Fish River rocks contain Cambrian fossils, and the Schwarzrand Group contains Ediacara faunas. A Late Sinian affinity is suggested if that was a widespread event. Equatorial paleolatitudes have been obtained.

CONCLUSIONS

The present conclusion is the tentative arrangement of widespread, if not global, glaciations in the sequence considered here. The sequence is arranged regionally under broad headings of glacial eras, periods, and epochs and is listed below. It is not a comprehensive list and should not be used without the qualifications outlined above.

Late Archean to Early Proterozoic Glacial Era
- Witwatersrand glacial period with four or more epochs (about 2.65 Ga)
- Huronian glacial period with three or more epochs (about 2.3 Ga)
  - possible younger glaciations

Mid-Proterozoic Interglacial Era (2.0 to 1.0 Ga)

Late Proterozoic Glacial Era
- Lower Congo glacial period (about 0.9 Ga)
- Sturtian glacial period (with two main epochs) (about 0.8 Ga)
- Varangian glacial period (with two main epochs) (about 0.65 Ga)
- Late Sinian glacial epoch (0.60 Ga)

A fuller critique of the rocks coupled with a review of their potential palinspastic distributions is in progress. Many tillite and tilloid units, whether mentioned above or omitted from this account, lack adequate independent control of their ages (for example, the extensive South American and many African Precambrian records). Climatic fluctuations must have been broadly synchronous regionally, if not globally, and so provide a powerful correlation potential. However, until a sequence in time has been established, ages deduced by miscorrelation can be, and have been, thoroughly misleading. This paper indicates some of the bases on which such a sequence can be established.

It has been assumed by some that the glacial record results from polar wandering rather than from global climatic changes. Both no doubt operated, but the latter must have controlled at least one Varangian glacial epoch. This has already been argued (for example, Harland, 1964a, 1964b; Harland and Herod, 1975; Frakes, 1979). This new review supports the hypothesis of low-latitude Varangian glaciation (Harland, 1964a, 1964b; Harland, 1981; Frakes, 1979) and also suggests that the Sturtian glaciations may have been similarly widespread. These matters will be more fully investigated elsewhere, together with a review of likely mechanisms from amongst those considered (for example, Harland and Herod, 1975; Hambrey and Harland, 1981a; Harland, 1981).

ACKNOWLEDGMENTS

I am indebted to W.G.M. Young and C. Matsch for improvements to the text in the course of editing.

REFERENCES CITED

Chumakov, N. M., 1978, Precambrian tillites and tilloides (problems of Precambrian glaciations): Moscow, Academy of Sciences of the USSR, Transactions, v. 308, 202 p. [text in Russian].

Crowell, J. C., 1964, Climatic significance of sedimentary deposits containing dispersed megaclasts, *in* Nairn, A.E.M., ed., Problems in palaeoclimatology, Proceedings of the NATO Palaeoclimates Conference, Newcastle-upon-Tyne, January 1963: London, Interscience Publishers (John Wiley & Sons), p. 86–99.

Frakes, L. A., 1979, Climates throughout geologic time: Amsterdam, Elsevier Scientific Publishing Company, 310 p.

Hambrey, M. J., and Harland, W. B., 1981a, The evolution of climates, *in* Cocks, L.R.M., ed., The evolving Earth (Volume 1 of Chance, change and challenge, ed. P. H. Greenwood): London, British Museum (Natural History)/Cambridge University Press, p. 137–152.

Hambrey, M. J., and Harland, W. B., eds., 1981b, Earth's Pre-Pleistocene glacial record: Cambridge, Cambridge University Press, xv + 1004 p.

Harland, W. B., 1964a, Evidence of Late Precambrian glaciation and its significance, *in* Nairn, A.E.M., ed., Problems in palaeoclimatology, Proceedings of the NATO Palaeoclimates Conference, Newcastle-upon-Tyne, January 1963: London, Interscience Publishers (John Wiley & Sons) p. 119–184.

—— 1964b, Critical evidence for a great infra-Cambrian glaciation: Geologischen Rundschau, v. 54, p. 45–61.

—— 1981, Chronology of Earth's glacial and tectonic record: Journal of the Geological Society, London, v. 138, p. 197–203.

Harland, W. B., and Herod, K. N., 1975, Glaciations through time, *in* Wright, A. E., and Moseley, F., Ice ages: Ancient and modern, Proceedings of 21st Inter-University Geological Congress, Birmingham, January 1974, Geological Journal Special Issue No. 6: Liverpool, Seel House Press, p. 189–216.

Harland, W. B., Herod, K. N., and Krinsley, D. H., 1966, The definition and identification of tills and tillites: Earth-Science Reviews, v. 2, p. 225–226.

Kulling, O., 1934, Scientific results of the Swedish-Norwegian Arctic Expedition in the summer of 1931 [Vol. II] Part XI, the "Hecla Hoek Formation" round Hinlopenstredet: Stockholm, Geografiska Annaler, v. XVI, no. 4, p. 161–254.

Schermerhorn, L.J.G., 1974, Late Precambrian mixtites: Glacial and/or nonglacial?: American Journal of Science, v. 274, no. 7, p. 673–824.

Schwarzbach, M., 1961, Das Klima der Vorzeit, eine Zinfuhrung in die Palaoklimatologie: Stuttgart, Ferdinand Enke, 175 p.

Spencer, A. M., 1971, The Late Pre-Cambrian glaciation in Scotland: Memoirs of the Geological Society of London, v. 6, 98 p.

MANUSCRIPT ACCEPTED BY THE SOCIETY APRIL 14, 1983

Printed in U.S.A.

Geological Society of America
Memoir 161
1983

The recognition of ancient glaciations

John C. Crowell
Department of Geological Sciences
University of California
Santa Barbara, California 93106

ABSTRACT

Documentation of an ancient ice age depends on both direct and indirect evidence, all fitted into an acceptable paleogeographic reconstruction. The direct evidence consists of striated and polished basement surfaces, commonly displaying friction cracks, roches moutonnées, and other geomorphic forms. Sedimentary strata overlying may be identifiable as lodgment and other tillite and glacial facies. Where icebergs have carried glacial debris to distant basins and have dropped the material into contrasting facies, the existence of glaciers someplace may be shown but their locations are uncertain. Regional reconstructions of facies within a limited time slice, utilizing all methods of correlation available, provide the most trustworthy method of ice age documentation. In the Proterozoic, however, correlations are imprecise so that our knowledge of ice ages is quite inexact.

Indirect results of continental glaciation include strong and rapid changes in sea level. These eustatic changes contrast with those resulting from other causes, including tectonics, which are likely to be very much slower or of much less magnitude. Transgressions and regressions in the Proterozoic record need comparison and correlation with known glacial sequences. They should be traced from stratigraphic section to section employing every correlation technique available, including magnetostratigraphic and seismostratigraphic methods.

Some paleomagnetic observations indicate glaciation at equatorial and low latitudes, whereas the Phanerozoic record shows that glaciation takes place in near-polar regions. Controversy has therefore arisen between those investigators who accept low-latitude glaciation and those who are skeptical and look for a way to explain the paleomagnetic measurements that is compatible with high-latitude glaciation. It may be that rapid crustal movements in combinations with postdepositional imprint of the magnetic vector by 10 or 15 m.y. have carried glaciated localities from a high- to a low-latitude region during the interval. More research is therefore called for on rock and mineral magnetics with respect to diagenetic changes. Searches are also needed for other geological consequences of such a marked climatological or orbital reorientation over the 120 or so m.y. interval between the latest Proterozoic glaciations, and the polar Ordovician-Silurian glaciations.

INTRODUCTION

Scrutiny of the geological record shows that continental ice sheets have waxed and waned upon the Earth, at intervals, including several times during the Proterozoic Era. Going back from the present, the major ice ages include the Late Cenozoic Ice Age which culminated in the Pleistocene Epoch. In fact, we are living now during an interglacial stage of that ice age, and we expect the ice sheets to expand again in several thousand years. Before the advent of the Late Cenozoic glaciation in the Oligocene Epoch about 30 m.y. ago, continental ice sheets apparently did not reach the sea until we reach back into the Paleozoic Era, although there may have been local ice caps that have left no direct record (Barron and others, 1981). Within the Late Paleozoic, however, Earth witnessed a major ice age upon the Gondwana continents. This long ice age came in slowly in the mid-Carboniferous, expanded rapidly so that ice sheets covered large regions of the Gondwana supercontinent in the early Permian, and then waned during mid-Permian times (Crowell and Frakes, 1975; Crowell, 1978). It lasted for about 90 million years, or about eight times longer than the Late Cenozoic Ice Age has lasted so far.

Continental ice sheets expanded in central South America and adjoining Gondwanan terranes during the Early and Middle Paleozoic. In mid-late Devonian times, a possible record is preserved in the Amazon Basin of Brazil (Caputo and others, 1972; Carozzi and others, 1973). Previously, ice sheets grew during the transition from the Ordovician into the Silurian periods, and spread from the central Sahara to the Bolivian Andes (Beuf and others, 1971; Crowell and others, 1980). Paleozoic continental glaciation older than this has not been recognized, although the waning stages of glaciation in the latest Proterozoic may have reached up in time into the earliest Cambrian (Deynoux and others, 1978).

In the late Proterozoic, continental glaciers flourished intermittently from about 950 m.y. to about 560 m.y. ago (Williams, 1975; Harland and Herod, 1975; Frakes, 1979). During this interval of nearly 400 m.y., ice sheets lay upon all of the continents, with the possible exception of Antarctica, and in some regions waxed and waned more than once. There may have been three culminations in glaciation during this long interval: one about 940 m.y. ago, another near 770, and a third near 615 (Williams, 1975), but the dating and geographical positioning of these events are insecure. An earlier Proterozoic glaciation occurred in southern Ontario and may have reached as far southwestward as southern Wyoming (2300 ± m.y. ago) (Young, 1970). Piecemeal evidence is also reported from southern Africa and Australia for poorly dated episodes that may extend as far back as 2720 m.y., (into Archean times) (Visser, 1971; Trendall, 1976; Harland, 1981). Glaciation therefore probably affected North America and perhaps other distant regions between 2700 and 2100 m.y. ago, a span of 600 m.y. Several glaciations may have come and gone during this long time span—an interval as long as all of Phanerozoic time!—and many questions remain unanswered concerning the nature, extent, and timing of these most ancient of recorded ice ages. In addition, we need to ask: Why is there no record of continental glaciation during the ensuing billion years?

Our purpose here in this paper, however, is to describe the nature of the record documenting these ancient ice ages, rather than to present a historical account of them through geologic time. The documentation of an ice age, to be useful to us, must be accompanied by information on the timing of the glaciation. At present, unfortunately, we are unable to date events satisfactorily within the Precambrian, and especially those events that are recorded within sedimentary rock sequences in which both isotopic and paleontological methods are so far too imprecise for our purposes.

DIRECT EVIDENCE OF GLACIATION

From the viewpoint of geologists attempting to find clues to past ice ages, it is fortunate that continental glaciers exist today in Greenland and Antarctica so that the investigators can study the record these glaciers leave behind. It is equally as fortunate that during the Pleistocene Epoch ice sheets covered large regions of the continents and have left a decipherable and unequivocal record that has now been widely studied by Quaternary geologists (Denton and Hughes, 1981). Moreover, the record from the sea floor, including cores and geophysical profiling, has added to our reconstruction of the extent and character of the Late Cenozoic Ice Age (CLIMAP Project Members, 1976, 1981; Anderson and others, 1979, 1980; Clark and others, 1980). Of particular importance to us now, is the knowledge gained concerning the products formed during glaciations, and especially those products that may be preserved within the rock record.

Glaciers scour into bedrock beneath them, leaving behind a telltale geomorphic and erosional record which may provide uncontestable evidence of past glaciation. U-shaped valleys, roches moutonnées, and stoss and lee structures are characteristic geomorphic forms and have been identified at some locality for all of the main ice ages of the past. These landforms are veneered with glacially polished and striated surfaces wherever bedrock is of the appropriate lithology, that is, fine-grained and indurated. Glacial striae, if well preserved, can easily be distinguished from fault slickensides. The striae occur in sets with slightly divergent directions, associated with chattermarks, crescentic gouges, lunate fractures, and other types of friction cracks (Embleton and King, 1975). In fact, many of these same friction features are recognized on striated stones carried downflow by glaciers and incorporated in till and outwash sedimentary debris.

Unsorted sedimentary debris, usually consisting of large clasts dispersed and mixed into clay and silt, is deposited at the base of glaciers as they flow or waste, and as morainal material at their downflow ends. In modern glacial environments, a distinction can usually be made between the debris (till) that is transported upon or within the ice, that deposited as lodgment till as the glacier melts, and that at and near the front of a wasting glacier by flowage of water-saturated material (Goldthwait, 1971). With the glacier still at hand and upflow, or with Quaternary landforms to show that a glacier has but recently departed, the till origin of the unsorted debris is established. Where such debris is preserved in an ancient sequence of strata, however, it may be difficult or impossible to determine its glacial origin inasmuch as such unsorted material (diamicton when unconsolidated; diamictite when an indurated rock) can form in many other ways as well (Crowell, 1957; Dott, 1963). It is therefore necessary to find other evidence of glaciation in addition to the occurrence of a diamictite within the stratigraphic section before a glacial origin for the deposit is acceptable.

Till and tillite consist of unsorted rock debris, ranging in grain size from clay to boulders or blocks. Some of the larger stones may have been transported by ice for great distances, and if their distant source can be recognized or inferred, ice was probably the transporting agent. If, in addition, a number of the stones are faceted and striated, and carry the characteristic pattern of glacial striae, the case is markedly strengthened. At places, boulder pavements are formed, where trains of large clasts have their tops ground off resulting in stratal levels with aligned, faceted, and striated stones. Other characteristics are helpful. In tillite the finest material is indurated rockflour, consisting of rock material mechanically ground down to silt and clay size. The fine fraction of tillites therefore results in a massive, even texture in outcrop that results in conchoidal fracturing and spheroidal weathering, a feature especially noticeable where the stones within the tillite are widely dispersed. Study of stone fabrics (Holmes, 1941; Drake, 1971) may be revealing, but such studies are time-consuming in indurated strata and are infrequently undertaken. However, these investigations may disclose the pattern of glacial flow in a lodgment till, and ideally should involve the measurement of the long axes of nonspheroidal clasts, in order to show imbrication. Where digging out of stones is precluded, however, a two-dimensional concept of the flow may be obtained by measurements of long axes of stones on bedding planes (Stratten, 1969).

Mineral grains carried by moving ice and pressed firmly against each other and the bedrock below the glacier are fractured and scarred with percussion markings and etchings. Quartz grains, under the electron microscope, display marks that may be characteristic of glacial transport (Krinsley and Doornkamp, 1973). Garnet grains, viewed with a petrographic microscope, show trains of chattermarks, perhaps also caused by englacial transport (Folk, 1975; Gravenor, 1979). If continuing studies confirm that these two types of markings are truly distinctive of glacial transport, a powerful tool will be in hand, but very similar markings are also caused by chemical etching during diagenesis. Research is now needed to find criteria so that glacial percussion marks can be differentiated from chemical etching marks (Gravenor and Leavitt, 1981). Although the markings will eventually be worn away as quartz and garnet grains are carried by fluviatile and other agents, while they remain they may provide a clue to their glacial derivation. Such clues are especially needed within outwash and transitional deposits where the mode of transport is nonglacial and the resulting textures and sedimentary structures overshadow the glacial origin of the sedimentary debris.

Bedrock sculpturings and patches of tillite may document an ancient glaciation in the vicinity where the glaciers previously existed. For a glacier terminating on land, however, fluviatile and other processes will very quickly rework the glacial debris so that within a few hundred meters or at most a few kilometers, no vestige within the deposits of the glacial origin may be discernible (Crowell, 1978). Textures and sedimentary structures reveal instead the new mode of transportation and deposition. Only where a glacier actually extends into a large body of water, such as the sea or ocean, is the situation favorable for the preservation of a glacial clue through rafting. When and where icebergs, calved from a glacier front, drift away in currents is the stage set for providing a clue for glaciation at distances from the glacier itself. Such icebergs may contain englacial debris that is eventually deposited when the berg melts or overturns, dumping till and boulders onto the sea floor in an environment where it can be recognized.

Two sedimentary facies involving rafting are significant. First, if the material falls into an environment where very thin beds or laminations are being deposited, rafting may be clearly inferred. Under these circumstances stones falling from an ice raft will lie at the bedding surface, and ideally will puncture the bedding or even splash up fragments of the substrata as they penetrate. Such isolated stones, known as "lonestones" descriptively, may be designated as "dropstones" when the reconstruction of the manner of their emplacement indicates rafting. This origin is best inferred where the diameter of the stone is many times, perhaps 10 or 15 times, the thickness of individual beds or laminations. Confidence in this interpretation is enhanced where the stones are truly alone, and penetration and splash-up structures can be identified. If they are strewn out with unsorted sedimentary debris, bedding characteristics need careful scrutiny in order to eliminate from consideration lateral currents. For example, currents washing into the site laterally may bring over-sized clasts, and then move on, carrying away the fine material and leaving behind only the larger stones. These lonestones are known as "lagstones." Cross bedding and other sedimentary structures may provide the clue indicating the efficacy of such lateral currents, and make suspect the interpretation that the lonestones are indeed dropstones. On the other hand, ice rafts may dump debris upon the depositional floor, but such material is usually unsorted and occurs in clumps or clusters and may even form pea-sized "till pellets" (Ovenshine, 1970).

Second, at places rafted glacial debris falls into environments where massive silt and clay are accumulating without discernible bedding. Such environments may lie seaward of calving ice fronts where huge volumes of rockflour, brought in by glacial streams, settle quietly to the sea floor to form massive and featureless deposits. Only here and there, dispersed within the massive siltstone, are isolated dropstones and clots of unsorted debris.

Research is needed to enable the identification of consolidated rockflour using petrographic or geochemical criteria. In the field, however, the massive matrix with distinctive blue-gray color where unweathered, and spheroidal structure where weathered, are suggestive. On the other hand, such a facies may closely resemble one formed by downslope sliding and mixing of unconsolidated mud and silt with rare interbedded conglomerate (Crowell, 1957). In view of a total association where the deposits grade laterally into those of assured glacial origin, thick sequences of sparse-stone diamictite are interpreted as of glacial origin also. One of the thickest sections (1100 m) of this type makes up the Whiteout Conglomerate, Sentinel Range, Antarctica, of Carboniferous and Permian age (Frakes and others, 1971).

Whether these types of deposits are marine or nonmarine is usually problematic, especially for Proterozoic rocks. Diagnostic fossils are rare at best in aqueous glacial deposits, even for Phanerozoic deposits. Some investigations show that glacial marine deposits are depleted in iron like most nearshore marine sediments, whereas tills deposited on land are enriched (Frakes and Crowell, 1975). Plots of total weight per cent of manganese against iron may therefore be useful in making the distinction.

In summary, an ice age is best documented where a facies reconstruction fitting together many different types of evidence requires continental glaciation. Seldom are there enough clues to glaciation in a single stratigraphic section. Instead, regional paleogeographic reconstructions, dovetailing facies interpretations from many correlated sections, are most satisfactory. This approach, however, depends on confidence in correlation from section to section. For Proterozoic strata, isotopic and paleontologic methods of correlation do not as yet have the time resolution for correlation over great distances. Correlation in the Proterozoic largely depends on methods in physical stratigraphy, and these are most useful on a regional scale only. Much of the controversy in regard to the extent and timing of Proterozoic glaciations hinges on differing judgments concerning how far and for how long correlations are extended.

Where nonmarine glacial strata lie upon a striated surface, and especially where different facies of till such as lodgment and flow till can be identified, the sediments are most likely to have been deposited during a waning stage as the glaciers retreated (Crowell, 1978). Geomorphic forms were carved by the glaciers in the basement, and glacial polish and striations probably originated just previously. Those manufactured earlier during the same long ice age were eroded away as the glaciation continued. A record of the earlier parts of the glaciation is therefore expected only in sedimentary sections at a distance from the glacier front where deposition rather than erosion has prevailed during the full span of time represented by the waxing, culmination, and final dwindling of the ice age. Where continental ice sheets grow on highlands through the enlarging and coalescing of alpine glaciers, first an ice cap and then an ice sheet develops. As the ice age progresses, glacial and periglacial sediments peripheral to the growing and waning ice sheet will quickly be reworked by fluviatile and other agents before the material reaches its resting place in a nearby basin. All vestige of glacial origin will be worn away. The glaciation is documented in the stratigraphic section only when the dropstone facies appears, but this may be a very long time after the ice cap began to grow. Beds in a continuous stratigraphic section older than the layers with dropstones are therefore pictured as deposited during the growth of glaciers at distance on land, for which there will be no record in the stratigraphic section at hand. According to this evolutionary model—that is, ice caps growing on uplands—the preserved basinal record will lack documentation for both the early stages of glacier growth and for dwindling stages. The record tells only when the glaciers reached the sea (or a large lake) so that icebergs were calved and carried exotic debris to the depositional site.

Synthesis studies of the last great glaciation of the Late Cenozoic Ice Age (for the Wisconsin-Weichselian stages of the Pleistocene between 17,000 and 21,000 years ago) suggest quite another model for the growth of ice sheets (Denton and Hughes, 1981). The west Antarctica, Greenland, Laurentian, and Scandinavian ice sheets grew over shallow seas and not over highlands. With the onset of coldness, sea ice on shallow marine shelves froze to the sea floor. Rivers carrying river ice coming down from nearby lands were inhibited in their oceanward flow and so added to the growing ice mass as snow fell upon it. Through time ice domes and ridges grew, some restrained in their outward flow by encircling islands. The Laurentian Ice Dome developed over Hudson Bay, the Scandinavian over the Gulf of Bothnia, the West Antarctic Ice Dome over the coalesced Ross and Weddell Seas, and the Greenland Ice Cap today sits within a marine saucer surrounded by restraining islands. This model of glacier growth allows the calving of icebergs very early in their development and must be considered in reconstructing the paleogeography and paleoclimatology of ice ages of the distant past, such as for those of the Proterozoic Era.

During the Pleistocene, ice domes and ridges also grew above mountain ranges, as shown by the waxing and waning of the Cordilleran Ice Sheet (Denton and Hughes, 1981), and so there are two distinctly different modes for glacier growth that must be evaluated in reconstructing ancient times of refrigeration (Fig. 1): 1) Ice domes growing over shallow seas; and 2) ice domes growing over mountains, highlands, or uplands through the coalescing of alpine glaciers to make first an ice cap and then an ice sheet. For Proterozoic reconstructions it may be difficult, in view of lack of information on tectonic setting and timing, to decide which mode prevailed.

With respect to reconstructing the location of ice sheets of the remote geologic past, ice-rafted debris may be carried by bergs swept along in oceanic currents for great distances before the bergs melt. Today, for example, bergs from West Greenland enter the Davis Straits and float southward across the Labrador Sea to finally melt off the Grand Banks at the margins of the Atlantic Ocean. Many bergs will therefore travel through 30 degrees of latitude, and some of these presumably will dump identifiable debris into sediments at the end of their long journey (Crowell, 1964). From this example we conclude that ice-rafted material preserved within a stratigraphic section documents the occurrence of glaciation somewhere at the time the beds were deposited but gives little if any information on where the glaciers were situated. The Greenland-Grand Banks example shows us that not even the nearest lands, in this case Nova Scotia, Newfoundland, and Labrador, are glaciated. Only if we have enough data and confidence in our paleoceanographic reconstruction of the remote past to show the flow of ocean currents, would we be able to infer much concerning the location of continental glaciers. And, unfortunately, we are never likely to have this confidence for limited time slices in the Proterozoic. The record for such ancient times is just too sparse and time resolution too crude. To arrive at a less pessimistic stance concerning reconstructing Precambrian glaciations, we must turn to the indirect ways to document ancient ice ages.

INDIRECT EVIDENCE OF GLACIATION

One of the causes of the rise and fall of sea level on a worldwide scale is the waxing and waning of ice sheets. By analogy with the Pleistocene Wisconsin-Weichselian Ice Stage, continental glaciations may take place synchronously over the Earth and are the result of worldwide refrigeration (Hughes and others, 1981). In the Pleistocene, at the same time as ice domes developed in the Northern Hemisphere, they also grew in Antarctica and so did alpine glaciers in high mountains in intermediate latitudes. A powerful method is therefore in hand to give both the timing of an ancient glaciation as well as its strength. Sea level drops in proportion to the amount of ice tied up in continental glaciers, if the amount involved in the eustatic changes can be uncontrovertibly related to glaciation. In addition, because of the instantaneous response of sea level to ice-volume fluctuations, dating at one place may be extrapolated over large distances to stratigraphic sections where the dating is insecure if the same eustatic response can be identified and traced. In combination with correla-

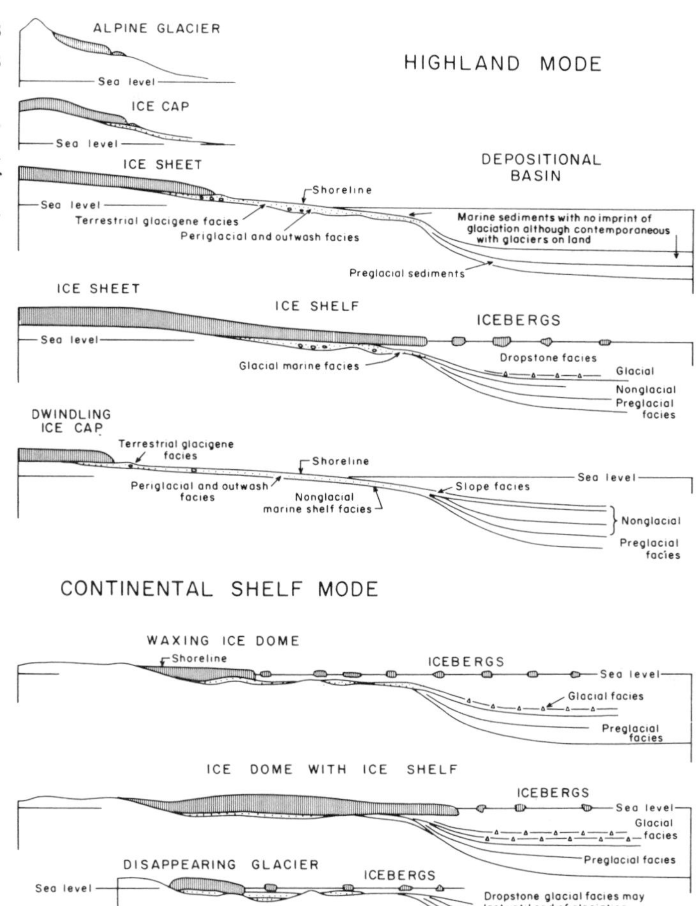

Figure 1. Facies relations associated with growth, culmination, and dwindling of continental glaciers. In the *Highland Mode,* alpine glaciers grow together to form an ice cap that enlarges through time to make an ice sheet. This sheet may expand to sea level and extend seaward as an ice shelf that may calve icebergs. In the *Continental Shelf Mode,* the glaciers grow in shallow water at and near sea level. Icebergs may spawn early in the glacier's history, and the iceberg phase may last nearly throughout its life. Refer to text for discussion.

tion through facies interpretations, seismic stratigraphy, and magnetostratigraphy, eustatic changes purport to be very useful in timing glaciations.

Eustatic changes in sea level may be caused by several other processes in addition to the waxing and waning of ice sheets, and these changes need to be sorted out from the sea level record before inferences can be drawn concerning glaciation. These processes will be those that both change the volume of water available to fill the ocean basins and those that change the shape of the sea and ocean floor. Under the accepted assumption that the volume of water on the Earth has either been constant or has changed but slowly over the last 2.5×10^9 years, only the amounts drawn into ice caps remove water from the seas and oceans and therefore lower sea level. At the same time, loading by ice depresses the crust isostatically and may tend to raise sea level slightly. Calculations of the drop in sea level for the Wisconsin-Weichselian Ice Stage, including allowance for isostatic loading, give a range between 127 and 163 m depending on whether a minimum or maximum reconstruction of ice sheet area and volume is selected (Hughes and others, 1981). This range, which fits well with local geomorphic observations of sea level changes (Milliman and Emery, 1969) and from oxygen isotope calculations (i.e., Fairbanks and Matthews, 1978), leads to the general inference that marked ice ages of the past, similar in strength to the Wisconsin-Weichselian, can account for rapid sea level drops of up to, say, 200 m. Such a sea level change should show up clearly in the geologic record. We need also to recognize that if huge, synchronous ice caps are advocated for times in the geologic past, an even greater lowering of sea level should be discernible in the stratigraphic record. In addition, since eustatic changes greater than those of the Pleistocene have not been documented for ice ages of the past, including those of the Proterozoic, it can be argued that these glaciations were not of greater severity.

Sea level changes also result from several other causes. Tectonic activities, in particular those related to rates of sea floor spreading and the positioning and size of midocean ridges, will modify the shape and volume of ocean basins (Sclater and Francheteau, 1970). With rapid sea floor spreading, midocean ridges are broad and large, and so displace water up upon the continental shelves. When spreading rates are slow, the ridges shrink, and sea level falls. These changes are the consequence of contraction during cooling; cooling rates are more or less constant in a vertical column of sea floor. With rapid sea floor spreading, the flanks of a midocean ridge moving outwards and away from a ridge shrink less vertically than when the movement is slow; the flanks are broad and stand high. Such changes probably account for the broad flooding of cratonic areas, such as those during the Cretaceous (Hays and Pitman, 1973), but they are slow and take place over tens of millions of years. The capacity of ocean basins may also be influenced by the amount of continental compression involved in orogenic processes (Rona, 1973). Such processes squeeze continents laterally so that they stand higher, bringing about a lowering of sea level. Continents may also stand high because they have moved onto parts of the upper mantle that are less dense than the average, as in western North America during the Cenozoic Era (Menard, 1973; Crough and Thompson, 1977). Local sagging or arching of continental margins may also occur due to tectonic processes. In addition, the world pattern and types of plate boundaries with respect to their distribution and arrangement beneath continents or oceans will affect the ocean volume. These movements, all related to plate-tectonic processes, are slow and bring about only gradual and small changes in sea level.

Large basins, such as the Mediterranean basin today, may dry up with a transfer of water to the world ocean, and fill up when they become connected to it. In the late Miocene, such events may have happened to the Mediterranean Sea (Hsü and others, 1973) with related changes in sea level of about 10 m, first up and then down (Berger and Winterer, 1974). Similar events may have occurred in the middle to late Jurassic when an isolated North Atlantic basin originated, grew, and was then flooded (Sclater and others, 1977; Schopf, 1980). This basin was larger than the Mediterranean today, and so its effect on sea level would be potentially greater. The filling of the North Atlantic may account for the sharp regression at the end of the Jurassic (Callovian) (Schopf, 1980). Smaller basins, such as those along the Dead Sea Rift and the Salton Trough at the head of the Gulf of California, have potential for altering sea level when they flood but only slightly because the volumes of water are small in proportion to the volume of the ocean as a whole.

Sediments eroded from the land and deposited in the sea displace ocean water, bringing about a sea level rise. The balance between continental erosion, deposition, and tectonic rejuvenation seems to be in relative equilibrium, however, well back into the Proterozoic. Fluctuations where one part of the chain gets either ahead or behind the other may bring about small sea level changes. On a local scale, deltas may load the crust, depressing it, and so deform the local record of sea level stands. Perhaps, at places, moderately sized basins have originated this way and then have continued to deepen as the result of induced phase changes in the lower part of the lithosphere (Joyner, 1967; Schopf, 1980).

This cursory review of the causes of sea level changes suggests that the waxing and waning of a continental ice stage may bring about fluctuations of as much as 200 m, and over rapid time periods of 10,000 to 50,000 years. The other processes can individually cause fluctuations but about an order of magnitude less, and most are geologically slow. We may therefore be able to document the occurrence of an ice age or stage on the basis of an analysis of the eustatic record. If the magnitude is large, worldwide, and not just local or even regional, and involves relatively rapid fluctuations, the cause may be glacial.

For the Proterozoic, it may be difficult to apply these criteria because the record is piecemeal and correlation inexact. For the Late Paleozoic Ice Age—an ice age that lasted for about 90 m.y. until the mid-Permian—a fair case can be made that cyclothems in North America and Europe are caused in part by the waxing and waning of glacial centers on Gondwanan continents in the Southern Hemisphere (Crowell, 1978). For the Precambrian, we must therefore begin to look for parts of the stratigraphic record that show cyclothems and larger scale transgressions and regressions. The careful analysis of relations between sea level, sedimentary facies, and shoreline position utilizing the techniques of seismic stratigraphy for the Phanerozoic record has been revolutionary (Vail and others, 1977). Vail and his associates have constructed a sea level curve for the Phanerozoic, a curve that, with revisions as new data come in, will provide a worldwide reference for eustacy through time. Such a curve should be extended downward into the Proterozoic as data become available. In fact, broad transgressions and regressions are already recognizable in strata of upper Proterozoic age (Bjørlykke, 1978; Christie-Blick and others, 1980). If these transgressions and regressions can be followed from place to place aided by magnetostratigraphic and other methods, our ability to correlate may be much enhanced, and along the way, understanding acquired of the basic causes of sea-level changes. On the one hand, research may disclose the dating of the eustatic fluctuations; and on the other, some changes may be clearly related to epochs of glaciation.

PROBLEMS CONCERNING LATE PROTEROZOIC GLACIATIONS

As reviewed earlier, ice ages flourished intermittently from about 950 m.y. to 560 m.y. ago in the late Phanerozoic. During this interval of nearly 400 m.y., continental glaciations occurred at times upon all the continents, with the possible exception of Antarctica, and at places came and went more than once. Correlation from place to place is uncertain, however, so we do not know whether distant occurrences are of the same age. Three glaciation peaks are suggested, however: one at about 940 m.y. ago, another near 770, and a third near 615 (Williams, 1975).

A body of paleomagnetic work indicates that some of these ice sheets accumulated at sea level in low latitudes and even equatorial regions (Tarling, 1974; McWilliams and McElhenny, 1980). Controversy has therefore arisen because equatorial glaciation is so obviously in contrast with polar- or high-latitude glaciation, established beyond question for the Late Cenozoic Ice Age, including the remnants today in Greenland and Antarctica. Paleomagnetic data show an acceptable polar fit for ice ages of the Late Paleozoic (Crowell and Frakes, 1970; Crowell, 1978) and for the late Ordovician-early Silurian glaciation, which began about 440 m.y. ago (Crowell, 1980, 1981). The question immediately arises: Why should there be a switch within the 120 m.y. interval between the latest Precambrian glaciations and that of the latest Ordovician, a switch from a near-equatorial to a near-polar siting? One group has placed credence in the straightforward interpretation of the paleomagnetic data (Williams, 1975; Harland, 1981) and has searched for an explanation for low-latitude continental glaciation, including an explanation involving changes in the obliquity of the Earth's ecliptic. According to the Williams hypothesis, in the late Proterozoic the spin axis of the earth was tipped at an angle of more than 54° with respect to the plane of the Earth's orbit. With this orientation, it moved about the sun in its annual cycle in such a way that first one pole and then the other were angled toward the sun, receiving radiation directly. In contrast, equatorial regions were relatively shadowed and therefore cooler during all seasonal changes. Research is needed on the geophysics and on other geological consequences of such an orbital scheme, since not only would the glaciation record be affected. Moreover, additional paleomagnetic points are needed because there is still uncertainty concerning the polar wander path during the late Precambrian. Published paths are significantly different (compare McElhinny and others, 1974, Fig. 3 with Morel and Irving, 1978, Fig. 1).

Another group has taken a more uniformitarian stance and has looked for evidence and arguments to extend the Phanerozoic pattern of polar glaciation back into the Proterozoic. This group is not challenging the paleomagnetic observations, and there is no reason to question the method of field sampling or the quality of the paleomagnetic determinations in the laboratory. On the other hand, perhaps the magnetic vector was imprinted in the glacial strata some time after the glaciation, or the vector was modified by diagenetic changes in the sediments. This group therefore first pleads for more research on the fundamentals of rock and mineral magnetism so that we understand fully the timing and process of the magnetic imprint. Is it possible that if the crust were as mobile during the late Proterozoic as during the Phanerozoic, the site moved through several tens of degrees of latitudes between the time when the glacigene sediments were deposited and when the magnetic vector was imprinted within them? If we take a recently published polar wander path at face value (Morel and Irving, 1978), the united supercontinent of Gondwana moved across the South Pole at a rate of nearly 1.5 degrees of latitude per million years during the Paleozoic Era (Crowell, 1981). If the magnetic vector were fixed in the rocks 15 or 20 million years after their deposition, the site could have moved from, say, 50° to 30° of latitude, from a region where glaciation is conceivable under the polar hypothesis to where it is not. Speculating further, such rates would permit Proterozoic sites to move in and out of high-latitude positions several times during the 400 m.y. or so between 970 and 570 m.y. ago. This line of thought also suggests that the glacial centers have laid down strongly diachronous strata as they moved. Such beds cannot be used for time correlation except on a relatively local scale.

CONCLUSIONS

Ice ages have occurred at several times during the late Proterozoic, but lack of good dating information prevents both understanding of them and some other fundamental aspects of the Earth history. The direct record of glaciation, contained in both terrestrial and marine strata, documents the ice ages; but the record in the Precambrian is sparse and piecemeal. By analogy with the Phanerozoic record, the glaciations should also affect sea level position markedly, and the fluctuations should be both of greater magnitude and shorter frequency than eustatic changes due to other causes. Over the decades ahead, research on transgressions and regressions preserved within patches of Proterozoic strata, and dovetailed with chronologic information from magnetostratigraphy, polar wander curves, paleontology, isotopic geochronology, and refined methods in physical stratigraphy, purports to add much to our understanding of the fundamental causes of climate change, including the comings and goings of continental glaciers.

ACKNOWLEDGMENTS

I am grateful to the U.S. National Science Foundation and the University of California, Santa Barbara, for research support, and to many colleagues for pertinent discussions.

REFERENCES CITED

Anderson, J. B., Kurtz, D. D., and Weaver, F. M., 1979, Sedimentation on the Antarctic continental slope: Society of Economic Paleontologists and Mineralogists Special Publication no. 27, p. 265–283.

Anderson, J. B., Kurtz, D. D., Domack, E. W., and Balshaw, K. M., 1980, Glacial and glacial marine sediments of the Antarctic continental shelf: Journal of Geology, v. 88, p. 399–414.

Barron, E. J., Thompson, S. L., and Schneider, S. H., 1981, An ice-free Cretaceous? Results from climate model simulations: Science, v. 212, p. 501–508.

Berger, W. H., and Winterer, E. L., 1974, Plate stratigraphy and the fluctuating carbonate line: International Association of Sedimentologists, Special Publication no. 1, p. 11–48.

Beuf, S., Biju-Duval, B., DeCharpal, O., Rognon, P., Gariel, O., and Bennacef, A., 1971, Les gres du Paleozoique inferieur au Sahara-sedimentation et discontinuities, evolution structurale d'un craton: Institute Francaise du Pétrole, Science et Technique du Pétrole, no. 18, 464 p.

Bjørlykke, Knut., 1978, The eastern marginal zone of the Caledonide orogen in Norway: Geological Survey of Canada Paper 78–13, p. 49–54.

Caputo, M. V., Rodrigues, R., and de Vasconcellos, D.N.N., 1972, Nomenclatura estratigráfica da bacia do Amazonas: Annas do XXVI Congresso Brasileira de Geologia, Sociedade Brasileira de Geologia, v. 3, p. 35–46.

Carozzi, A. V., Pamplona, H.R.P., de Castro, J. C., and Contreiras, C.J.A., 1973, Ambientes deposicionais e evoluçao tecto-sedimentar da seçao clástica paleozóica da bacia do Médio Amazonas: Annais do XXVII Congresso Brasileiro de Geologia, Sociedade Brasileira de Geologia, v. 3, p. 279–314.

Christie-Blick, N., Link, P. K., Miller, J.M.G., Young, G. M., and Crowell, J. C., 1980, Regional geologic events inferred from Upper Proterozoic rocks of the North American cordillera: Geological Society of America Abstracts with Programs, v. 12, p. 402.

Clark, D. L., Whitman, R. R., Morgan, K. A., Mackey, S. D., 1980, Stratigraphy and glacial-marine sediments of the Amerasian basin, central Arctic Ocean: Geological Society of America Special Paper 181, 57 p.

CLIMAP Project Members, 1976, The surface of the ice-age earth: Science, v. 191, p. 1131–1137.

——1981, Seasonal reconstructions of the earth's surface at the last glacial maximum: Geological Society of America, Map and Chart Series no. 36.

Crough, S. T., and Thompson, G. A., 1977, Upper mantle origin of Sierra Nevada uplift: Geology, v. 5, p. 396–399.

Crowell, J. C., 1957, Origin of pebbly mudstones: Geological Society of America Bulletin, v. 68, p. 993–1010.

——1964, Climatic significance of sedimentary deposits containing dispersed megaclasts, *in* Nairm, A.E.M., ed., Problems in Palaeoclimatology: London, Interscience, p. 86–99.

——1978, Gondwanan glaciation, cyclothems, continental positioning, and climate change: American Journal of Science, v. 278, p. 1345–1372.

——1981, Early Paleozoic glaciation and Gondwana drift: *in* McElhinny, M. W., and Valencio, D. A., eds., Paleoreconstruction of the continents, American Geophysical Union, Washington, D.C., and Geological Society of America, Boulder, Colorado: Geodynamic Series, v. 2, p. 45–49.

Crowell, J. C., and Frakes, L. A., 1970, Phanerozoic glacation and the causes of ice ages: American Journal of Science, v. 268, p. 193–224.

Crowell, J. C., and Frakes, L. A., 1975, The Late Palaeozoic Glaciation: *in* Campbell, K.S.W., ed., Gondwana Geology, Canberra, Australian National University Press, p. 313–331.

Crowell, J. C., Rocha-Campos, A. C., and Suárez-Soruco, R., 1980, Silurian glaciation in central South America: Proceeding Fifth International Gondwana Symposium, Wellington, New Zealand, p. 105–110.

Denton, G. H., and Hughes, T. J., eds., 1981, The last great ice sheets: New York, Wiley-Interscience, 484 p., 28 plates and tables.

Deynoux, M., Trompette, R., Clauer, N., and Sougy, J., 1978, Upper Precambrian and lowermost Palaeozoic correlations in West Africa and in the western part of central Africa. Probably diachronism of the late Precambrian tillite: Geologische Rundschau, v. 67, p. 615–630.

Dott, R. H., Jr., 1963, Dynamics of subaqueous gravity depositional processes: American Association of Petroleum Geologists Bulletin, v. 47, p. 104–128.

Drake, Lon, 1971, Evidence for ablation and basal till in east-central New Hampshire: *in* Goldthwait, R. P., ed., Till: a symposium: Columbus, Ohio State University Press, p. 73–91.

Embleton, C., and King, C.A.M., 1975, Glacial Geomorphology: New York, John Wiley & Sons, 573 p.

Fairbanks, R. G., and Matthews, R. K., 1978, The marine oxygen-isotope record in Pleistocene corals, Barbados, West Indies: Quaternary Research, v. 10, p. 181–196.

Folk, R. L., 1975, Glacial deposits identified by chattermark trails in detrital garnets: Geology, v. 3, p. 473–475.

Frakes, L. A., 1979, Climates throughout geologic time: Amsterdam, Elsevier, 310 p.

Frakes, L. A., and Crowell, J. C., 1975, Characteristics of modern glacial marine sediments—application to Gondwana glacials, *in* Campbell, K.S.W., ed., Gondwana Geology: Canberera, Australian National University Press, p. 373–380.

Frakes, L. A., Matthews, J. L., and Crowell, J. C., 1971, Late Paleozoic glaciation: Part III, Antarctica: Geological Society of America Bulletin, v. 82, p. 1581–1604.

Goldthwait, R. P., ed., 1971, Till: a symposium: Columbus, Ohio State University Press, 402 p.

Gravenor, C. P., 1979, The nature of the Late Paleozoic glaciation in Gondwana as determined from an analysis of garnets and other heavy minerals: Canadian Journal of Earth Sciences, v. 16, p. 1137–1153.

Gravenor, C. P., and Leavitt, R. K., 1981, Experimental formation and significance of etch patterns on detrital grains: Canadian Journal of Earth Sciences, v. 18, p. 765–775.

Harland, W. B., 1981, Chronology of Earth's glacial and tectonic record: Geological Society of London Journal, v. 138, p. 197–203.

Harland, W. B., and Herod, K. N., 1975, p. 189–216, *in* Wright, A. E., and Moseley, F., eds., Ice ages: ancient and modern: Geological Journal Special Issue no. 6, Liverpool, Sell House Press, 320 p.

Hays, J. D., and Pitman, W. C., 1973, Lithospheric plate motion, sea level changes and climatic and ecological consequences: Nature, v. 246, p. 18–22.

Holmes, C. D., 1941, Till fabric: Geological Society of America Bulletin, v. 52, p. 1299–1354.

Hsü, K. J., Ryan, W.B.F., and Cita, M. B., 1973, Late Miocene desiccation of the Mediterranean: Nature, v. 242, p. 240–244.

Hughes, T. J., Denton, G. H., Anderson, B. G., Schilling, D. H., Fastook, J. L., and Lingle, C. S., 1981, *in* Denton, G. H., and Hughes, T. J., eds., The last great ice sheets: New York, Wiley-Interscience, p. 263–317.

Joyner, W. B., 1967, Basalt-eclogite transition as a cause of subsidence: Journal of Geophysical Research, v. 72, p. 4977–4998.

Krinsley, D. H., and Doornkamp, J. C., 1973, Atlas of quartz sand surface textures: Cambridge University Press, 91 p.

McElhinny, M. W., Giddings, J. W., and Embleton, B.J.J., 1974, Palaeomagnetic results and late Precambrian glaciations: Nature, v. 248, p. 557–561.

McWilliams, M. O., and McElhinny, M. W., 1980, Late Precambrian paleomagnetism of Australia: the Adelaide geosyncline: Journal of Geology, v. 88, p. 1–26.

Menard, H. W., 1973, Epeirogeny and plate tectonics: EOS (American Geophysical Union Transactions), v. 54, p. 1244–1255.

Milliman, J. D., and Emery, K. O., 1969, Sea level changes during the past 35,000 years: Science, v. 162, p. 1121–1123.

Morel, P., and Irving, E., 1978, Tentative paleocontinental maps for the early Phanerozoic and Proterozoic: Journal of Geology, v. 86, p. 535–561.

Ovenshine, A. T., 1970, Observations of iceberg rafting in Glacier Bay, Alaska, and the identification of ancient ice-rafted deposits: Geological Society of America Bulletin, v. 81, p. 891–894.

Rona, P. A., 1973, Relations between rates of sediment accumulation on continental shelves, sea-floor spreading and eustacy, inferred from the Central North Atlantic: Geological Society of America Bulletin, v. 84, p. 2851–2871.

Schopf, T.J.M., 1980, Paleoceanography: Cambridge, Massachusetts, Harvard University Press, 341 p.

Sclater, J. G., and Francheteau, J., 1970, The implications of terrestrial heat flow observations on current tectonic and geochemical models of the crust and upper mantle of the earth: Royal Astronomical Society Geophysical Journal, v. 20, p. 509–542.

Sclater, J. G., Hellinger, S., and Tapscott, C., 1977, The paleobathymetry of the Atlantic Ocean from the Jurassic to the present: Journal of Geology, v. 85, p. 509–552.

Stratten, Thomas, 1969, A preliminary report of a directional study of the Dwyka Tillites in the Karroo Basin of South Africa: *in* Gondwana stratigraphy, Paris U.N.E.S.C.O., v. 2, p. 741–762.

Tarling, D. H., 1974, A palaeomagnetic study of Eocambrian tillites in Scotland: Geological Society of London Journal, v. 130, p. 163–177.

Trendall, A. F., 1976, Striated and faceted boulders from the Turee Creek Formation—evidence for a possible Huronian glaciation on the Australia continent: Geological Survey of Western Australia Annual Report, p. 88–92.

Vail, P. R., Mitchum, R. M., Jr., and Thompson, S., III, 1977, Global cycles of relative changes of sea level: American Association of Petroleum Geologists Memoir 26, p. 83–97.

Visser, J.N.J., 1971, The deposition of the Griquatown Glacial Member in the Transvaal Supergroup: Geological Society of South Africa, Transactions, v. 74, p. 186–199.

Williams, G. E., 1975, Late Precambrian glacial climate and the Earth's obliquity: Geological Magazine, v. 112, p. 441–465.

Young, G. M., 1970, An extensive early Proterozoic glaciation in North America? Palaeogeography, Palaeoclimatology, Palaeocology, v. 7, p. 85–101.

Manuscript Accepted by the Society April 14, 1983

Printed in U.S.A.

Geological Society of America
Memoir 161
1983

Quaternary glacial deposits: Implications for the interpretation of Proterozoic glacial deposits

A. Dreimanis
Department of Geology
University of Western Ontario
London, Ontario N6A 5B7
Canada

ABSTRACT

Glacial activity during a part of the Proterozoic was probably similar to that of the Quaternary. Therefore, the studies of recently glaciated areas, of recent near-glacial and periglacial environments on land and in oceans, and investigations of the deposits and erosional features of the extensive areas that were covered by the Pleistocene glaciers can assist in the deciphering of Proterozoic glacigenic deposits: the environments of their formation and their stratigraphic sequences.

Among glacial deposits, the most important is till. A relatively broad definition of till is used here to include flow tills, water-lain tills, and deformation tills besides the more conventional lodgement and melt-out varieties of till, since all of them, if correctly identified, imply glacial deposition, without or with penecontemporaneous resedimentation. Landforms will not be discussed here, as they seldom are preserved in Proterozoic glacial sequences. The macroscale and microscale glacial erosional features, glacio-dynamic deformation structures, fabric, and compositional characteristics will be considered as evidence of various glacial origins.

The following environments of glacial deposition and varieties of till are recognized: (a) supraglacial and ice-marginal environment, producing subaerial varieties of supraglacial tills and subaquatic flow till; (b) subglacial environment, producing subglacial tills under a glacier that is either in contact with the substratum or is separated from the substratum by a thin layer of water or a cavity. Dropstones in aquatic sediments, particularly if they bear surface marks of glacial transport, are useful indicators of the presence of glaciers, but they alone do not make the aquatic sediment a till.

INTRODUCTION

The atmosphere and hydrosphere of the Proterozoic may have been different from that of the Quaternary. Still, in some areas local Proterozoic climatic conditions permitted development of mountain glaciers and even ice sheets (Crowell, 1977; Hambrey and Harland, 1981). The causes of the Proterozoic glaciations (Harland and Herod, 1975; Schermerhorn, 1983), also may have differed from those of the Quaternary, but they will not be discussed here. However, the general physical rules that governed the behaviour of glaciers must have been the same during various times of the Earth's history. The main differences between the Proterozoic and the Quaternary were in the composition of biosphere and its environments. These factors influenced particularly the development of interglacial and interstadial sediments and those aquatic sediments that were deposited during the Proterozoic glaciations that interfinger with the glacial deposits.

Considering the above similarities and differences, we may apply, with some caution and possible restrictions, the uniformitarian principle—that the present is the key to the past—to Proterozoic glacigenic deposits. This can be done by using the results of glaciologic and sedimentologic investigations of present-day glaciers in the same way as Boulton (1972) or Lawson (1979) have used this information to interpret Pleistocene glacial deposits. Since Pleistocene glacigenic deposits have greater variety and wider spatial distribution than their present-day equivalents, additional investigation of Pleistocene glacigenic deposits is essential for the proper interpretation of the Proterozoic glacigenic deposits. The proposed similarities between the present-day and Pleistocene geologic processes and those of the Proterozoic apply not only to glacial environments but also to the areas surrounding the glaciers.

Studies of the recent and Pleistocene diamicts and also of sorted and stratified sediments have shown that glacigenic and nonglacigenic sediments are occasionally similar (Schermerhorn, 1974), for instance, flow tills resemble mudflow deposits, glaciofluvial deposits may look like fluvial deposits unrelated to glaciers, and dropstones may derive from icebergs or from various other floating objects. Also, erosional and deformational features such as striae, folds, shear planes, and joints may be of glacial and nonglacial origin and may appear similar. Therefore, a good knowledge of present-day and Pleistocene glacigenic processes and their effects alone are not sufficient for applying them to an interpretation of similar Proterozoic features. In addition, broad knowledge of nonglacial sedimentation processes and geotectonics is essential for correct interpretation of potential glacigenic sediments. If the suspected Proterozoic glacigenic deposits have been metamorphosed, the effect of metamorphism also has to be considered, particularly because most varieties of subglacial tills resemble dynamically metamorphosed rocks. Considering the above possible complications, we must apply multiple working hypotheses and multiple criteria for the interpretation of those Proterozoic sediments and erosional features that are suspected to be glacigenic.

TILL—THE MEANING OF THE TERM

When dealing with glacial deposits, first it is necessary to define till, called also "moraine" in most non-English languages. First, we have to decide whether we consider till as a petrological term, as used by Harland and others (1966), or as a genetic term with petrological implications, as used by most glacial geologists (Dreimanis, 1980, p. 14), or as a purely genetic term (Dreimanis, 1982b, p. 21).

While using till as a petrological term, Harland and others (1966) still emphasized its glacial origin among the petrogenetic aspects of its definition, but they also included deposits (allochthonous tills, tilloids) that have resulted from nonglacial or unknown transport, and polygenetic tills that contain some glacial components (Harland and others, 1966, p. 232). Such a wide petrogenetic usage of the term "till" causes confusion, since the terms "till" and "tillite" have been associated with glaciers in the minds of most geologists and all non-geologists for several generations. Therefore, I will further refer to till as a glacial deposit and also try to point out some criteria that differentiate till from similar looking nonglacial diamicts or mixtites, considering the last two as petrographic nongenetic terms (for their definitions, see Hambrey and Harland, 1981, p. 23, 28, 29).

Goldthwait (1971, p. 3, 4) wrote that "till is the only sediment stemming directly and solely from glacial ice." However, "till has more variations than any other sediment with a single name," and Flint (1971, p. 148) wrote that "no sharp dividing line separates till from stratified drift; one grades into the other . . . It is the non-size-sorted end member of a series whose opposite end member is well-size-sorted stratified drift. Ideally till is formed without the cooperation of water, but actually size sorting is present to an indefinite degree in deposits to which the term is applied." Most size-sorting is caused by water or wind, and sorting is rather weak in tills unless large quantities of water- or wind-sorted sediments have been incorporated. This means that the participation of glacial melt-water as a sorting agent is not an important factor during the deposition of till.

The above-mentioned variability of till and tillite and their grading into some other varieties of glacial drift is discussed, for instance, by Harland and others (1966). This wide range of variability makes it hard to define and to classify till to everybody's satisfaction.

Goldthwait (1971, p. 3–5), after discussing what is considered to be till and "when is till not a till," concluded that "everyone agrees that the word 'till' *does* mean glacial handling." That might be one of the broadest definitions.

One of the strictest and narrowest definitions of till is by Lawson (1979, p. 102): "Till is defined as sediment deposited directly from glacial ice that has not undergone subsequent disaggregation and resedimentation." It is based upon studies of a recent glacier in Alaska and would include only two varieties of till: melt-out till and lodgement till. It leaves out all the other varieties of till considered by most other authors. In Lawson's own area of study, according to him (Lawson, 1979, p. 103) 95% of the deposits in the ice terminus region are resedimented, sediment flow being the primary process of resedimentation. By his definition, they are not tills. If 95% of glacigenic diamicts that are related in their process of formation to glaciers are excluded from tills by definition, the term "till" loses its meaning as being a characteristic glacial deposit. In many cases, resedimentation accompanies melting out or lodgement so closely that their products are hard to differentiate. Therefore, Lawson's (1979) definition is too narrow, and we shall look for a broader one.

Another definition and genetic classification, which is based upon observations along present-day glaciers and theoretical considerations, but is less restrictive, is that of Boulton (1980): "Till is a sediment whose components are brought into contact by the direct agency of glacier ice, and which, although it may suffer subsequent glacially induced flow, is not disaggregated." This definition includes all ortho-tills (defined here later), some flow tills, and all glacially deformed sediments, but it leaves out water-lain tills that are common among tillites.

Both of the above definitions are based upon sound theoretical reasoning, but complications arise when they have to be applied in the field. It is often difficult to decide whether a Pleistocene or pre-Pleistocene diamict or mixtite should be considered a true glacial deposit and be called till. These difficulties arise particularly because the diamicts accepted as tills by Lawson (1979) or Boulton (1980) often grade imperceptibly into other genetically related diamicts that are excluded by them from tills, as has been admitted even by Lawson (1979, p. 104)

Considering the above theoretical and practical problems, we shall use the following broad definition of till and tillite in this paper that has been also tentatively adopted by the Till Work Group of the INQUA Commission on genesis and lithology of Quaternary deposits (Dreimanis, 1982b, p. 21). *Till is a sediment that has been transported and deposited by or from glacier ice with little or no sorting by water.* This definition of till would include all the varieties of till (and tillite) listed in Table 1, since all of them either have been deposited directly by a glacier or have derived from debris carried by a glacier, with little or no sorting by water. Since most varieties of till, even the lodgement and melt-out tills, are deposited by melting of the ice containing glacial debris, some participation of water even in their deposition is unavoidable. For those who would like to differentiate more rigorously between the tills formed by primary deposition from glacier ice and the tills where some secondary disaggregation or redeposition may be expected on theoretical grounds or even observed by certain physical properties, the designation *ortho-till* is proposed for the tills of primary deposition and *allo-till* for those tills where penecontemporaneous disaggregation or resedimentation may be proven or is strongly suspected (see Table 1). It may be noted here that the term "ortho-till" as used here corresponds to "ortho-till" as proposed by Harland and others (1966, p. 231) at the beginning of the paragraph defining this term: "Tills may be formed by immediate release from transporting ice (for example by ablation and melting), and these we term *ortho-tills*." Though the continuation of this description by Harland and others (1966) would include also the flow till, here separated as an allo-till, the newly published definition of ortho-till by Hambrey and Harland

TABLE 1. FORMATION OF TILLS AND THEIR GENETIC CLASSIFICATION

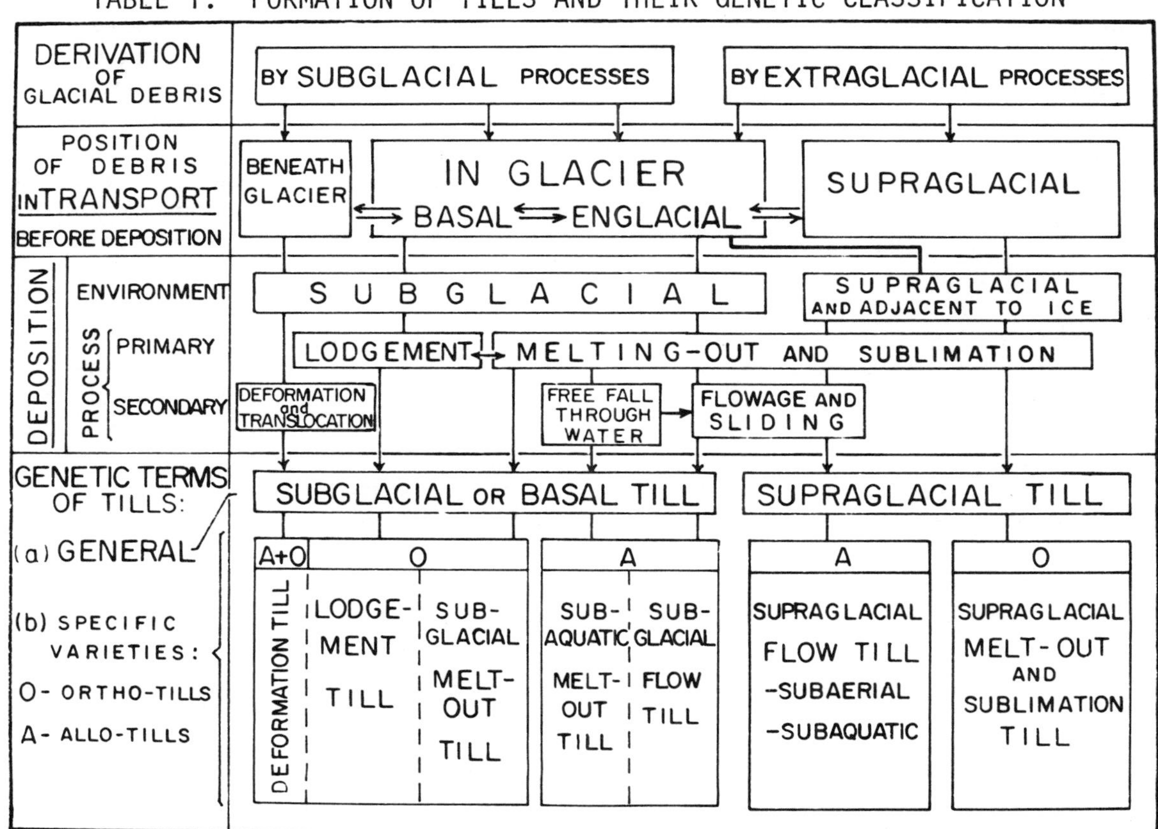

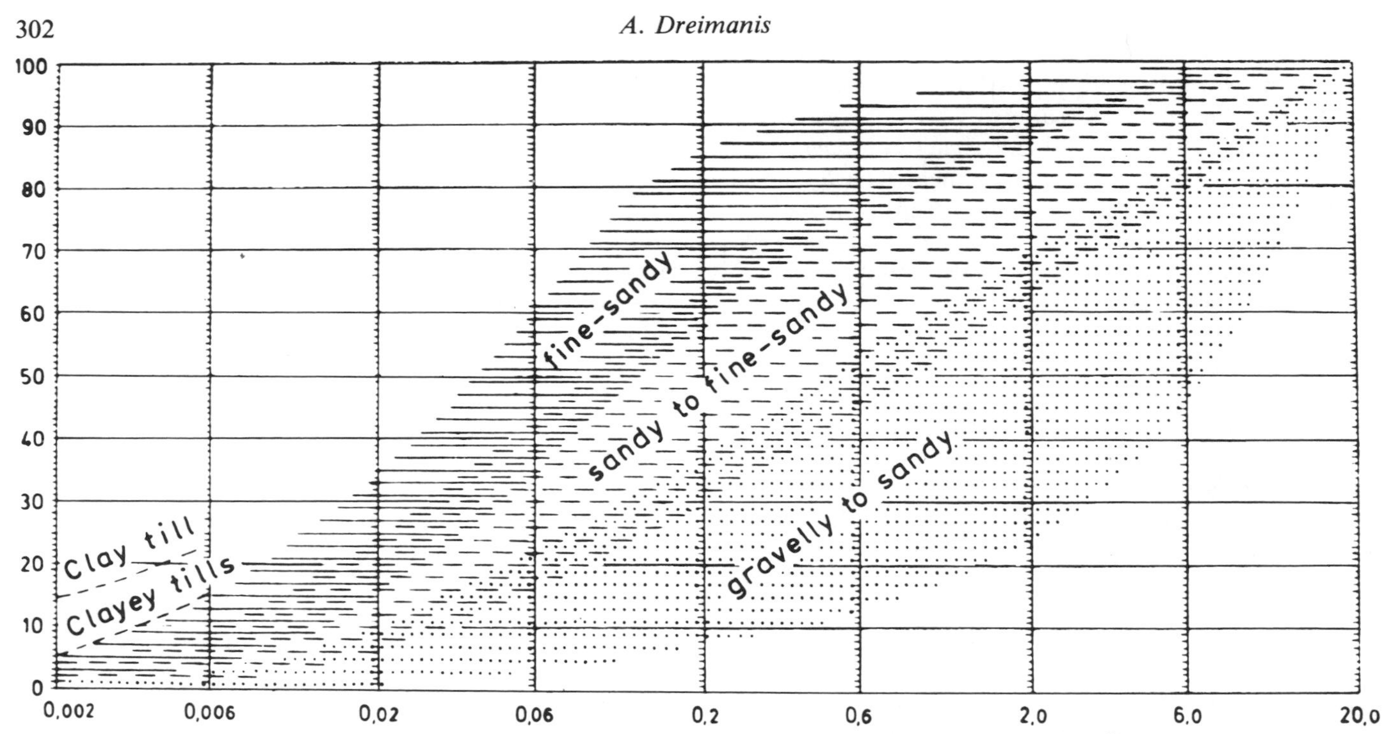

Figure 1. The Swedish classification of tills by their granulometric composition. The figures along the ordinate are percentages; those along the abcissa are millimetres (from Lunqvist, 1977, Fig. 1).

(1981, Glossary, p. 29) is essentially the same as the above brief quotation from Harland and others (1966). The ortho-tills correspond to the primary tills of Boulton and Deynoux (1982), and the allo-tills correspond in part to the secondary tills of Boulton and Deynoux (1982).

Most tills have the following characteristics: (1) They usually are poorly sorted: diamicts or mixtites. (2) They consist of a variety of rocks and minerals, some of them distantly transported. (3) The surfaces of many basally and englacially transported clasts are glacially abraded and show percussion and traction marks, even on brittle sand grains. (4) The fabric and structures of tills deposited directly by glacier (ortho-tills) are laterally consistent and related to the direction of glacial stress. (5) An ortho-till is underlain by glacially striated and/or glacially deformed substratum.

CLASSIFICATION OF TILLS

Two kinds of classifications of tills are used—descriptive and genetic. Descriptive classifications, such as in Figure 1 from Sweden, are applied to describing tills when mapping them, or evaluating them for engineering-geological purposes. For interpretation of Proterozoic geology, genetic classification of tills and tillites may be more useful. Therefore, a genetic classification is proposed for tillites and related sediments (for instance, see Hambrey and Harland, 1981, p. 25).

Table 1 lists a variety of factors significant for genetic classification of tills: derivation of glacial debris, their transport, and their deposition. However, the deposition only is emphasized here in the genetic names of tills, since the environment and process of deposition of till is of main interest to a Proterozoic geologist.

Why is it useful to differentiate several genetic varieties of till rather than to identify a sediment as till or tillite and to describe it only according to some observable criteria; for instance, as gray, silty, massive clay till? A diamict called gray, massive, silty clay till or its equivalent gray, massive, fine-textured tillite may be an ortho-till of lodgement or melt-out origin, or it may be an allo-till—a deformation till—or it may not be till at all; it may be a glaciomarine sediment. In order to place it in the proper environmental and stratigraphic setting, its correct genetic identification is essential, in addition to its description. Another example applies to stratigraphic interpretation. A till or tillite section may appear to consist of two units: (a) if they belong to two separate glaciations, or (b) they are merely two genetically different subunits—supraglacially and subglacially deposited during a single glaciation and may thus belong to a single stratigraphic unit. Application of multiple criteria and proper identification of the genetic varieties of the above two till layers would lead to two differing stratigraphic interpretations: two stratigraphically different tills versus one. In Pleistocene stratigraphy this problem has been solved easily in some areas, but it has been bothering the students of some areas for many years (Goldthwait, 1971); it is often a problem of distinguishing the two major general varieties of till, the supraglacial and the subglacial tills (or according to Flint's, 1971, terminology: the ablation till and the lodgment till, *sensu lato*).

SUBGLACIAL TILLS

These tills have been deposited underneath glacier ice, subglacially, and therefore the term "subglacial till" is preferred here to another widely used term "basal till" (Dreimanis, 1976, 1980). This would avoid a confusion with 'basal debris'—a glacial material carried in the basal part of a glacier. Most of the subglacial tills (Table 1)—lodgement and melt-out tills—are ortho-tills, and they bear evidence of transport of their materials inside dynamically active ice prior to their deposition. Even the subglacial allo-tills—deformation tills, flow tills, and water-lain melt-out tills—show some effect of pressure and traction by the overlying moving ice, mainly in their upper part that was in contact with moving ice.

1. Lodgement and subglacial melt-out tills are the most common and most typical subglacial tills. They are deposited directly by or from the base of glacier ice, and range in their variety from lodgement till as one end member to melt-out till (Table 1) as another.

A typical lodgement till is deposited, as observed by Boulton (1975, p. 20–22), by active lodging of glacial basal debris, particle-by-particle, underneath a moving glacier with its base at the pressure melting point. A typical subglacial melt-out till, on the other hand, lacks the effect of glacial movement and traction during its deposition; it is deposited from stagnant ice that gradually and slowly melts out its basal and even englacial debris due to the geothermal heat flux and warming by subglacial groundwater, as described, for instance, by Lawson (1979) and Shaw (1977).

The bedded (Virkkala, 1952) or stacked (Moran, 1971) ortho-tills and the subglacial tills with vertically changing strong pebble fabric (Mickelson, 1973) probably combine both above processes of deposition: first lodging of debris-rich basal ice, but in sheets of various thickness rather than particle-by-particle, followed by melting out of these sheets, beginning with their base. Such a till may be called lodged melt-out till. This kind of deposition has been described from present-day glaciers in Svalbard by Boulton (1970) and from Alaska by Mickelson (1973). Lavrushin's (1980) theoretical basal exfoliation appears to be similar.

All the above lodgement and melt-out processes, as discussed previously by Goldthwait (1971, p. 16), may combine or alternate in one and the same subglacial till layer, depending upon thermal conditions at the sole of the glacier and upon the load of basal debris that retards the movement of the glacier base. All the lodged and subglacially melted out components bear evidence of active glacial transport of debris in glacier ice, while the more specific evidence of lodgement versus passive melt-out may vary in its strength. The following characteristics of active glacial transport may be mentioned: (a) strong consistent orientation of elongate clasts and even matrix grains parallel to the direction of glacial movement as measured by Derbyshire (1980) in ice; (b) various deformation structures of debris bands in ice described by Lavrushin (1976) and Shaw (1977); (c) glacial abrasion and impact marks on clasts, described by many authors, and even on sand grains (Gravenor, 1979) if the glacial transport distance was sufficiently long; (d) presence of bullet-shaped (also called flat-iron-shaped or pentagonal) clasts with most striae parallel to their long axes. The above-listed characteristics of glacial transport in debris-rich ice are accentuated by the lodgement process (Boulton, 1970, 1975; Krüger, 1979), and lodgement adds the following related characteristics: up-glacier imbrication of clasts, sigmoidal shears continuing downglacier as attenuated smudges, some clasts having stoss-and-lee characteristics and faceted upper surfaces, and others (Krüger, 1979). Additional glaciodynamic structures (shears, fissility) are added by glacial drag against the surface of its own lodgement till (Boulton and others, 1974), producing deformed lodgement till (Boulton, 1976, 1980). Since lodgement tills and lodged melt-out tills are deposited by gradual or intermittent accretion, these post-lodgment deformations may be present throughout the above two varieties of subglacial tills and also in any other subglacial tills affected by glacial drag. Therefore, they may be considered as general characteristics of subglacial tills.

2. Subglacial allo-tills are deformation tills as originally proposed by Elson (1961), subglacial flow and slide tills (leeside till of Lundqvist, 1977), and subaquatic melt-out tills (Dreimanis, 1979, 1982; Gibbard, 1980) called also undermelt till (Gravenor and others, in press).

Deformation till (Elson, 1981) "comprises weak rock or unconsolidated sediment that has been detached from its source, the original structures distorted or destroyed, and some foreign material admixed," particularly in its top portion. It is "thought [by Elson] to be formed and deposited primarily beneath the glacier and generally does not become incorporated in it." Deformation till "commonly occurs in situations where drainage is impeded" (Elson, 1981). Deformation till structures and fabric are at least partially related to the direction of movement of the overlying glacier. Since the deformation till consists of material that has been moved or transported through short distance by glacial drag prior to its deposition, this variety of till may be considered an ortho-till (see the general genetic terms in Table 1).

Subglacial flow and slide tills are formed mainly in subglacial leeside cavities downglacier of substratum heights, such as shown in Figure 11.3 of Sugden and John (1976) and described by Hillefors (1969) from several locations in West Sweden. They resemble in their initial appearance supraglacial and proglacial flow tills. Their structures and fabric are related to their own mass movement rather than to glacial flow. These tills may also be interbedded with subglacial meltwater sediments.

Another subglacial variety of allo-tills is the subaquatic melt-out till, formerly (for example, in Dreimanis, 1976, 1979, 1980) classified as one of the water-lain tills. According to the model proposed by Dreimanis (1979) and Gibbard (1980), it is deposited by basal or englacial debris melting out at the base of moving or stagnant glacier and continuously falling down through such a shallow depth of water that no noticeable sorting takes place. Though the resulting diamict is crudely stratified, its sorting is as poor as that of the related ortho-tills (Evenson and others, 1977; Gibbard, 1980). The pebble fabric is either random or related to local penecontemporaneous flowage; dropstones are abundant (Gibbard, 1980).

The top portion of all the above-mentioned subglacial allo-tills may be strongly deformed by frictional drag of the overriding glacier (Dreimanis, 1976, 1982a) and may even grade imperceptibly into lodgement till (Dreimanis, 1982a) if the overriding glacier became grounded after the deposition of the allo-tills.

SUPRAGLACIAL AND ICE-MARGINAL TILLS

These tills have been commonly called ablation tills (Chumakov, 1978; Dreimanis, 1976, 1980; Flint, 1971; Goldthwait, 1971; Harland and others, 1966; Lavrushin, 1980; Lundqvist, 1977; and others), since they have been deposited mainly as a result of ablation. The place of their deposition is either on the surface of the ice or adjacent to it in the marginal area of the glacier (called often "proglacial"), on land or in water. Their usual group name, ablation till, is not recommended for future usage, as ablation also may occur subglacially or along englacial cavities or crevasses. Two main varieties are distinguished (Table 1): (a) supraglacial melt-out till (Boulton, 1970), which is an ortho-till, and (b) flow till (Hartshorn, 1958; Boulton, 1968), which is an allo-till, having resulted from resedimentation of supraglacial melt-out till or even other varieties of tills that have become exposed in contact with glacier ice. In some places it is possible to recognize and differentiate these two varieties of supraglacial till, while in many places, particularly if the tills are thin, their specific origin cannot be established, and the group term "supraglacial till" has to be applied. Such undifferentiated supraglacial tills still can be distinguished in some places from their subglacial equivalents by their position at the top of a till unit, a looser and generally coarser texture, and a greater lithologic and textural variability (Dreimanis, 1976). Also, they are often interstratified with meltwater deposits.

*1. **Supraglacial melt-out till*** derives either from extraglacial debris that have been carried passively on and in the surface part of a glacier, or from englacial debris originally of basal or supraglacial derivation that have been carried deeper in the ice and eventually melted out by supraglacial ablation. In most mountainous areas, debris of both derivations are present in various proportions, while in continental ice-sheet deposits the extraglacial component is lacking. Of similar multiple derivation are the sublimation tills formed in arid glacial environment such as Antarctica (Shaw, 1977) where the surficial melting is replaced to great extent by sublimation.

If the extraglacially derived debris dominate, the resulting till is usually very coarse textured and has angular clasts (Sharp, 1949), and its process of deposition is mainly by lowering due to the underlying ice melting out. Even if glacial debris have melted out of snow, firn, or from the uppermost rigid part of glacial ice, they lack features of active glacial transport, such as glacial abrasion marks and fabric related to glacial movement. Boulton and Deynoux (1981) called it supra-till.

Typical supraglacial melt-out till that derives from englacially transported debris resembles its subglacial counterpart by preserving most of the characteristics of the glacial transport. A greater chance exists that the supraglacial melt-out and sublimation tills are deposited from glacial debris bands carried in the englacial rather than in the dynamically more active basal zone of glacier ice, where crushing dominates. Therefore, their clasts are more abraded and rounded than crushed, and they contain more distantly transported debris than in subglacial tills (Dreimanis, 1976). In areas of mountain glaciers, the supraglacial melt-out and sublimation tills may also contain an admixture of angular supraglacial debris that have fallen into ice crevasses. Also, these tills are usually less compact than their subglacial equivalents.

2. ***Flow tills*** of supraglacial terrestrial origin have been investigated thoroughly along the present-day glaciers of Spitsbergen by Boulton (1968) and in Alaska by Lawson (1979: sediment flows). They derive as sediment flows from supraglacial melt-out till and may be deposited either on glacier ice or beside masses of stagnant ice on land in fluvial, lacustrine, or marine environments. While Boulton (1970, 1971, 1972) and Lawson (1979) emphasized their terrestrial deposition, Evenson and others (1977) and Hicock and others (1981) also described lacustrine and marine varieties that are characterized by debris flow cones deposited as ice-contact sediments in water. Whether deposited on land or in water, the flow tills develop clast fabrics that are related to their local flows but unrelated to glacial movements. The clayey and silty flow tills are usually enriched in silt (Evenson and others, 1977, Dreimanis, 1979), while their sandy varieties have about the same grain-size composition as their lodgement equivalents (Hicock and others, 1981). Flow structures are visible if stratified drift

layers or lenses are incorporated, but some flow tills are massive.

Recently, Boulton (1980), and Boulton and Deynoux (1981) have been distinguishing, theoretically, true flow till from non-till flows. The latter ones are "remobilized flow till—not glacially induced, derived from flow with zero effective stress" (Boulton, 1980, Fig. 4). For practical reasons, both varieties of flows may be considered as flow till if they interdigitate, and even Boulton and Deynoux (1981, Table 1) list several "non-till" characteristics among the criteria for the recognition of flow tills.

GLACIOMARINE DIAMICTS AND MIXTITES, SUBMARINE DEBRIS FLOWS

Glaciomarine diamicts or mixtites often resemble tills, and therefore some authors (e.g., Chumakov, 1978; Harland and others, 1966; Kurtz and Anderson, 1979) consider them as tills (para-tills or aqua-tills). Since they could be deposited in the sea either outside calving glaciers or possibly even underneath floating ice shelves and floating termini of glaciers (Lavrushin, 1968; Kurtz and Anderson, 1979), they may form transitions from proglacial marine sediments to subaquatic melt-out tills. Still, most of them are probably proglacial sediments, since they usually contain marine fossils *in situ.*

It should be mentioned here that in the Soviet Union the so-called marinists tend to misinterpret some authentic tills as glaciomarine sediments if they contain marine fossils, without testing if these fossils have not been incorporated by glacial erosion (see discussions in Dreimanis, 1970; Troitskiy, 1975). Therefore, the glaciomarine sediments of the marinists have to be considered with caution.

Modern glaciomarine diamicts have been investigated in the Arctic and Antarctic regions, and their Pleistocene equivalents both from presently submerged continental shelves and their slopes and from the post-glacially uplifted, formerly submerged, regions have been described in many papers. For their annotated bibliography, see Andrews and Matsch (1983); a few selected references will be mentioned here.

The polygenetic—marine, glacial, and their meltwater—origin of glaciomarine diamicts is reflected in the combination of predominantly current-derived and suspension-derived fine matrix and iceberg-derived or ice shelf–derived clasts and sand-size particles. Therefore, the particle-size composition is usually bimodal, the fine-grained clay and silt mode dominating over the coarse mode, except for the direct vicinity of ice margin where winnowing by meltwater currents has concentrated the coarse components (Armstrong, 1981; Boltunov, 1970; Hicock and others, 1981; Kurtz and Anderson, 1979; Lavrushin, 1968; and others). The structure of glaciomarine diamicts ranges from massive to stratified. Clasts often show dropstone orientation, and they have deformed the bedding by impact. Marine fossils are always present in the present-day or Pleistocene marine diamicts, but in various abundances, probably depending upon the degree of the turbidity of the water and other environmental factors. Armstrong (1981) has noted that the marine diamicts are usually thicker than the associated tills.

Away from the glaciers, glaciomarine diamicts grade into normal marine sediments without a sharp boundary, because icebergs can transport glacial debris for thousands of kilometres. (For data on ice-rafted sand in North Atlantic oceanic sediments during the last interglacial-glacial cycle, see Ruddiman, 1977).

Another group of marine diamicts that are similar in their appearance to many tills are submarine debris flow deposits. They are found on continental shelves and their slopes that may derive from glaciomarine or other sediments (Kurtz and Anderson, 1979). According to Kurtz and Anderson (p. 1159), the Antarctic debris flow deposits are "poorly sorted, massive, texturally homogenous throughout their thickness, and have sharp upper and lower boundaries. A crudely developed pebble fabric may be present in some units and all contain displaced shelf faunas or are unfossiliferous." They appear texturally so similar to tills deposited by grounded ice that it is difficult to differentiate them by texture alone. For their descriptions in relation to tillites see Gravenor and others (in press).

SUMMARY

Till is used here as a genetic term and defined broadly as a sediment deposited by or from glaciers with little or no sorting by water. This broad definition permits inclusion of flow tills, deformation tills, and subaquatic melt-out tills. These allo-tills have undergone penecontemporaneous disaggregation and/or resedimentation, but their deposition is part of authentic glacial deposition process, since they often grade into ortho-tills (lodgement and melt-out tills). However, the glaciomarine diamicts and such debris flows that are unrelated to glaciers are excluded from tills, even though they may look very similar to tills and contain some glacial debris. The reason for their exclusion is their deposition away from glacier ice.

Tills may be classified genetically either into ortho-tills and allo-tills or into subglacial and supraglacial tills, and each of them into several more specific varieties (Table 1), if the presence of multiple criteria warrant such classifications. Several varieties of till have gradational contacts. Recognition of the specific or even general varieties and distinction of tills from other till-like diamicts or mixtites permits identification of the environments and processes of their deposition. All the above comments on tills also apply to tillites.

ACKNOWLEDGMENTS

The research on definition and genetic classification of tills has been part of a project supported by the National Research Council of Canada grant 4215 for many years, but it has been shared also with several tens of members of the INQUA Commission on genesis and lithology of Quaternary deposits from all over the world and with my students and other co-workers—too many to be listed here. My sincere gratitude to all of them; particularly to the critical reviewers of the manuscript: Lee Clayton, W. B. Harland, and D. M. Mickelson.

REFERENCES CITED

Andrews, J. T., and Matsch, C. L., 1983, Glacial marine sediments and sedimentation—An annotated bibliography: Geo Abstracts, Bibliography No. 11, 227 p.

Armstrong, J. E., 1981, Post-Vashon Wisconsin Glaciation, Fraser Lowland, British Columbia: Geological Survey of Canada Bulletin 322, 34 p.

Boltunov, V. A., 1970, Certain earmarks distinguishing glacial and moraine-like glacial-marine sediments, as in Spitsbergen: International Geological Reviews, v. 12, p. 204–211.

Boulton, G. S., 1968, Flow tills and related deposits on some Vestspitsbergen glaciers: Journal of Glaciology, v. 7, p. 391–412.

—— 1970, On the deposition of subglacial and melt-out tills at the margins of certain Svalbard glaciers: Journal of Glaciology, v. 9, p. 231–245.

—— 1971, Till genesis and fabric in Svalbard, Spitsbergen, *in* Goldthwait, R. P., ed., Till/a symposium: Columbus, Ohio State University Press, p. 41–72.

—— 1972, Modern Arctic glaciers as depositional models for former ice sheets: Journal of the Geological Society of London, v. 128, p. 361–393.

—— 1975, Processes and patterns of subglacial sedimentation: A theoretical approach, *in* Wright, A. E., and Moseley, F., eds., Ice ages: Ancient and modern: Geological Journal Special Issue No. 6, p. 7–42.

—— 1976, A genetic classification of tills and criteria for distinguishing tills of different origin, *in* Stankowski, W., ed., Till, its genesis and diagenesis: Universytet im. Adama Mickiewicza w Poznaniu, Seria Geografia Nr. 12, p. 65–80.

—— 1980, Classification of till: Quaternary Newsletter No. 31, p. 1–12.

Boulton, G. S., and Deynoux, M., 1981, Sedimentation in glacial environments and the identification of tills and tillites in ancient sedimentary sequences: Precambrian Research, v. 15, p. 397–420.

Boulton, G. S., Dent, D. L., and Morris, E. M., 1974, Subglacial shearing and crushing, and the role of water pressures in tills from south-east Iceland: Geografiska Annaler, v. 56, Ser. A, p. 135–145.

Chumakov, N. M., 1978, Dokembriyskie tilliti i tilloidi: Moscow, Nauka, 202 p.

Crowell, J. C., 1977, The significance of glaciations in Precambrian correlations, *in* Sidorenko, A. V., ed., Correlation of the Precambrian: Moscow, Nauka, v. 1, p. 115–131.

Derbyshire, E., 1980, The relationship between depositional mode and fabric strength in tills: Schema and test from two temperate glaciers, *in* Stankowski, W., ed., Tills and glacigene deposits: Universytet im. Adama Mickiewicza w Poznaniu, Seria Geografia Nr. 20, p. 41–48.

Dreimanis, A., 1970, Are marine fossils in the Quaternary deposits a sufficient evidence for marine deposition? *in* Gudelis, V., ed., Baltica, v. 4, p. 313–322.

—— 1976, Tills, their origin and properties, *in* Legget, R. F., ed., Glacial till: The Royal Society of Canada Special Publication No. 12, p. 11–49.

—— 1979, The problems of waterlain tills, *in* Schlüchter, Ch., ed., Moraines and varves: Rotterdam, A. A. Balkema, p. 167–177.

—— 1980, Terminology and development of genetic classifications of materials transported and deposited by glaciers, *in* Stankowski, W., ed., Tills and glacigenic deposits: Universytet im. Adama Mickiewicza w Poznaniu, Seria Geografia Nr. 20, p. 5–10.

—— 1982a, Two origins of the stratified Catfish Creek, Till at Plum Point, Ontario, Canada: Boreas, v. 11, p. 173–180).

—— 1982b, Work group (1)—Genetic classification of tills and criteria for their differentiation: Progress report on activities 1977–1982, and definitions of glaciogenic terms, *in* Schlüchter, Ch., ed., INQUA Commission on genesis and lithology of Quaternary deposits, Report of activities 1977–1982; ETH, Zurich, p. 12–31.

Elson, J. A., 1961, The geology of tills, *in* Penner, E., and Butler, J., eds., Proceedings of 14th Canadian Soil Mechanics Conference: National Research Council of Canada Associate Committee on Soil and Snow Mechanics Technical Memorandum 69, p. 5–36.

—— 1981, Deformation till, INQUA Commission on genesis and lithology of Quaternary deposits, Work group no. 1, Genetic classification of tills and criteria for their recognition: Circular No. 20, Appendix, 4 p.

Evenson, E. B., Dreimanis, A., and Newsome, J. W., 1977, Subaquatic flow tills: A new interpretation for the genesis of some laminated till deposits: Boreas, v. 6, p. 115–133.

Flint, R. F., 1971, Glacial and Quaternary geology: New York, John Wiley and Sons, 892 p.

Gibbard, P., 1980, The origin of stratified Catfish Creek Till by basal melting: Boreas, v. 9, p. 71–85.

Goldthwait, R. P., 1971, Introduction to till, today, *in* Goldthwait, R. P., ed., Till/a symposium: Columbus, Ohio State University Press, p. 3–26.

Gravenor, C. P., 1979, The nature of the late Paleozoic glaciation in Gondwana as determined from an analysis of garnets and other heavy minerals: Canadian Journal of Earth Sciences, v. 16, p. 1137–1153.

Gravenor, C. P., von Brunn, V., Dreimanis, A., in press, Nature and classification of waterlain glaciogenic sediments, exemplified by Pleistocene, Late Paleozoic and Late Precambrian deposits: Earth-Science Reviews.

Hambrey, M. J., and Harland, W. B., 1981, editors, Earth's pre-Pleistocene glacial record: Cambridge University Press, Cambridge, 1004 p.

Harland, W. B., and Herod, K. N., 1975, Glaciations through time, *in* Wright, A. E., and Moseley, F., eds., Ice ages: Ancient and modern: Geological Journal Special Issue No. 6, p. 189–216.

Harland, W. B., Herod, K. N., and Krinsley, D. H., 1966, The definition and identification of tills and tillites: Earth-Science Reviews, v. 2, p. 225–256.

Hartshorn, J. H., 1958, Flowtill in southeastern Massachusetts: Geological Society of America Bulletin, v. 69, p. 477–482.

Hicock, S. R., Dreimanis, A., and Broster, B. E., 1981, Submarine flow till at Victoria, British Columbia: Canadian Journal of Earth Sciences, v. 18, p. 71–80.

Hillefors, Å., 1969, Västsveriges glaciala historia och morfologi: Meddelanden från Lunds Universitets geografiska Institution, Avhandling 60, 319 p. (Swedish with English summary).

Krüger, J., 1979, Structures and textures in till indicating subglacial deposition: Boreas, v. 8, p. 323–340.

Kurtz, D. D., and Anderson, J. B., 1979, Recognition and sedimentologic description of recent debris flow deposits from the Ross and Weddell Seas, Antarctica: Journal of Sedimentary Petrology, v. 49, p. 1159–1169.

Lavrushin, Yu. A., 1968, Features of deposition and structure of the glacial-marine deposits under conditions of a fiord coast (based on the example of Spitsbergen); translated from Litologiya i Polezniye Iskopaemye, v. 3, p. 63–79: in English in Lithology and Mineral Resources, v. 3, p. 298–310.

—— 1976, Stroenie e formirovanie osnovnikh moren materikovikh oledenenii: Moscow, Nauka, 237 p.

—— 1980, Vital problems of till sedimentogenesis, *in* Stankowski, W., ed., Tills and glacigene deposits: Universytet im. Adama Mickiewicza w Poznaniu, Seria Geografia Nr. 20, p. 19–40.

Lawson, D. E., 1979, Sedimentological analysis of the western terminus region of the Matanuska Glacier, Alaska: U.S. Army Corps of Engineers, Cold Regions Research and Engineering Laboratory Report 79-9, 112 p.

Lunqvist, J., 1977, Till in Sweden: Boreas, v. 6, p. 73–85.

Mickelson, D. M., 1973, Nature and rate of basal till deposition in a stagnant ice mass, Burroughs glacier, Alaska: Arctic and Alpine Research, v. 5, p. 17–27.

Moran, S. R., 1971, Glaciotectonic structures in drift, *in* Goldthwait, R. P., ed., Till/a symposium: Columbus, Ohio State University, p. 127–148.

Ruddiman, W. F., 1977, Late Quaternary deposition of ice-rafted sand in the subpolar North Atlantic (lat. 40°-65°N): Geological Society of America Bulletin, v. 88, p. 1813–1827.

Schermerhorn, L.J.G., 1974, Late Precambrian mixtites: Glacial and/or nonglacial?: American Journal of Science, v. 274, p. 673–824.

Schermerhorn, L.J.G., 1983, Late Proterozoic glaciation in the light of CO_2 depletion in the atmosphere, *in* Medaris, L. G., Jr., and others, eds., Proterozoic geology: Selected papers from an international Proterozoic symposium: Geological Society of America Memoir 161 (this volume).

Sharp, R. P., 1949, Studies of superglacial debris on valley glaciers: American Journal of Science, v. 247, p. 289–315.

Shaw, J., 1977, Tills deposited in arid polar environments: Canadian Journal of Earth Sciences, v. 14, p. 1239–1245.

Sugden, D. E., and John, B. S., 1976, Glaciers and landscape, a geomorphologic approach: London, Edward Arnold, 376 p.

Troitskiy, S. L., 1975, Sovremenniy antiglacializm: Moscow, Nauka, 163 p.

Virkkala, K., 1952, On the bed structure of till in eastern Finland: Commission Geologique de Finlande Bulletin No. 156, p. 97–109.

Manuscript Accepted by the Society April 14, 1983

Printed in U.S.A.

Geological Society of America
Memoir 161
1983

Late Proterozoic glaciation in the light of CO_2 depletion in the atmosphere

L.J.G. Schermerhorn
Institut für Mineralogie
Freie Universität Berlin
Takustr. 6
1000 Berlin 33
Federal Republic of Germany

ABSTRACT

Compared to established glacial formations of Early Proterozoic, Early and Late Paleozoic, and Pleistocene age, the supposed glacial formations of Late Proterozoic age present aberrant features indicating a different geotectonic, tectono-sedimentary, and climatic framework. They are mostly found in geosynclines where they may be very thick and also occur on unstable platforms but are absent on stable platforms. They are associated with tectonic uplift of source areas including basin margins so that they rest on a variable disconformity. Also, they contain interbedded warm facies (carbonate, glauconite, iron formation). These formations range from glacially deposited tillites or aquatillites and dropstone strata to nonglacially deposited tilloids that may contain varying amounts of glaciclastic material.

This paradox—occurrence of glacial material in a warm depositional environment—may be resolved as follows: tectonic uplift of source areas gave rise to altitude glaciation. This provided glaciclastic detritus and, locally, glacier tongues descended to sea level, depositing glacial intercalations. From the scarcity of volcanism and the extent of carbonate deposition during the Late Proterozoic, atmospheric CO_2 depletion is deduced. This would have led to a thinner atmosphere with a steeper vertical temperature gradient and hence a lower snowline. Thus, moderate tectonic elevation may have resulted in ice-crowned ranges overlooking tropical seas.

INTRODUCTION

During the Proterozoic both the best-established and the most controversial of Precambrian glacial formations were deposited.

Glaciation means the covering of part of the land surface with glacier ice, and there is little doubt that part of North America was glaciated during the Early Proterozoic, giving rise to the Gowganda Formation and correlated glacials (Young, 1970).

There is, again, little doubt that glaciation occurred in at least some parts of the world during the Late Proterozoic. However, the resulting formations are so aberrant when compared to undoubted glacial formations like the Gowganda that it seems dubious that they could have originated in the same way, that is, by glaciation of wide areas. Briefly, the geotectonic, tectono-sedimentary, and climatic framework of supposed glacial formations of the Late Proterozoic is very different and these formations have no real analogues among earlier or later glacials.

These differences far outnumber the similarities. This paper will examine them and will try to arrive at a synthesis, bringing in a hitherto unrecognized factor.

ESSENTIAL TERMINOLOGY

What constitutes a glacial or a presumed glacial formation? In the first place, prominence of boulder beds showing a till-like lithology. That is, such megaclastic units are not conglomerates but diluted conglomerates, usually called mixtites or diamictites (strictly, the latter term by definition excludes calcareous rocks and includes greywackes). These are purely descriptive all-purpose terms. Genetic designations—once the mode of deposition has been reliably established—are as follows.

glacial mixtites	terrestrial:	tillite
	aqueous:	aquatillite
nonglacial mixtite		tilloid

The terminology is reviewed and discussed elsewhere (Schermerhorn, 1966, 1974, 1975).

Truly glacial tillites, meaning continental glacier-laid deposits, and aquatillites, deposited from floating till-bearing ice, should be associated with glaciofluvial, glaciolacustrine, and glaciomarine sediments, the latter two subaqueous deposits containing admixed coarser material up to boulder size that was dropped from melting ice shelves, floes, and bergs. This ice-rafting process produces a dropstone lithology unlike till or aquatill. Well-developed dropstone strata carrying abundant coarse erratics provide strong evidence for glacial conditions in the source area and hence glaciation, but not of course in the depositional area, since the ice melted there. Faceted and striated stones, when reasonably abundant, also point to the existence of glacier ice.

A word of warning. The mixtite lithology alone is not enough to label a rock a tillite or aquatillite, which entails a glacial origin and mode of deposition. Tilloids laid down by nonglacial massflow processes have been interpreted as tillites, and no doubt some tillites have been mislabeled tilloids.

One further point: *glacial* means ice-produced, *glacigene* (or glaciogenic) ice-derived (literally ice-born), and *glaciclastic,* a narrower term, refers to detritus resulting from glacial erosion. These terms are not synonymous. If a rock or formation contains glacigene material (e.g., glacially striated pebbles or ice-rafted detritus), this does not make it a glacial deposit. The reason for this restriction is that glacigene material may enter, and even constitute the bulk of, nonglacial sediments. Examples are given by Schermerhorn (1974, p. 690).

GEOGRAPHIC DISTRIBUTION AND PALEOLATITUDES

The Early Proterozoic Gowganda glaciation, the Early and Late Paleozoic glaciations, and the Pleistocene glaciation all cluster in high to polar paleolatitudes.

Not so the Late Proterozoic (Proterozoic Z, 800 to 570 Ma) glacial or pseudoglacial formations: they are much more widespread, and many successions of this age in most parts of the world contain mixtite units or formations (Schermerhorn, 1974, 1975). The ages of the Late Proterozoic mixtites apparently range through some 200 Ma. There is, however, a great lack of reliable age determinations.

The Huronian Supergroup is ca. 2,150 to 2,400 Ma old, during which time the Gowganda glaciation occurred. Yet few other coeval sequences elsewhere contain glacial or glacial-looking mixtites. Though many Late Proterozoic formations thought to be glacial have been discovered during the past twenty years, no second Gowganda Formation has come to light in Middle or Early Proterozoic strata. There are of course the thin mixtite horizons in the Witwatersrand and Transvaal Supergroups in South Africa, but they do not present the spectacular development of thick mixtites and dropstone beds characteristic for the Gowganda, and they are not as well established as glacial formations (Beukes, 1973).

Equally, the Ordovician, Permian-Carboniferous, and Pleistocene glaciations were restricted to areas around the contemporaneous poles, away from which no widespread glacial mixtites are found (excepting local mountain glaciations). Within these areas the glacial formations show good continuity and synchroneity (discounting the effects of polar wandering): international correlation is possible. However, the Late Proterozoic mixtite formations are much more widespread, being of worldwide occurrence, but they are markedly discontinuous and diachronous. That is, unlike the great extent of the above-mentioned glacials, the Late Proterozoic mixtite formations, even when geosyncline-wide, are discontinuous, hence of much smaller extent, and diachronous. They were deposited in detached areas and are not correlatable over larger distances, often not even within the same basin, as in Spitsbergen (Schermerhorn, 1974, p. 729).

Though continuity and synchroneity would be expected of formations supposedly laid down from immense icecaps, no Late Proterozoic mixtite formation approaches the vast area covered by the Paleozoic or Pleistocene icesheets. Certainly enough has been preserved of the Gowganda, Early and Late Paleozoic tillites—even if the Pleistocene tills seem less likely to survive in the geological record—to trace their extent and continuity. Also, in the seas adjacent to these icesheets a narrow aquatill fringe formed, passing to a wide zone of ice-rafted glaciomarinites (Schermerhorn, 1974, p. 684). Such is not known from the Late Proterozoic.

Considering their widespread occurrence, it comes as no surprise that paleomagnetic data show many of the Late Proterozoic mixtite formations—notably those around the North Atlantic—to have been deposited in low to equatorial paleolatitudes (Schermerhorn, 1974, p. 709). Again, if these are glacial formations, this would be something completely unknown from earlier or later glaciations. Several explanations for this phenomenon have been offered, such as the occurrence of one or more Late Proterozoic global ice ages of such severity that icecaps covered the continents even in the tropics, strong tilting of the Earth's spin axis, and icebergs on the equator. None of these are sound (Schermerhorn, 1974, 1975, 1976). The problem is aggravated by the fact that several Late Proterozoic presumed glacial units enclose carbonate beds and other warm-facies indicators intercalated among mixtites thought to be tillites and dropstone strata. This, added to the evidence for and against glacial deposition, next to be discussed, gives rise to a paradox which this paper proposes to resolve.

EVIDENCE FAVOURING GLACIAL DEPOSITION

At the outset it should be stated that although there is evidence for glacial deposition or derivation for some Late Proterozoic mixtite formations, most of the "evidence" adduced by proponents of the great Late Precambrian ice age is spurious.

The *mixtite lithology,* as stated, is certainly not proof for or against glacial deposition. Tilloids may look like till but they are not till, since they are nonglacial: mere resemblance does not prove identity. It is therefore not justified to uncritically classify a mixtite as a tillite or aquatillite on the basis of lithology alone, although this has often been done.

Striated pavements beneath tillites, if of glacial origin, offer excellent evidence of glacial action but not necessarily of glacial origin of the overlying rocks (oyster beds resting on Pleistocene striated floors are known). Unfortunately, striated pavements of glacial origin are very rare indeed in Late Proterozoic successions, considering the ubiquity and extent of mixtite formations of this age, and certainly much rarer than in Permian-Carboniferous or Pleistocene glacial formations. Moreover, not every striated or grooved pavement is glacial, as is instanced by the disproved glacial floor associated with assumed tillites in the Late Proterozoic Adelaide geosyncline (Daily, Gostin, and Nelson, 1973).

Striated and faceted stones likewise are proof of glacial abrasion, if they can be shown to be glacial. Nonglacial striations are known also (Schermerhorn, 1974). In the Late Proterozoic, striated and faceted stones are too rare to be of much use. Then, glacially abraded clasts are glaciclastic detritus and as such may find their way into nonglacial deposits such as deltas or turbidites. They are thus not proof for or against a glacial mode of origin of the enclosing rocks.

If glacial pavements and stones are present, this does not mean, without supporting evidence, that the associated sediments are glacial deposits, and if they are absent, it does not follow that the associated sediments are of nonglacial origin.

Dropstones when abundant constitute excellent evidence for the rafting-in of erratic clasts by floating ice (discounting, for the present, other rafting agents such as kelp). However, there are two kinds of glaciomarine dropstone strata or *glaciomarinites,* one evidencing glaciation because it is produced by seagoing glaciers or icesheets, and the other unrelated to glaciation because it is produced by sea and shore ice rafting rounded beach gravel, as a result of seasonal freezing (Schermerhorn, 1974).

The first type of dropstone beds is characterized by a complete lack of sorting in the rafted detritus, by the presence of glacially abraded clasts, and by the occurrence of till pellets. This is because it derives from a glaciated landmass where till is being laid down, and till-carrying ice when seaborne must release all the components of till on thawing, from boulders down to till matrix, thus yielding till pellets and larger masses. The resulting iceberg-rafted glaciomarinites are thick and extensive and contain large numbers of dropped-in clasts from silt and sand to boulder grade. Such rocks are well known from the Dwyka and Pleistocene glaciations, where they cover large areas. However, few Late Proterozoic formations contain glaciomarinites of the first type, and when they occur they are with few exceptions thin and discontinuous. One of the exceptions is the Late Proterozoic Mount Rogers Formation in Virginia, which consists of tillites or aquatillites interbedded with dropstone strata and other rocks. It was deposited when a highland adjacent to a marine bay or large lake was glaciated (Blondeau and Lowe, 1972).

The second type of dropstone bed carries in contradistinction mostly gravel-grade material, and this selectivity is unlike till. Most of the dropstone strata described from Late Proterozoic sequences are of this type (for instance, Spencer, 1971) and hence are not evidence of glaciation but only of transport by sea ice (Stanton and Schermerhorn, 1977).

Furthermore, scattered stones in laminated or massive sediments need not have been dropped in but may have been emplaced by lateral transport (Schermerhorn, 1974, p. 683), even in thin-bedded carbonates (Jansa and Carozzi, 1970). In addition, dropstones need not be ice-rafted and ice-rafted dropstones need not be related to glaciation. It should also be remembered that ice-crystal casts produced by freezing at sea level are known from Cambrian and Ordovician rocks deposited in low paleolatitudes.

Summing up, although there is some evidence favouring glacial derivation and deposition of at least some of the material in some of the Late Proterozoic mixtite formations, it is meagre in comparison to the abundant, much more varied glacial evidence available for glaciation of other ages. It follows that Late Proterozoic glacial action was less extensive.

EVIDENCE FAVOURING NONGLACIAL DEPOSITION

We will restrict ourselves to the geotectonic setting, the tectono-sedimentary framework, and the warm climatic conditions of Late Proterozoic mixtite deposition; other nonglacial aspects are discussed elsewhere (Schermerhorn, 1974).

Most, or perhaps all, of the Late Proterozoic mixtite formations are marine and intercalated in thick geosynclinal successions or in the thinner sequences laid down on unstable platforms (Schermerhorn, 1974, 1975). None are found on stable platforms such as the Siberian Platform. Thus the lower mixtite formation in the Adelaide Geosyncline of South Australia is extremely thick, attaining nearly 6 km, but across the strike it wedges out completely before reaching the stable Stuart Shelf on the west of the basin (Schermerhorn, 1975). It is a general rule that mixtites in thick Late Proterozoic successions pinch out when these successions pass to the thin sorted sediments laid down, during the same time, on stable borderlands (Schermerhorn, 1975, 1976).

The marked preference of the Late Proterozoic mixtite formations for geosynclines and their absence on adjacent stable platforms is hard to explain on a climatic basis alone. It is in fact a strong argument against icecap glaciation. A link with tectonism, in this case uplift and erosion of source areas seems indicated: mixtites develop in a tectonically active environment and not in a stable environment. As a result, the mixtite formations are thickest in the thick successions in actively subsiding basins and thinner in the thin sequences deposited on weakly subsiding platforms. The next section will enlarge upon this concept.

TECTONO-SEDIMENTARY ENVIRONMENT

Late Proterozoic mixtite formations generally overlie older strata belonging to the same succession (in places they rest on basement) conformably to weakly disconformably in the central parts of the depositional basin, but the basal contact becomes a strong erosional disconformity towards the basin margins (Schermerhorn, 1975). This means increased downcutting in the direction of the source area. Moreover, the material eroded from underlying formations appears as abundant intrabasinal clasts in the mixtites. This locally derived intrabasinal detritus from slightly older, barely lithified rocks is often angular, while the far-traveled extrabasinal crystalline clasts are mostly rounded and not freshly eroded, and hence are recycled debris.

These features—the disconformity and the intrabasinal clasts—lead to conclude to tectonic uplift and erosion of the basin edges. However, authors explaining these mixtites as tillites or glaciomarine deposits rule out tectonism and substitute glacio-eustatic control of sedimentation (see Schermerhorn, 1974, p. 704; 1975, p. 251). Now, if no elevation of the basin edges took place, on the nontectonic glacial hypothesis, then the surface on which the mixtites were deposited would have sloped away from the basin interior to the source area. That is, the basin edges would have lain deeper than the basin interior. This is incompatible with the other evidence. Hence tectonic uplift of the basin edges must have occurred at the hinge zone between the subsiding basin where the eroded material accumulated and the elevated source area supplying debris from ever deeper horizons (over 1,000 m deeper in East Greenland). Local glaciation may have accompanied tectonic uplift, as is argued in this paper.

The mixtite deposits cover a smaller area than do earlier and later formations in the same succession; this basin shrinkage follows logically from the uplift and erosion of the basin edges.

Also, often some volcanic activity (mostly mafic extrusives such as spilites) accompanies the opening of Late Proterozoic mixtite cycles. This indicates that due to tectonic activity mixtite source areas were uplifted along fault lines that served as volcanic feeders.

Thus, whether or not the climate was cold, there must have occurred tectonic movements of an epeirogenic nature, in the sense that while the basin subsided, the source area and the basin margins were uplifted. This means *tectonic differentiation* of a previously uniform environment, resulting in rejuvenation of basin-source relations, and it has been argued elsewhere that this tectonic differentiation is the primary cause of the mixtite cycle (Schermerhorn, 1974, 1975). Although this does not rule out glaciation, it can explain a mixtite cycle without glaciation.

WARM PALEOCLIMATIC INDICATORS

An important clue to the warm climatic conditions under which many Late Proterozoic presumed glacials were deposited is furnished by carbonate beds and by associated glauconite and iron formation.

Dolomite interbeds in Late Proterozoic mixtite formations are fairly common. For instance, the Portaskaig Formation of the Dalradian in Scotland and Ireland is a thick (over 1,100 m) succession of mixtites alternating with sandstone, siltstone, conglomerate, and dolomite beds. The dolomite beds are numerous, reach 26 m in thickness, and contain possible stromatolites in one place (Spencer, 1971). Spencer interprets this sequence as produced by a vast icecap in equatorial paleolatitudes, advancing and retreating many times under extreme climatic oscillations. The Numees tillite in Namibia also is frequently interbedded with dolomite and contains a stromatolite reef that apparently grew during aqueous mixtite deposition (Kröner, 1977). This formation is likewise ascribed by Kröner to a severe glaciation.

The dolomite interbeds in Late Proterozoic mixtite formations range from true dolomite to dolomitic limestone. They are generally very fine grained, may be bedded, and show mostly sharp contacts with overlying and underlying beds. On these and other grounds (notably dolomite pebbles enclosed in siltstones very poor in carbonate) Spencer (1971) considered the abundant dolomites in the Portaskaig Formation to have formed by direct precipitation or by penecontemporaneous or early dolomitization, which implies that "conditions around the time of deposition of the mixtites were suitable for the formation of dolomites" (Spencer, 1971, p. 34).

Dolomitic interbeds like these occurrences, whether primary precipitates or penecontemporaneous dolomitizations, are *hot paleoclimatic indicators,* while mixtites in themselves are not climatic indicators. Four lines of evidence—experimental, uniformitarian, paleomagnetic, glaciological—converge to show conclusively that dolomite is not deposited at low temperatures: not in the laboratory, not in present-day cold seas, not in ancient seas at high paleolatitudes, not among glacials. *The occurrence of dolomite interbeds is not compatible with a glacial regime in the site of deposition.*

The main point is that *no tillite-dolomite interstratification is known from established glaciations,* such as the Gowganda, the Dwyka, the Ordovician, or the Pleistocene. So why would the low-latitude Late Proterozoic mixtite formations present an exception to the rule? Moreover, the dolomite interbeds among these mixtites are not freak occurrences easily explained away; they are plentiful and may attain remarkable thicknesses: 26 m in Scotland and 23 m in Australia.

Glauconite, the next warm indicator, is somewhat rarer, but Late Proterozoic mixtite formations may be contemporaneous and intertongue with glauconitic sediments, as in Siberia (Schermerhorn, 1975). The mixtite formation around the Taoudeni basin in West Africa is thought to consist of tillites laid down from an immense icecap (Deynoux and Trompette, 1976). Yet the supposedly glaciofluvial outwash sandstones interbedded with the mixtites are commonly glauconitic, and even the mixtites may carry glauconite. Still, glauconite is characteristic of warm shelf seas and is associated particularly with marine transgression (McRae, 1972), not with glaciers.

Iron formation, a laminated chemical sediment, is mostly of Lower Proterozoic age but is also known to occur in later times. It has been found associated with Late Proterozoic mixtite formations. Young (1976) described iron formation enclosing mixtite beds underlying the mixtite formation of the Rapitan Group in Northwest Canada. It also contains dropstones and casts of evaporite minerals. Young discussed the view that iron formation accumulates by evaporitic processes, causing rhythmic precipitation of iron and silica in the sea under hot conditions, and suggested that the same effect could also have resulted from freezing of seawater to precipitate iron and silica-rich beds. If this were true, one would expect the Gowganda and other glacial formations also to be interbedded with iron formation, which they are not.

Summarizing, the close association of supposedly glacial mixtites with warm-facies indicators is only found in the Late Proterozoic. Furthermore, it appears extremely unlikely that vast icecaps, necessary to produce thick (up to several kilometres) tillite or aquatillite sequences, could have existed in tropical paleolatitudes. This would have meant, since these formations are widespread, that the larger part of the continents would have been sheathed in ice, a climatic upset so extreme (and probably self-sustaining: latent heat and an increase of albedo operate to delay melting) that it seems doubtful whether normal conditions could ever have been restored, certainly not so abruptly as is shown by mixtites that are sharply covered by thick carbonate successions lacking dropstones, as is quite common in the Upper Proterozoic rock column.

SYNTHESIS: CONDITIONS FOR LATE PROTEROZOIC ALTITUDE GLACIATION

How can this paradox—glacial indications in a warm environment—be resolved? Briefly, by tectonically induced upland glaciation next to the depositional sites.

First, Late Proterozoic glaciation, as shown above, cannot have taken the usual form of continental icesheets. The occasional appearance of glacial and glacigene features can only be explained satisfactorily by highland glaciation, but the mountain glaciers did not grow into major icecaps.

Glaciers develop in uplands when snow precipitates abundantly from rising moist air. As we have seen, the opening of mixtite cycles in the Late Proterozoic by tectonic differentiation modified the existing paleogeographic configuration: source areas were uplifted next to marine basins. This altered circulation patterns, causing moist air from the warm sea to rise upon coastal ranges. If these were high enough—and this is the crucial point—they would have become covered with snow and in time glaciers would have developed.

At present the vertical temperature gradient in the lower atmosphere is 0.5°C to 0.6°C per 100 m altitude. This means that in low to equatorial latitudes the zero isotherm lies at an altitude of about 4.5 km.

Rough correlation of mixtite formation thicknesses with elevation of source areas indicates that for most Late Proterozoic mixtite formations the amount of source uplift must have been rather less than 4.5 km. This constitutes a first unfavourable factor, and two others are represented by the unfavourable composition of the Proterozoic atmosphere and the temperature of the earth and the seas that was probably higher than at present (the latter, incidentally, applies unfavourably to all hypotheses trying to explain Late Proterozoic glaciation at sea level in low latitudes).

The Proterozoic atmosphere contained much CO_2 and water vapour, together with very little free oxygen. Because of the abundance of infrared-absorbing, heat-retaining atmospheric components, warm conditions obtained at sea level.

When air rises in the atmosphere and cools adiabatically, its temperature lapse rate is about 1°C per 100 m altitude—this is the dry adiabatic rate, and for moist air a lesser rate of cooling is found, the saturation adiabatic lapse rate. Thus an atmosphere rich in H_2O and CO_2 would imply a lower lapse rate, hence an upward shifting of the zero isotherm.

However, another factor should be considered. The Late Proterozoic is remarkable because volcanism appears to have been much less active than during earlier or later epochs. Late Proterozoic mobile belts contain successions that are of the miogeosynclinal rather than the eugeosynclinal type in that volcanic horizons are very rare and thin. In consequence, ore deposits related to volcanism, notably the stratiform massive sulphides of the pyritite type, are lacking from the younger Proterozoic. Hutchinson (1973) remarked on this and correctly ascribed it to the rarity of subaqueous volcanic sequences of this age. Likewise, Miller (1980) listed a gap between 1,000 Ma and 550 Ma when no massive pyritic copper-zinc orebodies occur, although these are eugeosynclinal deposits and not time-dependent.

The Late Proterozoic is also remarkable for its abundant thick carbonate sequences in many parts of the world, for instance, in Africa and China. The deposition of very extensive carbonate levels with thicknesses measured in kilometres must have fixed much atmospheric CO_2. Normally the withdrawal of CO_2 from the atmosphere is balanced by replenishment from volcanic sources, but as volcanism was on the wane during the Late Proterozoic, the CO_2 content of the atmosphere must have decreased steadily.

As a result of this *secular CO_2 depletion,* the Late Proterozoic atmosphere must have lost a considerable volume of CO_2. Since CO_2 is heavier than most of the other atmospheric constituents, the atmosphere may have been shallower, with a steeper density gradient caused by gravitational stratification. If this is correct, the cooling rate in the lower atmosphere may have been steep enough for the snowline to shift downward. Then mountain glaciation could have taken place at moderate altitudes (Schermerhorn, 1977).

This hypothesis combines the apparent scarcity of volcanism and the abundance of carbonate deposits in the Upper Proterozoic—a combination unparalleled in other epochs—to deduce a decrease in the CO_2 content of the atmosphere over the hundreds of millions of years that the Late Proterozoic lasted, and this of course is still highly speculative.

No sudden great climatic change is suggested, such as the short-range extreme oscillations from hot to glacial that Spencer (1971) proposed for the depositional environment of the Portaskaig tillite; rather, a slow secular lowering of the snowline—because of the reasons sketched above or perhaps on other grounds—until tectonically uplifted source areas of mixtite basins could sustain glaciers, even in equatorial latitudes (where the Portaskaig tillite was laid down). Mountain glaciers in the tropics are known at the present time, but do not flow down to the sea. The hypothesis advanced here requires that glaciated or partly glaciated uplands existed next to depositional basins.

SUMMARY AND CONCLUSION

The widespread mixtite formations in the Upper Proterozoic present the problem that they, though glacial-

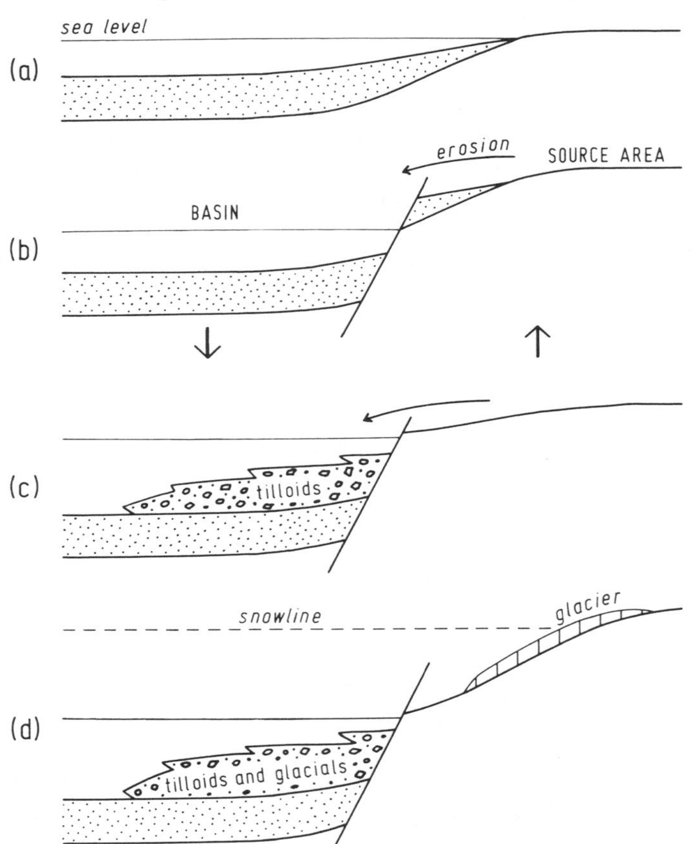

Figure 1. Diagrammatic reconstruction of the tectono-sedimentary framework of Late Proterozoic mixtite formations. (a) Stable environment of preceding formations. (b) Tectonic differentiation into a subsiding basin and a rising source area sets in. (c) Unsorted clastics derived from the uplifted hinterland are deposited as tilloids in the basin. (d) When source area elevation is sufficiently high so that glaciers can develop, glacial and glacigene sediments, mostly aquatillites and glaciomarinites, are deposited in addition.

looking, exhibit many features that strongly diverge from the circumpolar setting characteristic for the established glacial formations of Gowganda, Ordovician, Permian-Carboniferous, and Pleistocene age. Unlike these four formations, the Upper Proterozoic mixtite formations are discontinuous and diachronous, that is, they are not restricted to a single correlatable horizon, they are widespread in equatorial paleolatitudes, they are found in geosynclines and on unstable platforms but are absent on stable platforms, they are associated with uplift of their source areas due to tectonic differentiation of the stable environment in which underlying formations were deposited, and they often are associated with warm-facies interbeds. On the other hand, they may contain glacial or glacigene material, in particular aquatillites and dropstone beds (glaciomarinites), although these are much rarer than in the established glacial formations listed above.

Paradoxically, therefore, both warm conditions at sea level and glaciation at altitude are indicated for at least part of the Late Proterozoic mixtite formations.

The possibility that vast icesheets formed at sea level in tropical paleolatitudes and deposited thick tillite sequences interbedded with dolomite, only during the Late Proterozoic, is rejected. For those Late Proterozoic mixtite formations that show glacial influences, the following depositional model is proposed.

Tectonic differentiation into positive and negative areas (uplifted sourcelands and subsiding basins) created favourable conditions for glaciation in highlands next to the seas where the mixtite formations were deposited (Fig. 1). From these highlands, glaciclastic debris was transported into the basins, and glacier tongues descended locally to sea level (as in the Mount Rogers Formation of Virginia). These glacial incursions are superposed on normal sedimentation, from dolomite and sand, silt and gravel to unsorted tilloid flows.

To explain glaciation in the uplifted hinterland, it is suggested that the snowline descended to such an extent that glaciers could form. This is deemed to have been an effect of the abundant carbonate deposition and rare volcanism in the Late Proterozoic. The combination of these two factors is peculiar to this epoch and is here interpreted as meaning that CO_2 withdrawn from the atmosphere to build up immense carbonate sequences was not replenished ina commensurate way from volcanic sources. Such would have resulted in secular CO_2 depletion during the Late Proterozoic, possibly causing a steeper cooling rate in the lower atmosphere and hence a lowering of the snowline, so that glaciers could grow in uplands acting as source areas to mixtite basins. One way of testing this admittedly very speculative hypothesis would be to calculate and compare the volumes of the Late Proterozoic carbonate and volcanic rocks, when reliable worldwide information on thickness and extent of these deposits will become available.

REFERENCES CITED

Beukes, N. J., 1973, Precambrian iron-formations of southern Africa: Economic Geology, v. 68, p. 960–1004.

Blondeau, K. M., and Lowe, D. R., 1972, Upper Precambrian glacial deposits of the Mount Rogers Formation, Central Appalachians, U.S.A.: International Geological Congress, 24th, Montreal, Proceedings, Section 1, p. 325–332.

Daily, B., Gostin, V. A., and Nelson, C. A., 1973, Tectonic origin for an assumed glacial pavement of Late Proterozoic age, South Australia: Journal of the Geological Society of Australia, v. 20, p. 75–78.

Deynoux, M., and Trompette, R., 1976, Discussion *of* Late Precambrian mixtites: Glacial and/or nonglacial? Dealing especially with the mixtites of West Africa: American Journal of Science, v. 276, p. 1304–1314.

Hutchinson, R. W., 1973, Volcanogenic sulfide deposits and their metallogenic significance: Economic Geology, v. 68, p. 1223–1246.

Jansa, L. F., and Carozzi, A. V., 1970, Exotic pebbles in La Salle Limestone (Upper Pennsylvanian), La Salle, Illinois: Journal of Sedimentary Petrology, v. 40, p. 287–293.

Kröner, A., 1977, Non-synchroneity of Late Precambrian glaciations in Africa: Journal of Geology, v. 85, p. 289–300.

McRae, S. G., 1972, Glauconite: Earth-Science Review, v. 8, p. 397–440.

Miller, L. J., 1980, Distribution of ore deposits through geological time: Bureau de Recherches Géologiques et Minières, Mémoire 106, p. 67–76.

Schermerhorn, L.J.G., 1966, Terminology of mixed coarse-fine sediments: Journal of Sedimentary Petrology, v. 36, p. 831–835.

—— 1974, Late Precambrian mixtites: Glacial and/or nonglacial? American Journal of Science, v. 274, p. 673–824.

—— 1975, Tectonic framework of Late Precambrian supposed glacials, *in* Wright, A. E., and Moseley, F., eds., Ice ages: Ancient and modern: Geological Journal Special Issue 6, p. 241–274.

—— 1976, Reply *to* Discussions *of* Late Precambrian mixtites: Glacial and/or nonglacial?: American Journal of Science, v. 276, p. 375–384.

—— 1977, Discussion *of* Late Precambrian dolomites, Vendian Glaciation, and synchroneity of Vendian glaciations: Journal of Geology, v. 85, p. 247–250.

Spencer, A. M., 1971, Late Pre-Cambrian glaciation in Scotland: Geological Society of London, Memoir 6, 98 p.

Stanton, W. I., and Schermerhorn, L.J.G., 1977, Discussion *of* Late Precambrian glacial climate and the Earth's obliquity: Geological Magazine, v. 114, p. 57–60.

Young, G. M., 1970, An extensive Early Proterozoic glaciation in North America?: Paleogeography, Paleoclimatology, Paleoecology, v. 7, p. 85–101.

—— 1976, Iron-formation and glaciogenic rocks of the Rapitan Group, Northwest Territories, Canada: Precambrian Research, v. 3, p. 137–158.

MANUSCRIPT ACCEPTED BY THE SOCIETY APRIL 14, 1983